VIIIA/18
								2 **He** 4.0026 Helium
			IIIA/13	IVA/14	VA/15	VIA/16	VIIA/17	
			5 **B** 10.81 Boron	6 **C** 12.011 Carbon	7 **N** 14.0067 Nitrogen	8 **O** 15.9994 Oxygen	9 **F** 18.9984 Fluorine	10 **Ne** 20.179 Neon
			13 **Al** 26.9815 Aluminum	14 **Si** 28.0855 Silicon	15 **P** 30.9738 Phosphorus	16 **S** 32.06 Sulfur	17 **Cl** 35.453 Chlorine	18 **Ar** 39.948 Argon
VIIIB/10	IB/11	IIB/12						
28 **Ni** 58.69 Nickel	29 **Cu** 63.546 Copper	30 **Zn** 65.39 Zinc	31 **Ga** 69.72 Gallium	32 **Ge** 72.59 Germanium	33 **As** 74.9216 Arsenic	34 **Se** 78.96 Selenium	35 **Br** 79.904 Bromine	36 **Kr** 83.80 Krypton
46 **Pd** 106.42 Palladium	47 **Ag** 107.868 Silver	48 **Cd** 112.41 Cadmium	49 **In** 114.82 Indium	50 **Sn** 118.71 Tin	51 **Sb** 121.75 Antimony	52 **Te** 127.60 Tellurium	53 **I** 126.9045 Iodine	54 **Xe** 131.29 Xenon
78 **Pt** 195.09 Platinum	79 **Au** 196.967 Gold	80 **Hg** 200.59 Mercury	81 **Tl** 204.383 Thallium	82 **Pb** 207.2 Lead	83 **Bi** 208.980 Bismuth	84 **Po** (209) Polonium	85 **At** (210) Astatine	86 **Rn** (222) Radon

64 **Gd** 157.25 Gadolinium	65 **Tb** 158.925 Terbium	66 **Dy** 162.50 Dysprosium	67 **Ho** 164.930 Holmium	68 **Er** 167.26 Erbium	69 **Tm** 168.9341 Thulium	70 **Yb** 173.04 Ytterbium	71 **Lu** 174.967 Lutetium
96 **Cm** (247) Curium	97 **Bk** (247) Berkelium	98 **Cf** (251) Californium	99 **Es** (252) Einsteinium	100 **Fm** (257) Fermium	101 **Md** (258) Mendelevium	102 **No** (259) Nobelium	103 **Lr** (260) Lawrencium

FOUNDATIONS

of CHEMISTRY

SECOND EDITION

FOUNDATIONS
of CHEMISTRY

Ernest R. Toon
George L. Ellis
Larry Doyle
John Ivanco
Stan Percival

S E C O N D   E D I T I O N

Harcourt Canada

Toronto Orlando San Diego London Sydney

Canadian Cataloguing in Publication Data

Main entry under title:
Foundations of chemistry

2nd ed.
For use in secondary schools.
ISBN 0-03-922287-X

1. Chemistry. I. Toon, Ernest R.

QD33.F68 1989   540   C90-093122-1

Cover: A computer-generated model of the framework structure of ZSM-5, a microporous high-silica zeolite. Zeolites are a class of minerals that act as catalysts in petroleum refining, as molecular sieves in water treatment and as absorbents in pollution control. The zeolite shown is used as a catalyst to convert toluene, a by-product of petroleum refining, into commercially valuable benzene. The structure is displayed using filled polyhedra to illustrate connectivity, with benzene in the central channel. The region of zero electrostatic potential is mapped in white. (Credit: Chemical Design Ltd)

Printed and bound in Canada.

3 4 5 6 7   04 03 02 01 00

CONTENTS

CHAPTER 7

POLYMERS: SYNTHETIC AND NATURAL MACROMOLECULES 277

CHAPTER 8

ENERGY ASSOCIATED WITH CHEMICAL AND NUCLEAR REACTIONS 311

CHAPTER 9

RATES OF CHEMICAL REACTIONS 373

PREFACE

hemistry is like a skyscraper. The foundation of chemistry consists of countless experimentally observed facts. The theories, principles and laws developed from these observations are like an elevator that runs from floor to floor. At each level, new observations are made and new ideas—essential to continued progress—are proposed.

Foundations of Chemistry, Second Edition, and *Foundations of Chemistry Laboratory Manual* have been completely rewritten and updated. These new versions are intended for students who have already taken an introductory course in chemistry. The extensive revision has substantially shortened both the text and the manual so that the content can be covered in a one-year course. Together, the revised text and manual provide an enriched chemistry program that is designed to help the student understand how chemical principles and concepts are developed from experimental observations and data, and how these principles can be used to explain certain phenomena. Students are also exposed to the development of solutions to quantitative and qualitative problems through investigation and verification.

The historical evolution of important scientific ideas is described to give the student an insight into the way in which scientists develop theories and unifying principles from experimental data. The observations that the student makes in the laboratory and the discussions given in the laboratory manual provide added meaning and depth to the concepts discussed in the text.

In this text, chemical concepts are introduced after the necessary background has been developed and after a need for them has been established. Concepts are first introduced qualitatively, in simple terms, and are then discussed in detail, illustrated with examples and applied at every opportunity. After this extensive investigation, the quantitative aspects of a concept are introduced.

One of the unique features of this text is the treatment of organic chemistry. Its position near the beginning of the book is designed to help students understand senior-level biology and review or reinforce the concepts of atomic structure, chemical bonding and molecular structure. Our discussion of organic chemistry is divided into three chapters: Chapter 5 introduces the different organic families and discusses their functional groups, structures, and physical and chemical properties. In Chapter 6, the various types of organic reactions are examined. Finally, Chapter 7 discusses the reactions and functions of synthetic and natural polymers.

The *Foundations of Chemistry* text and laboratory manual contain many features that are designed to make the study of chemistry interesting, rational, understandable and relevant. These features are presented so that students, regardless of their ability or objectives, are able to
– understand the reason and logic behind the development of facts, concepts and principles
– learn the principles, concepts and facts in a systematic way
– understand the significance and application of chemistry
– develop an interest in chemistry
The following is a summary of the major features of the *Foundations of Chemistry* text, laboratory manual and solutions manual.

Chapter Previews and Summaries

At the beginning of each chapter is a short preview that provides a smooth transition from one chapter to another. These previews outline the ideas and sequence of topics developed within the chapter. Short summaries at the end of each chapter review the highlights of the chapter and set the stage for the presentation of the next chapter.

Chapter Presentation

Each chapter is divided into closely related units, which are further divided into specifically labelled, closely related sections.

Each section begins with a short summary that briefly describes the major ideas of the topic. This arrangement not only helps the student understand the logical sequence of ideas but also makes short, digestible reading assignments possible.

Interspersed throughout each chapter are a variety of captioned tables, two-colour illustrations and figures that supplement the text discussion.

Important principles, laws, concepts and key statements are highlighted in italics and/or bold type.

Biographies

Biographies of important scientists are presented in each chapter to put the study of chemistry into historical perspective. These biographies reveal some aspects of the personalities of these scientists, some of the problems they faced and, in addition, the significance and impact of their discoveries. Interesting, thought-provoking quotations by well-known scientists and writers open each chapter.

Special Feature Articles

Each chapter contains articles that have been written to spark the student's interest in chemistry in relation to society, medicine, industry and the environment, and to explore practical applications of the specific chemical principles treated within the chapter. These articles will help the student develop an awareness of how chemistry affects our lives as well as a respect for the environment and an appreciation of technology.

Margin Notes

Margin notes appear throughout each chapter. These notes, which are in colour, emphasize important points, extend a discussion, define new terms, review chemical concepts or supply incidental relevant information.

Questions and Problems

A number of example problems and their solutions appear in quantitative discussions throughout each chapter. These are accompanied by follow-up problems that will help the student develop proper problem-solving techniques and also consolidate the concepts discussed in the example problem.

Graded questions and problems are located at the end of each chapter and are designed so that students can answer them successfully. The questions are directly related to the concepts developed in the chapter.

Laboratory Manual

The experiments outlined in the laboratory manual have been extensively reduced in number and rewritten so that the student can succeed in mastering the relationship between experiment and theory. The manual is closely integrated with the text and contains specific experiments that relate to the concepts developed in each chapter in the text. Additional experiments have been included as possible extensions of concepts developed in the text.

A wide selection of quantitative experiments is provided to emphasize the importance of careful observation and accurate measurement. Each experiment is introduced with a discussion of the purpose of the lab, an objectives section, a detailed section on materials and procedures, and a follow-up discussion section. At the end of each lab is a section of follow-up questions containing directions and questions to help students evaluate their understanding of the experimental work.

Solutions Manual

The solutions manual provides teachers with the answers to all of the follow-up problems in the body of the text and the problems and questions at the end of each chapter. Possible answers to the questions in the laboratory manual are also included for each lab.

ACKNOWLEDGEMENTS

The publication of a book of this size requires the efforts of many people. We would like to thank the following reviewers for their criticisms and suggestions:

Stuart McLean   University of Toronto

Lyle Sadavoy   Westdale Secondary School, Hamilton

A. Tanin   University of Toronto

James Thompson   University of Toronto

We are grateful for the managerial support and encouragement given to us by the staff at HBJ-Holt Canada, including Kevin Ford, Ken Leland, Murray Lamb, Winnie Siu, Theresa Thomas, Mary Opper, Patricia Hall, Lisa Dimson and Sharon Latta-Paterson. Thanks also to Paul McCusker for his artistic portraits and cartoons. We would also like to thank the writers of the special-feature articles: Julie Bedford, Tom Shields (Creative and Editorial Services), Mary Kay Winter, Mike Wevrick, James Leahy, Larry Bedford and Craig Lewis.

We would like to express our sincere appreciation and gratitude to the editor of this project, Julie Bedford, who worked tirelessly to maintain the high standard of this book through her creativity and dedication.

Finally, we would like to thank our families for their support and encouragement throughout this project.

Many of the scientists at the 1933 Solvay Conference in Brussels were responsible for the development of the model of the atom. Seated, from left: E. Schrödinger, I. Joliot-Curie, N. Bohr, A. Joffé, M. Curie, P. Langevin, O. Richardson, E. Rutherford and T. De Donder. Standing: F. Perrin, F. Joliot-Curie, W. Heisenberg, H. Kramers, E. Stahel, E. Fermi, E. Walton, P. Dirac, P. Debye, N. Mott, B. Cabrera, G. Gamow, W. Bothe, P. Blackett (at back), M. Rosenblum, J. Errera, E. Bauer, W. Pauli, J. Verschaffelt and M. Cosyns (at back).

The Composition of Atoms

D o we have any proof that such things as atoms exist? The answer is that science can never prove anything in the way, say, mathematics can, by eliminating all the alternative possibilities. In science, it is not possible to determine all the alternative possibilities. Although scientists have not yet developed an alternative to the atomic theory, that does not preclude the possibility that such a theory will someday be proposed.

The theory of atoms is, therefore, not considered fact, but it can be rendered highly probable. The lines of evidence for the existence of atoms are numerous. If one experiment to measure an atom is performed, and this same experiment is repeated over and over, it is not considered proof of the existence of atoms. However, if atoms are measured in a variety of different experiments that give similar results, *it is highly probable that atoms do exist*. The evidence for atoms is, in fact, so strong that it is very *improbable* that anyone will ever propose an alternative theory to the atom. Thus, scientists are justified in believing in the existence of atoms.

In this chapter, we will trace the evolution of the model of the atom from its simple beginnings in ancient Greece, through the turn of the 19th century, to its highly sophisticated form used by scientists in the last part of the 20th century.

ATOMS AND MODELS

1-1

The Development of Scientific Theories and Models

"Physical concepts are free creations of the human mind, and are not, however it may seem, uniquely determined by the external world. In our endeavour to understand reality we are somewhat like a man trying to understand the mechanism of a closed watch. He sees the face and the moving hands, even hears its ticking, but he has no way of opening the case. If he is ingenious he may form some pictures of a mechanism which could explain his observations. He will never be able to compare his picture with the real mechanism and he cannot even imagine the possibility of such a comparison."
Albert Einstein,
The Evolution of Physics (1938)

Democritus's ideas were popular among the founders of modern physics two centuries before Dalton proposed his atomic theory in 1808. Galileo, Newton and most of their contemporaries were, indeed, atomists. The intuitive feeling that matter was somehow composed of particles had shown up again and again in scientific thought of the period. For example, Galileo reasoned that the appearance of a new substance through chemical change could be explained in terms of rearrangement of parts too small to be seen, and Robert Boyle and Isaac Newton used atomic concepts to interpret certain chemical and physical laws.

Because of the indirectness of physical science, scientists must be constantly searching for new theories and models to explain phenomena.

In science, the words theory and model are often used interchangeably. However, a ***model*** is a fairly simple representation that provides a structural similarity to the phenomena being studied. In contrast, a ***theory*** is a broader, more detailed attempt to explain the phenomena.

Physical science is full of magnificent theories and models. One of the most successful theories is the theory of light. Although indirect in its definition of light, this theory is very thorough in explaining light's properties.

The development of the theory of light illustrates the importance of the *crucial experiment*. When two different theories are developed to explain the same phenomena, a crucial experiment is performed on one theory. The results from the experiment allegedly "prove" one theory over the other. As an example, let us consider the corpuscular theory of light, attributed to Sir Isaac Newton (1642–1727), which proposed that light was made of little corpuscles. In the early 1800s, the wave theory, which proposed that light was made of waves and travelled more slowly in water than in air, replaced Newton's theory because it better explained the properties of light. In the late 19th century, the Michelson-Morley experiment measured the velocity of light and showed that light did travel more slowly in water than in air. Scientists, therefore, concluded that the corpuscular theory had been wrong and that the wave theory was right. The elegant Michelson-Morley crucial experiment was regarded as one of the high points in science.

In time, however, the corpuscular theory was revived. It was discovered that light has some properties that can only be explained by assuming that light comes in separate packets, called *quanta*. However, the wave theory was so successful in explaining many of the properties of light that it could not be easily abandoned. Thus, it became necessary to devise a new model of light that incorporated features of both theories.

The evolution of the model of light illustrates the constant changes and adaptations to which scientific models and theories are subjected. Physical science is not a body of indisputable and immutable truth; it is a body of well-supported opinion whose ideas may be modified at any time. In the same way, our concept of the atom and its structure may be modified at any time as new evidence appears.

1-2
The Atom: A Model of Model Building

The development of the model of the atom originated with the concepts of Democritus, around 400 BC.
The idea of the atom as an indivisible building block was proposed around 400 BC by the Greek philosopher Democritus (460–370 BC). Although his theory never gained wide acceptance in Greek thought, the word *atom* from the Greek *atomos*, meaning indivisible, is still used today.

Democritus believed that all matter was made up of tiny, indestructible particles that could not be divided. According to Democritus, all atoms consisted of the same basic material and there was no limit to the types of atoms that existed. Democritus sought to explain the properties of substances in terms of the way the different types of atoms associated to form the macrostructure.

Although Democritus's atomic theory was limited in scope and application, it did explain, in simple terms, some well-known phenomena such as evaporation, condensation, diffusion and crystal growth. Central to Democritus's thinking was the idea that simplicity was to be found by examining nature on a small scale. This notion is embedded in current scientific thought.

1-3
Dalton's Atomic Theory

John Dalton thought of the atom as an indivisible, uniformly dense, solid sphere that could enter into, but was not changed by, a chemical reaction.
The late eighteenth and early nineteenth centuries saw the development of a number of important scientific theories. In 1789, the French chemist Antoine Lavoisier (1743–1794) established the *law of conservation of mass*, which states that a chemical reaction does not result in a gain or loss in mass. In 1792, the French chemist Joseph Proust (1754–1826) proposed the *law of constant composition* (the law of definite proportion), which says that the percentage composition by mass in specific compounds never varies. English chemist John Dalton was the first person to realize that these laws gave strong support to the idea of atoms, and, in 1808, he published his ***atomic theory of matter***.

During this period, atomism and the whole intellectual style of

JOHN DALTON
1766–1844
One of the most important milestones in the progress of science was the introduction of the atomic theory by the English chemist, John Dalton. All science is fundamentally based on the concept of the atomic nature of matter. Although the idea that matter was composed of atoms had been proposed before 1800, it was Dalton who converted it into a real and usable hypothesis. He also assigned symbols to the elements and prepared a list of atomic masses for 14 elements. Although his symbols were later improved on by Berzelius, they were a great step ahead of the hieroglyphics of the alchemists. In alchemical writings, for example, there were over 200 names and symbols for mercury.

Dalton published his hypothesis in "A New System of Chemical Philosophy." He theorized that atoms of a given element had the same mass. Dalton chose hydrogen, the lightest element, as a standard for atomic mass and based the masses of other atoms on the mass of hydrogen.

Dalton considered atoms to be similar to billiard balls. Thus, his model of the atom is often referred to as the *billiard-ball model*.

It is interesting to note that Dalton was able to make many scientific observations and contributions in spite of the fact that he had red-green colour blindness.

Röntgen Rays
In 1895, German physicist Wilhelm Röntgen (1845–1923) was operating a cathode-ray tube when he noticed that a fluorescent chemical in a bottle on a nearby shelf was glowing and continued to glow even when a piece of cardboard was placed between it and the cathode-ray tube. Penetrating rays were obviously coming from the tube. Because of their mysterious nature, Röntgen named these rays X rays.

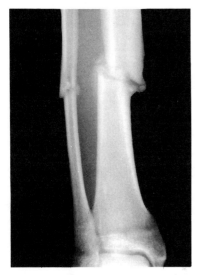

Figure 1-1
X-ray photograph of a human leg. Both the tibia and fibula are fractured.

Radioactivity
While studying the nature of X rays in 1896, the French scientist Henri Becquerel (1852–1908) discovered that some chemical substances spontaneously decomposed and radiated penetrating rays. This phenomenon is called *radioactivity*.

model building were mainly the domain of the physicists. Chemists, historically, have tended to be more conservative than physicists, sticking to the empirical roots of the scientific discipline. The chemists had virtually ignored the theory of atomism until Dalton showed that his theory of atomic structure could explain the law of conservation and the law of constant composition.

Dalton's new concept of the atom was based on the idea that atoms of specific elements have their own characteristic masses. The basic ideas of Dalton's atomic theory are as follows:

1. All substances are made up of tiny, indivisible particles.

2. Each chemical element is composed of its own kind of particles, called atoms.

3. The atoms of a given element are alike and have the same mass. The atoms of different elements differ in mass and properties.

4. Atoms cannot be created or destroyed during physical or chemical changes.

5. Atoms unite in simple whole-number ratios to form compounds.

In the light of current chemical knowledge and theory, many of Dalton's original statements have required some modification. For example, the processes of fission and fusion have shown that atoms can be created and destroyed, thus disproving Dalton's ideas. Generally, however, Dalton's model of the atom approached more closely the realities of nature than previous models.

Up until the end of the 19th century, Dalton's atomic model was widely accepted because it explained many of the chemical and physical laws known at the time. Around the turn of the century, however, certain experimental facts were discovered that were in direct conflict with Dalton's atom. These facts necessitated major modifications of Dalton's theory, even though many of his ideas were retained and incorporated into later atomic theories.

One vexing problem remained to cloud the success of Dalton's model: no one knew the size of an atom or the number of atoms in a particular substance. It was not until Albert Einstein (1879–1955) calculated the quantitative details of Brownian movement, initially discovered by Robert Brown (1773–1858) in 1827, that scientists were able to estimate atomic weights. The results indicated that atoms are relatively similar in size, about 10^{-10} m in diameter, despite the differences in mass. By the beginning of the twentieth century, the atom was no longer regarded as a hypothetical and unobservable entity.

The word atom originally meant indivisible, but two discoveries at the turn of the century made it obvious that atoms were made of and could be split into subparticles: the discovery of X rays in 1895 by Wilhelm Röntgen (1845–1923) and of radioactivity in 1896 by Henri Becquerel (1852–1908). These were closely followed by the discovery of the electron in 1897 by J. J. Thomson (1856–1940), which provided him with the information to develop his own model of the atom.

1-4
The Thomson Model of the Atom

Thomson's rice-pudding model of the atom was the first modification of Dalton's original model.

In 1874, the English physicist C. J. Stoney (1826–1911) identified electricity as being composed of particles and, in 1891, named the unit particle an *electron*. Further experiments by J. J. Thomson, using Crookes tubes, identified cathode rays as beams of electrons.

Thomson recognized that the electron was a component of the atom. His rice-pudding model of the atom (Fig. 1-2), developed in 1903, led the rush to develop new models that would explain the new knowledge of atomic structure.

1-5
The Rutherford Atom

Rutherford's experimental results could only be explained by discarding all previous models of the atom and developing a new model based on the nuclear atom.

Ernest Rutherford (1871–1937) was one of Thomson's research students. In 1909, while at Manchester University, Rutherford had little doubt that Thomson's model was correct. A routine, corroborative experiment, hardly worth Rutherford's personal attention, was initially undertaken by a young research assistant, Ernest Marsden (1889–1970) and his supervisor, Hans Geiger (1882–1945). Their anomalous results intrigued Rutherford and his co-workers so much that they continued with the research over the next four years.

Rutherford used alpha particles emitted from a sample of radioactive substance as subatomic "bullets" for probing into atoms. His targets were the atoms in a piece of very thin gold foil, and his detectors were fluorescent screens. Figure 1-3 shows the set-up of the experiment.

Rutherford had already learned that an alpha particle is a fragment of a helium atom, which carries two units of positive

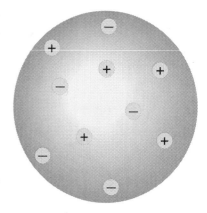

Figure 1-2
In Thomson's "rice-pudding" model of the atom, the electrons and protons of the atom are likened to the raisins (electrons) and rice (protons) in a bowl of rice pudding.

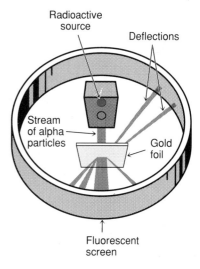

Figure 1-3
Rutherford used the newly discovered alpha particles as a probe to study the interior of atoms. From the results of scattering experiments using the above set-up, the model of the nuclear atom was developed.

About his experiment, Rutherford remarked, "It was almost as incredible as if you fired a 15-inch shell at a piece of tissue paper, and it came back and hit you."

LORD ERNEST RUTHERFORD
1871–1937
Ernest Rutherford grew up on a farm in New Zealand and studied mathematics and physics at the University of New Zealand. In 1895, he won a scholarship to Cambridge to study radioactivity and worked for three years in the Cavendish Laboratory as an assistant to English physicist J. J. Thomson.

In 1898, Rutherford moved to Montreal to take a post as professor of physics at McGill University. During his nine years at McGill, Rutherford and his assistants conducted experiments that related radioactivity to the structure of atoms and established the nature of alpha and beta particles. In 1908, Rutherford proved that alpha particles consist of a helium nucleus and that an electron is a beta particle. For this work, he received the Nobel Prize in chemistry.

At Manchester University in 1907, Rutherford used alpha particles in the famous gold-foil scattering experiments. The surprising results led Rutherford to develop his own atomic model in 1909.

Rutherford was knighted in 1914 and returned to Cambridge as director of the Cavendish Laboratory. That same year, he announced the discovery of the proton. Rutherford also succeeded in making an isotope of oxygen by bombarding a nitrogen atom with alpha particles.

In 1931 Rutherford received a peerage and was made First Baron Rutherford of Nelson. The element *rutherfordium* was named after Rutherford.

charge (2+) and has a mass of 4 u. As such, it was sufficiently small to serve as a probe to study the interior structure of the atoms.

By placing the screens at different positions around the source, Rutherford was able to determine the path of the alpha-particle bullets. To his astonishment, most of the alpha particles passed through the gold foil without being deflected. This observation helped refute Dalton's idea that atoms were solid spheres. Rutherford found that single flashes occasionally occurred far off to the side of the source. Most astonishing were the occasional flashes he observed on the screen almost directly behind the source. This meant that several of the relatively massive alpha particles were bouncing almost straight back to the source (Fig. 1-4). It was not possible that an electron with its negligible mass could be responsible for the deflection of a massive alpha particle.

From the experimental data, Rutherford reasoned that the atoms of gold must be nearly empty space. Rutherford assumed that, because some alpha particles were deflected, each atom contained an extremely tiny, dense core bearing a positive charge. He named this dense central portion of the atom the *nucleus*.

Calculations based on the data collected by Rutherford, Geiger and Marsden revealed that almost the entire mass of an atom was concentrated in the nucleus and that the diameter of the entire atom was over 100 000 times that of the nucleus. In other words, atoms are mostly empty space. They consist of a tiny, dense, positively charged nucleus surrounded by electrons moving at inconceivable speeds at great distances from the nucleus. The following analogy will give you an idea of the vast emptiness of an atom. If the nucleus of a hydrogen atom were enlarged to the size of a tennis ball, the outside of the atom, represented by the average distance of its single electron from the nucleus, would be about 6 km away.

Although an atom is mostly space, an electron moves around the nucleus so rapidly that it effectively occupies all of the space around the nucleus. This situation can be visualized by comparing an electron with an airplane propeller. The area swept by the propeller blade is mostly empty space, as is the region surrounding the nucleus of an atom. Although the blade *actually occupies* only a small part of the total area, it *effectively occupies* the entire area when it is spinning at the rate of 100 revolutions per second. Placing your finger in the "empty space" within the radius of the spinning blade for more than a small fraction of a second would result in the loss of your finger. The electron, which never stops moving, *does not actually occupy* a significant amount of space about a nucleus but *would appear to effectively fill all of the space* because of its rapid motion.

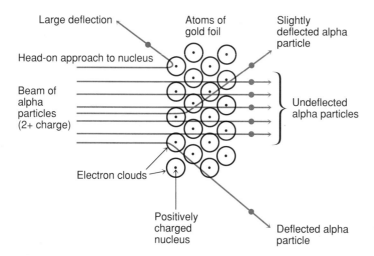

Figure 1-4
Alpha particles shot at gold foil, which is only a few atoms thick. Most alpha particles pass straight through the sample; however, some particles are deflected. The nearer the alpha particle comes to the nucleus, the greater the angle of deflection.

THE NATURE OF THE ELECTRON

In science, the results of one experiment often form the basis of another experiment. Such was the case with the investigations into the nature of the electron in the late nineteenth and early twentieth centuries.

The experiments used to study the electron involved observing the passage of electricity through gases in tubes known as gas-discharge tubes, or Crookes tubes. The following is a brief account of some of the experiments, apparatus and results that were involved in the search for the nature of the electron.

Cathode Rays

In 1879, Sir William Crookes (1832–1919) devised an apparatus that consisted of a glass tube containing two metal plates he called *electrodes*. The electrodes were connected to a source of electricity, as shown in the diagram below.

Crookes found that when the electric current was flowing and the anode was in a horizontal position, the glass opposite the cathode glowed with a greenish fluorescence. This is because the rays travelling in a straight line from the cathode struck the cross (as shown) but did not penetrate it. As a result, the shadow of the cross appeared on the glass.

This experiment shows that a ray coming from the cathode travels in a straight line, transmits energy and does not penetrate a metal sheet. Such a ray is called a *cathode ray*.

The Charge-to-Mass Ratio of an Electron

In 1897, English physicist J. J. Thomson deflected a beam of cathode rays by applying an electric field of known strength. He then varied the magnetic field, which was perpendicular to the electric field, until the beam returned to its original position (see diagram).

Using the data from his experiments, Thomson determined the ratio of charge to mass (*e/m*) of an electron and thus showed that cathode rays consisted of discrete particles of matter. By varying the voltage, using different metals for the electrodes and different gases in the tube, Thomson demonstrated that the cathode rays always had the same properties, and

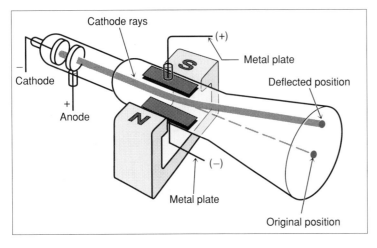

Cathode rays

(+)

Metal plate

Deflected position

Cathode

+

Anode

(−)

Metal plate

Original position

because the different charges on the droplets were all multiples of a fundamental charge, this charge was the absolute charge of a single electron.

The knowledge acquired by Crookes, Thomson and Millikan made it possible for other scientists to qualify and quantify the existence of the electron. For example, the charge determined by Millikan and the e/m ratio determined by Thomson enabled scientists to calculate the mass of an electron, which is approximately 9.1×10^{-31} kg, or 5.5×10^{-4} u. This is about $1/1837$ the mass of a hydrogen atom. For practical purposes, the mass of an electron is considered to be negligible compared to the total mass of an atom.

concluded that all atoms contained the same type of negative particles, called *electrons*. In 1906, he was awarded the Nobel Prize for his discovery of the electron.

From our exploration of the history of the electron, we can see that the discovery of the electron was not the achievement of just one scientist, but was, rather, a collaboration among scientists.

The Charge of an Electron

In 1909, American physicist Robert A. Millikan (1868–1953) accurately determined the charge of an electron by performing his "oil-drop" experiment (as shown). In this experiment, Millikan measured the time required for an electrically charged oil droplet to rise a specific distance when subjected to an electric field. He also measured the time required for the droplets to fall a specific distance in the absence of an electric field. He repeated these measurements with droplets containing various amounts of charge. However, when Millikan calculated the charges on the droplets, he found that they were always a multiple of the same number. He concluded that

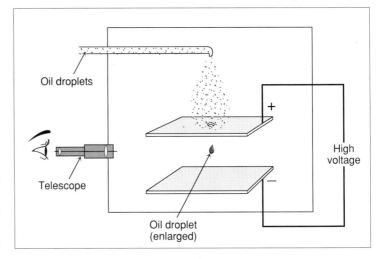

Oil droplets

+

High voltage

Telescope

Oil droplet (enlarged)

1-6

The Atomic Number

The chemical properties of an atom are determined by its atomic number.

Rutherford postulated that the nucleus carried a positive charge, but it was another Englishman, H. G. J. Moseley, who actually determined the charges on the nuclei of most of the atoms.

Moseley proposed that the increase in positive charge on the nucleus represented an increase in the number of protons in the nucleus.

In 1914, after completing his study of the X-ray beams emitted by different elements, Moseley wrote, "The atomic number of the element is identified with the number of positive units of electricity contained in the atomic nucleus." The **atomic number** of an element is equal to the number of protons contained in the nucleus. This is also equal to the number of electrons outside the nucleus of each uncharged atom of the element. *The atomic number of each element is unique*. Since no two elements can have the same atomic number, it is a fundamental property of an atom. As such, the atomic number is an index of the chemical and also of many of the physical properties of atoms.

Rutherford showed that *the mass of an atom is concentrated in the nucleus*. He could not, however, account for the total known mass of the atom in terms of the number of protons in the nucleus. For example, a helium nucleus (alpha particle) has a charge of 2+ furnished by the two protons, which also contribute approximately two units of mass. Since helium atoms have a mass of 4 u, there are still two units of mass to be accounted for. Rutherford postulated the existence of a neutral particle to account for the missing mass. The existence of this particle was not proved for 20 years because its lack of charge made it difficult to detect.

1-7

Neutrons

The atomic mass is determined by the sum of the neutrons and protons in the nucleus.

In 1932, James Chadwick (1891–1974), a British physicist, bombarded the element beryllium (atomic number 4) with alpha particles. He found that a beam of rays of highly penetrating power was emitted from the beryllium. These rays were not affected by a magnet. This meant that they were neutral and, in this respect, similar to X rays. Chadwick also noticed that the new rays travelled at about one-tenth the speed of light. Since X rays travel at the speed of light, the new beam could not be pure radiant energy. When other atoms were bombarded by these new rays, the nature of the collisions indicated that the new beam must be composed of particles. On the basis of his experiments, Chadwick was able to show that these nuclear particles had a mass of approximately 1 u and were electrically neutral. Accordingly, the particle was called a **neutron**. The mass of a neutron is now known to be 1.008 665 4 u, or 1.6748×10^{-24} g.

HENRY GWYN JEFFREYS MOSELEY 1887–1915
Occasionally a man will accomplish an amount of work in his youth that few could do in an entire lifetime. Such was the case with Henry Moseley.

After graduating from Trinity College, Oxford, Moseley went to work for Ernest Rutherford at Manchester. Moseley's experiments involved bombarding targets made of different metals with a beam of electrons. He noted that each metal emitted X rays of a characteristic frequency. He repeated this experiment for numerous elements and found that the heavier the element, the shorter was the wavelength and the more penetrating were the X rays. When he organized the observed X rays in order of increasing frequency, Moseley found an occasional gap, which indicated to him that an element was missing. He interpreted the regular increase in the frequency of the X rays in terms of a regular increase in positive charge on the nuclei of atoms.

Moseley's atomic-number concept solved the riddle of the rare-earth (inner-transition) elements, and explained the irregularities in the location of such elements as potassium and argon in the periodic table. In addition, his work stimulated further search for new elements.

Moseley volunteered for military service during World War I and became a signal officer. He was killed in action in Gallipoli in 1915 at age 27.

In 1935, James Chadwick was awarded the Nobel Prize in physics for his discovery of the neutron.

The discovery of neutrons completed the roster of particles that make up the three major building blocks of an atom. These particles and their characteristics are summarized in Table 1-1.

TABLE 1-1
FUNDAMENTAL PARTICLES OF ATOMS

Particle	Charge	Mass (u)	Mass (g)
Electron	1−	0.000 548 597	9.1091×10^{-28}
Proton	1+	1.007 276 63	1.6725×10^{-24}
Neutron	0	1.008 665 41	1.6748×10^{-24}

The Discovery of the Proton
Since atoms are electrically neutral particles, the discovery of electrons in 1897 as the negative components of atoms naturally led to the search for a positive component. A beam consisting of positive particles had been discovered in 1885 by E. Goldstein (1850–1931) and was investigated by J. J. Thomson.

In 1919, Ernest Rutherford showed that when an electron is removed from a hydrogen atom, a positively charged particle remains; he called this particle a *proton*. A proton has a mass of 1.007 267 u (approximately 1837 times the mass of an electron) and carries a unit positive charge that is equal and opposite to that of an electron.

Rutherford's concept that an atom consists of a tiny, positively charged nucleus surrounded by a cloud of rapidly moving electrons is an improvement on Dalton's indivisible, hard-sphere model. It does not, however, satisfactorily explain the arrangement and behaviour of electrons around the nucleus. The ***electron configuration*** in atoms may be determined by analysing the light absorbed or emitted by atoms. In order to relate the electron structure of an atom to the light absorbed or emitted by it, we must first examine the nature and characteristics of radiant energy. You are already familiar with many types of radiant energy, including visible light, infrared and ultraviolet light.

1-8

The Dispersion of Visible Light

Knowledge of the properties of light will help us to understand how electrons are positioned around the nucleus of an atom. Light may be dispersed by a glass prism into its component colours. When sunlight (white light) is passed through a prism, the light is dispersed, resulting in a rainbow of colours (Fig. 1-5). This rainbow, or series of colour bands, constitutes a continuous solar spectrum of all the visible wavelengths. A discontinuous spectrum differs in that certain wavelengths are missing. This dispersion of light by a prism was explained by Sir Isaac Newton. From his experiments, Newton came to the following conclusions:

1. White light is a mixture of many colours (wavelengths).

2. A prism does not make colours; it merely separates colours that already exist.

Violet
Blue
Green
Yellow
Orange
Red

Sunlight

Prism

Figure 1-5
When sunlight is passed through a prism, it is dispersed into its component colours. Red light travels faster through the glass medium of the prism and is bent the least.

3. Each component of the white light is bent (refracted) through a different angle by a prism, resulting in the spectrum.

Violet light, with the shortest wavelength, is refracted to the greatest extent, and the longer-wavelength red light is refracted the least. Refraction occurs when light passes from one medium to another, for example, from the air into the glass of a prism and then back into the air. This is explained by the fact that the speed of light varies in different media, and speed depends on two factors: the nature of the medium and the wavelength of the light. Thus, white light is dispersed by a prism because each of the component wavelengths travels with a different velocity through the glass. Red light travels the fastest and is refracted the least. It appears on the side of the spectrum toward the apex of the prism. Violet light travels the slowest and is refracted to the greatest extent. Consequently, it appears on the side of the visible spectrum toward the base of the prism (Fig. 1-5).

In 1859, Robert Bunsen (1811–1899) and Gustav Kirchhoff (1824–1887) developed the *spectroscope*, an instrument used to study the spectra of luminous sources. A spectroscope contains a prism or a diffraction grating for dispersing the light, and a telescope to enable the observer to examine the spectra. In some spectroscopes, the telescope is replaced by photographic film on which the spectrum is reproduced. This instrument is called a *spectrograph*, and the photograph of the spectrum is called a *spectrogram*. A spectrogram enables a scientist to measure the wavelengths of the components of various light samples. A cut-away view of a spectroscope is shown in Fig. 1-6.

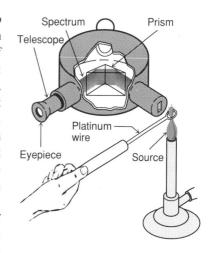

Figure 1-6
A simple prism spectroscope. Light from the source is separated into its component colours by the prism. Analysis of the distribution of the colours provides data related to the structure and composition of the source.

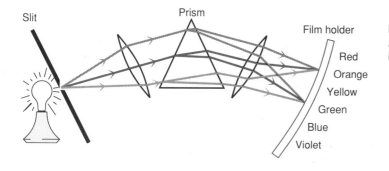

Figure 1-7
A prism spectroscope separates light into its component wavelengths.

1-9

Atomic-Emission Spectra

Knowledge of atomic-emission spectra will help us understand how electrons are positioned around the nucleus of an atom of a particular element.

When the light emitted by energized atoms, such as the mercury atoms in a mercury lamp or the sodium atoms in a sodium lamp, is examined with a spectroscope, a series of coloured lines separated by dark spaces is observed. Each line corresponds to a specific wavelength. A spectrum containing only specific wavelengths is called a *discontinuous* or *line spectrum*. The line, or *atomic-emission*, spectrum of an element is unique; that is, no two elements have the same spectrum. Spectroscopic analysis, therefore, may be used to identify an element.

In 1884, Johann Balmer (1825–1898) of Switzerland energized atoms of hydrogen gas and examined the visible radiation with a spectroscope. He found four prominent coloured lines in the hydrogen spectrum, as illustrated in Colour Plate II. They were:
– a red line with wavelength 6.563×10^{-7} m
– a blue-green line with wavelength 4.861×10^{-7} m
– a blue line with wavelength 4.340×10^{-7} m
– a violet line with wavelength 4.102×10^{-7} m

It was not until 1913 that the origin of the spectral lines was satisfactorily explained by Niels Bohr (1885–1962), the great Danish physicist. A revolutionary proposal by Max Planck in 1900 provided the clue that enabled Bohr to explain the line spectra of atoms. The *quantum theory*, proposed by Planck and confirmed by Einstein, led to the development of a new model of the atom.

THE STRANGE TRUTH ABOUT QUARKS

In the late 1960s, an American physicist, Murray Gell-Mann, developed a theory to explain observations from experiments with high-energy proton beams that showed that protons and neutrons have three separate centres of electric charge. Gell-Mann proposed the existence of a new kind of subnuclear particle, which he called a *quark*. According to Gell-Mann, quarks, under the influence of strong nuclear forces, combine to form protons, neutrons and other nuclear particles.

The idea behind this theory is that all nuclear particles, including protons and neutrons, are built out of quarks. Quarks are quantum particles that are similar to the electron. They have the same spin as an electron but have a fractional electric charge compared to the electron's one-unit charge. However, unlike the electron, the quark has never been seen. In fact, quarks seem to exist as a mathematical trick played by theoretical physicists.

It has been mathematically hypothesized that there are six quark "flavours," as shown in the quark table. ("Flavour" is an acceptable generic term for labelling quarks.) The key difference between the six quarks is in their electric charges.

A proton and a neutron are composed of up and down quarks, according to the formulas:

proton ~ 2 ups + 1 down
neutron ~ 1 up + 2 downs

The fractional electric charges of the quarks combine to produce an overall charge of 1+ in the proton and 0 in the neutron.

Quark Name	Letter Symbol	Electric Charge
Up	u	$2/3+$
Down	d	$1/3-$
Strange	s	$1/3-$
Charmed	c	$2/3+$
Beauty	b	$1/3-$
Truth	t	$2/3+$

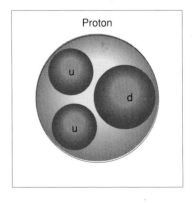

Proton

The distance between the quarks in nuclear particles is less than the distance between the nuclear particles themselves. Because of this small distance, it would be expected that the force between quarks is very strong. Experiments show that the quark-to-quark force is ten times as strong as the nuclear force between particles.

The quark model represents the most recent development in our understanding of the structure of atoms because it simplifies the intricacies of an infinite set of nuclear particles into the dynamics of six quarks. It remains to be seen if the quarks themselves are made of more fundamental particles or if the breakdown of atoms into nuclei and electrons, nuclei into protons and neutrons, and protons and neutrons into quarks, stops here.

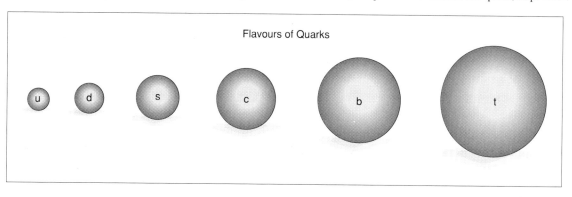

Flavours of Quarks

THE QUANTUM THEORY

1-10

The Particulate Nature of Radiant Energy

The work of Planck and Einstein led to the understanding that light has the properties of both waves and particles.
As a result of studying the relative energy of the light of different frequencies radiated from incandescent bodies (those that glow because of intense heat), Max Planck proposed that radiant energy, such as light and heat, is not emitted continuously but in little packets called **quanta**. He suggested that the *quantum of energy* depends on the frequency of the radiation. Assuming that the source of the light from the hot bodies was vibrating atoms, he proposed that these atoms could have only certain allowed energy values (quantized energy). In other words, *energy could only be emitted or absorbed in discrete units by vibrating atoms*. This is analogous to a tuning fork that remains motionless until another fork in the room is vibrating at its own specific frequency.

To explain his theory quantitatively, Planck developed an equation that related the allowed energy of a vibrating atom to its frequency. This equation is

$$E = hf \qquad [1\text{-}1]$$

where E is the energy in joules, f is the frequency in reciprocal

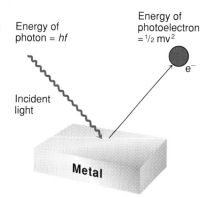

Figure 1-8
In the photoelectric effect, a photon of energy, equal to *hf*, ejects a photoelectron (pe⁻) from a metal. The velocity of the photoelectron depends on the frequency of the incident photon and not on the total number of photons.

MAX PLANCK
1858–1947

Max Planck, a German theoretical physicist, is best known for his revolutionary suggestion that radiation emitted by matter consists of packets of energy, or quanta. This was the first suggestion that the classical laws of physics might not always apply to atomic systems. This quantum theory was used by Einstein to describe the photoelectric effect, by Bohr to develop his concept of quantized energy levels and by many other scientists who played leading roles in the development of modern physical theories.

Planck was a versatile man with many interests. When he entered the University of Munich, he seriously considered a career in music rather than physics. He chose physics in spite of the suggestion from his adviser that little remained to be discovered in the field of physics. In 1918, at the age of 60, he was awarded the Nobel Prize in physics.

Planck was a man of unflinching courage. In 1934, while at the Kaiser Wilhelm Institute in Berlin, Planck attended a memorial service for Fritz Haber even though the Reichministry of Education had warned him against doing so because of Haber's non-Aryan background. Planck was held in disfavour by the Nazis because of his support of Jewish scientists. One of his own sons was executed for participating in a plot to assassinate Hitler.

seconds (s^{-1}) and h is a fundamental constant of nature, *Planck's constant*, equal to 6.626×10^{-34} J·s. According to Planck's hypothesis, atoms would not start vibrating until energy corresponding to a certain allowed value was absorbed. The atoms would then start vibrating with an amplitude corresponding to this quantized value of energy. Planck further postulated that when more energy was added, the amplitude would not gradually increase but would change suddenly when energy corresponding to twice the original quantum had been supplied.

Equation 1-1 can be used to show that high-frequency violet light has more energy than lower-frequency red light. If you have had experience with sun lamps, which emit ultraviolet light, and heat lamps, which emit infrared energy, you might conclude that heat lamps give off more energy because of the warmth you feel. According to Equation 1-1, this is not the case. The infrared energy from a heat lamp increases the motion of atoms and molecules, resulting in an increase in temperature. The rays from the ultraviolet lamp, in contrast, have sufficient energy to produce chemical changes in your skin. X rays and gamma rays have even higher frequencies and are more energetic.

Albert Einstein expanded Planck's idea of the particulate nature of radiant energy to include light or free radiant energy dissociated from all matter. Einstein assumed that the energy of electromagnetic radiation was not distributed over the entire wave front but was concentrated in packets of energy called **photons**. Photons are not material bodies as are atoms; they may be thought of as "massless" bundles of energy. The energy of a short-wavelength photon is greater than that of a long-wavelength photon. We may visualize these bundles of energy as being guided by the waves associated with them. Although it is rather difficult to visualize something that has both particle and wave characteristics, Einstein did not deny the possibility of this coexistence.

The best we can do is say that a wave of frequency, f, carries its energy in bundles (photons) of size hf. In other words, a wave guides the flow of energy, which is transported in bundles of definite size. As a result of these discoveries, *light is said to have a dual nature*. Under certain conditions it exhibits particle characteristics. Under other conditions, it behaves like a wave. For example, light is exhibiting wave characteristics when it undergoes *diffraction* and particle characteristics when it dislodges electrons from certain metals (exhibits the photoelectric effect). The **photoelectric effect** refers to the ability of photons (i.e., light) to eject electrons from a piece of metal (Fig. 1-8). Thus, energy is transferred either by means of waves or by means of particles.

Let us now investigate the role played by the quantum theory in the development of Bohr's model of the atom.

THE BOHR MODEL OF ATOMIC STRUCTURE

1-11

Energy States of a Hydrogen Atom

The work of Niels Bohr indicated that the electrons are found only in discrete energy levels within the atom.

In 1913, using Rutherford's concept of a nuclear atom, Planck's quantum theory and great imagination, Niels Bohr proposed a new model of atomic structure. This new model explained two important observations that could not be explained by either the Dalton or the Rutherford model. These were the stability of atoms and the wavelength of the lines in the hydrogen spectrum.

According to classical electrodynamic theory, the electrons whirling around the nucleus in Rutherford's model of atoms would be attracted to and spiral into the nucleus. In other words, the atom would be unstable and collapse readily. The observation that matter exists is evidence that Rutherford's atomic model is incorrect and incomplete. In addition to the instability of atoms, the classical theory predicts that a continuous range of energies would be emitted by an atom, so that a continuous atomic-emission spectrum should be observed.

Bohr's theory of atomic structure was based on Planck's quantum theory and contained the following three postulates:

1. *Electrons can occupy only certain specific energy levels, which are sometimes referred to as orbits or shells.* An electron does not emit energy when it is in one of these permitted energy levels. This postulate explains the stability of atoms because it does not permit an electron to lose energy continuously and spiral into the nucleus.

2. *Energy is radiated only when an electron falls from a higher to a lower energy level.* Atoms can emit or absorb energy only in specific amounts (quanta). The amount of energy absorbed or liberated is equal to the difference in energy possessed by the electron in the two different energy levels. This postulate, which incorporates Planck's quantum concept, explains the discontinuous atomic-emission spectra of atoms. That is, it permits an atom to emit radiation of a specific wavelength only.

3. *The angular momentum of an electron revolving about the nucleus is quantized.* That is, the angular momentum can take only specific values that are equal to

$$\frac{nh}{2\pi}$$

NIELS BOHR
1885–1962
Niels Bohr, one of the greatest atomic physicists of the twentieth century, proposed the familiar solar-system model of the atom. The influence exerted by Bohr and his many students on the modern atomic theory cannot be overestimated.

Bohr received his doctorate in 1911, the same year that Ernest Rutherford announced his discovery of the atomic nucleus. In Denmark it was the custom to treat the oral examination of a doctoral thesis as a public event. When Bohr defended his thesis, he did so before packed houses and to rave reviews in the press.

After studying with J. J. Thomson and Rutherford in England, Bohr formulated his own model of the atom. For this work, he received the 1922 Nobel Prize in physics.

Bohr's theories on the nature of the nucleus enabled him to play a leading role in the development of nuclear energy. It was Bohr who informed the United States that it was possible to split the uranium nucleus.

At the end of World War II, Bohr returned to Denmark to the Copenhagen Institute for Theoretical Physics. For his intense interest and work on the peaceful use of atomic energy, he received the first Atoms for Peace Award in 1957.

where h is Planck's constant and n is an integer that is restricted to any whole-number value. It turns out that n identifies the energy level in which the electron is located.

Bohr's model of the atom can be visualized as a miniature solar system, with the electrons representing planets. In the case of stable atoms, Bohr assumed that an electron is kept in its orbit by an inward centripetal force that was caused by and equal to the electrostatic force of attraction exerted by the nucleus. By expressing these relationships in quantitative terms and then introducing his quantized angular momentum requirement, Bohr was able to derive an expression that allowed him to calculate the radii of shells that represent the different energy levels within a hydrogen atom. This expression is simplified to

$$r = n^2 \ (52.9 \text{ pm})$$

If we wish to describe the energy state of a single atom, then a convenient unit of energy to use is one ***electron volt*** (eV). One electron volt is the amount of energy a single electron absorbs when it passes through a potential difference of one volt. One electron volt is an extremely small energy unit. It represents about the same amount of energy that the smallest imaginable particle of chalk dust would lose if it were to fall over a cliff as high as the thickness of this page.

$$1 \text{ eV} = 1.60 \times 10^{-19} \text{ J}$$

The energy associated with a hydrogen atom when its electron is in the first level can be calculated to be -13.6 eV. At this point, it may be instructive to interpret the significance of this negative number. It is possible to do an experiment that will measure the energy required to remove an electron completely from an atom. Applied to a neutral hydrogen atom with an electron in its lowest energy level, the experiment reveals that 13.6 eV is required to overcome the attractive force between the electron and its nucleus. In other words, energy is added to the atomic system to remove an electron. This means that *the atomic system has a greater potential energy when an electron is far from the nucleus than when close to it*. If we arbitrarily assign the atomic system zero potential energy when the electron is completely free from the nuclear attraction, then the value of the potential energy decreases and has a negative sign as the electron approaches the nucleus. Applied to a hydrogen atom, we can say that the atomic system has 13.6 eV less energy when the electron is in the first energy level than when it is at infinity. Since the potential energy with the electron at maximum distance from the nucleus is zero, it must have a negative value at all other distances. Hence, the energy value of the atomic system

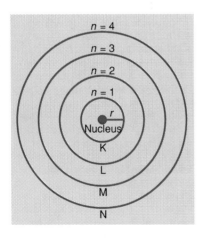

Figure 1-9
Bohr's solar-system model of the hydrogen atom. With Bohr's equation, the distance from the nucleus to the lowest-energy electron shell (r_1) is calculated to be 0.0529 nm.

in its lowest energy state (electron closest to the nucleus) is −13.6 eV. Interpretation of the atomic-emission spectrum of hydrogen shows that 13.6 eV is evolved when an electron that has been removed from the attraction of the nucleus returns to the first, or lowest possible, energy level of a hydrogen atom.

The potential energy of a hydrogen atom is at a minimum when its electron is in the energy level nearest the nucleus; thus, the total energy of a hydrogen atom is at a minimum. For all other levels, the potential energy is greater and has a more positive value. Thus, the energy associated with an electron occupying the second energy level is −3.4 eV, which is more positive than −13.6 eV. The allowed radii and energies associated with each energy level may be calculated and represented schematically by the solar-system diagram (Fig. 1-9) or the energy-level diagram (Fig. 1-10).

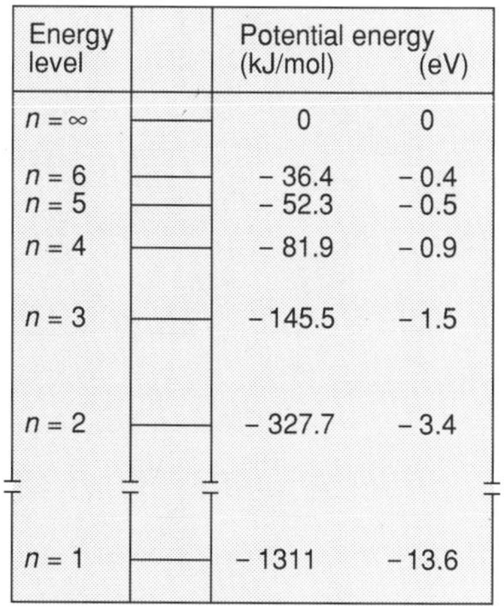

The energy associated with a mole of hydrogen atoms is usually expressed in terms of kJ/mol. Using the conversion factor, we can express the energy associated with a mole of hydrogen atoms as

$$\frac{-2.18 \times 10^{-18} \text{ J}}{\text{atom}} \times \frac{6.02 \times 10^{23} \text{ atoms}}{1 \text{ mol atoms}} = -1.312 \times 10^6 \text{ J/mol}$$

$$\text{or}$$

$$-1.312 \times 10^3 \text{ kJ/mol}$$

This value indicates that 1312 kJ is evolved when a mole of electrons free from the nuclear attraction drops into the first energy levels of a mole of hydrogen atoms. Conversely, it means that 1312 kJ is required to remove a mole of electrons from the first energy levels and away from the nuclear attraction of a mole of hydrogen atoms. A more accurate value for this energy is 1311 kJ/mol. Thus, the energy states of a hydrogen atom may be calculated using the equation

$$E_n = \frac{-1311}{n^2} \text{ kJ/mol of electrons}$$

We are now able to explain the origin of atomic-emission spectral lines.

Energy level		Potential energy (kJ/mol)	(eV)
$n = \infty$		0	0
$n = 6$		− 36.4	− 0.4
$n = 5$		− 52.3	− 0.5
$n = 4$		− 81.9	− 0.9
$n = 3$		− 145.5	− 1.5
$n = 2$		− 327.7	− 3.4
$n = 1$		− 1311	− 13.6

Figure 1-10
An energy-level diagram for the hydrogen atom. Negative values indicate the energy evolved when a mole of electrons drops from $n = \infty$ to a lower level. Positive values indicate the energy absorbed in removing a mole of electrons from a given level to $n = \infty$.

Electron volts per atom may be converted directly into kilojoules per mole of atoms by using the following relationship:

$$\frac{\text{eV}}{\text{atom}} \times 96.5 = \frac{\text{kJ}}{\text{mol atoms}}$$

1-12
The Origin of Atomic-Emission Spectral Lines

Atomic-emission spectral lines arise from the energy emitted when electrons move from an outer energy level to a lower level.

The energy levels in a hydrogen atom can be identified in terms of a principal quantum number known as n. Thus, the energy level closest to the nucleus is designated as either the $n = 1$ level, or the first level. Succeeding levels are designated as $n = 2$, $n = 3$, $n = 4$, $n = 5$, $n = 6$ and $n = 7$. When an electron is completely indepen-

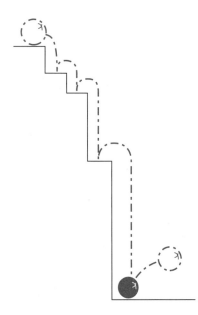

Figure 1-11
A ball rolling down a staircase can be likened to an electron dropping from a higher to a lower energy level within an atom. The bottom of the staircase would represent the lowest energy level within the atom.

dent of the nuclear attraction, $n = \infty$. The atom has minimum potential energy and is said to be in the **_ground state_** when an electron is in the first energy level. When electric energy is applied to hydrogen gas in a discharge tube, energy is absorbed by the atoms as electrons are raised to higher energy levels. That is, work is done in separating an electron from the nucleus that attracts it.

Let us compare the energy levels in an atom to the steps on a staircase (Fig. 1-11). A ball resting on the floor represents a position of minimum potential energy similar to the ground state in a hydrogen atom. On the top step, the ball has maximum potential energy. This is analogous to a free electron that is completely away from the influence of the nucleus. When the ball falls from the top step, it bounces down the stairs to a position of minimum potential energy on the floor below. Similarly, the potential energy of an atom is greater when the electron is in the second level than when it is in the first level.

When an electron is in a level other than the first level, the atom is said to be in an **_excited state_**. Since the excited state is unstable, the electrons return almost immediately (10^{-8} s) to their more stable lower energy levels. The difference in the energy possessed by an electron in the two different energy levels is emitted by the atom as a discrete amount of radiant energy. For example, when an electron drops from the second to the first energy level, the energy evolved is equal to $E_2 - E_1$. That is,

$$E_{\text{evolved}} = -3.4 \text{ eV} - (-13.6 \text{ eV}) = 10.2 \text{ eV}$$

This value may be converted to kJ/mol of atoms by using the proper conversion factors.

Since photon units are involved in this transfer of energy, we may represent the emission of radiation by an excited atom as

$$E_2 - E_1 = hf$$

where E_2 is the energy of the atom in the higher energy state, E_1 is the energy of the atom in the lower energy state, and hf is the energy of the photon. The frequency of the wave associated with a photon may be expressed as

$$f = \frac{E_2 - E_1}{h}$$

Frequency is related to wavelength by the equation

$$\lambda = c/f$$

Thus, each electron transition from a higher to a lower level produces a photon of specific wavelength that contributes to the "line" in the spectrum of the element. The greater the distance between the levels, the greater is the energy and the shorter is the wavelength of the emitted radiation.

In making transitions from outer to inner levels, the electrons release energy, the emission of which is indicated by the production of spectral lines. In a sample of hydrogen gas, individual atoms absorb and liberate different amounts of energy. For example, an electron in some of the hydrogen atoms may drop from the fourth to the second energy level. These particular atoms emit energy that corresponds to the difference in energy between the fourth and second energy levels. This transition contributes to the blue-green line observed in the hydrogen spectrum. In other hydrogen atoms, an electron may drop from the third energy level to the second level. This transition represents a smaller energy gap; hence, these atoms emit radiation of longer wavelength, which is observed as the red line in the visible spectrum of hydrogen. The visible lines in the hydrogen spectrum constitute what is known as the ***Balmer series***. It can be shown that these lines are produced when an electron jumps from the 3rd, 4th, 5th or 6th level to the 2nd energy level (Fig. 1-12). The intensity of the colour of a particular line depends on the number of electrons simultaneously making the transition represented by the line.

The "line," as it is called, is merely the image of a vertical slit through which the light travels. The light that one sees comes from the contributions of many photons of the same energy being emitted simultaneously by identical electron transitions in a large number of atoms.

Figure 1-12
When an electron falls from a higher energy level to a lower level, a photon is emitted. The greater the difference in energy between levels, the greater will be the energy of the emitted photon.

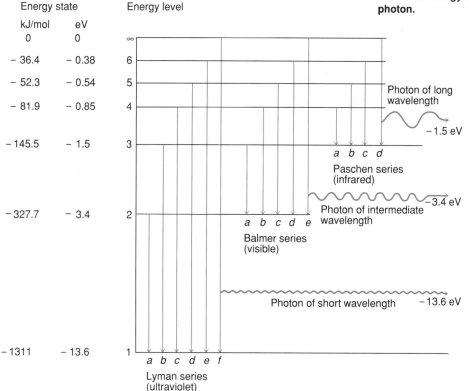

Bohr was able to calculate theoretically the wavelength of the known visible lines in the hydrogen spectrum and also to predict the existence of an undiscovered series of lines in the ultraviolet region of the hydrogen spectrum. From his own theoretically derived equation, he predicted the wavelengths of these unknown lines. The subsequent discovery of the **Lyman series** of lines, with wavelengths similar to those predicted by Bohr, gave added support to Bohr's original theory. This series originates when electrons fall from the 6th, 5th, 4th, 3rd and 2nd levels to the first energy level. Perhaps you can use the energy-level diagram in Fig. 1-12 to explain why the Lyman series is in the ultraviolet rather than the visible region of the spectrum.

The following example illustrates how the wavelength of a spectral line can be calculated using the different energy states of a hydrogen atom.

"At the final stage you tell me that this multicoloured universe can be reduced to the atom and that the atom itself can be reduced to the electron. All this is good and I wait for you to continue. But you tell me of an invisible planetary system where electrons gravitate around a nucleus. You explain this to me with an image. I realize then that you have been reduced to poetry: I shall never know. Have I the time to become indignant? You have changed theories. So that science that was to teach me everything ends up in a hypothesis, that lucidity founders in metaphor, that uncertainty is resolved in a work of art."
Albert Camus, *The Myth of Sisyphus*

EXAMPLE 1-1
Determining the Wavelength of a Spectral Line

Show that the transition of an electron from $n = 4$ to $n = 2$ in a hydrogen atom gives rise to the blue-green spectral line with a wavelength of 486 nm.

SOLUTION

1. The energy evolved when one electron falls from energy level 4 to energy level 2 can be determined by referring to the energy-level diagram shown in Fig. 1-12.

$$E_{\text{evolved}} = E_4 - E_2 = -0.85 \text{ eV} - (-3.40 \text{ eV})$$
$$= 2.55 \text{ eV}$$

2. Substitute known values for the factors in the equation $(E_4 - E_2) = \dfrac{hc}{\lambda}$ and solve for λ. Using electron volts, the equation is:

$$-0.85 \text{ eV} - (-3.40 \text{ eV})$$
$$= \frac{(6.62 \times 10^{-34} \text{ J·s})(3.0 \times 10^8 \text{ m/s})}{\lambda}$$

$$\lambda = \frac{(6.62 \times 10^{-34} \text{ J·s})(3.0 \times 10^8 \text{ m/s})}{(2.55 \text{ eV})(1.6 \times 10^{-19} \text{ J/eV})}$$

$$= 4.87 \times 10^{-7} \text{ m}$$

When excited, each element emits radiant energy with a unique set of wavelengths. In other words, no two elements have the same spectrum. Therefore, the spectrum of an element is like a set of fingerprints and can be used to identify the element (see Colour Plate II). For example, helium in the sun's atmosphere was first "discovered" by means of spectral analysis. When it was later found on earth, it was again identified by its spectrum. The composition of a star billions of kilometres away can be determined by spectroscopic analysis of its emitted light.

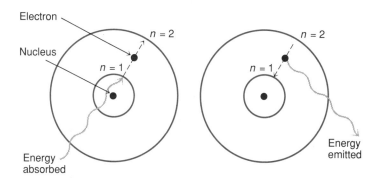

Figure 1-13
When the electron in the first energy level of the hydrogen atom absorbs 10.2 eV of energy, it makes a *quantum jump* to the second level. When it returns to the first level, it gives up 10.2 eV of energy. This energy is associated with ultraviolet radiation.

1-13
Quantum Jumps

The following demonstration can be used to show that atoms can absorb or emit energy of only specific values.

In this demonstration, two different sources of ultraviolet light are used. Try to predict which lamp uses mercury atoms as a source of light.

In a darkened room, mercury vapour is allowed to pass between a source of ultraviolet light and a fluorescent screen (filter paper coated with anthracene), as shown in Fig. 1-14. Although mercury vapour is invisible, dark clouds of "smoke" can be seen drifting across the screen. (***Do not try this demonstration yourself***. Mercury vapour is extremely poisonous.) The "smoke" is the shadow of mercury atoms that have absorbed the ultraviolet light that strikes them. In the case of the short-wavelength ultraviolet light, the photons contain the exact amount of energy needed to effect a *quantum jump* or, in other words, to promote an electron in a mercury atom from its unexcited (ground) state to a higher energy level. Thus, the energy is absorbed by the atom and does not reach the screen as light energy. As a result, the atom casts a shadow. If ultraviolet light of a longer wavelength is used, a shadow is not produced. Since the longer-wavelength photon does not have sufficient energy to promote an electron from one specific level to a higher level, the energy of the photon is not absorbed. As you may have predicted, the lamp emitting the longer-wavelength light does not use mercury as the source of the radiation.

Figure 1-14
The invisible cloud of mercury atoms absorbs the ultraviolet light from the lamp and casts a shadow on the fluorescent screen. Since only light of the specific wavelength 253 nm is absorbed, an ultraviolet lamp emitting this wavelength must be used.

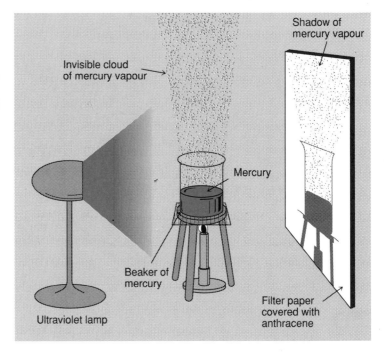

Shadow of mercury vapour

Invisible cloud of mercury vapour

Mercury

Beaker of mercury

Filter paper covered with anthracene

Ultraviolet lamp

1-14
The Electron Population of Energy Levels

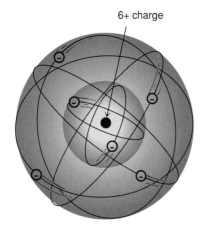

6+ charge

Figure 1-15
The Bohr model of a carbon atom. Two electrons occupy and fill the first energy level, and four electrons occupy but do not fill the second energy level.

The electron population of each energy level in atoms having more than one electron can be determined by spectroscopic analysis and explained in terms of the more advanced atomic theory discussed in Chapter 2.

The maximum number of electrons that are allowed in a given principal energy level is $2n^2$, where n is the number of the principal energy level. Thus, the maximum number of electrons in any energy level is limited by the value of n.

Using the $2n^2$ formula, we can show that the first energy level can contain a maximum of 2 electrons and that the second level can contain a maximum of 8 electrons. Figure 1-15 shows Bohr's model of a carbon atom. How many electrons can be accommodated in the second energy level of the carbon atom? Isolated atoms in the ground state have minimum potential energy. This means that the electrons occupy the lowest available energy levels. Thus, for example, an isolated chlorine atom, which has a total of 17 electrons, has 2 electrons in the first level, 8 electrons in the second level and 7 electrons in the third level. However, beyond calcium (element 20), Bohr's model could not account for the distribution of the electrons about the nucleus, and, thus, a new model was developed.

As we discussed earlier, our concept of the atom is not based on a single body of indisputable truth but, rather, on a body of well-supported opinion that can be modified as new evidence comes to light. Table 1-2 gives a summary of the models of the atom, culminating in the most complete atomic theory proposed to date—the quantum, or wave-mechanical, model.

TABLE 1-2
A CHRONOLOGICAL SUMMARY OF THE DEVELOPMENT OF THE ATOM MODEL

Date	Model	Proponent
c. 400 BC	Atoms as tiny, indivisible particles	Democritus
1808	Billiard-ball model	John Dalton
1903	Rice-pudding model	J. J. Thomson
1909	Nuclear model	Ernest Rutherford
1913	Solar-system model	Niels Bohr
1926	Quantum, or wave-mechanical, model	Erwin Schrödinger

Figure 1-16
Ernest Rutherford in his laboratory. Rutherford is known as one of the century's greatest experimental physicists and was able to obtain his outstanding results using makeshift equipment. Once, when invited to view a modern, well-equipped laboratory, he muttered to an assistant, "Too much equipment—too little brains."

1-15

Introducing the Quantum, or Wave-Mechanical, Model

Bohr's model of the atom, although it introduced the concept of energy levels, did not explain the nature of multi-electron atoms. This discrepancy in Bohr's model led to the development of a more complete model—the quantum, or wave-mechanical, model.

Bohr's theory satisfactorily explained the stability and atomic-emission spectra of a hydrogen atom. It also contributed the important concept of fixed energy levels, or states, and enabled scientists to construct a model of an atom that is easy to visualize.

Unfortunately, this model does not satisfactorily explain the electron configuration, nature and behaviour of atoms containing many electrons. First of all, Bohr's model does not explain the spectra of multi-electron atoms or account for the observed energy differences between the electrons that occupy the same principal energy level. In addition, it fails to explain the shapes and characteristics of molecules. Furthermore, some of the factors found in Bohr's equations were not a natural outcome of his theory. They were arbitrarily introduced by Bohr because they fixed the positions of electron orbits, enabling him to predict correctly the experimentally observed wavelengths of the hydrogen spectrum.

To explain the electron configuration and behaviour of multi-electron atoms, it is necessary to develop a more complex theory and model of atomic structure. The need for a more adequate model leads us to investigate the modern concept of an atom in the next chapter. The model is known as the quantum, or wave-mechanical, model.

SERENDIPITY

Everyone is familiar with the story of how Isaac Newton was sitting in an apple orchard when he was struck on the head with a falling apple. This accident was said to have prompted Newton's discovery of gravity. Whether this story is true or just a legend is not important. What is important, however, is the critical role that serendipity seems to play in many important scientific discoveries.

Serendipity is defined by the Oxford Dictionary as "the faculty of making happy and unexpected discoveries by accident." The myth associated with many scientific discoveries is that they are assumed to be serendipitous; that is, great breakthroughs can neither be planned nor predicted because they depend, to a large extent, on luck. The testing of a scientific hypothesis, on the other hand, is believed to be a more valid and logical operation that only a trained scientific mind can perform. Many philosophers of science suggest that a discovery is a product, not of logical inquiry, but of being in the right place at the right time, and that it could happen to anyone.

There are many stories of "serendipitous" discoveries, including Wilhelm Röntgen's discovery of X rays. However, Röntgen did not stumble on the existence of X rays by accident. After observing fogged photographic plates and fluorescing screens, Röntgen began searching for the explanation for these observations and concluded that the effects were created by rays being emitted from a nearby cathode-ray tube. Many people, including Röntgen's colleague, William Crookes, had observed the same phenomena but had not reached the same conclusions. The ability to make detailed and accurate observations, coupled with intellectual curiosity, can lead to unexpected discoveries, but, as French chemist Louis Pasteur (1822–1895) said, "Chance favours the prepared mind."

Thus, "serendipitous" discoveries should be attributed to the scientist's intellectual curiosity, willingness to explore the unexpected and ability to detect the unusual. William Crookes did not discover X rays, because he was not looking for them. Henri Le Châtelier (1850–1936), known for his principle of equilibrium, missed the opportunity to discover the synthesis of ammonia when a violent explosion interrupted his work on the reaction. Convinced the experiment was a failure, Le Châtelier later lamented, "I let the discovery of ammonia synthesis slip through my hands. It was the greatest blunder of my scientific career."

Intellectual curiosity is not the only requirement for a successful discovery; the scientist must be intuitive enough to perceive the principles behind and the patterns within observed phenomena. Ernest Rutherford, for example, while performing a simple experiment to verify J.J. Thomson's model of the atom, obtained aberrant results. However, Rutherford did not discount his observations and, instead, searched for the principles behind what he saw. Subsequently, he developed his own atomic theory.

Being able to recognize patterns in phenomena and organize facts facilitated Russian chemist Dmitri Mendeleyev's (1834–1907) development of the periodic table. Although the German chemist Lothar Meyer (1830–1895) had already discovered periodicity in the properties of the elements, the credit for recognizing the periodic law and for promoting its usefulness is attributed to Mendeleyev. Instead of forcing the elements into a preconceived pattern, Mendeleyev organized the elements according to their atomic masses such that chemically related elements appeared in specific intervals. He also correctly predicted the existence of elements not yet discovered and left gaps in his table for them.

Scientific discoveries are never entirely accidental. Even Newton had to be receptive to the idea that such a thing as gravity existed. As American chemist Albert Szent-Györgyi (1893–1986) stated, "Discovery consists of seeing what everybody has seen and thinking what nobody has thought." Often, the most important discoveries arise not from serendipitous experiments but from recognizing and exploring unexpected avenues of thought.

QUESTIONS

1. (a) What do we mean by the term "model" as it is used in science? (b) Why do we use models in science? (c) What are the limitations of models? (d) What is the difference between a model and a theory?

2. How did Dalton's theory account for the law of conservation of mass and the law of definite proportions?

3. Why do we not consider the atomic nature of matter, as suggested by the early Greek philosophers, a true scientific model?

4. (a) Outline the main postulates of Dalton's atomic theory. (b) What are the limitations of Dalton's atomic theory? (c) In what ways does Dalton's theory differ from modern atomic theory? In what ways are they similar?

5. Which property is most closely related to the chemical behaviour of an element—atomic mass or atomic number? Explain.

6. (a) What two atomic models followed Dalton's model? (b) What are the distinguishing features of each model? (c) What are the problems with each model?

7. What does the atomic number of an atom reveal about its composition?

8. What experimental evidence requires that the emission of energy by an atom be quantized?

9. (a) Explain why scientists continue to view electromagnetic radiation as having a dual nature? (b) Why do they not exclusively use either the wave model or the particle model?

10. Copy the table and fill in the blanks. *Do not write in this book*.

Element	Atomic Number	Mass Number	No. of Protons	No. of Neutrons	No. of Electrons
	13	27			
	19			20	
Nickel				30	
Xenon				78	
		238	92		

11. Write the number of electrons in each principal energy level of the following atoms in the ground state: (a) He, (b) F, (c) Na, (d) P, (e) Ar.

12. Calculate the maximum number of electrons that may be contained in each of the first six energy (quantum) levels of an atom.

13. The atomic masses given in the periodic table are not whole numbers. Explain.

14. How do radiant-energy waves differ from sound or water waves?

15. The wavelengths of X rays are much shorter than those of ultraviolet or visible light. Using the relationships $E = hf$ and $c = \lambda f$, show qualitatively why continued exposure to X rays is more damaging than exposure to sunlight.

16. Describe Max Planck's contribution to the understanding of the nature of light.

17. (a) What problems did the Bohr model of the atom resolve? (b) Why was the Bohr model replaced by the quantum, or wave-mechanical, model?

18. (a) What were the two major assumptions of Bohr's theory of atomic structure? (b) Outline the differences between Rutherford's and Bohr's models of the atom.

19. Why does the spectrum of hydrogen contain several lines when a hydrogen atom has only one electron?

20. State Planck's law both in words and in mathematical symbols.

21. If Planck's constant were larger than it is, how would this affect our everyday lives?

PROBLEMS

1. Approximately 14 eV of energy is required to remove an electron from the first energy level of a hydrogen atom. It can be shown that approximately 10 eV is required to cause the electron to go from the first to the second level. What is the energy in eV required to remove the electron completely from the atom when it is in the second energy level?
   Answer: 4eV

2. Calculate the energy in eV required to cause an electron transition in a hydrogen atom from (a) $n = 1$ to $n = 2$ and (b) from $n = 3$ to $n = 4$.
   Answer: (b) 0.66 eV/atom

3. (a) Calculate the energy state of a hydrogen atom when the principal quantum number of the electron is 7. (b) What is the significance of the minus sign in your answer?

4. The characteristic colour imparted to a bunsen-burner flame when ordinary salt (NaCl) is heated is the result of an electron transition involving 2.1 eV. What is the wavelength of this radiation and what colour is imparted to the flame? The approximate wavelengths for different colours are: red, 650 nm; yellow, 600 nm; blue, 450 nm; violet, 400 nm.
   Answer: 5.9×10^2 nm

5. In an oil-drop experiment designed to determine the charge on an electron, the charges found on different oil droplets are

2.24×10^{-18} C	1.28×10^{-18} C
1.76×10^{-18} C	9.59×10^{-19} C
1.44×10^{-18} C	4.80×10^{-19} C

   Use this data to calculate (a) the charge on an electron in C and (b) the number of electrons attached to an oil drop with a charge of 2.72×10^{-18} C.
   Answers: (a) 1.60×10^{-19} C, (b) 17 electrons

6. Some dwarf stars are believed to be composed of almost pure nuclear material. If a dime were made up of pure nuclear material, calculate its mass in tonnes. Assume that a dime occupies 1 cm^3 and that nuclear particles have a density of about 5×10^{17} kg/m^3.
   Answer: 5×10^8 t

7. Millikan's oil-drop experiment involved determining charges on thousands of oil drops. Each oil drop contained an unknown number of unit charges, yet Millikan was able to calculate the charge on a single electron. Assume that you are measuring samples of uniformly large oranges on a balance with a sensitivity of ±1 g. Each sample being measured contains an unknown number of oranges. (a) Explain how you would determine the mass of a single orange with ±1 g. (b) Would one or two measurings be adequate?

8. Some experimental lights use salts of lithium because excited lithium atoms emit a photon that is in the red ($\lambda = 7.0 \times 10^2$ nm) region of the spectrum. Calculate the number of electron volts emitted from an excited lithium atom as it returns to its ground state. There are 1.6×10^{-19} J/eV.
   Answer: 1.8 eV

9. If the gold target in Rutherford's experiment were 6.0×10^{-5} cm thick, approximately how many atoms thick was the target? Make the following assumptions: (a) The radius of a gold atom is 0.144 nm. (b) The atoms line up just touching one another from one side of the foil to the other. (c) They are hard spheres.

Neon signs, such as the one outside this Montreal restaurant, contain mixtures of noble gases. When electric energy is absorbed by these gases, their atoms become excited and emit visible light in a range of colours as they return to their ground state.

The Electron Configuration of Atoms

In order to explain the behaviour of multi-electron atoms, we must know their electron configurations. The Bohr atom model provided the important concept of specific (quantized) energy states, or levels, and an easy-to-visualize picture of an atom. Modern quantum, or wave-mechanical, theory, developed during the 1920s, retains the concept of quantized energy states but abandons (invalidates) the easy-to-visualize satellite model with its electrons in fixed trajectories (orbits).

Modern theory views the atom as a positively charged nucleus surrounded by pulsating electron waves. Although we will continue to refer to an electron as a particle, it is important to remember that scientists use the solutions to a complicated wave equation to describe mathematically the behaviour of an electron in terms of its wave characteristics.

The transition from the easy-to-visualize satellite model is made easier if we draw analogies to it. In the Bohr model, we visualized electrons as travelling around the nucleus in orbits of fixed radius. In the wave-mechanical model, we will see that the electrons are moving about in such a way as to occupy designated regions of space around the nucleus, called *orbitals*. We will attach recognizable shapes and spatial orientations to electron orbitals.

Orbitals may be viewed as *electron charge clouds* produced by the rapid motion of electrons. In other words, a charge cloud represents the distribution of electron charge that would be obtained by observing the motion of an electron over a period of time. Modern theory describes the location of the electron in terms of probability. Probability information tells us in which regions of space an electron spends most of its time.

The models and illustrations of electron orbitals represent the boundaries of the volume within which an electron with a given energy might be found a given percentage (90%) of the time. The shapes and spatial orientations of the orbitals are important because they will help us to understand and predict the way in which atoms react.

As you might expect, the wave-mechanical theory is abstract and mathematical. Therefore, in this chapter we will first present a simplified version of electron configuration in terms of the concepts of the wave-mechanical theory. In our discussion, we will explain the form of the periodic table and the observed periodicity in the properties of the elements in terms of the electron configuration of the atoms.

The essential features of electron configuration are presented in Sections 2-1 through 2-8. After completing these sections, we will be able to use energy-level diagrams and quantum, wave-mechanical, principles to designate the electron population of the orbitals and principal energy levels.

In the second half of the chapter, we will discuss the origin and theoretical basis of the wave-mechanical model. These sections will give us a better idea of how scientists view an atom.

THE ELECTRON CONFIGURATION OF MULTI-ELECTRON ATOMS AND IONS

TABLE 2-1

MAXIMUM NUMBER OF ELECTRONS FOUND AT EACH ENERGY LEVEL

Energy Level (n)	Number of Electrons ($2n^2$)
1	2
2	8
3	18
4	32
5	50

2-1

Energy Sublevels

Each principal energy level is divided into a number of energy sublevels. The number of these sublevels is equal to the principal quantum number.

Experimental data shows that all of the electrons that occupy a given principal energy level of a multi-electron atom do not have the same energy. A clue to the energies of the electrons in a principal energy level is found in the energy required to remove them from the attractive force of the nucleus. Consider an isolated magnesium atom (atomic number 12), which has 12 electrons.

Using the $2n^2$ rule noted in Chapter 1, we find that the lowest energy level ($n = 1$) has two electrons, the second energy level ($n = 2$) has eight electrons and the third energy level ($n = 3$) has two electrons (Table 2-1). Spectroscopic analysis can be used to determine the energy required to completely remove any one of the electrons from a magnesium atom. The results of such an analysis applied to the first 20 elements are in Table 2-2.

TABLE 2-2
ENERGIES (ELECTRON VOLTS) REQUIRED TO REMOVE ELECTRONS FROM ATOMS

Total Electrons	1	2	3	4	5	6	7	8	9	10	11	12	13	14	15	16	17	18	19	20
Principal Energy Level	1		2								3								4	
Orbital	1s		2s		2p						3s		3p						4s	
Hydrogen	14																			
Helium	25	25																		
Lithium	65	65	5																	
Beryllium	120	120	9	9																
Boron	200	200	13	13	8															
Carbon	300	300	17	17	11	11														
Nitrogen	450	450	20	20	15	15	15													
Oxygen	550	550	28	28	14	14	14	14												
Fluorine	700	700	38	38	17	17	17	17	17											
Neon	900	900	50	50	22	22	22	22	22	22										
Sodium	1000	1000	60	60	40	40	40	40	40	40	5									
Magnesium	1200	1200	85	85	52	52	52	52	52	52	8	8								
Aluminum	1600	1600	110	110	75	75	75	75	75	75	10	10	6							
Silicon	1800	1800	140	140	100	100	100	100	100	100	13	13	8	8						
Phosphorus	2200	2200	180	180	130	130	130	130	130	130	17	17	11	11	11					
Sulfur	2400	2400	220	220	160	160	160	160	160	160	20	20	10	10	10	10				
Chlorine	2800	2800	260	260	190	190	190	190	190	190	24	24	13	13	13	13	13			
Argon	3000	3000	320	320	225	225	225	225	225	225	29	29	16	16	16	16	16	16		
Potassium	3400	3400	380	380	280	280	280	280	280	280	35	35	26	26	26	26	26	26	4	
Calcium	3600	3600	430	430	320	320	320	320	320	320	43	43	28	28	28	28	28	28	6	6

Principal Energy Level (n)	Number of Energy Sublevels ($= n$)	Designation and Relative Energies of Energy Sublevels
1	1	s
2	2	$s < p$
3	3	$s < p < d$
4	4	$s < p < d < f$

Let us see how the data in Table 2-2 provides evidence for energy sublevels. Consider a magnesium atom. Removal of either of the two electrons in the third energy level requires 8 electron volts. Apparently, these two electrons are located in the same sublevel. It should be noted that after one of the electrons in the third level is removed, the inter-electron repulsion decreases so that the remaining electron is closer to the nucleus and held more firmly than before. Thus, 15 eV is required to remove the other electron. Of the eight electrons located in the second energy level, any one of a group of six can be removed by 52 eV, while either of the remaining pair can be removed by 85 eV. This data suggests that the electrons in the second energy level are arranged in two energy sublevels that have different energy values. Either of the two electrons in the first energy level may be removed by 1200 eV. This suggests that there is only one energy sublevel in the first principal energy level. An extension of Table 2-2 would show that *the number of different kinds of energy sublevels in a principal level is equal to the principal quantum number, n*.

Within a given energy level, the energy sublevels are designated in order of increasing energy as s, p, d and f. Thus, the first principal energy level contains only an s sublevel; the second contains s and p sublevels; the third contains s, p and d sublevels; and the fourth contains s, p, d and f sublevels. We can represent the relative energies of the sublevels and their relationship to the principal energy levels as shown in the margin above.

Assuming that the electrons are found in the lowest energy sublevels first, we can say that in a gaseous neon atom that has ten electrons, two electrons occupy the s sublevel of the first energy level, two electrons occupy the s sublevel of the second energy level and six electrons occupy the p sublevel.

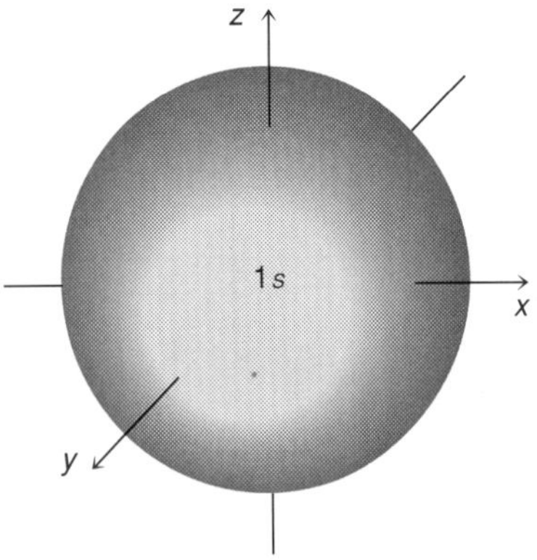

2-2
Orbitals

Orbitals are regions in space in which the electrons in the energy sublevels are most likely to be found. The total number of orbitals available in a given energy level is equal to n^2.

It can be shown that under the influence of a magnetic field, the electrons in the energy sublevels are most likely to be found in certain preferred regions of space about the nucleus. These regions of space are called **orbitals**. The spatial orientation of the orbitals is illustrated in Figs. 2-1, 2-2 and 2-3. To help us visualize orbitals, boundaries are established that define their shapes. These boundaries enclose the region in space within which the electron is most likely to be found. It can be seen in Fig. 2-1 that s orbitals are spherical regions of space and in Fig. 2-2 that p orbitals, which

Figure 2-1
The 1s atomic orbital. The nucleus is at the intersection of the x, y and z axes. The 1s electron, the lowest-energy electron in an isolated atom, is most likely to be found within the boundary of the spherical region of space.

have two major lobes, are oriented with their axes along one of the three axes in space. Furthermore, the three p orbitals are perpendicular to each other. They are identified as p_x, p_y, p_z, where the subscripts refer to the orientation of the orbital axis with respect to the space axes (Cartesian co-ordinates). The d orbitals are shown in Fig. 2-3 on page 35.

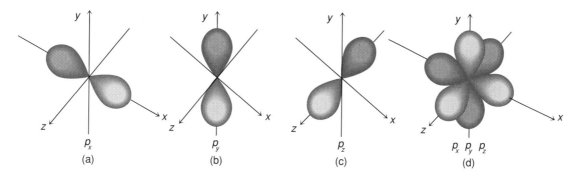

| p_x | p_y | p_z | p_x p_y p_z |
| (a) | (b) | (c) | (d) |

Figure 2-2
The p orbitals. Unlike s orbitals, p orbitals have directional characteristics. p electrons are most likely to be found in the regions of space directed along the x, y and z axes. In an atom, the three $2p$ orbitals are oriented as shown in (d).

Application of quantum mechanics shows that the first principal energy level in an atom has only an s orbital; the second energy level has one s and three p orbitals; the third energy level has one s, three p and five d orbitals; and the fourth energy level has one s, three p, five d and seven f orbitals. It follows that *the total number of orbitals available in a given energy level is equal to n^2.* More detailed analysis and calculations reveal that *each orbital can contain a maximum of two electrons.* This means that *the maximum number of electrons in a given energy level is $2n^2$.* The relationships discussed above are tabulated in Table 2-3 and schematically summarized in Table 2-4 on the next page.

2-3

Distribution of Electrons in Orbitals

Specific rules govern the order in which energy levels are filled by electrons. This "order of filling" is correct for the ground, or lowest-energy, state of all atoms.

Up to this point we have identified the orbital composition and maximum electron population of the principal energy levels. We found that each orbital, each energy sublevel and each energy level can accommodate only a specific number of electrons. We are now ready to explain how the electrons are distributed in the orbitals of specific gaseous atoms in their ground (lowest-energy) states. This means we must indicate the number of electrons in each orbital of each energy level.

To acquaint you with the electron configuration of atoms, we will employ a useful, but *imaginary*, process. In this process we

TABLE 2-3

PRINCIPAL ENERGY LEVEL, ENERGY SUBLEVEL AND ORBITAL DISTRIBUTION OF ELECTRONS

Principal Energy Level	Principal Quantum Number (n)	Energy Sublevels	Orbitals per Sublevel	Orbital Designation	Maximum Electrons per Orbital	Maximum Electrons per Energy Sublevel	Maximum Electrons per Energy Level
1	1	s	1	$1s$	2	2	2
2	2	s	1	$2s$	2	2	8
		p	3	$2p_x\ p_y\ p_z$	2	6	
3	3	s	1	$3s$	2	2	18
		p	3	$3p_x\ p_y\ p_z$	2	6	
		d	5	$3d_{xy}\ d_{xz}\ d_{yz}$ $d_{x^2-y^2}\ d_{z^2}$	2	10	
4	4	s	1	$4s$	2	2	
		p	3	$4p_x\ p_y\ p_z$	2	6	
		d	5	$4d_{xy}\ d_{xz}\ d_{yz}$ $d_{x^2-y^2}\ d_{x^2}$	2	10	32
		f	7	unimportant for our purpose	2	14	

TABLE 2-4

PRINCIPAL ENERGY LEVEL AND ELECTRON CONFIGURATION OF ORBITALS

Principal Energy Level (n)	Number (n)	Type	Orbital diagram	Orbitals per Sublevel	Total Number of Orbitals per Energy Level (n^2)	Maximum Number of Electrons per Energy Level ($2n^2$)
1	1	{ s	(↑↓)	1 }	1	2
2	2	{ p	(↑↓)(↑↓)(↑↓)	3 }	4	8
		{ s	(↑↓)	1 }		
3	3	{ d	(↑↓)(↑↓)(↑↓)(↑↓)(↑↓)	5 }	9	18
		{ p	(↑↓)(↑↓)(↑↓)	3 }		
		{ s	(↑↓)	1 }		
4	4	{ f	(↑↓)(↑↓)(↑↓)(↑↓)(↑↓) (↑↓)(↑↓)	7 }	16	32
		{ d	(↑↓)(↑↓)(↑↓)(↑↓)(↑↓)	5 }		
		{ p	(↑↓)(↑↓)(↑↓)	3 }		
		{ s	(↑↓)	1 }		

begin with a hydrogen atom that contains one proton in its nucleus and one electron in the $1s$ orbital. We then "add" particles to construct an atom with any atomic number we wish. Each time we "add" a proton to the nucleus, we "add" an electron to an available orbital. In other words, we imagine that electrons "enter and finally fill" the system of empty orbitals shown in Fig. 2-4 on the next page. Figure 2-4 schematically depicts the relative energies of the orbitals in multi-electron atoms.

In reality, elements are not formed in this way. There is no magical process in which protons are "added" to a nucleus and electrons are systematically "added," one at a time, to empty orbitals. Thus, the term "entering and filling of orbitals" is actually misleading and erroneous if you interpret it literally.

Let us now examine rules and devices that will enable us to properly represent the electron configuration of atoms in the ground state. The energy-level diagram shown in Fig. 2-4 and the rules listed below may be used to write the electron configuration of gaseous atoms in the ground state. If an energy-level diagram is not available, the mnemonic diagram shown in Fig. 2-5 on page 37 will help you remember the sequence. Both show that, in order of increasing energy, the orbital sequence is

$$1s\,2s\,2p\,3s\,3p\,4s\,3d\,4p\,5s\,4d\,5p\,6s\,4f\,5d\,6p\,7s\,5f$$

Remember that this is an "order-of-filling" diagram and not a sequence of energy levels that is correct for the ground state of *all* atoms. Because of the close spacing of some of the higher-energy sublevels, experiments indicate some overlapping and "criss-crossing" of these sublevels occurs. This makes it impossible to construct an "all-inclusive" energy-level diagram. You will, however, find that the sequence above is consistent with the arrangement of atoms in the periodic table. Hence, we find it useful for making correlations and predictions.

RULES FOR WRITING ELECTRON CONFIGURATIONS OF GASEOUS ATOMS IN THE GROUND STATE

1. Electrons occupy the lowest-energy orbital of the lowest energy level first.

2. No electron pairing takes place in p, d or f orbitals until each orbital of the given set contains one electron. This is known as *Hund's rule*.

3. No orbital can contain more than two electrons.

When writing electron configurations, you must identify each orbital with a principal quantum number. For example, a p orbital

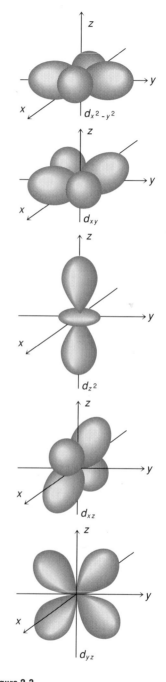

Figure 2-3
The spatial orientations and shapes of *d* orbitals. Each orbital can accommodate a maximum of two electrons. An electron in a d_{yz} orbital has an equal probability of being found in any one of the four lobes.

Figure 2-4
Relative energies of orbitals in iso-
lated multi-electron atoms. Each cir-
cle represents an orbital capable of
holding two electrons. The lowest-
energy orbitals are filled first.

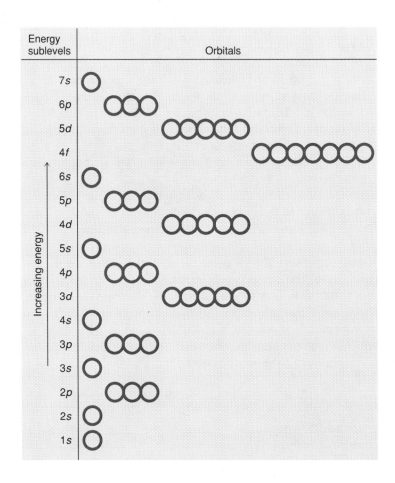

in the fourth energy level is called a $4p$ orbital. The number of electrons in each orbital is indicated by a superscript. A single electron in a $4p$ orbital would be represented as $4p^1$. In Fig. 2-4, each circle represents an orbital capable of holding two electrons. Arrows pointing in opposite directions are used to denote electrons having opposite spin direction. A filled orbital is represented as ⑪.

There are several ways to represent the electron configuration of an atom. The starting point is to locate the element in the periodic table. The atomic number of the element represents the positive charge on the nucleus and the number of electrons outside the nucleus of a neutral atom of the element. Knowing the total number of electrons available, we can then distribute them by following the energy-level diagram or mnemonic diagram and applying the rules noted above. Consider nitrogen, atomic number 7, as an example. According to the atomic number, there are 7 electrons in a nitrogen atom. The first two electrons are located in the $1s$ orbital. The third and fourth electrons are located in the $2s$

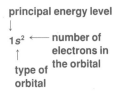

orbital. The fifth, sixth and seventh electrons occupy, respectively, the $2p_x$, $2p_y$ and $2p_z$ orbitals. This distribution may be represented as $1s^2$, $2s^2$, $2p_x^1$, $2p_y^1$, $2p_z^1$, or as

$$1s \; \underline{\textcircled{\text{\small ↑↓}}} \quad 2s \; \underline{\textcircled{\text{\small ↑↓}}} \quad 2p \; \underline{\textcircled{↑}\textcircled{↑}\textcircled{↑}}$$

where the letters s and p represent the orbital, the coefficients in front of the letters represent the principal energy levels and the superscripts represent the number of electrons in each orbital. If less detail is desired, the configuration may be shown as

$$1s^2 2s^2 2p^3$$

The imaginary process of building up the electron structures of the elements in the ground state is known as the **Aufbau principle**. Let us illustrate its application.

A hydrogen atom has atomic number 1. This indicates that the atom has 1 electron. The single electron occupies the lowest-energy orbital (s) in the lowest energy level ($n = 1$). Accordingly, the electron configuration of a hydrogen atom in the ground state is represented as

$$1s^1$$

Helium, atomic number 2, has 2 electrons. One of these electrons occupies the s orbital in the first level, as in the case of the hydrogen atom. The second electron also occupies the $1s$ orbital. Thus, the first two electrons form an electron pair and completely fill both the orbital and the first energy level. These two electrons must have opposite spins, since they occupy the same orbital. The configuration may be designated as

$$1s^2$$

Helium is chemically inert. This experimental fact suggests that the helium atom has a very stable structure. Consequently, we assume that two electrons complete the first energy level and represent a stable electron configuration for the first energy level.

An atom of lithium, atomic number 3, contains 3 electrons. Since the first level is complete, the third electron is found in the lowest-energy orbital (s) of the second energy level. The electron configuration of lithium in the ground state is

$$1s^2 2s^1$$

Let us next write the electron configuration of potassium, atomic number 19. Figure 2-4 shows that for an atom in the ground state, a $4s$ orbital is slightly lower in energy than the $3d$ orbital. Thus, the 19th electron is found in the $4s$ orbital, which is the

Main energy level	s	p	d	f
1	s			
2	s - - → p			
3	s - - → p		d	
4	s	p	d	f
5	s	p	d	f
6	s	p	d	
7	s	p		

Sequence: 1s, 2s, 2p, 3s, 3p, 4s, 3d, 4p, 5s, 4d, 5p, 6s, 4f, 5d, 6p, 7s, 5f

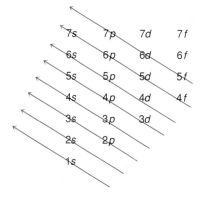

Figure 2-5
Memory aid for determining the ground-state electron configuration of a multi-electron atom.

The Aufbau Principle Analogy
To visualize the $4s$-$3d$ relationship, we can use the analogy of apartment buildings perched on a hill next to a river that sometimes overflows its banks.

Each of the buildings is higher than the preceding building. The first building has only one floor ($1s$); the second building has two floors ($2s$, $2p$); the third has three floors ($3s$, $3p$, $3d$); the fourth building has four floors ($4s$, $4d$, $4p$, $4f$). However, the top floor of the third building is actually higher than the bottom floor of the fourth building. Thus, the flooding order of the buildings would be: $1s$, $2s$, $2p$, $3s$, $3p$, $4s$, $3d$, $4p$, and so on, just as predicted by the Aufbau principle. (Adapted from *Chem 13 News*, January 1988)

lowest-energy orbital available. Starting with potassium, all of the atoms of the elements in Groups IA and IIA contain electrons in an outer s orbital before any electrons are found in the underlying d orbital. The configuration of a potassium atom is

$$1s^2 2s^2 2p^6 3s^2 3p^6 4s^1$$

The ten elements following calcium are known as the *transition elements*. The ground-state configurations of these atoms show that underlying d orbitals are occupied only after the s orbital in the next higher energy level is occupied. The orbital configurations of these elements are shown in Table 2-5. Note that chromium, atomic number 24, and copper, atomic number 29, are exceptions to the general trend. The exception consists of an unpairing of the $4s$ electrons, yielding a $3d^5$ or $3d^{10}$ configuration. The electron configurations of these atoms are given below.

Cr $1s^2 2s^2 2p^6 3s^2 3p^6 3d^5 4s^1$
Cu $1s^2 2s^2 2p^6 3s^2 3p^6 3d^{10} 4s^1$

A detailed explanation for these irregularities is beyond the scope of this book. In general, it can be said that there is an unusual stability attached to a one-half or completely filled set of orbitals.

A second transition series of ten elements begins after strontium, atomic number 38. In this and in the third series of transition elements, there are several exceptions to the usual pattern. In general, we will not be concerned with the reasons for these irregularities. We will assume that the arrangement of electrons implied from experiments is more stable than one we would predict by following the rules.

To determine the ground-state electron configuration of cadmium, atomic number 48, we may use the memory aid shown in Fig. 2-5. The 48 electrons may be distributed in the proper orbitals by following the arrows in the diagram. The two electrons of lowest energy are located in the $1s$ orbital. Continuing in this pattern, the fifth through tenth electrons occupy the $2p_x$, $2p_y$ and $2p_z$ orbitals. These are followed by two electrons in the $3s$ orbital, six in the $3p$ orbitals, two in the $4s$ orbital, ten in the $3d$ orbitals, six in the $4p$ orbitals, two in the $5s$ orbital and ten in the $4d$ orbitals.

Using the energy-level diagram or the mnemonic, we find the configuration of a cadmium atom in the ground state is

$$1s^2 2s^2 2p^6 3s^2 3p^6 4s^2 3d^{10} 4p^6 5s^2 4d^{10}$$

Rather than show the exact sequence obtained by following the energy-level diagram, it is customary to show the ground-state configuration by grouping all the orbitals in a given energy level together. Thus, the ground-state configuration of cadmium is usually written as

$$1s^2 2s^2 2p^6 3s^2 3p^6 3d^{10} 4s^2 4p^6 4d^{10} 5s^2$$

This order makes it easier to recognize the outer-energy-level electrons.

TABLE 2-5
ELECTRON CONFIGURATION OF ATOMIC NUMBERS 1–36

Element	Atomic Number	1s	2s	2p	3s	3p	4s	3d	4p
H	1	↑							
He	2	↑↓							
Li	3	↑↓	↑						
Be	4	↑↓	↑↓						
B	5	↑↓	↑↓	↑					
C	6	↑↓	↑↓	↑ ↑					
N	7	↑↓	↑↓	↑ ↑ ↑					
O	8	↑↓	↑↓	↑↓ ↑ ↑					
F	9	↑↓	↑↓	↑↓ ↑↓ ↑					
Ne	10	↑↓	↑↓	↑↓ ↑↓ ↑↓					
Na	11	↑↓	↑↓	↑↓ ↑↓ ↑↓	↑				
Mg	12	↑↓	↑↓	↑↓ ↑↓ ↑↓	↑↓				
Al	13	↑↓	↑↓	↑↓ ↑↓ ↑↓	↑↓	↑			
Si	14	↑↓	↑↓	↑↓ ↑↓ ↑↓	↑↓	↑ ↑			
P	15	↑↓	↑↓	↑↓ ↑↓ ↑↓	↑↓	↑ ↑ ↑			
S	16	↑↓	↑↓	↑↓ ↑↓ ↑↓	↑↓	↑↓ ↑ ↑			
Cl	17	↑↓	↑↓	↑↓ ↑↓ ↑↓	↑↓	↑↓ ↑↓ ↑			
Ar	18	↑↓	↑↓	↑↓ ↑↓ ↑↓	↑↓	↑↓ ↑↓ ↑↓			
K	19	↑↓	↑↓	↑↓ ↑↓ ↑↓	↑↓	↑↓ ↑↓ ↑↓	↑		
Ca	20	↑↓	↑↓	↑↓ ↑↓ ↑↓	↑↓	↑↓ ↑↓ ↑↓	↑↓		
Sc	21	↑↓	↑↓	↑↓ ↑↓ ↑↓	↑↓	↑↓ ↑↓ ↑↓	↑↓	↑	
Ti	22	↑↓	↑↓	↑↓ ↑↓ ↑↓	↑↓	↑↓ ↑↓ ↑↓	↑↓	↑ ↑	
V	23	↑↓	↑↓	↑↓ ↑↓ ↑↓	↑↓	↑↓ ↑↓ ↑↓	↑↓	↑ ↑ ↑	
Cr	24	↑↓	↑↓	↑↓ ↑↓ ↑↓	↑↓	↑↓ ↑↓ ↑↓	↑	↑ ↑ ↑ ↑ ↑	
Mn	25	↑↓	↑↓	↑↓ ↑↓ ↑↓	↑↓	↑↓ ↑↓ ↑↓	↑↓	↑ ↑ ↑ ↑ ↑	
Fe	26	↑↓	↑↓	↑↓ ↑↓ ↑↓	↑↓	↑↓ ↑↓ ↑↓	↑↓	↑↓ ↑ ↑ ↑ ↑	
Co	27	↑↓	↑↓	↑↓ ↑↓ ↑↓	↑↓	↑↓ ↑↓ ↑↓	↑↓	↑↓ ↑↓ ↑ ↑ ↑	
Ni	28	↑↓	↑↓	↑↓ ↑↓ ↑↓	↑↓	↑↓ ↑↓ ↑↓	↑↓	↑↓ ↑↓ ↑↓ ↑ ↑	
Cu	29	↑↓	↑↓	↑↓ ↑↓ ↑↓	↑↓	↑↓ ↑↓ ↑↓	↑	↑↓ ↑↓ ↑↓ ↑↓ ↑↓	
Zn	30	↑↓	↑↓	↑↓ ↑↓ ↑↓	↑↓	↑↓ ↑↓ ↑↓	↑↓	↑↓ ↑↓ ↑↓ ↑↓ ↑↓	
Ga	31	↑↓	↑↓	↑↓ ↑↓ ↑↓	↑↓	↑↓ ↑↓ ↑↓	↑↓	↑↓ ↑↓ ↑↓ ↑↓ ↑↓	↑
Ge	32	↑↓	↑↓	↑↓ ↑↓ ↑↓	↑↓	↑↓ ↑↓ ↑↓	↑↓	↑↓ ↑↓ ↑↓ ↑↓ ↑↓	↑ ↑
As	33	↑↓	↑↓	↑↓ ↑↓ ↑↓	↑↓	↑↓ ↑↓ ↑↓	↑↓	↑↓ ↑↓ ↑↓ ↑↓ ↑↓	↑ ↑ ↑
Se	34	↑↓	↑↓	↑↓ ↑↓ ↑↓	↑↓	↑↓ ↑↓ ↑↓	↑↓	↑↓ ↑↓ ↑↓ ↑↓ ↑↓	↑↓ ↑ ↑
Br	35	↑↓	↑↓	↑↓ ↑↓ ↑↓	↑↓	↑↓ ↑↓ ↑↓	↑↓	↑↓ ↑↓ ↑↓ ↑↓ ↑↓	↑↓ ↑↓ ↑
Kr	36	↑↓	↑↓	↑↓ ↑↓ ↑↓	↑↓	↑↓ ↑↓ ↑↓	↑↓	↑↓ ↑↓ ↑↓ ↑↓ ↑↓	↑↓ ↑↓ ↑↓

The electrons in the highest, or outermost, energy level are generally involved in chemical reactions and are, therefore, of special interest to us. They are sometimes referred to as ***valence electrons***. *The number of valence electrons in an atom of any representative element (Group A elements in the periodic table) is numerically equal to the roman numeral at the top of the column.* For example, the atoms of the elements in Group VIIA all have 7 electrons in their outer energy level. With few exceptions, *the atoms of the transition elements (Group B elements) have only 2 electrons in their outer energy level.*

FOLLOW-UP PROBLEMS

1. Use orbital notation to represent the ground-state electron configuration of rubidium (atomic number 37), cesium (55), bromine (35) and iodine (53).

2. What is the orbital configuration of the outer energy level in each of the atoms in Group IA of the periodic table?

3. What is the outer-energy-level configuration in each of the atoms in Group VIIA?

4. Use the answers to the last two questions to suggest a reason for the similarities in the properties of the elements in a given group of the periodic table.

Answers:

1. **rubidium:** $1s^2 2s^2 2p^6 3s^2 3p^6 3d^{10} 4s^2 4p^6 5s^1$
   cesium: $1s^2 2s^2 2p^6 3s^2 3p^6 3d^{10} 4s^2 4p^6 4d^{10} 5s^2 5p^6 6s^1$
   bromine: $1s^2 2s^2 2p^6 3s^2 3p^6 3d^{10} 4s^2 4p^5$
   iodine: $1s^2 2s^2 2p^6 3s^2 3p^6 3d^{10} 4s^2 4p^6 4d^{10} 5s^2 5p^5$

2. **Group IA orbital configuration of the outer energy level is s^1.**

3. **Group VIIA orbital configuration of the outer energy level is $s^2 p^5$.**

4. **Similar electron configurations of the outer energy levels result in similar properties.**

With the ability to properly represent the electron configuration of atoms, we are now in a position to examine the relationship between the electron structure of atoms and their location in the periodic table. We will find that we can use the location of an element in the periodic table to help us write the orbital electron configuration of its atoms.

PERIODICITY IN OUTER-ENERGY-LEVEL ELECTRON CONFIGURATION

2-4

Electron Configuration of Outer Energy Levels

The outer-energy-level electron configurations of the atoms of the elements in each group of the periodic table are identical. The similarity in chemical behaviour shown by elements in a group is related to the electron configuration of the outer level. Electric and spectrographic measurements reveal that, in general, the atoms of all elements in a given group of the periodic table have the same electron population and orbital configuration in their outer energy levels. The electron population and configuration of the atoms in three of the groups, as revealed by experimental measurements, are listed in Table 2-6. Each group is composed of elements that have similar properties, but each group has properties that differ from those of the other groups. The noble gases have the same electron configurations as the inner energy levels of the Group IA elements. Therefore, the symbols of the noble gases in the configurations of the Group IA elements are used to represent the inner energy levels.

The data in Table 2-6 is summarized as follows:

1. The atoms of all Group IA elements have one electron in the s orbital of the outer energy level.

2. The atoms of all Group VIIA elements have two electrons in the s orbital and five electrons in the p orbitals of the outer level.

3. The atoms of all elements in Group O have completely occupied s and p orbitals in their outer levels. In general, these elements are characterized by chemical inactivity.

4. The atoms of all elements in Group IA have one electron more than the noble-gas atoms just preceding them in the periodic table. The elements in this group are all observed to be very reactive metals.

5. All the atoms of the elements in Group VIIA have one electron fewer than the noble-gas atoms that follow them in the periodic table. These elements are observed to be extremely inactive nonmetals.

6. The group number of the A families, known as the *representative elements*, is equal to the number of electrons in the outer energy level of the atoms in the family. For example, all atoms

TABLE 2-6
OUTER-ENERGY-LEVEL ELECTRON CONFIGURATIONS

Group O Noble Gases	
neon	$2s^2 2p^6$
argon	$3s^2 3p^6$
krypton	$4s^2 4p^6$
xenon	$5s^2 5p^6$

Group VIIA Halogens	
fluorine	$2s^2 2p^5$
chlorine	$3s^2 3p^5$
bromine	$4s^2 4p^5$
iodine	$5s^2 5p^5$

Group IA Alkali Metals	
sodium	$(Ne)3s^1$
potassium	$(Ar)4s^1$
rubidium	$(Kr)5s^1$
cesium	$(Xe)6s^1$

of elements in Group VIIA have seven electrons in their outer energy levels.

7. The number of the period (row) in which an element is located is equal to the number of major energy levels occupied by electrons in the ground-state atoms of the elements.

The observations above suggest the following conclusions:

1. Similarities in chemical and physical properties are paralleled by and reflect similarities in electron configurations.

2. Completed s and p orbitals are associated with high stability.

3. Chemical behaviour is related to the electron configuration of the outer level.

Let us now see how the periodic table can be used as a guide to help us determine the electron configuration of atoms.

2-5
Orbital Blocks of the Periodic Table

The main difference in electron configuration of the transition-element atoms and the lanthanide–actinide-element atoms is in their respective incomplete d and f orbitals.

A detailed examination of the experimentally determined outer-energy-level electron configuration of the atoms in the periodic table reveals these facts:

1. The outermost (highest-energy) electrons in the atoms of Group IA and IIA elements are located in s orbitals.

2. The outermost (highest-energy) electrons in the atoms of Groups IIIA, IVA, VA, VIA, VIIA and O elements are located in p orbitals.

3. In general, the atoms of the Group B elements contain one or two electrons in the s orbital of the highest energy level but differ from one another in the number of electrons in an underlying d orbital. These elements are known as the ***transition elements***. As you go from left to right across the fourth row (period 4) of the periodic table, the change in properties of the transition elements is not as drastic as in the elements of the A or representative groups. This is not totally unexpected, since the main difference in electron configuration of the transition-element atoms is in the population of the underlying d orbital rather than an outer s or p orbital.

4. In general, the atoms of the elements in the separate section at the bottom of the periodic table contain two electrons in the s

orbital of the highest energy level but differ from one another in the number of electrons in an underlying f orbital that has a principal quantum number two less than that of the outer s orbital. These elements are known as the *inner transition elements*. As you go from left to right across these long rows, there are marked similarities in the properties of the elements. This is to be expected, since the main difference in the electron configuration of the atoms is in the electron population of an underlying f orbital.

The analysis above suggests that the long form of the periodic table may be dissected into s, d, p and f orbital blocks. These blocks are shown in Fig. 2-6. The s block is two elements wide, corresponding to the maximum allowable number of two electrons in a given energy level. The p block is six elements wide, corresponding to the six electrons that can occupy a set of p orbitals. The d block is ten elements wide, corresponding to the ten electrons that can occupy a set of five d orbitals. The f block is fourteen elements wide, corresponding to the fourteen electrons that can occupy a set of seven f orbitals.

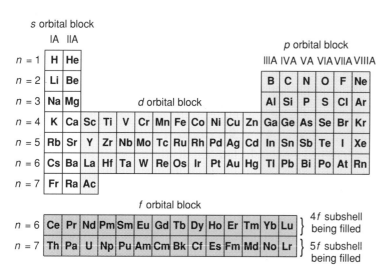

Figure 2-6
The *s, p, d* and *f* orbital blocks of the periodic table.

2-6

The Periodic Table as a Guide to the Electron Configuration of Atoms

The periodic table was originally developed to organize the elements according to their physical and chemical properties. We now know that these similarities are a result of similar electron configurations.

DMITRI MENDELEYEV
1834–1907
Dmitri Mendeleyev was born in Siberia, the youngest of seventeen children. Tutored in science by a political exile in Siberia, Mendeleyev went on to receive his doctor's degree in chemistry.

Mendeleyev's greatest contribution to the field of chemistry is the periodic table, which he published in 1869. Although he was not able to explain why the periodic table worked, we now know that elements in the same row have the same electron configuration in their outer shell. Mendeleyev also predicted the existence and properties of undiscovered elements and left gaps in his table for them. When gallium, scandium and germanium were discovered, their properties agreed so well with Mendeleyev's predictions that he became the most famous chemist in the world. The value of the periodic table for predicting the properties of newly discovered elements continued throughout the twentieth century.

Although scientists today would place Mendeleyev's discovery ahead of most work done by his contemporaries, he never received the Nobel Prize in chemistry. However, in 1955, scientists at Berkeley, California, named element number 101, mendelevium, in honour of the founder of the periodic classification of the elements.

Examination of the electron configuration of the atoms in a given row of the periodic table reveals that each atom differs from its neighbours by one electron. Inspection of the orbital energy-level diagram shows that the orbitals containing the outer electrons have closely related energy values. The length of each row is determined by the relative energies of the orbitals. After each p orbital is fully occupied, there is a relatively large energy gap. These gaps represent the difference in energy between two successive principal energy levels and are related to the great stability of the noble-gas atoms. Each noble-gas atom (except He) has completely occupied p orbitals and is surrounded by a symmetrical charge cloud. The negligible electron affinities of these atoms suggest that there is no room for another electron. Thus, the next electron occupies an s orbital of a new, higher energy level that is relatively distant from the completed p orbital. This corresponds to the beginning of a new row in the periodic table. The completion of a period in the table occurs when a p orbital of a noble-gas atom is completely filled.

Since a new period begins after each noble gas, the number of elements in a period is determined by the difference in the electron populations of successive noble-gas atoms. For example, argon, atomic number 18, is the noble gas located at the end of period 3. Krypton, atomic number 36, is another noble gas and is found at the end of period 4. The difference in electron populations between argon and krypton is $36 - 18 = 18$. Therefore, period 4 may be expected to contain 18 elements, and it does. In Fig. 2-7, orbitals with closely related energy values are grouped together. Examination of this figure reveals that there are only small energy differences between different orbitals in the same period. The relationship between the location of an atom in the periodic table and the electron configuration of its outer orbitals is shown in Fig. 2-8. Many of the relationships discussed above are depicted in this figure.

Again, the imaginary "order-of-filling'" concept serves a useful purpose because it helps rationalize the form of the periodic table and suggests a positive correlation between the electron configuration of an atom and its position in the table. This means we should be able to express in writing the electron configuration of an atom by noting its position in the periodic table. There are, of course, a number of deviations from the general pattern. This is to be expected, since each atom is unique and has an electron configuration that is in no way controlled by its neighbours. With these limitations in mind, we will use our imaginary "order-of-filling" process to deduce the electron configuration of osmium, element number 76, from its position in the periodic table.

Notice that osmium follows the lanthanide series of elements in which the $4f$ orbitals are completely filled. Since osmium is the sixth element in the $5d$ transition-element series, it is expected to have six electrons in the $5d$ orbitals. The $5d$ elements follow the $4f$ and the $6s$ elements in period 6 of the table. Therefore, the three highest sublevels that contain electrons in an osmium atom are expected to have an electron configuration of $6s^2$, $4f^{14}$ and $5d^6$. The remaining underlying orbitals are completely filled. Their configuration may be obtained by writing the completely filled orbitals of the atoms in the first five rows of the periodic table.

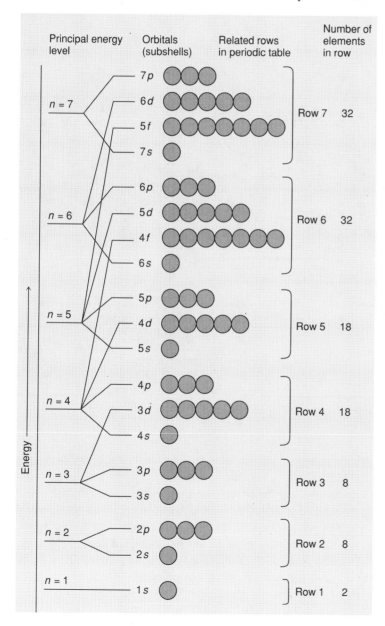

Figure 2-7
Energy-level diagram showing principal quantum levels, orbitals, related periods in the periodic table and the number of elements in each row.

PERIODIC TABLE OF THE ELEMENTS

Representative elements — Transition elements—d

Outer orbital configuration	s^1	s^2	$d^1s^2f^x$	d^2s^2	$(d^3s^2)^*$	$(d^5s^1)^*$	d^5s^2	$(d^6s^2)^*$	←
Period / Orbitals being filled	IA	IIA	IIIB	IVB	VB	VIB	VIIB		
$n=1$ $1s$	1.00797 **H** 1								
$n=2$ $2s2p$	6.939 **Li** 3 (2,1)	9.0122 **Be** 4 (2,2)							
$n=3$ $3s3p$	22.9898 **Na** 11 (2,8,1)	24.312 **Mg** 12 (2,8,2)							
$n=4$ $4s3d4p$	39.102 **K** 19 (2,8,8,1)	40.08 **Ca** 20 (2,8,8,2)	44.956 **Sc** 21 (2,8,9,2)	47.90 **Ti** 22 (2,8,10,2)	50.942 **V** 23 (2,8,11,2)	51.996 **Cr** 24 (2,8,13,1)	54.9380 **Mn** 25 (2,8,13,2)	55.847 **Fe** 26 (2,8,14,2)	
$n=5$ $5s4d5p$	85.47 **Rb** 37 (2,8,18,8,1)	87.62 **Sr** 38 (2,8,18,8,2)	88.905 **Y** 39 (2,8,18,9,2)	91.22 **Zr** 40 (2,8,18,10,2)	92.906 **Nb** 41 (2,8,18,12,1)	95.94 **Mo** 42 (2,8,18,13,1)	[99*] **Tc** 43 (2,8,18,13,2)	101.07 **Ru** 44 (2,8,18,15,1)	
$n=6$ $6s4f5d6p$	132.905 **Cs** 55 (2,8,18,18,8,1)	137.34 **Ba** 56 (2,8,18,18,8,2)	Lanthanide Series 57-71	178.49 **Hf** 72 (2,8,18,32,10,2)	180.948 **Ta** 73 (2,8,18,32,11,2)	183.85 **W** 74 (2,8,18,32,12,2)	186.2 **Re** 75 (2,8,18,32,13,2)	190.2 **Os** 76 (2,8,18,32,14,2)	
$n=7$ $7s5f6d7p$	[223] **Fr** 87 (2,8,18,32,18,8,1)	[226] **Ra** 88 (2,8,18,32,18,8,2)	Actinide Series 89-103						

$n=6$ $4f$	Lanthanide Series	138.91 **La** 57 (2,8,18,18,9,2)	140.12 **Ce** 58 (2,8,18,20,8,2)	140.907 **Pr** 59 (2,8,18,21,8,2)	144.24 **Nd** 60 (2,8,18,22,8,2)	[147*] **Pm** 61 (2,8,18,23,8,2)	
$n=7$ $5f$	Actinide Series	[227] **Ac** 89 (2,8,18,32,18,9,2)	232.038 **Th** 90 (2,8,18,32,18,10,2)	[231] **Pa** 91 (2,8,18,32,20,9,2)	238.03 **U** 92 (2,8,18,32,21,9,2)	[237] **Np** 93 (2,8,18,32,23,8,2)	

*Some variations in configuration of family members

Figure 2-8
The relationship between the outer-orbital electron configuration of an atom and its location in the periodic table.

These represent the Xe core and are $1s^22s^22p^63s^23p^64s^23d^{10}4p^6 5s^24d^{10}5p^6$. It is usually desirable to write the ground-state sequence so that the orbitals are grouped according to their principal quantum numbers. For osmium, the ground-state configuration could be written $1s^22s^22p^63s^23p^63d^{10}4s^24p^64d^{10}4f^{14}5s^25p^65d^66s^2$. There are irregularities in the configurations of certain atoms that cannot be predicted by following the general pattern. These exceptions need not concern us at this point. For quick reference, the orbital configurations for the first 36 elements in the periodic table are given in Table 2-5.

				Representative elements				Noble-gas elements	
$(d^7s^2)^*$	$(d^8s^2)^*$	$d^{10}s^1$	$d^{10}s^1$	s^2p^1	s^2p^2	s^2p^3	s^2p^4	s^2p^5	s^2p^6
⟵ VIII ⟶		IB	IIB	IIIA	IVA	VA	VIA	VIIA	VIIIA
									4.0026 **He** 2 (2)
				10.811 **B** 5 (2,3)	12.01115 **C** 6 (2,4)	14.0067 **N** 7 (2,5)	15.9994 **O** 8 (2,6)	18.9984 **F** 9 (2,7)	20.183 **Ne** 10 (2,8)
				26.9815 **Al** 13 (2,8,3)	28.086 **Si** 14 (2,8,4)	30.9738 **P** 15 (2,8,5)	32.064 **S** 16 (2,8,6)	35.453 **Cl** 17 (2,8,7)	39.948 **Ar** 18 (2,8,8)
58.9332 **Co** 27 (2,8,15,2)	58.71 **Ni** 28 (2,8,16,2)	63.54 **Cu** 29 (2,8,18,1)	65.37 **Zn** 30 (2,8,18,2)	69.72 **Ga** 31 (2,8,18,3)	72.59 **Ge** 32 (2,8,18,4)	74.9216 **As** 33 (2,8,18,5)	78.96 **Se** 34 (2,8,18,6)	79.909 **Br** 35 (2,8,18,7)	83.80 **Kr** 36 (2,8,18,8)
102.905 **Rh** 45 (2,8,18,16,1)	106.4 **Pd** 46 (2,8,18,18,0)	107.870 **Ag** 47 (2,8,18,18,1)	112.40 **Cd** 48 (2,8,18,18,2)	114.82 **In** 49 (2,8,18,18,3)	118.69 **Sn** 50 (2,8,18,18,4)	121.75 **Sb** 51 (2,8,18,18,5)	127.60 **Te** 52 (2,8,18,18,6)	126.9044 **I** 53 (2,8,18,18,7)	131.30 **Xe** 54 (2,8,18,18,8)
192.2 **Ir** 77 (2,8,18,32,15,2)	195.09 **Pt** 78 (2,8,18,32,16,2)	196.967 **Au** 79 (2,8,18,32,18,1)	200.59 **Hg** 80 (2,8,18,32,18,2)	204.37 **Tl** 81 (2,8,18,32,18,3)	207.19 **Pb** 82 (2,8,18,32,18,4)	208.980 **Bi** 83 (2,8,18,32,18,5)	[210*] **Po** 84 (2,8,18,32,18,6)	[210] **At** 85 (2,8,18,32,18,7)	[222] **Rn** 86 (2,8,18,32,18,8)

Inner transition elements—*f* orbital elements

150.35 **Sm** 62 (2,8,18,24,8,2)	151.96 **Eu** 63 (2,8,18,25,8,2)	157.25 **Gd** 64 (2,8,18,25,9,2)	158.924 **Tb** 65 (2,8,18,27,8,2)	162.50 **Dy** 66 (2,8,18,28,8,2)	164.930 **Ho** 67 (2,8,18,29,8,2)	167.26 **Er** 68 (2,8,18,30,8,2)	168.934 **Tm** 69 (2,8,18,31,8,2)	173.04 **Yb** 70 (2,8,18,32,8,2)	174.97 **Lu** 71 (2,8,18,32,9,2)
[242] **Pu** 94 (2,8,18,32,24,8,2)	[243] **Am** 95 (2,8,18,32,25,8,2)	[247] **Cm** 96 (2,8,18,32,25,9,2)	[249*] **Bk** 97 (2,8,18,32,27,8,2)	[251*] **Cf** 98 (2,8,18,32,28,8,2)	[254] **Es** 99 (2,8,18,32,29,8,2)	[253] **Fm** 100 (2,8,18,32,30,8,2)	[256] **Md** 101 (2,8,18,32,31,8,2)	[254] **No** 102 (2,8,18,32,32,8,2)	[257] **Lr** 103 (2,8,18,32,32,9,2)

The brackets indicate that the mass number is that of the isotope with the longest half-life.

The electron configurations of neutral, gaseous atoms in the ground state serve a useful function in providing a basis for our discussion in subsequent chapters of how atoms combine. Most of the situations we deal with involve atoms in the combined state. We have already noted that many solid compounds are composed of ions. Knowledge of the electron configuration of ions and the way they may be formed will help us to understand their properties and the characteristics of the aggregates they form. For these reasons, let us see how the electron configuration of ions is related to the configuration of neutral gas atoms.

2-7

Formation of Positive Ions

The formation of a positive ion depends on the ionization energy of an atom or the amount of energy required to remove an electron from an atom or ion in the gaseous phase.

It is reasonable to assume that the formation of a positive gas ion is related to the ease with which an electron can be removed from a neutral gas atom. The energy, or work, required to remove an electron from a gaseous atom is called the ***ionization energy (IE)***. Ionization energies may be determined spectroscopically or, in some cases, by means of electric measurements. The second method is easier to understand and is depicted schematically in Fig. 2-9. The experiment involves bombarding gaseous atoms with electrons in a cathode-ray-like tube. The kinetic energy of the bombarding electrons is related to and controlled by the applied voltage. Higher voltages increase the kinetic energies of the bombarding electrons. To determine the ionization energy of a gas atom, the voltage is increased until the kinetic energy of the bombarding electrons is equal to the energy needed to overcome the force of attraction between the nucleus and the easiest-to-remove electron of a gas atom. When this critical voltage is reached, positive gas ions are formed. The formation is signalled by a sudden change in current flow.

In theory, each atom has as many ionization energies as it has

Figure 2-9
(a) As the potential difference (*V*) is increased, electrons from the filament (F) gain sufficient energy to reach the plate (P) and cause a rise in the plate current (*I*), but do not have enough energy to dislodge the outer electron of sodium atoms. No loss of energy is suffered in the elastic collisions with the sodium atoms. (b) When voltage reaches a critical value, bombarding electrons have enough energy to dislodge an electron from a sodium atom. Kinetic energy of bombarding electrons is distributed between the two electrons (the bombarding electron and the "target" electron). Neither has enough energy to reach the plate, so the current drops. The ionization energy may be determined by analysing a plot of voltage versus current.

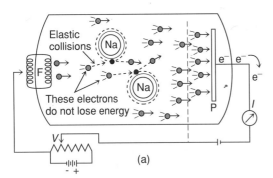

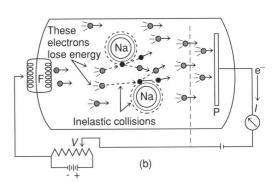

○ outer electron of sodium atom
● bombarding electrons from filament (F)

electrons. Experimental data shows that the energy required to remove a second electron is always greater than that to remove the first. The removal of the first electron reduces the number of electrons and, consequently, the total electron repulsion. This results in drawing the electron cloud closer to the nucleus (Fig. 2-10). There it is more compact, and, because of the smaller radius, each electron in the cloud is subjected to a greater force of attraction by the nucleus. This greater force of attraction between an electron and its nucleus means that more energy is required to dislodge the electron or to achieve ionization. Thus, the second ionization energy of a gaseous atom is always greater than the first. The first, second and third ionization energies of the first 20 elements are listed in Table 2-7.

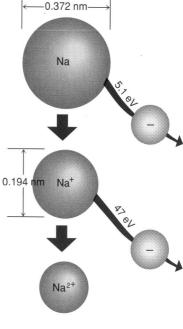

Figure 2-10
The removal of an outer electron from a sodium atom reduces the electron-to-proton ratio, the total electron repulsion and the radius of the particle.

TABLE 2-7
IONIZATION ENERGY OF GASEOUS ATOMS

Atomic Number	Element	Ionization Energies (IE)					
		$[IE_1]$		$[IE_2]$		$[IE_3]$	
		kJ/mol	eV	kJ/mol	eV	kJ/mol	eV
1	H	1313	13.6				
2	He	2370	24.6	5241.7	54.4		
3	Li	518	5.4	7289.9	75.5	11800	122
4	Be	848	9.3	1755.6	18.2	14831	154
5	B	798	8.3	2424.0	25.1	3658	37.9
6	C	1087.1	11.3	2349.2	24.4	4615	47.9
7	N	1400.3	14.5	2854.9	29.6	4573	47.4
8	O	1312.5	13.6	3390.0	35.2	5296	54.9
9	F	1680.4	17.4	3373.3	35.0	6040	62.6
10	Ne	2077.5	21.6	3958.5	41.1	6270	64.0
11	Na	493.2	5.1	4560.4	47.3	6905	71.7
12	Mg	735.7	7.6	1450.5	15.0	7725	80.1
13	Al	576.8	6.0	1814.1	18.8	2742	28.4
14	Si	785.8	8.1	1575.9	16.3	3227	33.4
15	P	1061.7	11.0	1893.5	19.6	2909	30.2
16	S	990.0	10.4	2257.2	23.4	3373	35.0
17	Cl	1254.0	13.0	2294.8	23.8	3846	39.9
18	Ar	1517.3	15.8	2662.7	27.6	3942	40.9
19	K	413.8	4.3	3068.1	31.8	4598	47.8
20	Ca	589.4	6.1	1145.3	11.9	4937	51.3

Analysis of the data in Table 2-7 will lead to the following observations:

1. In general, nonmetallic atoms have higher first-ionization energies than metallic atoms.

2. Certain gases such as helium (He), neon (Ne) and argon (Ar) have very high first ionization energies. This indicates that the electrons are held very firmly. The compactness and symmetry of their electron clouds also prevent them from taking on electrons. In general, the gases helium, neon, argon, krypton,

xenon and radon are chemically unreactive. They are the noble gases; with the exception of helium, they all have two *s* electrons and six *p* electrons in the outermost energy level.

3. There is an unusually large gap between the energy required to remove the first electron and the second electron from lithium (Li), sodium (Na) and potassium (K) atoms. This suggests that it is relatively easy for these atoms to form ions having a 1+ charge. The low ionization energy is consistent with the fact that the single outer *s* electron in each of these atoms is located at a relatively long distance from the nucleus. It is also consistent with the relatively high chemical reactivity of these elements.

4. There is an unusually large gap between the energy required to remove the second electron and the third electron from beryllium (Be), magnesium (Mg) and calcium (Ca) atoms. This suggests that it is relatively easy for these atoms to form ions having a 2+ charge.

Let us examine the electron configuration of a few of these simple positive ions.

2-8

Electron Configuration of Ions

Ions that attain a noble-gas electron configuration are particularly stable.

Examination of the electron configuration of many simple positive ions shows that they are *isoelectronic* (same number of electrons) with the atoms of the noble gases. For example, neon *atoms* and sodium *ions* (Na^+) both have 10 electrons and the same configuration. Let us examine the significance of this observation. Neon atoms have a ground-state configuration of $1s^2 2s^2 2p^6$. In neon atoms, all available orbitals in the first and second energy levels are fully occupied. Note that the outer level has 8 electrons. This outer-level octet structure is characteristic of all noble-gas atoms except helium, which has only one principal energy level. Because noble gases are chemically unreactive and extremely stable, it is assumed that *there is a special stability associated with the outer-octet structure and the configuration of the noble-gas atoms.* Apparently, the 8 electrons form a spherically symmetrical charge cloud about the nucleus.

Neutral sodium atoms have 11 electrons—one more than neon atoms. By losing one electron, sodium atoms achieve the electron configuration of neon and become stable sodium ions. Sodium ions have a nuclear charge of 11+ and only 10 electrons. This gives the ion an overall charge of 1+. Accordingly, the electron configuration of Na^+ is the same as that of neon, $1s^2 2s^2 2p^6$.

It is evident from the relatively high ionization energies of fluorine, chlorine, oxygen and sulfur that these and other non-metals do not readily lose electrons and form positive ions. Rather, they are observed to form simple negative ions quite readily. In doing so, they achieve the electron configurations of the noble gases. Consider fluorine atoms, which have one electron fewer than neon atoms. We would expect fluorine to gain one electron readily and thereby achieve the neon structure. The addition of one electron to a neutral fluorine atom produces a fluoride ion with a 1– charge. Thus, fluoride ions (F^-), sodium ions (Na^+) and neon atoms (Ne) all have the same electron configurations.

The charge cloud that forms around the nucleus of a noble-gas atom is, in effect, impenetrable, in that other atoms cannot "see" or "feel" the nucleus of a noble-gas atom. Hence, their stable structures are not disrupted by attracting the electrons of other atoms or by losing their own electrons. This suggests that other atoms might gain stability by acquiring the same electron configuration as a noble-gas atom.

These examples and other data indicate that the easiest-to-remove electrons are those with the highest principal quantum numbers. It is for this reason that we usually represent the ground-state configuration of an atom by grouping together all the orbitals in a given energy level and arranging them in order of increasing principal quantum number.

Positive ions have the same nuclear charge as the atoms from which they are formed but have fewer electrons. Let us write the electron configuration of a titanium(II) ion (Ti^{2+}). The atomic number of titanium is 22. This means that the neutral gas atom has 22 electrons and a nuclear charge of 22+. Accordingly, the electron configuration of a titanium atom is

$$1s^2 2s^2 2p^6 3s^2 3p^6 3d^2 4s^2$$

The 2+ charge on the ion indicates that the atom has lost two electrons. The two electrons that are lost come from the $4s$ orbital, even though, in our hypothetical process, a d electron was the last to "enter" in the "building up" of the atom in the ground state. This behaviour is explained in terms of the relative stabilities of electrons in the $4s$ and $3d$ orbitals. The relative stabilities are related to the energy changes associated with orbital overlap and increasing complexity of orbitals in the higher energy levels. A detailed explanation is beyond the scope of this text. We may represent the configuration of Ti^{2+} as $1s^2 2s^2 2p^6 3s^2 3p^6 3d^2$, or as

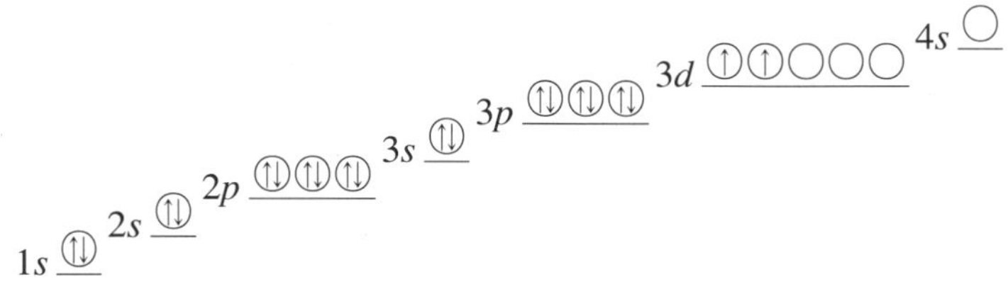

$$4s \, \bigcirc$$
$$3d \, ⬆️⬆️\bigcirc\bigcirc\bigcirc$$
$$3p \, ⬆️⬇️⬆️⬇️⬆️⬇️$$
$$3s \, ⬆️⬇️$$
$$2p \, ⬆️⬇️⬆️⬇️⬆️⬇️$$
$$2s \, ⬆️⬇️$$
$$1s \, ⬆️⬇️$$

FOLLOW-UP PROBLEM

Write the electron configuration for these species: (a) K^+, (b) Cl^-, (c) Ar, (d) Fe^{2+}, (e) Fe^{3+}, (f) Zn^{2+}.

Answers:
a) $1s^2 2s^2 2p^6 3s^2 3p^6$
b) $1s^2 2s^2 2p^6 3s^2 3p^6$
c) $1s^2 2s^2 2p^6 3s^2 3p^6$

In order to understand the nature of electron orbitals, it is necessary to examine the basics of the quantum, or wave-mechanical, theory. The quantum model of the atom proposes that electrons of particular energy sublevels occupy specific orbitals. Through the use of the quantum theory, we will be able to determine the shapes and spatial orientations of these electron orbitals.

THE EVOLUTION AND NATURE OF THE WAVE-MECHANICAL MODEL OF AN ATOM

2-9

"Matter Waves"

Scientists consider that every particle of matter possesses both particle and wave characteristics.

In 1923, a young French scientist, Louis de Broglie (1892–1960), supplied the creative spark that led to the development of the wave-mechanical model. De Broglie's imaginative proposal was that *matter, like light or any other type of radiant energy, has both particle and wave characteristics.* He reinforced this proposal by deriving an equation for the wavelength λ of a particle with mass m and velocity v. The equation was derived by equating the energy of a photon from Planck's equation, $E = hv$, to the mass energy from Einstein's equation, $E = mc^2$. That is,

$$mc^2 = h\nu$$

If we substitute c/λ for ν, then

$$mc^2 = \frac{hc}{\lambda}$$

Dividing both sides by mc^2 and multiplying both sides by λ yields

$$\lambda = \frac{h}{mc}$$

By substituting the velocity of a particle, v, for the speed of light, c, we can derive the de Broglie equation:

$$\lambda = \frac{h}{mv}$$

where h is Planck's constant, m is the mass of the particle and v is its velocity. Thus, de Broglie concluded that *every particle is associated with a wave, the frequency of the wave depending on the velocity of the particle.* At the time, de Broglie's concept of "matter waves" was looked on with a great deal of scepticism by other scientists who had no evidence of the existence of such waves. However, even the sceptics were forced to accept the idea when two American scientists experimentally verified de Broglie's hypothesis.

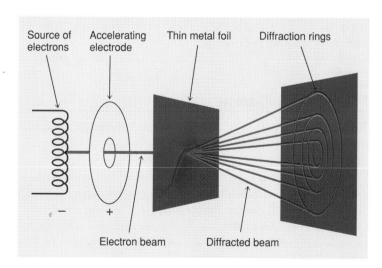

Source of electrons Accelerating electrode Thin metal foil Diffraction rings

Electron beam Diffracted beam

Figure 2-11
Schematic representation of the diffraction of electrons by a thin metal foil. The regular spacing of the atoms in a metallic crystal (foil) affects the beam of electrons in the same way that the slits in a diffraction grating or the pinhole in a piece of cardboard affect visible light. The spacing of the atoms in a crystal is about 0.1 nm. This approximates the wavelength of a 100 eV electron. The distance between the lines in an ordinary grating approximates the wavelength of visible light.

In 1927, C. J. Davisson (1881–1958) and L. H. Germer (1896–1971) conducted experiments that involved the "shooting" of electrons at a sample of nickel. To their amazement, they obtained diffraction patterns similar to those obtained when X rays (a form

Figure 2-12
Electron interference pattern resulting from the diffraction of electrons by a crystal. This experimental observation provides evidence that beams of electrons behave as waves.

"WONDER WHERE MY WAVE OF PROBABILITY IS GUIDING ME?"

Figure 2-13
Even an elephant has a wavelength that can be calculated. In order for a 2500 kg elephant to have a measurable wavelength (1.0 pm), it would have to move at a velocity of about 25×10^{-24} m/s. At this rate, it would take 40×10^{15} (million, billion) years for it to go 1 m.

of radiant energy) were diffracted by a crystal. Furthermore, the experimentally determined wavelength agreed with the value calculated by using the de Broglie equation. It has since been confirmed that beams of neutrons, hydrogen atoms and other small particles exhibit wave characteristics (see Fig. 2-12). Wavelengths can be calculated theoretically for material objects ranging from electrons to elephants. The wavelengths associated with large objects, however, are so small that there is no physical method available for detecting or measuring them. Hence, they have no practical significance (Fig. 2-13).

Practical use of the wave character of electrons is shown in the operation of the electron microscope. This instrument, shown in Fig. 2-14, uses a beam of electrons rather than light waves to produce the image of an object being viewed. The wavelength of "electron waves" is much smaller than that of visible light waves. The electron microscope, therefore, has a much greater resolving power than an ordinary microscope.

Although we can calculate a wavelength for "matter waves," such waves do not resemble electromagnetic waves, sound waves, water waves or any other waves associated with our normal, everyday experience. It was Max Born (1882–1970) who proposed the currently accepted interpretation of "matter waves." He suggested that these waves are waves of probability, indicating a region of space where we are most likely to find particles associated with these waves. We can consider electron waves as "pilot waves," which guide the motion of the particles (electrons), analogous to electromagnetic waves, which guide the flow of "particles" (photons) of energy.

2-10
The Uncertainty Principle

The uncertainty principle states that it is impossible to simultaneously predict the momentum and position of any atomic particle.

The inability to predict the exact location of atomic particles was rationalized by German physicist Werner Heisenberg (1901–1976). He proposed that the basis of the dilemma was the attempt to apply the rules and methods used in making observations on the macroscopic level to atomic phenomena. It is possible to carry out observations and measurements of everyday objects without disturbing the object being measured. For example, the exact path that a satellite follows can be precisely determined by applying the laws of classical mechanics. As long as the momentum (the product of mass and velocity) and the position of the satellite can be determined simultaneously, the path it will follow can be

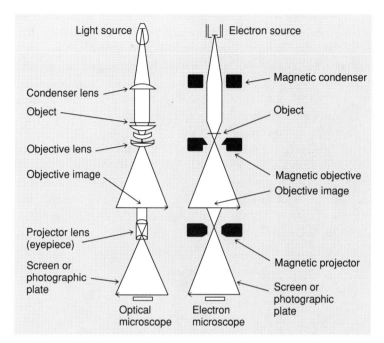

Light source · Electron source

Condenser lens

Object

Objective lens

Objective image

Projector lens
(eyepiece)

Screen or
photographic
plate

Magnetic condenser

Object

Magnetic objective
Objective image

Magnetic projector

Screen or
photographic
plate

Optical
microscope

Electron
microscope

Figure 2-14
Schematic diagrams of the optical (light) microscope and the electron microscope, inverted to make comparison easier.

predicted. Since the position of the massive satellite is not changed by the impact of the light rays that strike it, the image we observe is the actual point from which the rays are reflected.

A different situation exists in the world of atomic particles. Investigating the behaviour of an electron with photons of light is like investigating the working of a fine watch with a crowbar. For example, if we attempt to determine the position of an electron, the light reflected from a tiny electron has enough energy to·alter the electron's path completely. Thus, *we cannot simultaneously measure the momentum and the position of an electron.* Since we cannot observe the true position of an electron, we are unable to describe its trajectory. Consequently, an exact orbit such as that described by the Bohr theory cannot be determined for electrons.

Werner Heisenberg summarized these ideas in his famous **uncertainty principle**, which states that *it is impossible to determine simultaneously the exact momentum and position of a single atomic particle.* The uncertainty principle may be expressed mathematically as

$$(\Delta p)(\Delta x) = h \qquad [2\text{-}1]$$

where h equals Planck's constant, Δp represents *the uncertainty in momentum* and Δx *the uncertainty in position.* Equation 2-1 shows that the smaller the uncertainty in momentum or velocity ($\Delta p = m \, \Delta v$), the greater the uncertainty in position. It can be shown that an uncertainty of as much as 1% in the velocity of an electron in a hydrogen atom yields an uncertainty of 3.7×10^{-8} m in the position of an electron. This uncertainty is 700 times the actual radius of a hydrogen atom. More precise measurements of the velocity yield even greater uncertainty in the position of an electron. This example vividly illustrates that it is impossible to specify the location of an electron at any given time. Thus, Bohr's definite orbits have no real meaning and can never be experimentally demonstrated.

Since the value of h in Equation 2-1 is so small, we can ignore uncertainty on the macroscopic scale. It can be shown that an uncertainty of 16 km/h in the velocity of an ordinary automobile results in an uncertainty of only 1×10^{-37} m in its position. This example indicates that the uncertainty principle does not apply to events on the macroscopic scale.

Figure 2-15
A photon of light used to observe and determine the position of an electron would change the momentum (mass ×velocity) and alter the path of the electron. Therefore, we cannot simultaneously determine the momentum and position of an electron.

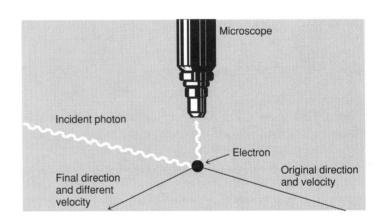

Microscope

Incident photon

Electron

Original direction and velocity

Final direction and different velocity

LOOKING AT ATOMS

When John Dalton proposed his atomic theory of matter in 1808, he based it entirely on indirect evidence—no one had ever seen an atom. Over the next 150 years, scientists accumulated more evidence for the existence of atoms, but that final proof—the sight of an atom—still eluded them.

Light microscopes were developed and improved during this time but were limited by the nature of light itself. For an object to be distinguished, or *resolved*, in a light microscope, its diameter must be greater than the wavelength of light. It is possible to resolve objects with a diameter as small as 250 nm, but anything smaller than that cannot be resolved. It is impossible to use light to "see" an atom.

A beam of electrons is similar to a beam of light, and under suitable conditions it can be reflected, refracted and focused with

lenses. Because of its very short wavelength, a beam of fast-moving electrons can be used in an *electron microscope* to resolve objects smaller than 1 nm.

In a *transmission electron microscope (TEM)*, an electron gun and its associated electromagnetic lenses produce a beam of electrons that is passed through a thin slice of a sample material. Additional lenses focus the transmitted electrons, forming a three-dimensional image. The image, which consists of electrons rather than light, is converted to a visual image on a TV screen or on film. During the 1950s and 1960s, transmission electronmicroscopy allowed great advances in the science of cell biology. Structures such as ribosomes, mitochondria and Golgi bodies, which have diameters smaller than 10 nm, could only have been discovered with a transmission electron microscope. The limit of resolution of

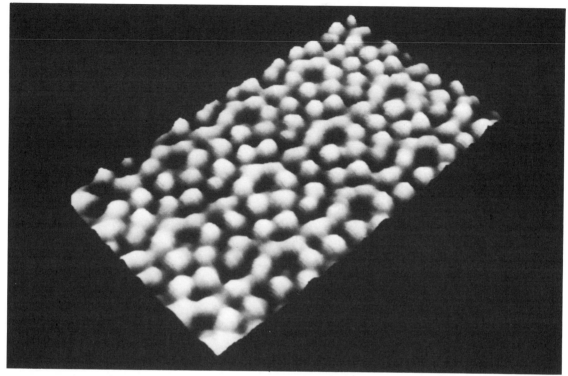

this technique is as small as 0.5 nm.

During the 1960s, a related device, the *scanning electron microscope (SEM)*, was developed. In this instrument, a beam of electrons is used to scan the surface of a three-dimensional object that has been thinly coated with a material that conducts electricity. The scanning electron beam causes the emission of secondary electrons from the surface. As these secondary electrons are detected on a scintillator, a computer analyses their distribution and produces a three-dimensional image on a TV screen. Startling images of tiny biological objects have been produced in this way, but because of the scattering of electrons, the absolute limit of resolution is about 20 nm.

The progress of electronmicroscopy has advanced as technical difficulties in the instruments have been overcome:

- Techniques of sample preparation and staining have been refined.
- Methods of maintaining a high vacuum within the instruments have been invented.
- The amount of mechanical vibration has been minimized.
- The power supplies necessary for the electromagnetic lenses have been made stable.

And, most important, computer programs necessary to process the data and produce the visual image have also been developed.

Since 1970, when the first images of individual thorium atoms were produced using a combination instrument—a *scanning transmission electron microscope (STEM)*—techniques of imaging atoms have advanced even further.

During the 1980s, a new device—the *scanning tunnelling microscope (STM)*—was developed by scientists at the IBM Zurich Research Laboratory and won for its inventors the Nobel Prize in 1986. The photograph on this page is a computer-generated image showing the surface atoms of silicon (Si) magnified millions of times. The scanning tunnelling microscope produces images of the surface of a sample by utilizing the electrons within the sample. Surface electrons "tunnel" out of a substance and form an electron cloud above the surface. A fine stylus, with a point one atom wide, scans the surface of the sample. The tunnelling current that flows between the stylus and the sample's electron cloud is monitored and kept constant by maintaining the stylus at a uniform height above the surface atoms as it passes laterally across the sample. Bumps as small as 0.01 nm in the surface result in vertical movements of the stylus—movements that are interpreted on the viewing screen to show, in a three-dimensional image, the position of individual atoms.

ERWIN SCHRÖDINGER
1887–1961
Schrödinger was an Austrian physicist who received his education at the University of Vienna and later served as professor of physics at Stuttgart, Breslau, Zurich and the University of Berlin. He became a Fellow of Magdalene College, Oxford, and in 1940 went to Dublin, Ireland, as a professor of physics at the Institute of Advanced Studies. In 1933, Schrödinger was awarded the Nobel Prize for his contribution to the development of the wave-mechanical model of an atom.

Schrödinger expressed his ideas of the wave-particle duality of the electron proposed by de Broglie in the following statement: "The electron revolving in the atom is a disturbance proceeding along the electron orbit in the form of a wave."

In 1926, Schrödinger developed the equation that bears his name. The wave equation is

$$\left(\frac{\delta^2\psi}{\delta x^2} + \frac{\delta^2\psi}{\delta y^2} + \frac{\delta^2\psi}{\delta z^2} \right) + \frac{8\pi^2 m}{h^2}(E - V)\psi = 0$$

where x, y and z are the space coordinates of the electron with the nucleus at 0, 0, 0, m is the mass of the electron, E is the total energy of the electron-proton system and V is the potential energy. The Greek letter ψ (psi) is called a "wave amplitude function" because in many solutions to the equation it exhibits a wave-like

The Quantitative Basis for the Wave-Mechanical Model

Schrödinger's wave-mechanical equation furnished the quantitative basis for the new atomic model. Wolfgang Pauli enunciated, in his exclusion principle, the configuration of the electrons about the nucleus.

In 1926, Austrian scientist, Erwin Schrödinger (1887–1961), furnished the quantitative basis for the new atomic model. Schrödinger, taking a cue from de Broglie, visualized an atom as *a positively charged nucleus surrounded by vibrating electron waves*. As a theoretical physicist, Schrödinger knew that a complete description of an atom required an equation for the waves associated with its electrons. However, the correct equation would have to yield solutions that would agree with experimental data. That is, it would have to predict energy states that agreed with those obtained spectroscopically. Schrödinger considered the pulsating electron waves surrounding the nucleus analogous to the periodic vibrations of water covering a uniformly flooded, spherical planet. Equations describing the wave motion on a hypothetical, flooded planet had been worked out 100 years earlier by the Irish mathematician, William Hamilton (1805–1865), while he was working on the problem of predicting tides.

Schrödinger adapted Hamilton's equations to an atomic system, introduced de Broglie's wavelength of an electron and applied conditions corresponding to the geometry of an atom. The result was his famous *wave equation*, the solution of which described the behaviour of a hydrogen atom in terms of its wave characteristics. This equation, or a modification of it, provides the theoretical basis for the current wave-mechanical model of atomic and molecular structures. The wave equation describes an electron as a three-dimensional wave in the electric field of a positively charged nucleus. The wave equation is briefly discussed in the biographical sketch of Erwin Schrödinger.

When the wave equation is solved for a hydrogen atom, the allowed energy values are in close agreement with the experimentally derived values. In addition, solutions to the equation provide data that enables scientists to identify regions of space (orbitals) about the nucleus where there is a high probability of locating an electron with a specific energy. Computers are used to solve the Schrödinger equation and to plot the probable locations of an electron as it moves about the nucleus.

The solution to the Schrödinger equation yields a quantity, psi (ψ), whose square (ψ^2) can be used to determine the probability of finding an electron with a specific energy in a tiny unit volume of space at a distance from the nucleus. By determining the probability at various distances from the nucleus, it is possible to outline regions of space where there is, for example, a 90% to 95% probability of finding a given electron.

The computer-produced plot is equivalent to plotting the results of a series of hypothetical experiments that are designed to determine the frequency of an electron's appearance at different points in the space surrounding the nucleus. If we were to plot the results of many such experiments on a three-dimensional graph, we would obtain an electron-charge-cloud picture that would have the size, shape and direction of the regions of space in which an electron could be found a given percentage of the time. These regions of space are called **orbitals** and are pictured as electron charge clouds. The probability of finding an electron at various regions in the cloud is proportional to the density of the cloud in those regions.

Each orbital is associated with and defined by a set of integers, called **quantum numbers**. These numbers are analogous to the three dimensions needed to describe anything occupying three-dimensional space. The three quantum numbers are derived from the mathematical solutions of the wave equations. These numbers are designated as n, l and m_l. The quantum numbers can have only specific values and are interrelated. That is, the value of l is limited by the value of n, and the value of m_l is limited by the value of l. The permitted values assigned to these numbers determine the specific (quantized) energies that a hydrogen atom can have. The quantum numbers are like an address for the electrons in an atom. To completely identify an electron in an atom, it is necessary to state the value of each of the quantum numbers. *No two electrons in a given atom can have the same set of quantum numbers*. This important principle, called the **Pauli exclusion principle**, after Wolfgang Pauli (1900–1958), underlies the electron arrangement about the nucleus.

The significant aspects of each of the quantum numbers are discussed in the next four sections.

series of maxima and minima. It is analogous to the wave amplitude of an ordinary wave. The expression $\delta^2 \psi / \delta x^2$ indicates the mathematical operation that must be carried out on ψ to solve the equation.

Solutions of the Schrödinger equation yield expressions for the wave function, ψ. Each wave function is associated with a set of quantum numbers that can have only certain allowed values. The values determine the allowed energy states of the atom. Thus, each acceptable wave function, ψ, is related to a given energy state as well as to the space co-ordinates that describe the atomic system. Psi squared, ψ^2, is interpreted as being proportional to the probability of finding the electron in a unit volume about the nucleus. If we think of the electron in a specific energy state as being smeared out over a certain region of space about the nucleus, then ψ^2 may be interpreted as being proportional to the "electron density" of the electron charge cloud in a given volume of the cloud.

Note the difference between an orbit, as in Bohr's model of the atom, and an orbital. An orbit is a defined path; an orbital is a region in which an electron will most likely be found.

2-12

The Principal Quantum Number, *n*

The value of the principal quantum number, n, determines the energy of an electron and indicates where an electron is least likely to be found in each orbital of a given energy level.

The principal quantum number, n, designates the principal energy level in which a given electron is located. The value of n determines the total energy of an electron as well as the average distance of an electron from the nucleus. The principal quantum number, n, is limited to any positive whole number value, excluding zero. An electron with $n = 1$ is in the lowest energy level of an atom. The value of n also indicates the number of nodal surfaces associated with each orbital in a given energy level. Nodal surfaces represent locations where the probability of finding the electron is zero.

A nodal surface for a three-dimensional vibrating object is analogous to a nodal point for a vibrating string. In Fig. 2-16(a) the string is fixed at both ends. Points A and B constitute the boundaries of the string system. When plucked, the string vibrates. The maximum displacement from the rest position at point C is called the *amplitude* of the vibration. There is no vibration at the ends; these points of zero displacement are called *nodes*. Only certain vibrations can occur, and these are determined by the boundaries of the system. A second mode of vibration is shown in Fig. 2-16(b). The vibration in this case has three nodes: one at each end and one in the centre. Note that on either side of the central node, the displacements of the curve are equal in magnitude but opposite in direction. The displacements are said to be *out of phase*. A change in phase always occurs at a nodal point. In an atom, there is a nodal surface at infinity for all orbitals. Thus, in theory, all orbitals extend to infinity. We are concerned with the regions relatively close to the nucleus, where there is a high probability of finding an electron. The most likely distance at which a given electron may be found is represented in terms of a probability graph, which we will discuss later. In addition to the number of nodal surfaces, n is equal to the number of different types of orbitals in the given energy level. For example, in the third energy level in which $n = 3$, there are three types of orbitals: s, p and d.

2-13
The Angular-Momentum Quantum Number, l

The angular-momentum quantum number, l, determines the shape of the orbital.

Although the total energy of an electron is represented by the principal quantum number, a portion of this energy can be associated with the orbital motion of the electron about the nucleus. This orbital motion is described by the angular-momentum quantum number, which is designated as l. The angular-momentum quantum number, l, is related to the angular momentum of the electron and the shape of the orbitals. The l quantum number is also related to the position of the nodal surfaces. Interpretation of this quantity reveals that for p orbitals there is a nodal plane through the nucleus. The p electrons have zero probability of being found in this plane. The value of l also indicates the type of sublevel and orbital in which an electron is located. Sublevels and orbitals are

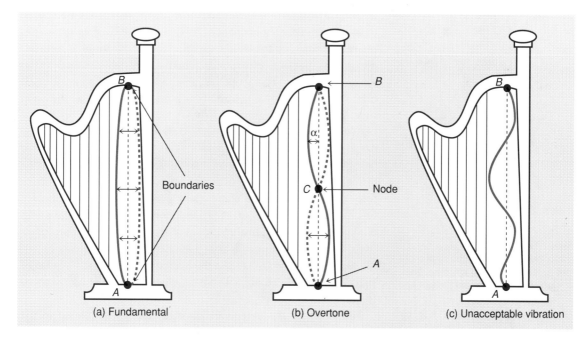

(a) Fundamental   (b) Overtone   (c) Unacceptable vibration

designated as s, p, d or f, depending on the value of l. The relationship is shown below.

Value of l	Type of Sublevel and Orbital
0	s
1	p
2	d
3	f

The value of l is determined by the value of n for that level and may assume all whole number values from 0 through $n - 1$. Thus, when $n = 1$, l has only one value, 0. This means there is just one type of sublevel or orbital in the first, or $n = 1$, energy level. Therefore, an electron in the first energy level can be identified as an s electron only. An electron with $n = 2$ might be located in either an s or p orbital in the second energy level.

Figure 2-16
(a) and (b) Allowed vibrations of a string. Note that in (b), the string is displaced in opposite directions on either side of the node. The two displacements are said to be *out of phase*. Any vibrations that would require displacement of the string at the boundaries are not allowed. When the string in (a) is plucked, standing waves shown in (b) appear. That is, the waves in (b) appear to be stationary. The wave-mechanical model treats electron waves as standing waves of energy. (c) An unallowed vibration is analogous to an unallowed set of quantum numbers for describing an electron.

2-14

The Magnetic Quantum Number, m_l

The magnetic quantum number, m_l, indicates the spatial orientation of the orbitals.

The magnetic quantum number is designated as m_l. As a result of an electron's angular momentum, a magnetic field is produced that can interact with an external electric or magnetic field. Under the influence of these fields, the electrons in the orbitals or sublevels are oriented in certain preferred regions of space about the

The number of m_l values is equal to the number of orbitals in an energy sublevel.

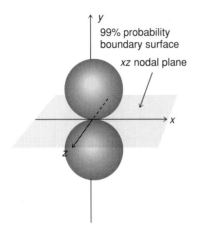

Figure 2-17
The p_y orbital showing the region of zero probability in the xz plane. The xz plane is called a nodal plane.

nucleus. The directional characteristics of these regions are related to the x, y and z axes in space. These letters are used as subscripts on the orbital letters. For example, there are three p orbitals designated, respectively, as p_x, p_y and p_z. The p_x orbital is directed along the x axis. The yz plane represents a nodal plane for this orbital. The directional nature of the p and d orbitals was shown in Figs. 2-2 and 2-3. Figure 2-17 shows that each p orbital is dumb-bell-shaped with two lobes separated by a nodal plane. It should be noted that an electron in a p orbital has an equal probability of being found in either lobe of the orbital. We will find that the directional characteristics of the p and d orbitals play an important role in determining the shapes and properties of molecules. In Fig. 2-1, we saw that s orbitals are spherically symmetrical about the nucleus and are non-directional. This means that the probability of finding an s electron at a given distance from the nucleus is the same in all directions from the nucleus. The spherical region of space represents the area where an electron is most likely to be found.

The value of the magnetic quantum number is related to the *spatial orientations of the orbitals* that result when the atom is subjected to the magnetic field. The m_l values depend on the value of l. Thus, m_l can assume all values from $+l$ through 0 to $-l$. For example, when $l = 0$, m_l can have only one value, 0. This means that there is one s orbital per energy level. When $l = 1$, m_l can have three values: $+1$, 0, -1. This means that there can be three p orbitals. It can be seen that for each value of l, there are $2l + 1$ different values of m_l. Thus, the number of each kind of orbital in a principal energy level is determined by the number of values that m_l has for a given value of l. An exercise for you is to show that d orbitals can have five spatial orientations (5 orbitals per level) and that f orbitals can have seven spatial orientations (7 orbitals per level). The relationships among the three quantum numbers, the principal energy levels and the orbitals are summarized in Table 2-8.

2-15

The Spin Quantum Number, m_s

The spin quantum number, m_s, distinguishes between the oppositely spinning electrons in an orbital.

In order to explain finer details of atomic spectra, it was proposed that an electron has an angular momentum of rotation about its own axis. In other words, it has a spin and behaves like a small magnet. It can spin in either of two directions and can have one of two possible values: $+\frac{1}{2}$ or $-\frac{1}{2}$. Thus, a fourth quantum number, called the *spin quantum number*, m_s, distinguishes between the oppositely spinning electrons in an orbital (Fig. 2-18 on the next page).

TABLE 2-8
RELATIONSHIPS BETWEEN QUANTUM NUMBERS, PRINCIPAL ENERGY LEVELS AND ORBITALS

Principal Energy Level	Principal Quantum Number (n)	Angular-Momentum Quantum Number (l)	Orbital or Sublevel	Different Types of Orbitals per Principal Energy Level	Magnetic Quantum Number (m_l)	Number of Each Type of Orbital per Energy Level
1	1	0	s	1	0	1
2	2	0	s	2	0	1
		1	p		+1, 0, −1	3
3	3	0	s	3	0	1
		1	p		+1, 0, −1	3
		2	d		+2, +1, 0, −1, −2	5
4	4	0	s	4	0	1
		1	p		+1, 0, −1	3
		2	d		+2, +1, 0, −1, −2	5
		3	f		+3, +2, +1, 0, −1, −2, −3	7

2-16

The Pauli Exclusion Principle

The Pauli exclusion principle sets the limits on the number of electrons that can occupy an orbital.

Since the values of the quantum numbers are restricted and interdependent, only certain combinations are possible. The Pauli exclusion principle states that no two electrons in an atom can have the same set of quantum numbers. Thus, *no orbital can contain more than two electrons and the two electrons must have opposite spins.* Application of this principle determines and limits the maximum number of electrons that can occupy a given energy level. Table 2-9 illustrates the possible combinations of quantum numbers for electrons in a neon atom and is consistent with our finding that the first energy level can hold only two electrons and the second level only eight.

The values of the four quantum numbers in the first row of the table constitute the "address" of the single electron in a hydrogen atom. The first- and second-row values are those that identify, respectively, the two electrons in a helium atom. The data in Table 2-9 shows that s orbitals contain a maximum of two electrons and that p orbitals contain a maximum of six electrons. An extension of this table would show that the d orbitals in the third or

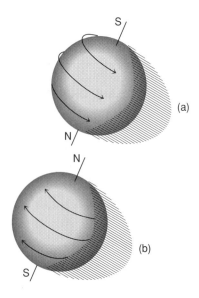

(a)

(b)

Figure 2-18
Electrons spinning about an axis produce a magnetic field that interacts
with an externally applied field and
the field produced by the electron's
motion around the nucleus. The electrons in (a) and (b) have opposite
spins and interact with the orbital
magnetic field, giving different energies. The differences can be determined spectroscopically.

Quantum numbers are used to identify the most probable location of an
electron, in much the same way an
address identifies the location of a
house. The principal quantum number (n) identifies the main energy
level (like a city or town); the angular-
momentum quantum number (l) identifies the energy sublevels (like the
street); and the magnetic quantum
number (m_l) identifies the orbital in
which an electron is most likely to be
found (similar to a house number). A
fourth number, the spin quantum
number (m_s) is needed to identify the
orientation of the electron.

higher energy level could contain a maximum of ten electrons and
that f orbitals in the fourth or higher energy level could contain a
maximum of 14 electrons. Application of the Pauli exclusion
principle shows that the general formula for the maximum number
of electrons that can be accommodated by a given energy level is
$2n^2$, where n is the principal quantum number of the energy level.
Thus, the fourth energy level can hold a maximum of $2 \times 4^2 = 32$
electrons.

TABLE 2-9
ALLOWED QUANTUM NUMBERS OF ELECTRONS
IN A NEON ATOM

Energy Level	n	l	Orbital	m_l	m_s	Possible Combinations of 4 Quantum Numbers (Maximum Number of Electrons)
1	1	0	$1s$	0	$+\frac{1}{2}$	2
	1	0	$1s$	0	$-\frac{1}{2}$	
2	2	0	$2s$	0	$+\frac{1}{2}$	8
	2	0	$2s$	0	$-\frac{1}{2}$	
	2	1	$2p$	-1	$+\frac{1}{2}$	
	2	1	$2p$	-1	$-\frac{1}{2}$	
	2	1	$2p$	0	$+\frac{1}{2}$	
	2	1	$2p$	0	$-\frac{1}{2}$	
	2	1	$2p$	$+1$	$+\frac{1}{2}$	
	2	1	$2p$	$+1$	$-\frac{1}{2}$	

Solutions to the Schrödinger wave equation yield quantum
numbers that define the energy levels and orbitals available to the
electrons of an atom. Support for the validity of the wave-mechanical model is found in the close agreement between the theoreti-
cally-calculated energy values for hydrogen and those determined
experimentally from atomic spectra. The relative energy values for
each state can be depicted in an energy-level diagram. The energy-
level diagram for hydrogen is shown in Fig. 2-19. As you can see
from this figure, all the orbitals in any given principal quantum
level represent the same energy; that is, they are *degenerate*.

The wave equation cannot be rigorously solved for atomic
systems containing more than one electron. Therefore, approximation methods are used. Prediction of the behaviour of the electrons
in more complicated atoms and molecules is made by analogy to
the solutions of the wave equation for a hydrogen atom. Since
solutions have been verified experimentally, predictions made on

this basis are valid. In multi-electron atoms, inter-electron repulsion is a factor, so that the orbitals in a given energy level have different energy values. In these atoms, a 3d electron has more energy than a 3p electron, which, in turn, has more energy than a 3s electron. The relative positions of the energy levels of a given atom depend on the nuclear charge and on the extent to which other orbitals are occupied. Therefore, energy-level diagrams of different atoms vary in terms of actual energies, but in a qualitative sense, they are similar and follow the general pattern shown in Fig. 2-4.

Orbitals having the same energy are said to be *degenerate energy levels*.

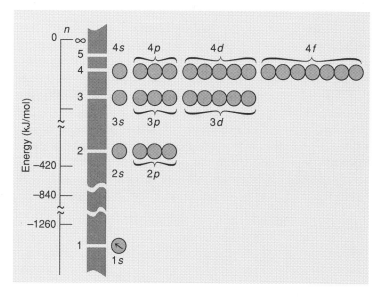

Figure 2-19
Energy-level diagram for hydrogen.
The circles represent empty orbitals.

In this chapter, we discovered that similarities in the properties of the elements are related to the similarities in the outer-energy-level electron configuration of their atoms. It was further observed that there is a correlation between the electron configuration of an element and its location in the periodic table. We also determined the electron configuration of atoms using the concepts of the quantum, or wave-mechanical, theory.

We will now use the orbital concept and the electron configuration of atoms to help explain how different types of bonds are formed, and to account for the shapes and characteristics of molecules. We will also use the quantum theory to help us explain the observed properties of matter and behaviour of the molecules we investigate.

In the next chapter we will examine in detail the atomic properties such as ionization energy and electronegativity. We will then consider the formation and nature of chemical bonds.

The electron configuration of atoms in the ground state may be written by using an energy-level diagram, Hund's rule and the Pauli exclusion principle. The procedure was illustrated earlier in some detail.

THE ORIGIN OF THE ELEMENTS

S ince ancient times, people have wondered about the origins of the earth and the heavens. Although the answers to such speculation have traditionally been sought in religion, scientists have assembled enough data to be able to hypothesize about one clue to this mystery. That clue is the origin of the chemical elements.

In the mid-nineteenth century, the French philosopher, Auguste Comte, predicted that we would never know the chemical composition of the stars. Not fifty years later, however, astronomical spectroscopy was providing us with this knowledge. In this procedure, the light emitted by various stars and galaxies is separated into a spectrum of lines, each of which represents a specific wavelength. Because the atoms of each element emit and absorb light at characteristic wavelengths, the presence or absence of each element in the light source can be detected. Similarly, the composition of dust clouds and gases can be determined by noticing which wavelengths of light have been absorbed.

Results to date reveal that the elements found in space are the same as those found on earth (with the important exceptions of certain artificially produced elements such as technitium and

californium). Identifying what elements are present is therefore fairly straightforward. Determining the quantities of each is considerably more difficult. Research indicates that the chemical composition of most stars is similar, although there are some differences that prove important to the question of the origin of the elements. Very old stars, for instance, tend to have fewer elements with masses greater than helium than do young stars. This implies that the universe originally contained little or none of these heavier elements.

The relative abundance (relative number of atoms) of each element appears to be more or less the same throughout the universe, in spite of the variations between individual stars and planets. This means that the processes that form elements must be uniformly available throughout the universe. It is therefore useful to chart these abundances against their atomic numbers so that we can visualize the parameters that must be accounted for when theorizing about the elements' origins. Part of such a chart appears below. A complete chart would reveal the following:

– Hydrogen and helium are the most common atoms in the universe. In fact, around 93% of the universe's atoms can

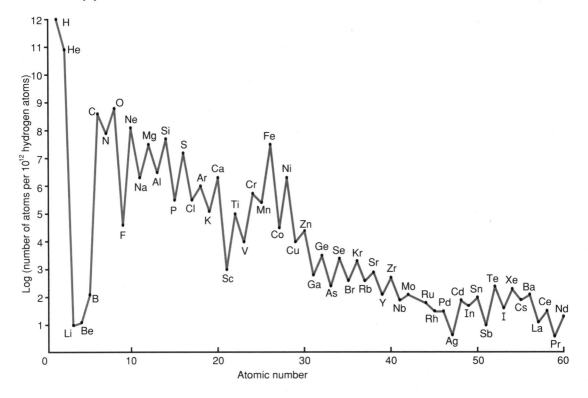

be accounted for by hydrogen, while around 6% are helium atoms.

- The other elements account for less than 1% of the universe's atoms, not only in number but also by mass.
- Elements with even atomic numbers are, on average, more abundant than those with odd atomic numbers.
- Lithium, beryllium and boron are curiously rare on a chart that generally shows a gradual decline in abundance toward the heavier elements.
- Defying this trend, there is a definite peak in abundance around iron.
- There are also some noticeable, though less remarkable, peaks around those nuclei containing 50, 82 or 126 neutrons. This is to be expected from the theory of nuclear structure, which indicates that such nuclei should be especially stable.
- No stable elements are found beyond bismuth, atomic number 83. (On earth, no elements are found beyond uranium, atomic number 92.)

To account for these observations, we must look back to the beginnings of the universe, some 20 billion years ago. The *big bang* theory considers the birth of the universe as an explosion of imponderable size and fury in which an incredibly hot, enormously dense ball of strongly interacting particles and antiparticles blew up. According to this theory, nearly equal amounts of matter and antimatter annihilated each other in the process, leaving a small amount of residual matter in the form of photons, electrons, positrons, neutrinos and quarks. These particles radiated and expanded outwards from the fireball core. As the fireball expanded, it cooled, and many of the particles immediately began to combine to form protons and neutrons. After only a few minutes, the protons and neutrons combined to form deuterium ($_1^2H$):

$$_1^1p \ + \ _0^1n \ \longrightarrow \ _1^2H \ + \text{energy}$$
$$\text{proton} \quad \text{neutron} \quad \text{deuterium} \atop \text{nucleus}$$

At first, the deuterium quickly dissociated. As the temperature continued to drop, however, deuterium formed more quickly than it could decay. The deuterium nuclei then reacted with each other to form helium nuclei and energy.

Potentially, three helium nuclei could then have interacted to produce carbon nuclei. Additional helium nuclei could then have interacted with the carbon nuclei in a chain of fusion reactions to produce other nuclei up to iron. Note that the products of one set of reactions become the fuel for the next reaction.

This sequence of events appears to occur in the cores of high-temperature stars and neatly accounts for the greater abundances of elements with even atomic numbers. It also helps to explain the rarity of lithium, beryllium and boron. Scientists believe that the universe expanded and cooled too rapidly for more than a negligible amount of these elements to have formed in the immediate aftermath of the big bang.

After perhaps a million years, the density of the universe declined considerably and its temperature cooled to around 3000 K, making it possible for electrons to be captured by protons to form elemental hydrogen:

$$_1^1p \ + \ _{-1}^0e \ \longrightarrow \ _1^1H \ + \text{energy}$$
$$\text{proton} \quad \text{electron} \qquad \text{hydrogen}$$

Similarly, helium nuclei captured electrons to form elemental helium.

The two most abundant elements were now formed. One billion years after the big bang, the still cooler gas clouds of hydrogen and helium became gravitationally bound to eventually form galaxies, and within the galaxies, stars. As the gravitational force of each star increased, so did its density and temperature. Finally, when each star's core reached between 10 000 000 and 20 000 000 K, ionized hydrogen began to fuse into helium nuclei. This reaction, currently taking place in our own sun, marks the main sequence in a star's life and may last for billions of years. As the hydrogen fuel neared exhaustion, the temperature rose to between 100 000 000 and 200 000 000 K, and helium nuclei fused to form carbon nuclei, which could then fuse to form oxygen nuclei, and so on. Our sun can only burn helium to carbon because it is not hot enough to fuse carbon.

In the cores of massive stars known as Red Giants, this chain of fusion reactions can continue up to iron and nickel but not beyond. This explains the peak in abundance around iron. Elements with masses greater than iron and nickel can only be created by a great input of energy, unlike the exothermic fusion reactions. Such energy is available deep in the interior of the Red Giants, along with a supply of free neutrons that could be captured by nuclei to form elements up to bismuth.

The formation of the unstable elements beyond bismuth can only be explained by the awesome release of energy from a *supernova*, an exploding star. The material expelled into space from a supernova includes all the elements formed in that star. The photograph shows Supernova Shelton 1987A, the closest supernova to earth since 1604, and first seen on February 24, 1989 by Ian Shelton, an astronomer at the University of Toronto. The supernova apparently exploded on February 23, 1987. At some point, fusion ceases, and the star's core collapses under intense gravitational force in less than one second! This sudden collapse causes tremendous shock waves that heat the star's outer envelope of gases and blow them away with staggering force. So intense is the radiation from one of these explosions that it may surpass, in only a few hours, our sun's output for the last million years.

The presence of uranium, gold and other heavy elements on earth indicates that the material from which our planet was formed was produced in a supernova. It is only because of uranium-238's relatively long half-life (4.51×10^9 years) that it and its radioactive series of decay products are still found on earth. In fact, scientists who have studied the concentration of uranium and lead deposits in the earth's crust have concluded that our uranium was formed in a supernova some 6.6×10^9 years ago.

As for those rare elements—lithium, beryllium and boron—one recent proposal suggests that they are formed when cosmic ray protons collide with interstellar carbon, oxygen and nitrogen. If so, such chance encounters would explain their scarcity.

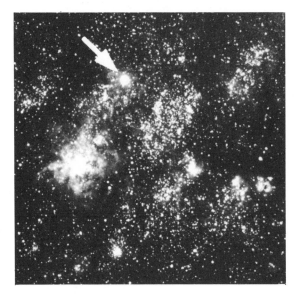

QUESTIONS

1. Calculate the maximum number of electrons with principal quantum number (a) 1, (b) 2, (c) 3, (d) 4.

2. How many electrons fill an orbital?

3. Describe the shapes of the s and p orbitals.

4. What is the maximum number of electrons that may be designated (a) $2s$, (b) $2p$, (c) $3s$, (d) $3d$, (e) $4f$?

5. What is the physical significance in our model of the x, y and z in the p orbital (p_x, p_y, p_z)?

6. Identify the elements whose neutral atoms have the following electron configurations: (a) $1s^2 2s^2$, (b) $1s^2 2s^2 2p^3$, (c) $1s^2 2s^2 2p^6 3s^2$, (d) $1s^2 2s^2 2p^6 3s^2 3p^3$, (e) $1s^2$

7. What kind of evidence was used by physicists and chemists to establish the relative energies of the energy levels?

8. What is the relationship between the principal quantum number of the last electron to "enter" an atom of an element and the period (row) in the periodic table in which we find the element?

9. Use the periodic table to write the electron configuration of (a) Sr, (b) the element with atomic number 52, (c) Ta, (d) Gd, (e) U.

10. Identify the group containing the element composed of atoms whose last electron (a) enters and fills an s orbital, (b) enters but does not fill an s orbital, (c) is the first to enter a p orbital, (d) is the next to the last in a given p orbital, (e) enters and fills a given p orbital, (f) is the first to enter a d orbital, (g) half-fills a d orbital.

11. Explain why we find noble-gas properties on completion of p orbitals rather than s orbitals.

12. Which of the following represents the electron configuration of an excited atom?

(a) $1s^2 2s^2 2p^6$, (b) $1s^2 2s^1 3s^1$,
(c) $1s^2 2s^2 2p^2 3s^1$, (d) $1s^2 2s^1 4d^1$.
Which is likely to give off a photon with the greatest energy on returning to the ground state?

13. Write the electron configuration for the following substances, using the orbital notation described previously: (a) zinc atom, (b) vanadium atom, (c) chloride ion (Cl^-), (d) aluminum ion (Al^{3+}), (e) gallium (Ga), (f) bromine (Br).

14. (a) Write the electron configuration for argon. (b) Name two positive and two negative ions that have this configuration.

15. Chemists often consult tables of atomic radii in order to compare sizes of atoms. Why is it not strictly correct to say that a hydrogen atom has a radius of 5.29×10^{-2} nm?

16. (a) Is it possible to define the exact path of an electron in a p orbital? (b) Which atomic principle do we rely on to answer this question?

17. The Bohr theory allows only specific orbits, which means that an electron is at some exact distance from the nucleus. The Schrödinger model indicates that the distance of an electron from the nucleus can be defined only in terms of probability. Discuss the possible truth of the following statement: An electron from an atom in the ink of this page may at this instant be on the moon.

18. What evidence is there to support the idea that matter has wave properties?

19. How does the wavelength of "matter waves" vary with (a) increasing mass, (b) decreasing velocity?

20. Show the permissible values of l and m for (a) $n = 1$, (b) $n = 2$, (c) $n = 3$.

21. Write a set of four permissible quantum numbers for the electron found in the outermost energy level of a potassium atom (atomic number 19).

22. How many nodal surfaces are there for (a) a $2s$ orbital, (b) a $3p_x$ orbital?

23. (a) What are the relative energies of the $3s$, $3p$ and $3d$ orbitals in a hydrogen atom? (b) Is the order the same for multi-electron atoms? Explain.

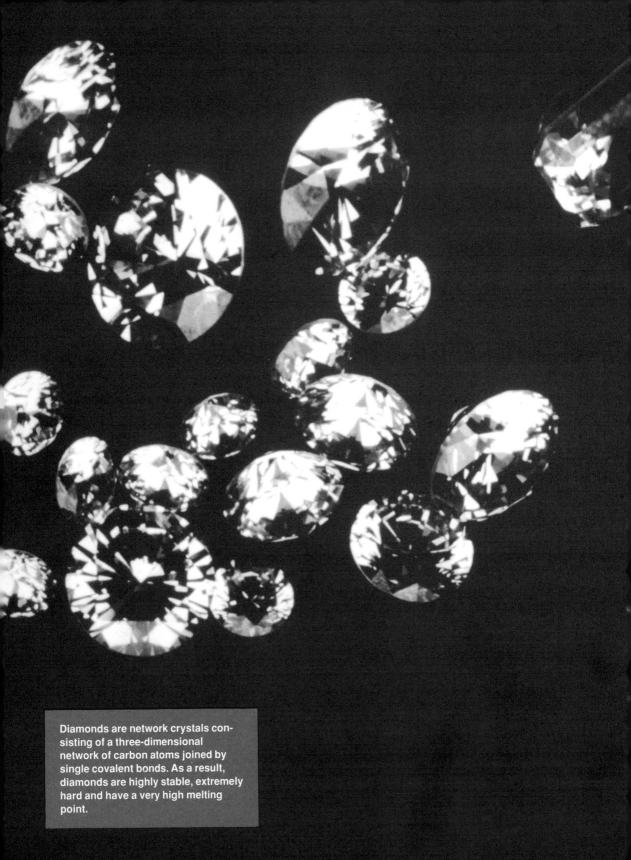

Diamonds are network crystals consisting of a three-dimensional network of carbon atoms joined by single covalent bonds. As a result, diamonds are highly stable, extremely hard and have a very high melting point.

CHEMICAL BONDING

You are no doubt aware of the countless chemical changes that occur every day in our environment. One of the goals of this text is to interpret, explain and predict chemical changes. To achieve this goal, we must understand the principles that underlie chemical changes and the nature of the particles that make up chemical systems.

We have now acquired a background knowledge and understanding of the structure and nature of atoms. Most chemical systems and changes involve molecules and polyatomic ions. For continued progress, therefore, it is necessary to investigate the structure and nature of these species. You are already aware that molecules and polyatomic ions are aggregates of chemically combined atoms. In this chapter we will discuss how atoms combine, the reason they combine in certain ratios and the characteristics of the species that result from their combination. We can then use this knowledge in Chapter 4 to help explain the properties of systems involving aggregates of molecules and ions.

Using the language of chemistry, we say that the atoms that compose a molecule or polyatomic ion are held together by *chemical bonds*. Because chemical bonding is the theme of this chapter, we will first define and describe the origin of bonds. This leads us to mention briefly and show the interrelationship between two major types of bonds: covalent and ionic. For the rest of the chapter, we will focus on developing a covalent-bond model, which will help us predict the shapes, electric nature and other properties of covalent molecules.

In this chapter we will use the concept of periodicity to extend and apply the principles of bond formation to a large number of substances. In our development of bonding concepts we will use ideas from several bonding theories. A bonding theory should account for polarity (electric nature) and shapes of molecules, as well as their stability, reactivity and other properties. There is no single theory that accomplishes all of these objectives equally well. Each one has its own strengths.

We will use *Lewis structures*, or *electron-dot formulas*, to represent structures involving covalent bonds. These structures will help us identify electron pairs when we use the electrostatic repulsion concept to determine the shapes of molecules and ions. We will use the *charge-cloud model* to emphasize the basic electrostatic nature of chemical bonding and to help predict the shapes of molecules. The *valence bond theory* supplies the concepts of *hybridization* and *resonance*, which are useful for describing, explaining and predicting the geometry (shapes) and other characteristics of molecules.

THE ORIGIN AND NATURE OF CHEMICAL BONDS

3-1

The Origin, Nature and Classification of Chemical Bonds

Chemical bonds are formed as the result of the simultaneous attraction of two or more nuclei for electrons. Equal sharing results in covalent bonds, while bonds that result from the transfer of electrons to form ions are called ionic bonds.

Structural investigation of most substances found in nature reveals that they are composed of an aggregate of atoms held together by electrostatic forces of attraction. For example, the oxygen (O_2) and nitrogen (N_2) gas in the air we breathe is made up of diatomic molecules. A great deal of energy is required to overcome the forces of attraction that bind together the atoms in these molecules. In nature, very few metals exist in the elemental state. The ones that do, such as gold and silver, are found in metallic crystals that are aggregates of atoms held together by electrostatic forces of attraction. In nature, most metals are found in the form of their compounds. For example, the element sodium (Na) is found in a variety of naturally occurring compounds, one of which is ordinary sodium chloride (NaCl). Laboratory tests show that a large number of these compounds are crystalline ionic solids composed of an aggregate of positive and negative ions held together by strong electrostatic forces of attraction.

The electrostatic forces of attraction that hold atoms, ions and molecules together are, in general, referred to as ***chemical bonds***. We know that electrostatic forces of attraction exist between oppositely charged bodies. Since the nuclei of atoms bear positive charges and electrons carry negative charges, we can say that *all chemical bonds are formed as the result of the simultaneous attraction of two or more nuclei for electrons.*

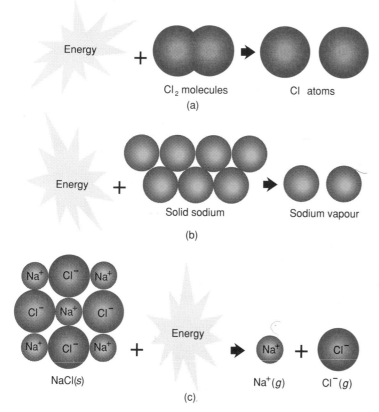

Figure 3-1
Energy is required to overcome the force of attraction (chemical bond) that binds atoms together in (a) molecules, (b) metallic crystals and (c) ionic crystals. The separated atoms are, therefore, in a higher energy state than the bound atoms. The force of attraction in (a) is called a *covalent bond*, in (b) a *metallic bond* and in (c) an *ionic bond*.

The dissociation of a chlorine molecule into chlorine atoms (a) is an endothermic process that absorbs 2.34 eV of energy (226 kJ/mol of chlorine).

In (b) the conversion of one mole of sodium atoms from the solid phase into the gaseous phase requires 109 kJ/mol.

In (c), 493 kJ/mol is required to convert one mole of solid sodium chloride into individual gaseous sodium and chloride ions.

It is apparent from our examples and discussion that a bonded condition is usually more energetically stable than an unbonded one. That is, the energy required to overcome attractive forces (break bonds) between bonded particles raises the energy of the system. Thus, bonded atoms are in a lower-energy, more stable state than unbonded ones. It is reasonable to assume that when

LINUS PAULING
1901–
Linus Pauling was born in Portland, Oregon. He received a PhD in chemistry in 1925 from the California Institute of Technology.

Pauling's greatest contribution to chemistry was his explanation of the nature of the chemical bond. He was the first person to apply the principles of quantum mechanics to chemical reactions. From 1931 to 1933, Pauling published seven papers on "The Nature of the Chemical Bond." His book by the same title, first published in 1938, became a classic in its field.

Pauling first recognized the hydrogen bond as a unique type of bond. In 1934, he began applying his knowledge of molecular structure to tissues. With chemist Robert Corey, Pauling studied the structure of amino acids and polypeptides and recognized that certain protein molecules had a helical shape. This concept helped Francis Crick and James Watson discover the structure of DNA.

Pauling expressed the idea that chemical bonds could have both a covalent and an ionic nature. He also developed an electronegativity scale and was the first to use the term *resonance* in chemical bonding.

For his work in chemistry, Pauling received the 1954 Nobel Prize in chemistry. Because of his concerns about peace, he was awarded the Nobel Peace Prize in 1962, the year the International Nuclear Test Ban

conditions are such that atoms can form bonds and thereby achieve structures that have lower energy, they do so.

To simplify and expedite our study of bonding, we will classify chemical bonds in terms of the behaviour and probable location of the bonding (outer-energy-level) electrons of the atoms involved. Such a classification will help us explain a large number of observations and predict the behaviour of many substances in terms of a relatively few general principles. Clues to the type of bond that exists between the component particles of a substance can be found by studying the properties of the substances and the structural characteristics of the particles.

One of the most revealing properties of a substance is its electric conductivity in the solid and liquid phases. You know from your introductory chemistry studies that a large number of substances classified as ionic salts conduct an electric current in the liquid phase but not in the solid phase. This evidence, coupled with data from X-ray diffraction studies of ionic crystals, suggests that these compounds are made up of oppositely charged ions. The model that accounts for these observations is called an *ionic-bond model*. This model explains the formation of positive and negative ions in terms of electron transfer from an atom having a low electronegativity to one having a high electronegativity. Electronegativity is discussed in the next section. The electrostatic force of attraction between the oppositely charged ions is called an **ionic bond**. We will develop and investigate the nature and significance of the ionic-bond model in Chapter 4.

It can be shown experimentally that many pure substances such as sulfur (S_8), carbon tetrachloride (CCl_4) and water (H_2O) do not conduct an appreciable electric current in either the solid or the liquid phase. This observation suggests that neither the solid nor the liquid phase of these substances contains ions. Rather, it suggests that they are composed of neutral molecules. The physical and chemical properties of these and many other substances lead us to the conclusion that the atoms in these substances are held together by non-ionic bonds. In 1916, an American chemist, Gilbert N. Lewis (1875–1946), suggested that atoms in molecules might be held together by an electrostatic force of attraction between atomic nuclei and electron pairs shared by the bonding atoms. Lewis called the electron-pair bond between atoms a **covalent bond**.

The characteristics of bonded species are related to the character of the bonds between the atoms. That is, the properties of covalently bonded aggregates differ from those of ionically bonded aggregates. It is apparent that it would be valuable to have a method for measuring the relative electron-attracting ability of bonded atoms and, hence, to be able to identify the nature of the bond and the characteristics of the bonded species. Fortunately, there is an experimentally-based periodic property that indicates the relative electron-attracting ability of bonded atoms. This property, known as *electronegativity*, will help us predict the nature of the bond between atoms when we investigate chemical bonding later in this chapter. The periodic nature of electronegativity suggests that the location of pairs of bonding atoms in the periodic table will help us predict the type of bond between them.

Treaty was signed. This made him the only person, other than Marie Curie, to receive two Nobel Prizes.

In 1965, Pauling became interested in vitamins and in 1970 developed the controversial theory that large doses of vitamin C prevent the transmission of the common cold. In 1986, he published the book, *How to Live Longer and Feel Better*. Presently, he works at the Linus Pauling Institute of Science and Medicine in California.

3-2

Electronegativity

Electronegativity is the ability of an atom to attract electrons to itself when combined with another atom. The concept of electronegativity helps us to identify the character of a chemical bond.

Electronegativity is a measure of the tendency of an atom in a molecule or aggregate of atoms to attract electrons. Atoms such as fluorine, which have a strong attraction for electrons, are said to be highly electronegative. Atoms such as cesium, with little electron-attracting ability, have low electronegativities.

Figure 3-2
A table of the electronegativity values of the elements. Notice that, generally, the electronegativity value increases across a period from left to right, and decreases down a group from top to bottom.

Group	1A	2A	3B	4B	5B	6B	7B		8		1B	2B	3A	4A	5A	6A	7A	0
1	1 H 2.1																1 H 2.1	2 He
2	3 Li 1.0	4 Be 1.5											5 B 2.0	6 C 2.5	7 N 3.0	8 O 3.5	9 F 4.0	10 Ne
3	11 Na 0.9	12 Mg 1.2											13 Al 1.5	14 Si 1.8	15 P 2.1	16 S 2.5	17 Cl 3.0	18 Ar
4	19 K 0.8	20 Ca 1.0	21 Sc 1.3	22 Ti 1.5	23 V 1.6	24 Cr 1.6	25 Mn 1.5	26 Fe 1.8	27 Co 1.8	28 Ni 1.8	29 Cu 1.9	30 Zn 1.6	31 Ga 1.6	32 Ge 1.8	33 As 2.0	34 Se 2.4	35 Br 2.8	36 Kr
5	37 Rb 0.8	38 Sr 1.0	39 Y 1.2	40 Zr 1.4	41 Nb 1.6	42 Mo 1.8	43 Tc 1.9	44 Ru 2.2	45 Rh 2.2	46 Pd 2.2	47 Ag 1.9	48 Cd 1.7	49 In 1.7	50 Sn 1.8	51 Sb 1.9	52 Te 2.1	53 I 2.5	54 Xe
6	55 Cs 0.7	56 Ba 0.9	57 La 1.1	72 Hf 1.3	73 Ta 1.5	74 W 1.7	75 Re 1.9	76 Os 2.2	77 Ir 2.2	78 Pt 2.2	79 Au 2.4	80 Hg 1.9	81 Ti 1.8	82 Pb 1.8	83 Bi 1.9	84 Po 2.0	85 At 2.2	86 Rn
7	87 Fr 0.7	88 Ra 0.9	89 Ac 1.1															

58 Ce 1.1	59 Pr 1.1	60 Nd 1.1	61 Pm 1.1	62 Sm 1.1	63 Eu 1.1	64 Gd 1.1	65 Tb 1.2	66 Dy 1.2	67 Ho 1.2	68 Er 1.2	69 Tm 1.2	70 Yb 1.2	71 Lu 1.2
90 Th 1.3	91 Pa 1.5	92 U 1.7	93 Np 1.3	94 Pu 1.3	95 Am 1.3	96 Cm 1.3	97 Bk 1.3	98 Cf 1.3	99 Es 1.3	100 Fm 1.3	101 Md 1.3	102 No 1.3	103 Lr 1.3

A number of methods have been used and a number of scales have been devised to determine the electronegativities of atoms. One of the more commonly used is the scale developed by American chemist Linus Pauling (1901–). Pauling's scale of electronegativities is based on energy changes accompanying chemical reactions. The electronegativity values obtained by Pauling are shown in Fig. 3-2. These values are plotted against the atomic numbers for the first eighty-six elements in Fig. 3-3. The graph shows the periodic nature of electronegativity. Note that electronegativity values are not listed for the noble-gas elements because they do not form many compounds.

Figure 3-3
The periodic nature of electronegativity.

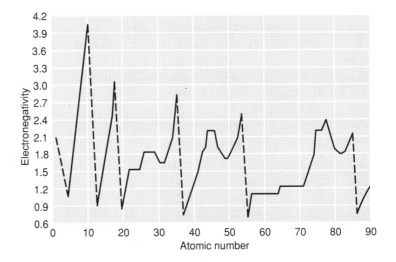

The data shows that *electronegativity generally decreases as you go down a given group in the periodic table.* This observation may be explained largely by the increase in atomic radius as the atomic number increases within a group. Since the force of attraction between the nucleus of an atom and an electron from another atom varies inversely with the square of the distance between them, we would expect a large atom to have much less electron-attracting ability than a smaller one. Thus, a cesium atom would have less tendency to attract an electron of another atom than would a sodium atom.

It is the difference between the electronegativity of two atoms that can be used to identify the character of the bond. Large differences are associated with a high degree of ionic character. On Pauling's scale, a difference of 1.7 is often used to denote a 50% ionic character. It should be noted that the concept of electronegativity is somewhat controversial; many chemists question the validity of the numerical values. Even the critics, however, admit they find the concept useful. The important thing is to be aware of the limitations and not expect 100% accuracy in the predictions you make using this concept. Remember that all predictive devices have shortcomings.

For quick reference, the general trends in certain properties are summarized in Fig. 3-4.

Figure 3-4
Composition of the periodic table and trends in periodic properties.

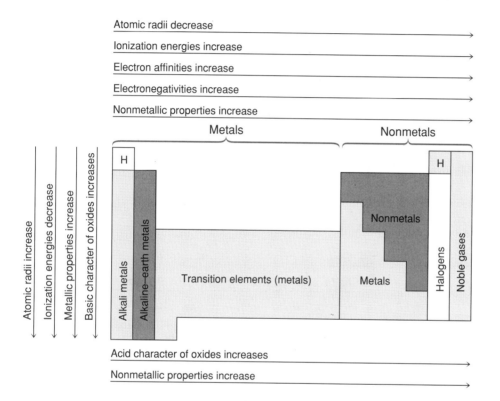

FOLLOW-UP PROBLEMS

1. Would you predict the bond between potassium and chlorine to be largely ionic or largely covalent?

2. Would you predict the bond between sulfur and oxygen to be largely ionic or largely covalent?

3. Make a generalized statement about the nature of the bonds that exist between the atoms of Group IA and Group VIIA elements.

4. Make a generalized statement about the nature of the bonds that exist between two nonmetallic atoms.

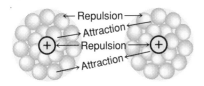

Figure 3-5
As two atoms approach each other, attractive and repulsive forces begin to operate. If the attractive forces predominate before the equilibrium bond distance is reached, as in the case of hydrogen, a bond is formed. If the repulsive forces predominate, as in the case of helium, no bond forms.

TABLE 3-1
FORCES BETWEEN INTERACTING ATOMS

Attractive Forces Operate Between

– the nucleus of an atom and its own electrons
– the nucleus of one atom and the electron clouds of another

Repulsive Forces Operate Between

– the negative electron clouds of two different atoms
– the positive nuclei of two different atoms

Recall from Chapter 2 that ionization energy is the energy required to remove an electron from a gaseous atom.

It is reasonable to assume that in molecules composed of different kinds of atoms with different electronegativities, the bonding electrons will not be shared equally between the atoms. In this situation, the bonding electrons are, on average, closer to the atom having the greater attraction for electrons (higher electronegativity). Therefore, the more electronegative atom acquires a *partial negative charge* and the less electronegative atom acquires a *partial positive charge*. This suggests that covalent bonds in molecules composed of different kinds of atoms have a *partial ionic character* and that there are no sharp boundary lines separating a covalent bond from an ionic bond. That is, as the difference in electron-attracting ability (electronegativity) between atoms increases, the degree of sharing decreases, and the ionic character of the bond increases. Thus, we may consider the ionic bond as an extension of the covalent bond in which there is minimum sharing of bonding electrons. Because of this relationship, we will first consider the covalent-bond model.

COVALENT BONDS

3-3

Energy Changes During Bond Formation

A covalent bond forms if the attractive forces between interacting atoms predominate over the repulsive forces.
Let us first consider the covalent bond formed by the interaction of two hydrogen atoms. The starting point is to examine the ground-state electron configuration of the atoms, the atomic properties related to the behaviour of the electrons and the forces that exist between the interacting atoms.

The ground-state electron configuration of a hydrogen atom is

$$1s^1$$

From this configuration it can be seen that hydrogen atoms need only one electron to fill their $1s$ orbital and to attain the configuration of helium, the noble-gas atom that follows hydrogen in the periodic table.

Hydrogen atoms have an electronegativity of 2.1 and an ionization energy of 13.6 eV. When the two atoms approach each other, the relative attraction of the two nuclei for their own (and for each other's) outer-energy-level electrons (bonding electrons) determines the extent to which electrons will be transferred from one atom to the other. Since two hydrogen atoms approaching each other have the same attraction for electrons (same electronegativity), there is essentially no tendency for an electron to be transferred from one atom to the other.

As the atoms approach each other, attractive and repulsive forces operate to change the energy of the atomic system (Fig. 3-5). These forces are listed in Table 3-1.

When the nuclei of the two hydrogen atoms are 74 pm apart, the atomic system has minimum potential energy. At this distance, the atoms are close enough for their half-filled 1s orbitals to overlap. Thus, the volume represented by the 1s orbitals of the two atoms is now available to the bonding electrons. Since the region between the positive nuclei represents a region of low potential energy for the negative electrons, there is a high probability of finding the bonding electrons in the internuclear region (Fig. 3-6). Thus, we can say that, in general, an electron from each atom shares a region of space between the two nuclei. Sharing a pair of electrons results in a filled s orbital and a stable, helium-like electron configuration for each atom (Fig. 3-7). The covalent bond formed by the overlap of the s orbital clouds is sometimes referred to as a *sigma (σ) bond*. The electron-dot and line formulas for the hydrogen molecule are as follows:

H : H   H—H

Note that a pair of dots or a single line may be used to represent a covalent bond.

The graph in Fig. 3-8 shows how the potential energy varies as two hydrogen atoms approach each other. As a reference for comparison, the potential energy of the separate atoms is assumed to be zero. The graph shows that the potential energy of the combined atoms is lower than that of the separated atoms (the potential energy has a negative value). As the atoms approach each other, the internuclear distance decreases, and attractive forces operate and increase their velocity and kinetic energy. As the kinetic energy increases, the potential energy decreases. At the internuclear distance represented by point B, the attractive force between the atoms is at a maximum, and the system has minimum potential energy. At internuclear distances less than that represented by point B (for example, at point A), repulsive forces predominate, kinetic energy decreases and potential energy increases. Finally, the atoms momentarily stop and then begin to move apart. Thus, the distance between the nuclei varies as the atoms in the molecule vibrate about the equilibrium bond length. In other words, the point on the curve that represents the internuclear distance moves back and forth about the equilibrium point.

Helium does not form He_2 molecules. The 1s orbitals of separate helium atoms already contain two electrons. When two

Figure 3-6
An electron-charge-distribution representation of a hydrogen molecule. It can be seen that maximum electron density occurs in the internuclear region of the molecule.

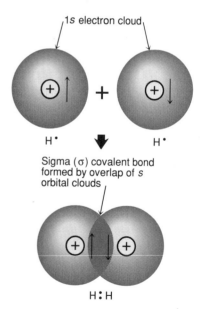

Figure 3-7
The covalent bond within an H_2 molecule is formed when the s orbitals of the two H atoms overlap and form a single electron cloud that is attracted to both nuclei. The arrows indicate that the paired electrons have opposite spins.

helium atoms approach each other, repulsive forces exceed the attractive forces, and the potential energy of the atomic system increases. An increase in potential energy is associated with a decrease in stability. Therefore, He_2 represents an unstable system. Although it goes beyond the scope of this book, there is another, more complicated, bonding theory that provides a method for predicting the relative stability of molecules.

Figure 3-8
Representation of potential energy changes that occur when two hydrogen atoms approach each other.

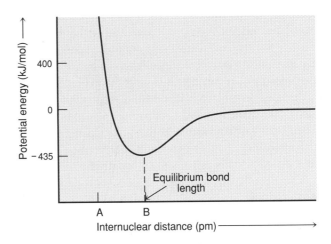

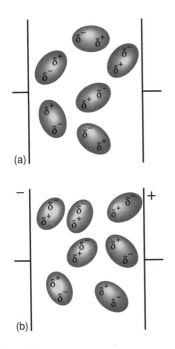

(a)

(b)

Figure 3-9
(a) In the absence of an electric field, polar molecules are randomly oriented. (b) In the presence of an electric field, the positive pole of the molecules is generally oriented toward the negative plate, and the negative pole of the molecules is generally oriented toward the positive plate. The more polar a molecule is, the greater its effect on the electric field.

3-4

Nonpolar Covalent Bonds

Nonpolar bonds are covalent bonds in which the bonding electrons are equally shared and symmetrically distributed.
Diatomic molecules such as H_2, Cl_2 and N_2 are made up of identical atoms with equal electronegativities or the same attraction for electrons. Thus, we would expect the electron-charge distribution in these molecules to be symmetrical about the two nuclei. Experiments designed to measure the symmetry of molecules (Fig. 3-9) verify this expectation. Covalent bonds in which the bonding electrons are equally shared and symmetrically distributed are called ***nonpolar bonds*** (Fig. 3-10).

3-5

Polar Covalent Bonds: Partial Ionic Character

Polar bonds are covalent bonds in which the bonding electrons are distributed asymmetrically.
Electric measurements made on diatomic molecules such as HF and HCl show that these molecules have an *electric dissymmetry*. This suggests that the bonding electrons are unequally shared by the two different atoms and asymmetrically distributed in the

molecule. Covalent bonds in which there is an asymmetrical distribution of electrons are called *polar bonds*. Molecules in which there is an asymmetrical distribution of electron charge are called *polar molecules*. As a result of the unequal sharing, the less electronegative atom acquires a partial positive charge, symbolized by the Greek letter delta (δ^+), and the more electronegative atom acquires a partial negative charge (δ^-) equal in magnitude to the partial positive charge. Thus, diatomic polar molecules are neutral but have positive and negative regions called *electric poles*. This means that *all polar covalent bonds have a partial ionic character.* Let us examine hydrogen chloride (HCl) as an example of a diatomic polar molecule.

The electronegativities and ground-state electron configurations of hydrogen and chlorine atoms are as follows:

Ground-state configuration	Electronegativity
H: $1s^1$	2.1
Cl: $1s^2 2s^2 2p^6 3s^2 3p_x^2 3p_y^2 3p_z^1$	3.0

The overlap of the half-filled $1s$ orbital of hydrogen and the half-filled $3p$ orbital of chlorine results in the formation of a covalent bond when the two atoms share the electron pair in their internuclear region (Fig. 3-11). The covalent bond formed by the overlap of s and p orbital clouds is also referred to as a *sigma bond*. Since chlorine has a much higher electronegativity than hydrogen, the electron-charge density is greater near the chlorine end of the molecule. The result is that the chlorine end of the molecule acquires a partial negative charge (δ^-), while the hydrogen end acquires a partial positive charge (δ^+) (Fig. 3-12). Thus, hydrogen chloride (HCl) is a polar molecule. Electronegativity differences are sometimes used to denote the partial ionic character of a bond. On Pauling's scale, a difference of 1.7 is used to denote a 50% ionic character. A larger difference suggests greater ionic character. Equations are available for calculating the percentage of ionic character in a bond. Calculations made for a few selected substances are listed in Table 3-2.

Centre of positive charge

Centre of negative charge

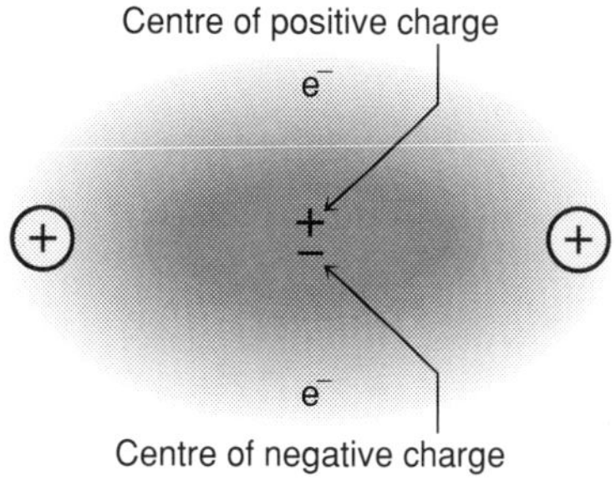

Figure 3-10
A nonpolar covalent bond results when two nuclei with the same number of protons simultaneously attract the electron cloud between them. In molecules composed of identical atoms, the centre of positive charge coincides with the centre of negative charge.

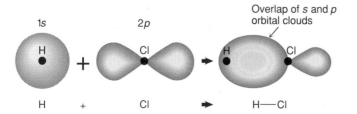

Figure 3-11
When a singly occupied *s* orbital from a hydrogen atom overlaps a singly occupied *p* orbital from a chlorine atom, a covalent bond is formed. Like *s-s* overlap, *s-p* overlap also forms a sigma (σ) covalent bond.

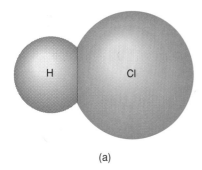

(a)

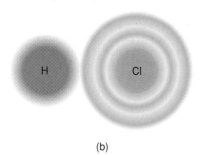

(b)

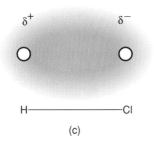

(c)

Figure 3-12
Three representations of an HCl mole-cule. (a) A space-filling model. (b) The greater electronegativity of the Cl atom is illustrated by the greater elec-tron density around the Cl atom. (c) In polar molecules, the centre of posi-tive charge does not coincide with the centre of negative charge.

TABLE 3-2
PARTIAL IONIC CHARACTER OF SELECTED SUBSTANCES

Name	Formula	Electro-negativity Difference	Partial Ionic Character
Cesium fluoride	CsF	3.3	94%
Sodium chloride	NaCl	2.1	67%
Hydrogen chloride	HCl	0.9	19%
Hydrogen bromide	HBr	0.7	12%
Hydrogen iodide	HI	0.4	4%
Bromine chloride	BrCl	0.2	1%
Hydrogen	H_2	0.0	0%

LEWIS STRUCTURES (ELECTRON-DOT FORMULAS)

3-6

The Octet Rule and Structure

In forming a compound, an atom will lose, gain or share electrons in order to have eight electrons in its outer shell. This octet rule determines the electron configuration and bonding of atoms in molecules.

It is observed that many stable molecules and polyatomic ions are composed of covalently bonded atoms having a noble-gas electron configuration. This configuration is sometimes referred to as an *octet structure*, and the atoms that achieve this structure are said to follow the *octet rule*. The rule is frequently used when con-structing *Lewis structures* (*electron-dot formulas*) to show the electron configuration and bonding of atoms in molecules. To construct an electron-dot formula for a molecule, we determine the total number of available outer electrons in the atoms that make up the molecule and then, if possible, arrange them about the atoms so that each atom (except for the hydrogen atom, which has only one electron) is surrounded by eight electrons. Shared electrons are common to two atoms and are counted as part of the outer-level population of each atom. The number of outer-level (bonding or valence) electrons in the atoms of the representative elements is given by the group number in the periodic table. For example, to construct the electron-dot formula for a chlorine molecule (Cl_2), we note that its atoms are in Group VIIA and thus contain seven valence electrons. It is apparent that each atom needs one electron to achieve an octet structure. By sharing a pair of electrons, each atom completes its outer octet. The electron-dot formula for Cl_2 is as follows:

$$: \overset{\bullet\bullet}{\underset{\bullet\bullet}{Cl}} {}^{x}_{x} \overset{xx}{\underset{xx}{Cl}} {}^{x}_{x}$$

Lewis structures for the first 20 elements of the periodic table are shown in Table 3-3. The dot symbols surrounding the symbol of the element represent the outer-level electrons.

TABLE 3-3
LEWIS STRUCTURES FOR THE FIRST TWENTY ELEMENTS

	I	II	III	IV	V	VI	VII	VIII
First row	H •							He •
Second row	Li •	Be •	B •	• C •	• N •	• O •	• F :	: Ne :
Third row	Na •	Mg •	Al •	• Si •	• P •	• S •	• Cl :	: Ar :
Fourth row	K •	Ca •						

FOLLOW-UP PROBLEM
Write electron-dot formulas for (a) F_2, (b) OF_2 and (c) H_2O.

Answers:

(a) $: \overset{\bullet\bullet}{\underset{\bullet\bullet}{F}} : \overset{\bullet\bullet}{\underset{\bullet\bullet}{F}} :$ (b) $: \overset{\bullet\bullet}{\underset{\bullet\bullet}{F}} : \overset{\bullet\bullet}{\underset{\bullet\bullet}{O}} : \overset{\bullet\bullet}{\underset{\bullet\bullet}{F}} :$ (c) $H : \overset{\bullet\bullet}{\underset{\bullet\bullet}{O}} : H$

3-7
Multiple Bonds

The sharing of two or three pairs of electrons between atoms produces multiple bonds.

In order to achieve the octet structure, some atoms must share two or even three pairs of electrons. Sharing two pairs of electrons produces a *double bond*; sharing three pairs of electrons produces a *triple bond*. The bonding in carbon dioxide (CO_2) illustrates this point (Fig. 3-13). Experimental data, to be discussed later, suggests that the CO_2 molecule is symmetrical and that two oxygen atoms are bonded to one carbon atom. From the location of the atoms in the periodic table, we can determine that, because the carbon atom is in Group IVA, it has four electrons available for bonding, and each oxygen atom (Group VIA) has six electrons in

$: \overset{\bullet\bullet}{\underset{\bullet\bullet}{O}} : {}^{x}_{x} C {}^{x}_{x} : \overset{\bullet\bullet}{\underset{\bullet\bullet}{O}} :$

carbon dioxide

Figure 3-13
Space-filling model of carbon dioxide (CO_2).

its outer level. This makes a total of 16 electrons to be arranged so that, if possible, each atom has an outer octet. We can arrange the two oxygen atoms around the carbon atom as follows:

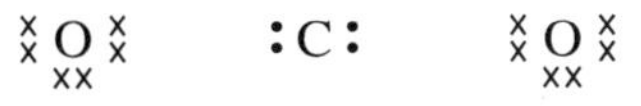

$$\overset{x}{\underset{xx}{x}} O \overset{x}{\underset{}{x}} \qquad :C: \qquad \overset{x}{\underset{xx}{x}} O \overset{x}{\underset{}{x}}$$

oxygen   carbon   oxygen

For a carbon atom to obtain an octet structure, it must share its four electrons with four from the two oxygen atoms. By sharing two of carbon's electrons, each oxygen atom will complete its outer octet. The electron arrangement, which involves two double bonds, is represented by an electron-dot formula as

$$\overset{x}{\underset{xx}{x}} O \overset{x}{\underset{}{x}} : C : \overset{x}{\underset{xx}{x}} O \overset{x}{\underset{}{x}}$$

and by a line formula as

$$O{=}C{=}O$$

It is reasonable to assume that there is a greater electron density between the nuclei and, hence, a greater attractive force between the nuclei. Experimental data verifies that greater energy is required to break double bonds than single bonds. Hence, *double bonds are stronger than single bonds*. Because stronger bonds tend to pull atoms closer together, atoms joined by double bonds are closer together than those joined by single bonds. It should be noted that more than one arrangement of electrons that yields an octet structure can be drawn for CO_2. This phenomenon is discussed in Section 3-9.

FOLLOW-UP PROBLEM

The large amount of energy required to decompose a nitrogen molecule (N_2) into nitrogen atoms suggests the presence of a triple covalent bond.

a) Write the electron-dot formula for N_2.

b) Are triple bonds stronger or weaker than double bonds? Explain.

c) Are triple bonds longer or shorter than double bonds? Explain.

Answers:
(a) $: N ::: N :$, (b) **stronger**, (c) **shorter**

3-8

Polyatomic Ions: Co-ordinate Bonds

Formulas of polyatomic ions can be explained through the use of Lewis structures and bonding concepts.

A large number of ionic substances contain polyatomic ions. Since there is no easy way to predict the formulas of these ions, we list them in Tables 3-4 and 3-5 and suggest that you memorize them.

TABLE 3-4
PARTIAL LIST OF SOME COMMON POSITIVE IONS

Formula	Name	Formula	Name	Formula	Name	Formula	Name
NH_4^+	ammonium	Ba^{2+}	barium	Al^{3+}	aluminum	Ce^{4+}	cerium(IV) or ceric
Cs^+	cesium	Cd^{2+}	cadmium	Sb^{3+}	antimony(III) or antimonous	Sn^{4+}	tin(IV) or stannic
Cu^+	copper(I)	Ca^{2+}	calcium	As^{3+}	arsenic(III) or arsenious	Ti^{4+}	titanium(IV) or titanic
H^+	hydrogen	Cr^{2+}	chromium(II) or chromous	Bi^{3+}	bismuth	Pb^{4+}	lead(IV) or plumbic
Li^+	lithium	Co^{2+}	cobalt(II) or cobaltous	Ce^{3+}	cerium(III) or cerous		
Hg_2^{2+}	mercury(I) or mercurous	Cu^{2+}	copper(II) or cupric	Cr^{3+}	chromium(III) or chromic		
K^+	potassium	Fe^{2+}	iron(II) or ferrous	Co^{3+}	cobalt(III) or cobaltic		
Rb^+	rubidium	Pb^{2+}	lead(II) or plumbous	Fe^{3+}	iron(III) or ferric		
Na^+	sodium	Mg^{2+}	magnesium	Ga^{3+}	gallium		
Ag^+	silver	Hg^{2+}	mercury(II) or mercuric	Tl^{3+}	thallium(III) or or thallic		
Tl^+	thallium(I) or thallous	Ni^{2+}	nickel(II)	Ti^{3+}	titanium(III) or titanous		
Au^+	gold(I) or aurous	Sr^{2+}	strontium	V^{3+}	vanadium		
		Sn^{2+}	tin(II) or stannous	Au^{3+}	gold(III) or auric		
		Zn^{2+}	zinc				

TABLE 3-5
PARTIAL LIST OF SOME COMMON NEGATIVE IONS

Formula	Name	Formula	Name	Formula	Name	Formula	Name
$C_2H_3O_2^-$	acetate	IO_3^-	iodate	CO_3^{2-}	carbonate	AsO_4^{3-}	arsenate
HCO_3^-	bicarbonate or hydrogen carbonate	I^-	iodide	CrO_4^{2-}	chromate	AsO_3^{3-}	arsenite
		NO_3^-	nitrate	$Cr_2O_7^{2-}$	dichromate	BO_3^{3-}	borate
		NO_2^-	nitrite	HPO_4^{2-}	mono- hydrogen phosphate	PO_4^{3-}	phosphate
$HC_2O_4^-$	bioxalate or hydrogen oxalate	ClO_4^-	perchlorate			$Fe(CN)_6^{3-}$	ferricyanide
		MnO_4^-	permanganate				
		SCN^-	thiocyanate	$C_2O_4^{2-}$	oxalate		
$HC_8H_4O_4^-$	biphthalate or hydrogen phthalate						

TABLE 3-5 (continued)
PARTIAL LIST OF SOME COMMON NEGATIVE IONS

Formula	Name	Formula	Name	Formula	Name	Formula	Name
HSO_4^-	bisulfate or hydrogen sulfate	$C_7H_5O^-$	benzoate	O^{2-}	oxide	$Fe(CN)_6^{4-}$	ferrocyanide
				SO_4^{2-}	sulfate	$P_2O_7^{4-}$	pyrophosphate
				S^{2-}	sulfide	SiO_4^{4-}	orthosilicate
HS^-	bisulfide or hydrogen sulfide			SO_3^{2-}	sulfite		
				$S_2O_3^{2-}$	thiosulfate		
BrO_3^-	bromate						
Br^-	bromide						
ClO_3^-	chlorate						
Cl^-	chloride						
ClO_2^-	chlorite						
CN^-	cyanide						
$H_2PO_4^-$	dihydrogen phosphate						
F^-	fluoride						
OH^-	hydroxide						

We are now able to rationalize the formulas of polyatomic ions in terms of electron-dot formulas and bonding concepts. Let us first investigate the formation of an ammonium ion (NH_4^+). We will find that the bonding is characteristic of that in many polyatomic ions.

We can experimentally demonstrate the formation of the ammonium ion with a simple reaction involving ammonia gas (NH_3) and hydrogen chloride gas (HCl). When a bottle of hydrogen chloride is inverted over a bottle of ammonia and the glass cover plates are removed, a white smoke (powder) is instantly observed. The reaction is exothermic. When the white powder is analysed, it is found to consist of two ions whose formulas are NH_4^+ and Cl^-. To explain the formation of ammonium ions, we start with the electron-dot formula of an ammonia molecule:

$$
\begin{array}{c}
H \\
\overset{\bullet x}{} \\
H \overset{\bullet}{\underset{\bullet x}{x}} N \overset{\bullet\bullet}{} \\
\overset{\bullet x}{} \\
H
\end{array}
$$

It can be seen that NH_3 has an unshared pair of valence electrons that are available for bond formation. The attractive force operating between the nucleus of the hydrogen atom in an HCl molecule and the unshared electrons of a nitrogen atom in an NH_3 molecule lowers the energy and increases the stability of the system.

When the hydrogen atom in the HCl molecule breaks away from the chlorine atom, the hydrogen electron remains with the more electronegative chlorine atom. Thus, the hydrogen atom becomes a positively charged hydrogen ion (H^+), and the chlorine, left with the extra electron, becomes a negatively charged chloride ion (Cl^-). An ammonium ion is formed when the vacant *s* orbital of the hydrogen ion overlaps the orbital of the nitrogen atom that contains the unshared electron pair. A covalent bond in which one atom donates both bonding electrons is called a ***co-ordinate covalent bond*** (or, simply, a ***co-ordinate bond***). The formation of such a bond requires that one atom have an orbital containing an unshared pair of electrons and the other atom an empty orbital available for bonding. The atom furnishing the pair of electrons is called an ***electron-pair donor;*** the atom furnishing the empty orbital is called an ***electron-pair acceptor.*** The above reaction is shown in Fig. 3-14 and can be represented by the following electron-dot equation:

$$\begin{array}{c} H \\ \bullet x \\ H \overset{x}{\bullet} N \colon \end{array} + \; H \overset{\bullet\bullet}{\underset{x}{\bullet}} Cl \colon \; \longrightarrow \; \left[\begin{array}{c} H \\ \bullet x \\ H \overset{x}{\bullet} N \colon H \\ \overset{x\bullet}{} \\ H \end{array} \right]^+ + \; \overset{\bullet\bullet}{\underset{x}{\colon}} Cl \colon ^-$$

The addition of a positively charged hydrogen ion to a neutral ammonia molecule yields a positively charged ammonium ion. In this reaction, NH_3 is the electron-pair donor and H^+ is the electron-pair acceptor. We can also describe NH_3 as a ***proton acceptor*** and HCl as a ***proton donor***.

The co-ordinate covalent bond may be represented in a line formula by an arrow pointing from the donor to the acceptor. The line formula for an ammonium ion is

$$\left[\begin{array}{c} H \\ | \\ H - N \rightarrow H \\ | \\ H \end{array} \right]^+$$

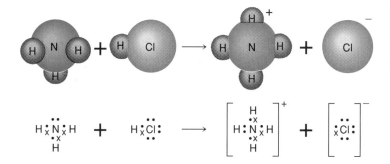

Figure 3-14
Representation of the reaction between gaseous HCl and gaseous NH_3, forming solid ammonium chloride (NH_4Cl).

EXAMPLE 3-1
Writing Electron-Dot Formulas
Write the electron-dot formula for a sulfite ion, SO_3^{2-}.

SOLUTION

1. Count up the available valence electrons plus the electrons giving the ion its charge. Because both sulfur and oxygen are in Group VIA, there are $6 \times 4 = 24$ valence electrons plus two more for the 2– charge.

2. Arrange the 26 dots around the atoms so that, if possible, the octet rule is followed. Note that we will later encounter many cases in which this rule is not followed by the central atom. We will find, however, that the rule can be invoked for all atoms in the second row of the periodic table.

3. The formula (SO_3^{2-}) implies that three oxygen atoms are bonded to one sulfur atom. Therefore, write the symbol for a sulfur atom and surround it with the symbols for three oxygen atoms:

$$\begin{array}{cc} O & O \\ & S \\ & O \end{array}$$

4. Draw four lines (representing eight electrons) from the central sulfur atom to the surrounding oxygen atoms. Recall that a single line represents two electrons common to two atoms. Since a sulfur atom must have eight electrons around it, we can show a single bond between the sulfur atom and each of the two oxygen atoms, and a double bond between the sulfur and the third oxygen atom.

5. Rewrite the single and double bonds with dots representing the bonding electrons and complete the outer octet of the oxygen atoms by using dots.

6. Count the total number of electrons in the tentative formula to see if this number agrees with the available electrons. Our electron-dot formula above shows a total of 24 electrons. The number available to be distributed in a sulfite ion (SO_3^{2-}) is 26. To make room for the extra electrons, we can shift the electron pair that represents one-half the double bond to the oxygen atom. This converts the double bond to a single bond and leaves the sulfur atom with six electrons.

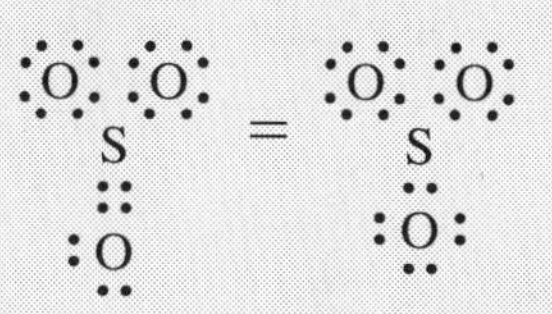

The other two electrons can then be placed as a lone pair on the sulfur atom:

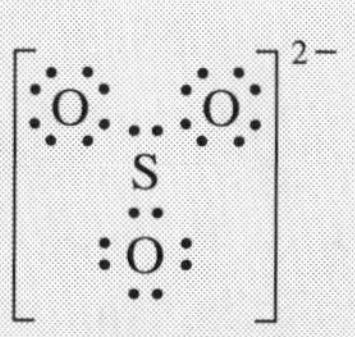

Note that the electron-dot formulas for ions should be bracketed and the charge shown outside of the bracket. The electron-dot formula shows that three identical atoms are bonded to a central atom that has an unbonded electron pair.

EXAMPLE 3-2
Writing Electron-Dot Formulas

Write the electron-dot formula for sulfur trioxide, SO_3.

SOLUTION

The steps are the same as in Example 3-1. In sulfur trioxide there are 24 outer electrons to be distributed. This suggests that there is a double bond in the molecule and that its electron-dot formula is

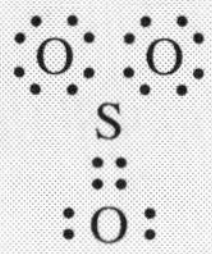

There are, however, two other ways to draw the electron-dot formula for SO_3. We could have placed the double bond between either of the other two oxygen atoms. The resulting formulas would be

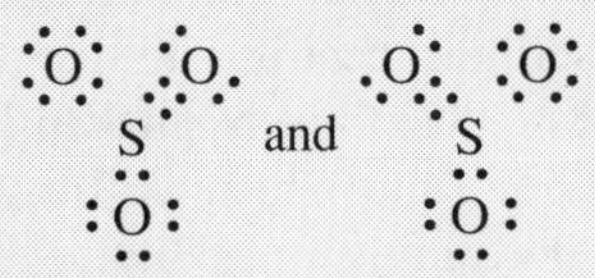

These three equivalent electron-dot formulas for SO_3 are known as *resonance structures*.

3-9

Resonance Structures

Imaginary resonance structures help to explain the structure of polyatomic ions that cannot be accurately represented by a single electron-dot formula.

Strangely enough, none of the three configurations shown in Example 3-2 agree with the experimental data that shows that the three sulfur-oxygen bonds are of the same length and the same strength. The three structures show a double bond between a sulfur atom and an oxygen atom. This would indicate that one oxygen atom is closer and more tightly bound to the sulfur atom than the other two singly bonded oxygen atoms. The experimentally determined bond distances and strengths fall between those of single and double bonds, indicating that the bonding between the electron-dot formulas shown above must be intermediate. It is apparent that the SO_3 molecule cannot be accurately represented by a single electron-dot formula. The concept invoked to explain such a situation is known as *resonance*, and the three diagrams shown below are called *resonance structures*. These structures do not actually exist; they are imaginary. It is not implied that the SO_3 molecule resonates between these three structures. Sulfur trioxide is a real substance with a definite electron structure. We may think of the real structure as a *hybrid* of the three imaginary electron-dot structures. It is conventional to show resonance structures joined by a double-headed arrow.

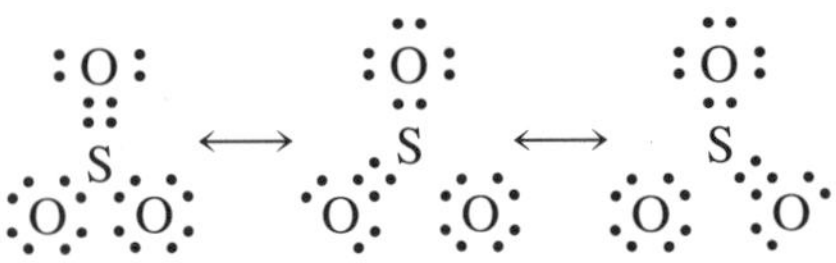

Sulfur trioxide is representative of a large number of substances for which no single, correct electron-dot formula can be written. These substances are classified as having structures that are **resonance hybrids** of the two or more structures that can be drawn. Substances for which resonance structures can be written are more energetically stable than would be predicted on the basis of any one of the individual structures. The increase in stability resulting from resonance is important in explaining bond strengths, heats of reaction and the rates of chemical reactions.

You will no doubt encounter a number of stable species for which no satisfactory electron-dot structures—resonance or non-resonance—can be written. Conversely, you may be able to write Lewis structures for species that cannot exist. In either case, the problem can be traced to deficiencies in the Lewis structure. Application of other bonding theories, however, will often solve the problem.

FOLLOW-UP PROBLEM

Write electron-dot formulas for the following species. Assume that the octet rule holds. Indicate which formulas are resonance structures.

(a) carbon tetrachloride (CCl_4) (f) sulfur dioxide (SO_2)

(b) phosphine (PH_3) (g) carbonate ion (CO_3^{2-})

(c) hydroxide ion (OH^-) (h) ozone (O_3)

(d) phosphate ion (PO_4^{3-}) (i) carbon monoxide (CO)

(e) nitrate ion (NO_3^-) (j) sulfate ion (SO_4^{2-})

Answers:

(a)

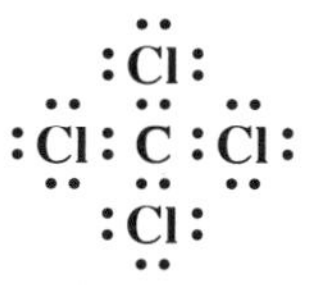

(c)

(e) 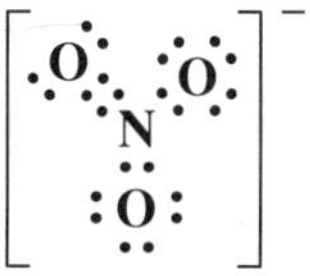
resonance structure

(f)
resonance structure

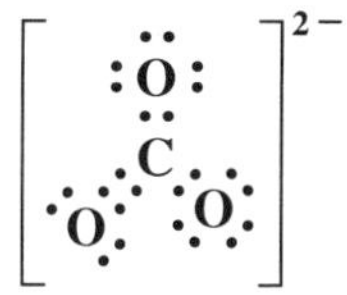

(g)
resonance structure

3-10

Species That Do Not Follow the Octet Rule

The octet rule cannot be applied to all molecules.
Examination of the outer-electron configuration of the atoms in certain molecules shows that not all atoms attain an octet structure. As mentioned in Section 3-6, hydrogen is an exception to the octet rule because it requires only two electrons to fill the valence shell. Helium is another species that requires only two electrons. Other species that do not follow the octet rule but form covalent compounds include:

1. *Molecules in which more than four atoms are bonded to a central atom.* An example is phosphorus pentachloride (PCl_5). In this molecule, a phosphorus atom is covalently bonded to five chlorine atoms. Since each bond involves two electrons, there are ten electrons in the outer energy level of the phosphorus atom. The Lewis structure is

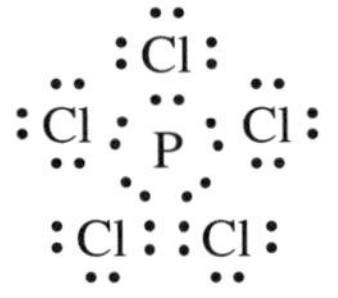

$$
\ddot{Cl}
$$
$$
:\!\ddot{Cl}:\overset{..}{\underset{..}{P}}:\ddot{Cl}:
$$
$$
:\!\ddot{Cl}::\!\ddot{Cl}:
$$

2. *Molecules containing an odd number of bonding electrons.* An example of an *odd-electron* molecule is nitric oxide (NO). This molecule is a resonance hybrid whose resonance structures may be written as

$$
:\!\overset{..}{N}::\!\overset{..}{O}\cdot \longleftrightarrow \cdot\overset{..}{N}::\!\overset{..}{O}:
$$

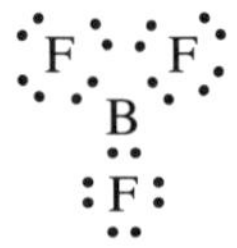

Application of the octet rule to BF₃ yields resonance structures involving a double bond. One structure is

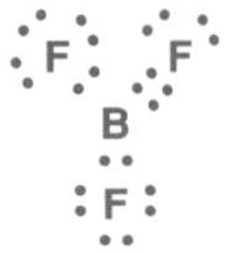

3. *Species that contain no multiple bonds (as shown by experiment) and whose central atom has fewer than four bonding electrons.* The most common examples are compounds that contain boron or beryllium. An example is boron trifluoride (BF_3). Boron has three bonding electrons. Thus, in BF_3 there are only six electrons in the outer level of the boron atom, as shown by its Lewis structure:

A knowledge of the shapes and sizes of molecules and polyatomic ions will help us explain the observed properties of substances. The shapes and sizes of molecules are related to the geometric arrangement of their component atoms. Let us now see how our models of electron configuration and chemical bonding can be used to help predict the geometric arrangement of atoms in molecules and polyatomic ions.

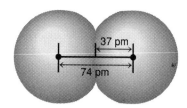

Figure 3-15
A cross-section of a hydrogen molecule (H_2). The covalent radius of a hydrogen atom within a hydrogen molecule is one-half the bond length (average distance between nuclei).

FOLLOW-UP PROBLEM
Write Lewis structures for the following species whose formulas do not follow the octet rule: (a) sulfur hexafluoride (SF_6), (b) nitrogen dioxide (NO_2), (c) beryllium fluoride (BeF_2).

Answers:

(b) $: \overset{\cdot \cdot}{\underset{\cdot \cdot}{O}} : \overset{\cdot}{N} : \overset{\cdot \cdot}{\underset{\cdot \cdot}{O}} :$ (c) $: \overset{\cdot \cdot}{\underset{\cdot \cdot}{F}} : Be : \overset{\cdot \cdot}{\underset{\cdot \cdot}{F}} :$

SHAPES OF COVALENT MOLECULES AND POLYATOMIC IONS

3-11

Bond Lengths and Bond Angles

The measurement of bond lengths and bond angles helps us develop models for making predictions about the shapes of molecules.

The arrangement of atoms in a molecule or ion is described in terms of bond lengths and bond angles. The average distance between the nuclei of two vibrating, covalently bonded atoms defines the length of a covalent bond. These distances can be determined by the detailed analysis of molecular spectra. For example, spectroscopic data shows that for a hydrogen molecule (H_2), the average distance or covalent bond length between the nuclei is 74 pm (Fig. 3-15). One-half of the internuclear distance represents the *covalent*, or *atomic, radius* of a hydrogen atom.

When a molecule is made up of just two atoms, it is not necessary to define a bond angle. When two or more atoms are bonded to a third atom, however, the bonds joining the atoms to the third atom form an angle with each other, called a ***bond angle***. Bond angles are measured experimentally by X-ray diffraction or molecular spectroscopy; the bond angles for some compounds are listed in Table 3-6. For example, spectroscopic data shows that the vibrating hydrogen atoms in a water molecule form an average angle of 104.5° between each other (Fig. 3-16).

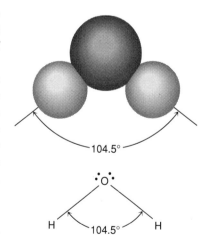

Figure 3-16
The angle formed by the imaginary lines joining the nuclei of the hydrogen atoms to the nucleus of the oxygen atom in a water molecule has been measured spectroscopically and found to be approximately 104.5°. Thus, H_2O is said to be an angular, or bent, molecule.

TABLE 3-6
BOND ANGLES

Compound	Formula	Angle Between Atoms Bonded to Central Atom
Water	H_2O	104.5°
Hydrogen sulfide	H_2S	92°
Ammonia	NH_3	107°
Methane	CH_4	109.5°
Boron trifluoride	BF_3	120°
Beryllium fluoride	BeF_2	180°

The concept of atomic orbitals (s, p, d, f) developed in Chapter 2 helped us construct energy-level diagrams and furnished the basis for the concept of electron-pair bonds. Furthermore, the orbital concept should help us to explain and predict the bond angles and shapes of covalent molecules. Consider a water molecule (H_2O) in which two hydrogen atoms are covalently bonded to an oxygen atom. The shape of the water molecule depends on the angle defined by imaginary lines joining the nuclei of the two hydrogen atoms to the nucleus of the oxygen atom. We can explain the experimentally observed 104.5° bond angle in terms of the directional characteristics of atomic orbitals. Let us examine the electron configuration of an oxygen atom in order to determine which orbitals are available for bond formation.

The ground-state configuration for an oxygen atom is

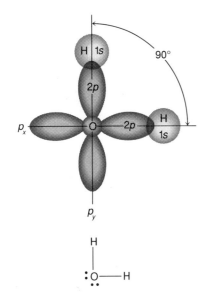

Figure 3-17
The hydrogen atoms in a water molecule would form a 90° angle if we assume that only pure _p_ orbitals of oxygen are involved (_p²_ bonding) and that there is no interaction between hydrogen atoms. The 1_s_, 2_s_ and 2_p_z orbitals of oxygen are not shown.

On the basis of this configuration we would predict that oxygen could form two covalent bonds by sharing two pairs of electrons with two hydrogen atoms. Each pair would consist of one p electron from oxygen and one s electron from hydrogen. This would complete the s orbitals of the hydrogen atoms and the p orbitals of the oxygen atom. The formation of the two covalent bonds requires that the s orbitals of each hydrogen atom overlap the p orbitals of the oxygen atom. Thus, the location of the hydrogen atoms depends on the directional characteristics of the p orbitals of the oxygen atom. Since pure p atomic orbitals are at right angles to each other, we might predict the bond angle between the two hydrogen atoms to be 90° (Fig. 3-17).

However, experiments show the bond angle is 104.5°. This suggests that *the directional characteristics of orbitals in bonded atoms differ from those in isolated atoms.* That is, the orientation of the orbitals in a bonded atom is influenced by the presence of other atoms. We will first explain observed bond angles in terms of the *electrostatic repulsion* between valence electron charge clouds and then later use the concept of *hybridization* to explain the same observations.

Keep in mind that the ideas expressed here are merely models to help us correlate experimental findings. The models are useful because they allow us to make predictions concerning molecular shapes that are reasonably correct in a large number of cases.

RONALD J. GILLESPIE
1924–

3-12

Valence Shell Electron-Pair Repulsion Theory

The valence shell electron-pair repulsion (VSEPR) theory allows us to readily predict the shapes of many molecules.
Let us visualize either bonded or unbonded electron pairs in the outer level of a bonded atom as negative charge clouds. Each negative charge cloud tends to repel all other charge clouds in the vicinity. To achieve a condition of minimum potential energy, it is necessary to locate the charge clouds so that they will be as far apart as possible. In this position, the electrostatic repulsion between the clouds is reduced to a minimum. The position of the charge clouds on the central atom will determine the directional characteristics of the covalent bonds and shapes of the molecules that the atom forms. This concept forms the basis of the *valence shell electron-pair repulsion theory (VSEPR)*, developed by chemists R. J. Gillespie (1924–) and R. S. Nyholm (1917–1971).

The spatial orientation of the charge clouds depends on the number present and on their size. The number of charge clouds equals the total number of electron pairs (bonded and unbonded) in the outer level of the central atom of the compound. The relative size of the charge cloud depends on whether the electron pair is a bonded or a lone (unbonded) pair. We would expect clouds associated with bonded electrons to be rather localized between nuclei and to take up less space than those associated with unbonded electrons.

The VSEPR model applies best to compounds in which a central atom is bonded to two, three, four or six identical atoms. We can use the VSEPR model to determine the nature of the geometric figure inscribed in the "atomic sphere" that joins, respectively, two, three, four or six electron pairs that are located as far apart as possible on the surface of the atomic sphere.

When the central atom is bonded to *two identical atoms*, the mutual repulsion of the two electron clouds forces them to opposite sides of the atomic sphere. Lines from the electron pairs to the

Ronald Gillespie was born in London, England, where he obtained his BSc and PhD degrees at University College, London. In 1958, he moved to Canada to teach at McMaster University in Hamilton, Ontario.

Gillespie's research has concentrated on the field of nonmetal chemistry, particularly superacid chemistry, noble gases and fluorine. He is best known for his work on the *valence shell electron pair repulsion (VSEPR) theory* with Dr Ronald S. Nyholm (1917–1971). Gillespie popularized and expanded the theory as a teaching aid, particularly as an alternative to the theory of hybrid orbitals. Today, the theory continues to be a useful tool in the study and teaching of inorganic chemistry.

Gillespie is the author of *Molecular Geometry*, an account of the VSEPR theory, and co-author of *Chemistry*, an introductory university textbook.

The recipient of numerous honours during his career, including the prestigious Izaak Walton Killam Memorial Prize for Pure Science in 1987, Gillespie is also a fellow of the Royal Society, London, and the Royal Society of Canada.

An avid traveller, Gillespie has spent periods of leave teaching and doing research in Europe, Australia and India. Closer to home, Gillespie enjoys sailing Ontario's Great Lakes.

centre of the sphere form a 180° angle. These lines represent the directional characteristics of the covalent bonds. When atoms are bonded to these electron pairs, the resulting molecule is said to be *linear* and the bond angle is 180°.

Figure 3-18
Minimum repulsion between two electron pairs occurs when the pairs are located at the opposite ends of the diameter of a sphere.

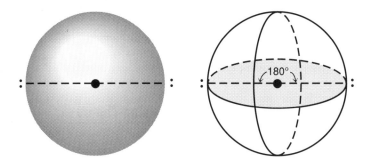

When the central atom is bonded to *three identical atoms*, the mutual repulsion of the three electron clouds forces them to the corners of an equilateral triangle where repulsive forces are at a minimum. Lines from the electron pairs to the centre of the sphere make an angle of 120°. Atoms bonded to these electron pairs lie in the same plane and make a bond angle of 120°. Accordingly, the molecule is said to be *trigonal planar*.

Figure 3-19
Minimum repulsion between three electron pairs occurs when each of the pairs is located at the vertices of an equilateral triangle inscribed in a great circle of the sphere.

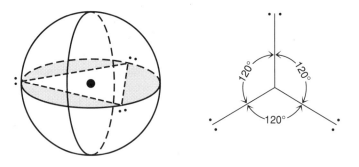

When the central atom is bonded to *four identical atoms*, the mutual repulsion of the four electron clouds forces them to the corners of an inscribed, regular tetrahedron (Fig. 3-20). A regular tetrahedron has four identical faces. Lines drawn from any two of the electron pairs to the centre of the sphere (and tetrahedron)

make an angle of 109° 28′. This angle, usually rounded to 109.5°, is called a *tetrahedral angle*. When four identical groups are bonded to the four electron pairs, the species is said to have a *tetrahedral shape*.

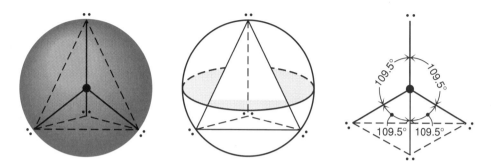

Figure 3-20
Four electron pairs are the farthest apart on the surface of an atomic sphere at the vertices of an inscribed tetrahedron.

When the central atom is bonded to *six identical atoms*, the mutual repulsion of the six electron clouds forces them to the six corners of an inscribed, regular octahedron where they are as far apart as possible (Fig. 3-21). Lines drawn from any two adjacent electron pairs to the centre of the atomic sphere make an angle of 90°. Thus, molecules or ions composed of six identical groups bonded to a central atom are said to have an *octahedral geometry*.

Note that an octahedral structure has only six atoms bonded to the central atom. There are, however, eight planar surfaces.

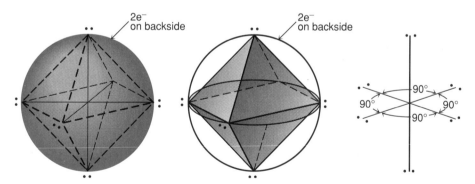

The four electron-pair arrangements that we described above are summarized in Table 3-7 on the next page.

We will now use these generalities to help predict the bond angles and shapes of some simple, covalent binary compounds that contain, as their central atoms, atoms from the Group A elements in the periodic table.

Figure 3-21
Six electron pairs are the farthest apart on the surface of an atomic sphere at the vertices of an inscribed octahedron.

TABLE 3-7
**ELECTRON-PAIR
ARRANGEMENT**

Pairs of Electrons	Geometric Shape of Molecules
2	linear
3	trigonal planar
4	tetrahedral
6	octahedral

3-13

Covalent Molecules Containing an Atom of a Group IA Element

The atoms in Group IA have only one bonding (valence) electron. A covalent molecule containing any of these atoms as a central atom would have only one covalent bond; therefore, no angle can be defined. Any diatomic molecule may be considered linear. In the next chapter we will find that most compounds containing these elements are ionic rather than molecular.

3-14

Covalent Molecules Containing an Atom of a Group IIA Element

The atoms of elements from Group IIA have only two bonding (valence) electrons and can, therefore, form a maximum of two regular covalent bonds. In beryllium fluoride (BeF_2), each of the two valence electrons in a beryllium atom is shared with an electron from a fluorine atom. Using the VSEPR theory, we would predict that the angle between the fluorine atoms is 180° and that BeF_2 is a linear molecule (Fig. 3-22(a)). *A linear arrangement is characteristic of molecules in which the central atom uses all of its bonding electrons to bond to two identical atoms.*

3-15

Covalent Molecules Containing an Atom of a Group IIIA Element

Boron trifluoride (BF_3) is a covalent molecule containing an atom from Group IIIA. Elements in this group have three outer-energy-level electrons and can form three regular covalent bonds. In a molecule such as BF_3, there are three electron pairs in the valence shell of the boron atom. Thus, all three fluorine atoms lie in the same plane at 120° from each other. The molecule is symmetrical (Fig. 3-22(b)) and is trigonal planar. *When all bonding electrons are used to bond three identical atoms to a fourth atom, the molecule is trigonal planar and the bond angles are 120°.*

3-16

Covalent Molecules Containing an Atom of a Group IVA Element

Methane (CH_4) is an example of a molecule in which four identical groups are bonded to a central atom. In methane, the outer level of the carbon atom contains four electron pairs. This means the electrostatic repulsion will be at a minimum when the angle between the hydrogen atoms is 109.5°. Since the hydrogen atoms are located at the corners of a regular tetrahedron, the molecule is tetrahedral. The symmetrical methane molecule is shown in Fig. 3-22(c). In general, *when an atom uses all of its outer electrons to bond to four other atoms, the resulting molecule is tetrahedral.*

3-17

Covalent Molecules and Ions Containing an Atom of a Group VA Element

The atoms of Group VA elements have five valence electrons and should be able to form five regular covalent bonds. The phosphorus in phosphorus pentachloride (PCl_5) is an example. Electrostatic repulsion is at a minimum when the five electron pairs are located at the vertices of a trigonal bipyramid (Fig. 3-23). Note that, although all five bond angles are not identical in PCl_5, measurements show that the trigonal bipyramid is the minimum energy shape. Because this molecule is relatively uncommon, we will be concerned primarily with the abundant and important molecules that contain nitrogen. We would not expect nitrogen to form five covalent bonds. The bonding level in nitrogen is the second quantum level, which can accommodate a maximum of four electron pairs. Furthermore, the bonding of five groups to a small atom like nitrogen would probably produce an unstable species. One of the most important compounds containing nitrogen is ammonia (NH_3). Examination of the Lewis structure of NH_3 reveals that there are three pairs of shared electrons and one pair of unshared electrons in the outer energy level of the nitrogen atom:

$$\begin{array}{c} H \\ \cdot\cdot \\ :N:H \\ \cdot\cdot \\ H \end{array}$$

If all pairs were equivalent, the four charge clouds would be identical. Mutual repulsion would force them apart until they made an angle of 109.5°. The charge cloud associated with the lone pair, however, has a distorting effect on the angle and reduces it to about 107°; the result is a distorted tetrahedron.

Lines joining the three hydrogen atoms outline an equilateral triangle; the nitrogen atom is located above the centre of the triangle. Lines from the nitrogen atom to each hydrogen atom form an angle of about 107° with each other. An ammonia molecule (Fig. 3-24), is said to be pyramidal. In general, *when three atoms bond to a central atom, the molecule or ion will be pyramidal if the central atom contains one unbonded electron pair.*

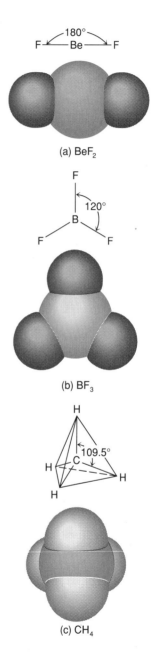

(a) BeF$_2$

(b) BF$_3$

(c) CH$_4$

Figure 3-22
BeF$_2$, BF$_3$ and CH$_4$ are all symmetrical molecules. BeF$_2$ is linear, BF$_3$ is trigonal planar and CH$_4$ is tetrahedral. All valence electrons of the central atoms are used in bond formation.

Figure 3-23
When the central atom uses all of its valence electrons to bond to five identical atoms, the resulting species has a trigonal bipyramidal shape. In this figure, the dark lines represent bonds and the light lines outline the shape of the bipyramid. Note that three chlorine atoms are found at the corners of an equilateral triangle.

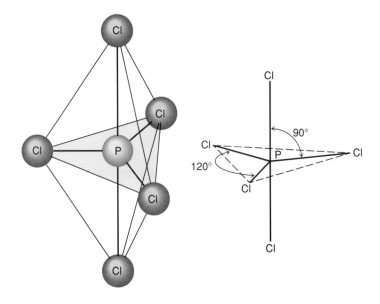

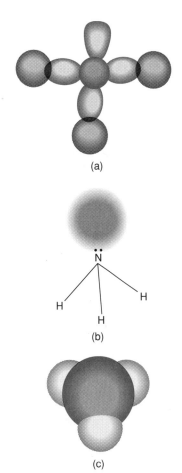

(a)

(b)

(c)

Figure 3-24
(a) The shape of NH_3 is related to a tetrahedron. The unbonded pair of electrons exerts a greater repulsion on a bond pair than bond pairs do on each other. The result is a distorted tetrahedron. (b) Three hydrogen atoms form the base of a pyramid with a nitrogen atom at the apex.
(c) Space-filling model of NH_3.

In an ammonium ion (NH_4^+) (Fig. 3-25), there are four identical groups with no lone electron pairs. Hence, we would predict that the ion is tetrahedral. Experimental data confirms this prediction.

3-18

Covalent Molecules Containing an Atom of a Group VIA Element

According to the VSEPR theory, atoms from Group VIA elements should be able to form six covalent bonds. The exception is oxygen, which, like nitrogen, is a small atom whose bonding level can contain only four electron pairs.

Let us apply the VSEPR theory to predict the shape of sulfur hexafluoride (SF_6), a molecule in which six fluorine atoms are bonded to one sulfur atom. The formula (SF_6) shows that six bonding positions are required. Since sulfur is in the third row of the periodic table, it has three energy levels that, in theory, can contain nine electron pairs. In SF_6, six electron pairs are used to form six covalent bonds. We have shown that, in this case, minimum repulsion occurs when the electron pairs are located at the vertices of a regular octahedron (Fig. 3-26(a)). The bond angles between any adjacent fluorine atoms are 90°. The SF_6 molecule shown in Fig. 3-26(b) is octahedral and symmetrical. *Most species (molecules or ions) in which six atoms or ions are bonded to a central atom or ion are octahedral.*

The most familiar and important molecule formed by an element of Group VIA is, of course, the water molecule. The Lewis structure shows that in a water molecule, the oxygen atom has two pairs of shared electrons and two pairs of unshared electrons in its outer energy level. If all pairs were equivalent, the four charge clouds would be identical, and the bond angle would be 109.5°. We would, however, predict that the charge clouds associated with the unbonded electron pairs would repel and force the bonding pairs closer together than 109.5°. This is confirmed by data showing that the bond angle in water is 104.5°. Note that the one lone pair in an ammonia molecule distorted the tetrahedral angle to a lesser extent than the two lone pairs in a water molecule. In general, *when two atoms are bonded to a central atom, the resulting molecules are angular (bent) if unbonded outer electrons are present in the central atom.* This shape is characteristic of triatomic molecules that contain as their central atoms the atoms of Group VIA elements.

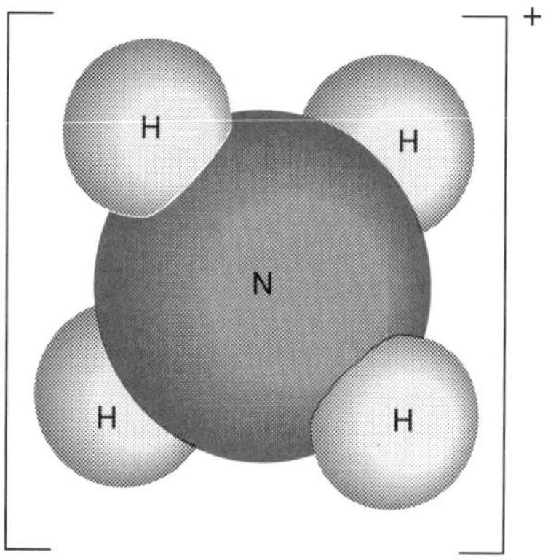

Figure 3-25
In NH_4^+, all bonding electrons are used to bond four hydrogen atoms. Thus, the ammonium ion is tetrahedral.

3-19
Covalent Molecules Containing an Atom of a Group VIIA Element

In theory, the larger atoms from Group VIIA elements can form seven covalent bonds. Molecules of this type are known—IF_7, for example (see Fig. 3-27 on page 104)—but are relatively unimportant for our purposes. We will concern ourselves mainly with molecules in which two, three and four atoms are bonded to a central atom from a Group VIIA element. Examples involving these species have already been discussed.

The possible shapes of molecules and ions that are related to the possible arrangements of valence electron pairs on the central atom are summarized in Tables 3-8 and 3-9. In the Lewis structures, A represents the central atom and B represents the attached atoms. In the geometric figures, the light lines outline three-dimensional geometric figures and the unbroken dark lines represent bonds. Dashed lines are used to give a three-dimensional effect. Note that the structures of all species in which there are four pairs of bonding electrons around the central atom are related to a tetrahedron. Similarly, the structures of all species in which there are five pairs of bonding electrons are shown as being related to the trigonal bipyramid. For example, chlorine trifluoride (ClF_3) has three pairs of bonding electrons and a total of five pairs of electrons. However, since only three positions on the bipyramid are occupied, the molecule is said to be T-shaped. Minimum repulsion occurs when the two lone pairs are in the central plane (see Fig. 3-28(a) on page 104).

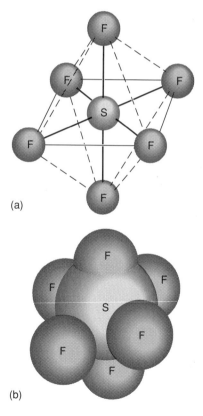

(a)

(b)

Figure 3-26
(a) In an SF_6 molecule, the fluorine atoms are located at the vertices of a regular octahedron. (b) Space-filling model of SF_6.

TABLE 3-8

POSSIBLE SHAPES OF SPECIES CONTAINING ATOMS OF REPRESENTATIVE ELEMENTS

No. of Electron Pairs in Valence Level of Central Atom	No. of Atoms Bonded to Central Atom	No. of Unbonded Electron Pairs (Lone Pairs)	Lewis Structure Showing Bonds and Unbonded Electron Pairs	Formula	Representation of Shape	Shape	Example
2	2	0	B—A—B	AB_2		linear	BeF_2
3	3	0	B, A, B, B	AB_3		trigonal planar	BF_3
3	2	1	A, B, B	AB_2		angular	$SnCl_2$
4	4	0	B, A, B, B, B	AB_4		tetrahedral	CCl_4
4	3	1	A, B, B, B	AB_3		pyramidal	NH_3
4	3	0	B, A, B, B	AB_3		trigonal planar	SO_3
4	2	2	A, B, B	AB_2		angular	H_2O
4	2	1	A, B, B	AB_2		angular	SO_2
4	2	0	B=A=B	AB_2		linear	CO_2

TABLE 3-9

POSSIBLE SHAPES OF SPECIES CONTAINING ATOMS WITH 5, 6 OR 7 ELECTRON PAIRS

No. of Electron Pairs in Valence Level of Central Atom	No. of Atoms Bonded to Central Atom	No. of Unbonded Electron Pairs (Lone Pairs)	Lewis Structure Showing Bonds and Unbonded Electron Pairs	Formula	Representation of Shape	Shape	Example
5	5	0		AB_5		trigonal bipyramidal	PCl_5
5	4	1		AB_4		seesaw	SF_4
5	3	2		AB_3		T-shaped	ClF_3
5	2	3		AB_2		linear	XeF_2
6	6	0		AB_6		octahedral	SF_6
6	5	1		AB_5		square-based pyramid	IF_5
6	4	2		AB_4		square planar	XeF_4
7	7	0		AB_7		pentagonal bipyramid	IF_7

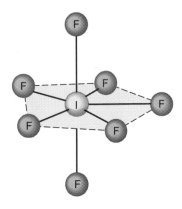

Figure 3-27
When the central atom uses all of its valence electrons to bond to seven identical atoms, the resulting species has a pentagonal, bipyramidal shape. In IF$_7$, the five fluorine atoms are found at the vertices of a regular pentagon. Lines drawn from the fluorine atoms at the poles to each of the atoms in the central plane outline the pentagonal bipyramid.

When there are six pairs of bonding electrons, the shape of the structure is related to the octahedron. When only five positions are occupied, as in iodine pentafluoride (IF$_5$), the bonded atoms define a square-based pyramid (see Fig. 3-28(b)).

Note that in the pictorial representation of molecular shapes, multiple bonds are not shown. As far as shape is concerned, they have the same orientation as single bonds. Note also that the shapes described in Tables 3-8 and 3-9 are idealized and represent general shapes. No bonding theory permits the accurate prediction of all bond angles because the angles are affected by the relative sizes of the atoms and their relative electronegativity. For example, in a T-shaped molecule, it is unlikely that the top of the T will be precisely perpendicular to the stem.

The relationship between the central atom (A), the bonded atoms (B) and the number of lone pairs (unbonded electron pairs), symbolized by E, is summarized in Table 3-10.

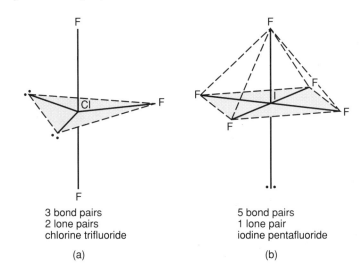

Figure 3-28
(a) The probable shape of species in which there are five pairs of electrons.
(b) The probable shape of species in which there are six pairs of electrons.

3 bond pairs
2 lone pairs
chlorine trifluoride

(a)

5 bond pairs
1 lone pair
iodine pentafluoride

(b)

You may have noticed that we have avoided identifying by name or letter any of the bonding orbitals used by the central atom. The reason is that the directional characteristics of pure atomic orbitals do not give rise to the observed bond angles. For example, we could not explain the 109.5° angles in CH$_4$ by assuming that one s and three p hydrogen-like orbitals in the carbon atom were used for bonding. The s orbital is non-directional, and the three p orbitals form right angles with each other. Furthermore, the electron configuration of the atom in the ground state is not consistent with the observed bonding capacity of carbon in most of its compounds. The ground-state configuration shows two unpaired electrons, but in most of its compounds, carbon exhibits a bonding capacity of four.

FOLLOW-UP PROBLEM

Write electron-dot formulas for and predict the shapes of
(a) BeH_2, (b) H_2S, (c) BCl_3, (d) H_3O^+, (e) SiH_4,
(f) $Sb(OH)_6^-$, (g) ClO_4^-, (h) CO_3^{2-}, (i) $Al(H_2O)_6^{3+}$, (j) CO_2,
(k) $SbCl_5$, (l) $TeCl_4$, (m) ClO_2^-, (n) BrF_3, (o) BrF_5, (p) NO_2^-,
(q) N_2O.

Answers:

(a) H : Be : H

linear

(d) $\left[\begin{array}{c} \text{H : O : H} \\ \text{H} \end{array}\right]^+$

pyramidal

(e) H
H : Si : H
H

tetrahedral

(m) $\left[\text{: O : Cl : O :} \right]^-$

angular

(n) : F :
: F : Br : F :

T-shaped

(o)

: F :
: F :   : F :
    Br
: F :   : F :

square-based pyramid

TABLE 3-10

RELATIONSHIP BETWEEN STRUCTURE OF A MOLECULE AND NUMBER OF LONE PAIRS

Molecule	Shape
AB_2	linear
AB_2E	angular
AB_2E_2	angular
AB_2E_3	linear
AB_3	trigonal planar
AB_3E	pyramidal
AB_3E_2	T-shaped
AB_4	tetrahedral
AB_4E	seesaw
AB_4E_2	square planar
AB_5	trigonal bipyramid
AB_5E	square-based pyramid
AB_6	octahedral
AB_7	pentagonal bipyramid

In order to relate experimentally observed bonding capacities and bond angles to the concept of pure atomic orbitals, scientists use a concept known as *hybridization*. Hybridization is one aspect of an important bonding theory known as the *valence bond theory*. Let us briefly examine this helpful concept.

3-20

Hybridization

Hybridization—the blending of atomic orbitals—helps explain observed bonding capacities and bond angles.

Hybridization of pure atomic orbitals means that two or more different pure atomic orbitals can be mixed (hybridized) to yield two or more hybrid atomic orbitals that are identical. For example, mixing one *s* and one *p* orbital in an atom yields two *sp* hybrid orbitals. Whereas the individual *s* and *p* orbitals have different energies and directional characteristics, the two *sp* hybrids are identical in every respect.

Atomic orbitals do not actually mix. Hybridization is a convenient mathematical model that helps to explain observations, but no real mixing occurs.

Figure 3-29
Hybridization analogy. Starting with one can of red paint and three cans of white paint, we mix one can of red paint with one can of white paint. Two cans of pink paint are formed, leaving no red paint and two cans of white paint. This is analogous to mixing one *s* and one *p* orbital to give two *sp* hybrid orbitals. This leaves two *p* and two *sp* orbitals available for bonding.

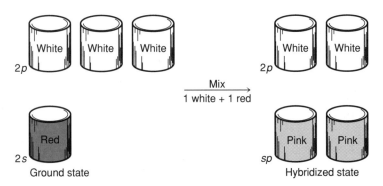

3-21

sp Hybrid Orbitals

An *sp* hybrid orbital is formed by mixing one *s* and one *p* orbital.

We will illustrate the application of the hybridization concept by showing how it can account for the experimentally observed bonding capacity of beryllium and the bond angles in BeF_2. The formula shows that a beryllium atom is bonded to two fluorine atoms and, therefore, has a bonding capacity of two. Spectroscopic measurements reveal that the bond angle between the fluorine atoms is 180° and that the bond lengths are equal. The ground-state electron configuration of beryllium is

$$1s^2 2s^2$$

It is apparent that this configuration is not consistent with the formation of two covalent bonds oriented at 180°. The valence bond theory must account for these observations; in other words, there must be two bonds of equal strength directed at an angle of 180° with respect to each other.

To explain these observations, *the valence bond theory invokes the hybridization concept in which a specific number of pure atomic orbitals are hybridized (mixed) to yield an equal number of identical hybrids*. If all valence electrons of the central atom are used in bond formation, we can assume that the angle between the hybrid orbitals is maximized. If all valence electrons are not used in bond formation, then the angle between hybrid orbitals may be slightly distorted.

A hypothetical sequence of steps can be used to illustrate the formation of hybrid orbitals in BeF_2. The approach of fluorine atoms causes a rearrangement of electrons and energy changes to take place in the beryllium atom. The ground-state electron configuration of a beryllium atom is

$2p$ ◯◯◯
$2s$ ⦿
$1s$ ⦿

We can imagine that the energy released as the fluorine atoms approach the beryllium atom promotes one of the s electrons into an empty p orbital. This provides two bonding orbitals, each with one electron. This intermediate configuration, which is strictly hypothetical, would be

$2p$ ①◯◯
$2s$ ①
$1s$ ⦿

However, since electrons in s and p orbitals have different energies, bonds involving the electrons in these pure atomic orbitals would not have the same strength. In order to make the bonding theory agree with experimental evidence, it is necessary to postulate that one s and one p orbital hybridize (mix) and yield two identical orbitals. We identify the hybrid by stating with superscripts the number of each pure orbital involved in the formation of the hybrid. Thus, the two hybrid orbitals formed by mixing one s and one p orbital are called sp hybrids. Each hybrid contains one electron and is, in nature, intermediate between a pure s and a pure p atomic orbital. The overall process can be represented schematically as

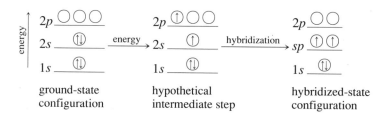

$2p$ ◯◯◯ $2p$ ①◯◯ $2p$ ◯◯
$2s$ ⦿   energy→ $2s$ ①   hybridization→ sp ①①
$1s$ ⦿ $1s$ ⦿ $1s$ ⦿

ground-state configuration   hypothetical intermediate step   hybridized-state configuration

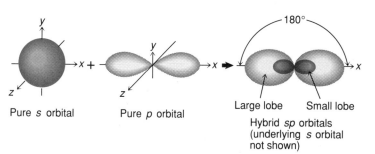

Pure s orbital   Pure p orbital   Large lobe   Small lobe
Hybrid sp orbitals (underlying s orbital not shown)

Figure 3-30
Two equivalent sp hybrid orbitals are formed by hybridizing one s and one p orbital. Each sp orbital consists of two lobes, one large and one small. The large lobe occupies a greater region of space than the pure p orbital. This permits a greater degree of overlapping with the orbital of another atom, resulting in the formation of a stronger bond.

The formation of *sp* hybrid orbitals from pure orbitals is shown in Fig. 3-30.

In the BeF_2 molecule, bonds are formed when a singly occupied *p* orbital of each fluorine atom overlaps a singly occupied *sp* orbital of a beryllium atom so that two electrons are common to both orbitals. The hybrid *sp* beryllium orbitals are directed at angles that keep them as far apart as possible (Fig. 3-31). Therefore, the bond angle in BeF_2 is 180°.

Figure 3-31
Representation of bond formation in BeF_2. The *s* orbitals of fluorine are not shown. The overlap of the p_x orbital of each fluorine atom with the *sp* orbitals of beryllium gives rise to the sigma-type (σ) covalent bond.

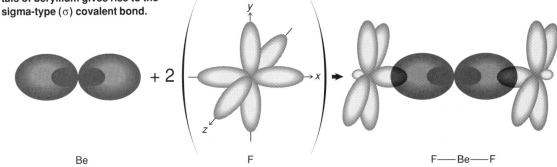

Be   F   F——Be——F

3-22

sp² Hybrid Orbitals

An *sp²* hybrid orbital results from the promotion of an *s* electron to a *p* orbital where hybridization occurs.

Earlier we used the VSEPR theory of chemical bonding to show that when a central atom uses all its bonding electrons to bond with three other atoms, the molecule is planar and the bond angles are 120°. Let us apply the valence bond theory of hybridization to this situation. Consider a boron trifluoride molecule (BF_3). This molecule is nonpolar with three identical bonds and trigonal planar geometry. The ground-state configuration of the boron atom is

$$1s^2 2s^2 2p^1$$

To exhibit a bonding capacity of three and form three identical bonds, boron must have three half-filled orbitals. We can imagine that a $2s$ electron is promoted to a $2p$ orbital, whereupon hybridization occurs. The three resulting hybrid orbitals are identified as *sp²* hybrid orbitals. The spatial orientation and the shape of a BF_3 molecule are shown, respectively, in Figs. 3-32 and 3-22(b).

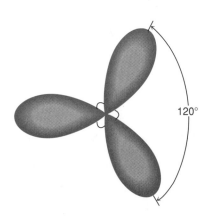

120°

Figure 3-32
Spatial orientation of *sp²* orbitals in a BF_3 molecule.

3-23

sp³ Hybrid Orbitals

An *sp³* hybrid orbital involves one *s* and three *p* orbitals.
In methane (CH_4), one *s* and three *p* orbitals of the carbon atom hybridize to give four identical *sp³* hybrid orbitals with 75% *p* character and 25% *s* character. The hypothetical steps involved in the formation of the four *sp³* orbitals are shown below. The formation of these orbitals is illustrated in Fig. 3-33. It can be seen that these orbitals are directed toward the corners of a regular tetrahedron and make an angle of 109.5° with each other.

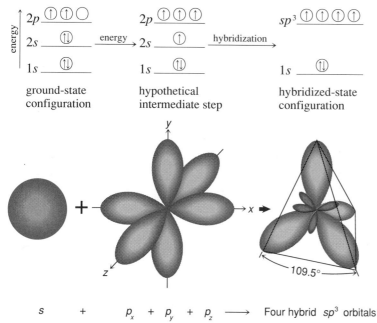

s + p_x + p_y + p_z ⟶ Four hybrid *sp³* orbitals

Figure 3-33
Hybridization of one *s* and three *p* orbitals yields four identical *sp³* orbitals, the larger lobes of which are directed toward the vertices of a regular tetrahedron.

3-24

Hybrid Orbitals in H₂O and NH₃

The *sp³* orbitals are used in the bonding of both H_2O and NH_3.
The *sp³* orbitals are the orbitals referred to in our discussion of the bonding in H_2O and NH_3. In H_2O and NH_3, however, the angles of the *sp³* orbitals are influenced and distorted by the presence of unbonded electron pairs. The ground-state and hybridized-state configurations of an oxygen atom are

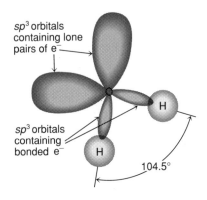

sp³ orbitals containing lone pairs of e⁻

sp³ orbitals containing bonded e⁻

104.5°

Figure 3-34
Orbital model for water. The electron clouds associated with lone pairs of electrons distort the tetrahedral angle from 109.5° to 104.5°.

The orbital model for water is shown in Fig. 3-34.

The ground-state and hybridized-state configurations for a nitrogen atom are

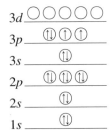

ground-state configuration

hybridized-state configuration

The orbital and space-filling models for NH_3 are shown, respectively, in Figs. 3-35 and 3-24.

3-25

sp³d² Hybrid Orbitals

When six identical bonds are formed, the central atom must use d orbitals. Consider a sulfur hexafluoride molecule (SF_6). The ground-state configuration of a sulfur atom is

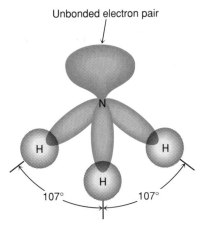

Unbonded electron pair

N

H H H

107° 107°

Figure 3-35
Orbital model for NH_3.

$$
\begin{array}{l}
3d\ \bigcirc\bigcirc\bigcirc\bigcirc\bigcirc \\
3p\ \underline{\textcircled{\scriptsize ↑↓}\ \textcircled{\scriptsize ↑}\ \textcircled{\scriptsize ↑}} \\
3s\ \underline{\textcircled{\scriptsize ↑↓}} \\
2p\ \underline{\textcircled{\scriptsize ↑↓}\ \textcircled{\scriptsize ↑↓}\ \textcircled{\scriptsize ↑↓}} \\
2s\ \underline{\textcircled{\scriptsize ↑↓}} \\
1s\ \underline{\textcircled{\scriptsize ↑↓}}
\end{array}
$$

To provide the necessary six bonding orbitals, an s and a p electron are promoted to d orbitals, whereupon sp^3d^2 hybridization occurs. The spatial orientation of the sp^3d^2 hybrid orbitals and the geometry of an SF_6 molecule are shown in Fig. 3-36.

Figure 3-36
Spatial orientation (a) and shape (b) of sp^3d^2 hybrid orbitals. In SF_6, four fluorine atoms are located at the corners of a square. The other two, located at the poles, make an angle of 90° with the central plane. See Fig. 3-26 for a space-filling model of SF_6.

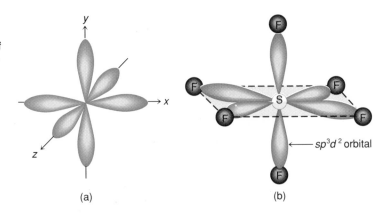

(a)

(b)

3-26

Relationships of Hybrid Orbitals

The relationships among the different types of hybrid orbitals and the characteristics of molecules are summarized in Table 3-11.

TABLE 3-11
RELATIONSHIPS AMONG TYPES OF HYBRID ORBITALS, FEATURES OF CENTRAL ATOM AND CHARACTERISTICS OF RESULTING MOLECULE

No. of Bonds	No. of Lone Pairs	Type of Hybrid Orbital	Angle Between Atoms Bonded to the Central Atom	Geometry of Molecule or Ion Formed	Example
2	0	sp	180°	linear	BeF_2
3	0	sp^2	120°	trigonal planar	BF_3
4	0	sp^3	109.5°	tetrahedral	CH_4
3	1	sp^3	90° to 109.5°	pyramidal	NH_3
2	2	sp^3	90° to 109.5°	angular	H_2O
6	0	sp^3d^2 or d^2sp^3	90°	octahedral	SF_6

The concept of hybridization is based on quantum mechanical calculations. In other words, it is possible to calculate the hybrid orbital angles and relative strengths. The calculated values agree closely with observed values. In general, hybrid orbitals permit a greater degree of overlap than the corresponding pure atomic orbitals. Hence, stronger bonds are formed by hybridization than with pure atomic orbitals. A summary of the orbitals used for bond formation and their relative strengths based on a value of 1.000 for a pure s orbital are given in Table 3-12.

TABLE 3-12
RELATIVE STRENGTHS OF BONDING ORBITALS

Orbitals Used	Number of Orbitals	Relative Strength
s	1	1.000
p	3	1.732
sp	2	1.932
sp^2	3	1.991
sp^3	4	2.000
sp^3d^2	6	2.923

FOLLOW-UP PROBLEM

Identify the hybrid orbitals used by the central atom in the following:

(a) BeH_2 (e) SeF_6
(b) BCl_3 (f) NO_3^-
(c) H_3O^+ (g) SO_3^{2-}
(d) SeH_4

Answers:
a) sp
c) sp^3
e) sp^3d^2 or d^2sp^3

BONDING IN CARBON COMPOUNDS

When writing Lewis structures, we encountered two carbon (organic) compounds that involved multiple bonds: ethene (ethylene, C_2H_4) and ethyne (acetylene, C_2H_2). Because of the importance of organic compounds, and to set the stage for the discussion of organic chemistry in later chapters, we will briefly examine the structural features of a few simple organic molecules. We have already considered methane (CH_4), commonly used as a fuel for heating and cooking. Three other carbon compounds closely related to methane are propane (C_3H_8), ethene (C_2H_4) and ethyne (C_2H_2). Experimental data related to these molecules is listed in Table 3-13.

TABLE 3-13
CHARACTERISTICS OF PROPANE, ETHENE AND ETHYNE

	Formula	Carbon-Carbon Bond Length (nm)	Carbon-Carbon Bond Energy (kJ/mol)	C—H Bond Angles	Molecular Shape	Relative Reactivity
Propane	C_3H_8	0.154	367.8	109.3°	–	low
Ethene	C_2H_4	0.134	698.1	120°	trigonal planar	moderately high
Ethyne	C_2H_2	0.120	961.4	180°	linear	high

Bonding energy may be defined as the energy required to break all the bonds in a mole of gaseous molecules that are in their lowest energy states.

The bond energy, or bond-dissociation energy, measures the force holding atoms together in a gaseous molecule. Table 3-14 lists the average bond energies for some compounds. Table 3-13 reveals that the carbon-to-carbon bond strength in ethyne is approximately one and one-half times that in ethene and almost three times that in propane. This factor, coupled with the corresponding changes in bond length, suggests the presence of single bonds in propane, a double bond in ethene and a triple bond in ethyne. These structures provide an outer octet of electrons for each carbon atom and a helium configuration for each hydrogen atom. The line formulas of the molecules are as follows:

TABLE 3-14
AVERAGE BOND ENERGIES

Bond	Energy (kJ/mol)
C—C	348
C—O	360
C—H	412
H—H	436
O—H	464
C=C	612
C=O	740
C≡C	836

$$
\begin{array}{ccc}
 & & \text{H} \quad\; \text{H} \quad\; \text{H} \\
 & & | \qquad | \qquad | \\
\text{Propane} & \text{H}- & \text{C}-\text{C}-\text{C}-\text{H} \\
 & & | \qquad | \qquad | \\
 & & \text{H} \quad\; \text{H} \quad\; \text{H}
\end{array}
$$

$$
\begin{array}{cc}
 & \text{H} \qquad\qquad \text{H} \\
 & \;\diagdown \qquad\quad \diagup \\
\text{Ethene} & \quad \text{C}=\text{C} \\
 & \;\diagup \qquad\quad \diagdown \\
 & \text{H} \qquad\qquad \text{H}
\end{array}
$$

$$\text{Ethyne} \qquad \text{H}-\text{C}\equiv\text{C}-\text{H}$$

A CHEMICAL SOCCER BALL

R. Buckminster Fuller (1895–1983), the American architect responsible for designing the geodesic dome, would have appreciated the structural intricacies of the 60-atom carbon molecule named after him—the *buckminsterfullerene* molecule. Formed in the lab when graphite is vaporized by laser irradiation, these highly symmetrical, stable carbon clusters are thought to exist within interstellar space as well as at the core of soot particles.

Chemists Harold Kroto and Richard Smalley, intrigued with the formation of lengthy carbon clusters, called fullerenes, discovered that, under certain conditions, 60-atom carbon molecules showed up in a mass spectra more often than other large-numbered carbon molecules. The reason the 60-atom molecule shows up more often than a 58- or 62-atom molecule is related to the stability of its structure. Buckminsterfullerene is made up of 12 pentagons and 20 hexagons, giving it 60 vertices. This pattern allows each carbon atom to have one double bond and two single bonds, linking it to three other carbon atoms. Although the structure for C_{60} is officially known as a truncated icosahedron, scientists liken the shape to a soccer ball or a hollow sphere.

It was this hollow, cage-like structure of fullerene molecules that fascinated the 1987 Nobel Prize winners in chemistry—Donald Cram and L. Lehn. Cram discovered that fullerene molecules can act as cages by forming around large ions and thus "trapping" them. Cram refers to the resulting molecule as a *carcerand*, from the Latin word for prison. Various configurations of these carcerands react selectively with certain molecules. This leads to the theory that carcerands may be used to trap ions such as calcium, or perhaps even gold, from seawater. Because some carcerands act as natural proteins, Cram feels that these molecular shells may eventually be used to deliver drugs or pesticides.

Scientists are also interested in the fullerene molecules because of their possible involvement in the origins of the universe. Smalley feels that because of the fullerene's stability, it may be so photon-resistant that nothing but a laser or a supernova would be able to destroy it. Although some scientists remain sceptical, Smalley and Kroto surmise that buckminsterfullerene, because of its stability and large size (the largest in interstellar space), may have played a critical role in the formation of the planets by absorbing the energy of colliding molecules after the "big bang." By absorbing this energy, the molecules may have slowed down and stuck together, forming dust, comets, asteroids and planets.

Although the existence of the fullerene molecules in interstellar space has yet to be proven, it is fascinating to think that the formation of the planets and the stars may have relied on a molecule known as buckminsterfullerene.

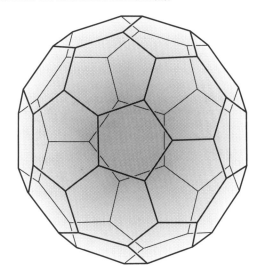

3-27

Single Bonds: Propane

Single bonds utilize sp^3 orbitals.

The bond orientation (109.5°) in propane (C_3H_8) shown in Fig. 3-37 may be explained by assuming that sp^3 hybrid orbitals are involved. One singly occupied sp^3 orbital from each adjacent atom overlaps endwise in the region between the carbon nuclei, forming a strong sigma covalent bond. The other singly occupied sp^3

orbitals from each carbon atom overlap the singly occupied *s* orbitals of the hydrogen atoms and form additional sigma bonds.

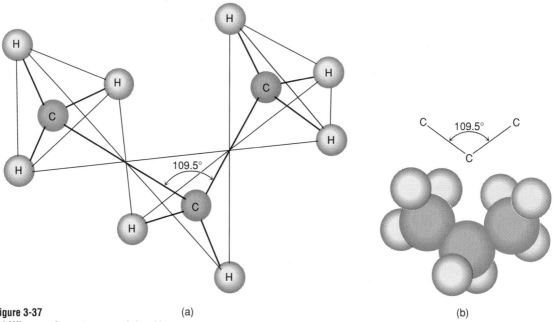

Figure 3-37
(a) When carbon atoms are joined by a single bond, it is possible to visualize two tetrahedrons meeting vertex to vertex. (b) A space-filling model of propane, showing the 109.5° angle between alternate carbon atoms.

(a)

(b)

3-28

Double Bonds: Ethene

Double bonds utilize sp² orbitals.

The observed trigonal planar geometry of an ethene molecule suggests the presence of sp^2 hybrid orbitals that form 120° angles with each other. The basic structure showing the single-bond orientation of ethene may be represented as

$$\begin{array}{ccc} \text{H} & 120° & \text{H} \\ & \diagdown \quad \diagup & \\ & \text{C}{-}\text{C} & 120° \\ & \diagup \quad \diagdown & \\ \text{H} & 120° & \text{H} \end{array}$$

A double or triple bond involving, respectively, two or three electron pairs is counted as a single electron charge cloud for purposes of determining spatial orientation.

All of the atoms lie in the same plane, and the angle between the atoms is 120°. The bond between the carbon atoms is a strong sigma bond formed by the endwise or head-on overlap of two singly occupied sp^2 orbitals. The C—H bonds are also sigma bonds formed by the overlap of a carbon sp^2 orbital with a hydrogen *s* orbital. These bonds are represented in Fig. 3-38.

Since the formation of three singly occupied sp^2 hybrid orbitals requires only two *p* orbitals and two electrons, each carbon atom still possesses an unused *p* electron. These electrons account for the double-bond nature of the carbon-to-carbon bond in ethene. The moderately high reactivity of ethene (a general chemical property) suggests that some of the outer electrons are more available for reaction than those of propane. These observations, along with spectroscopic data, suggest that all of the electrons in the double bond are not localized in the region between the carbon nuclei, where they would be rather confined and not readily available for reaction. It is the remaining p electrons that account for the greater reactivity of ethene.

The fourth bonding electron of each carbon atom is located in a p_y orbital. A minimum-energy condition occurs when the p_y orbitals on the two carbon atoms are parallel to each other. In this position, p orbitals overlap sideways (laterally) and form a relatively weak covalent bond. This bond is called a ***pi (π) bond***. Thus, the double bond in ethene consists of a strong sigma bond and a weaker pi bond. The structural formula for ethene is

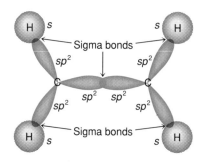

Figure 3-38
Five sigma bonds are formed in an ethene molecule. The sigma bond between the two carbon atoms constitutes half of the double bond in ethene. The p_y orbitals containing the fourth bonding electron of the carbon atom are not shown.

$$\begin{matrix} \text{H} & & \text{H} \\ & \diagdown \quad \diagup & \\ & \text{C}=\text{C} & \\ & \diagup \quad \diagdown & \\ \text{H} & & \text{H} \end{matrix}$$

It can be seen in Fig. 3-39 on page 116 that the pi-bond electron clouds are spread out over the entire upper and lower parts of the molecule. Unlike the electrons involved in sigma bonds, those involved in pi bonds are not localized and concentrated in the region between two positive nuclei. This means that pi-bond electrons can be easily affected by polar molecules or molecules that react with electron pairs.

3-29
Triple Bonds: Ethyne

Triple bonds utilize sp orbitals.
The chemistry of ethyne and other carbon compounds containing a triple bond is characteristic of the carbon-to-carbon triple bond. Let us examine the nature of this bond. The experimentally deduced linear geometry of ethyne suggests the presence of sp hybrid orbitals, which make angles of $180°$ with each other. The basic linear geometry of ethyne may be represented as

$$\text{H}-\text{C}-\text{C}-\text{H}$$

The bond between the carbon atoms formed by the endwise overlap of two singly occupied sp orbitals is a strong sigma bond. The C—H bonds are sigma bonds formed by the overlap of singly occupied sp and s orbitals.

Each carbon atom still has an electron in a p_z and a p_y orbital. A

Explain why ethene (C_2H_4) is more reactive than ethane (C_2H_6). Which is more reactive, ethene or ethyne (C_2H_2)? Explain.

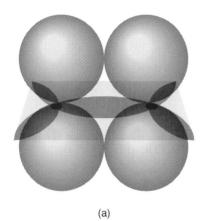

(a)

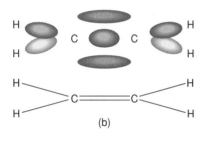

(b)

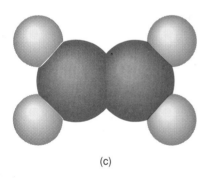

(c)

Figure 3-39
(a) Parallel p_y orbitals on adjacent carbon atoms of ethene. Sideways (lateral) overlap of these p orbitals results in the formation of a pi bond (in red). (b) Five sigma bonds (in black) and one pi bond (in red). Note that the pi-bond electron clouds are spread out over the top and bottom of the molecule. (c) A space-filling model of ethene.

Figure 3-40
Three sigma bonds and two pi bonds are formed in an ethyne molecule.

condition of minimum energy will be achieved when the p_z and p_y orbitals of each atom are parallel. In this position, sidewise (lateral) overlap of the p_z and p_y orbitals occurs (Fig. 3-40). Each overlap produces a pi bond. Thus, the triple bond in ethyne is composed of a strong sigma bond and two weaker pi bonds. The high chemical reactivity of ethyne may be attributed in part to the accessibility of the delocalized pi electrons to reagents that react with electrons. The structural formula for ethyne is

$$H-C\equiv C-H$$

BONDING IN NOBLE-GAS COMPOUNDS

3-30

Noble-Gas Compounds

Xenon, krypton and radon are considered to be the only noble gases that form compounds.
The noble gases had for many years been called the "inert" gases because of their very limited ability to react chemically. No noble-gas compound was made until 1962 when Neil Bartlett at the University of British Columbia made xenon tetrafluoride. Up until then, it was believed that the electron configuration of the noble-gas elements was so stable that they could not enter into covalent bond formation. Since that time, a number of covalent noble-gas compounds have been experimentally produced. For example, in addition to xenon difluoride (XeF_2) and xenon tetrafluoride (XeF_4), other compounds such as xenon hexafluoroplatinate ($XePtF_6$), XeO_3, $Na_4XeO_6 \cdot 8H_2O$ and XeF_6 have been prepared and found to be stable at room temperature. Compounds containing krypton (KrF_4) and radon (RnF_4) have also been synthesized, although compounds made from radon have not been studied

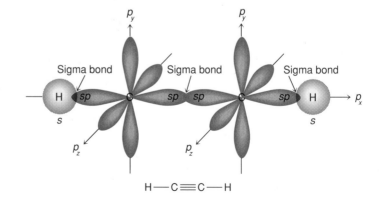

extensively because of their radioactivity. At present, there have been no compounds of helium, neon or argon reported. From a table of ionization energies (Table 2-7), you can see that helium and neon have first ionization energies that exceed that of fluorine, while those of the other noble-gas compounds are lower. Many scientists predict that it is unlikely that stable compounds will ever be formed with helium or neon. The first ionization energies are so high that combination even with fluorine, the most reactive nonmetal, would seem to be improbable.

Figure 3-41
A space-filling model of ethyne.

NEIL BARTLETT AND THE NOBLE-GAS COMPOUNDS

B y the year 1900, the inert gases had been isolated and identified. For more than 60 years after that, chemical bonding theories held that these gases were incapable of taking part in chemical reactions and forming compounds. Since inert gas compounds were thought to be impossible, no one looked for them and none were found.

In 1962, this situation changed suddenly as the result of the work of Neil Bartlett (1932–) at the University of British Columbia. Bartlett, who was born in Newcastle-upon-Tyne in England and obtained his PhD in chemistry from the University of Durham in 1957, accepted an appointment at UBC in 1958. Although Bartlett moved to the United States in 1966, it was during his stay at UBC that he changed the perception of the noble gases.

While working with platinum hexafluoride (PtF_6), Bartlett had a startling result—the platinum hexafluoride formed an ionic compound with oxygen ($O_2^+PtF_6^-$). Because oxygen has a very high ionization energy, Bartlett did not expect that an electron could be pulled away from it, even by platinum hexafluoride, with its high electron affinity. Since he knew that the ionization energy of the noble gas xenon (12.13 eV) is very close to that of oxygen (12.2 eV), Bartlett set up an experiment to see if xenon would react in a similar way with platinum hexafluoride.

Although working with such an extremely reactive substance can never be easy, the design of Bartlett's experiment was simple: In a container, he put the dark red platinum hexafluoride gas on one side of a diaphragm and the clear, colourless xenon gas on the other. When the diaphragm was broken, the gases mixed and reacted, forming a yellow powder. Through this simple reaction of platinum hexafluoride with xenon, Bartlett obtained the first chemical compound of a rare gas, xenon hexafluoroplatinate

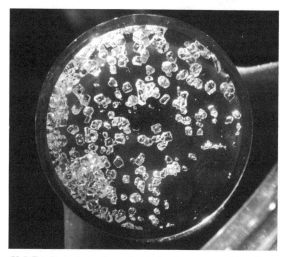

($XePtF_6$). Bartlett also found that by heating xenon and fluoride at 750°C, crystals of xenon tetrafluoride (shown above) could be made.

When the report of this synthesis was published in 1962, it immediately prompted scientists to search for other noble-gas compounds. Within a few years, several compounds of xenon, including xenon difluoride, had been synthesized. Other chemists soon made compounds from krypton and one compound from radon—radon fluoride. However, no compounds of helium, neon or argon have yet been synthesized.

Bartlett's work forced chemists to modify their theories of chemical bonding. During his eight years in Canada, Bartlett changed our perception of and, ultimately, our nomenclature for the "inert" gases and opened up the possibilities for further investigation into the structure of the noble gases.

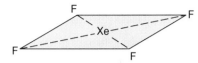

Figure 3-42
An XeF₄ molecule has a square planar geometry. The xenon atom in the centre is surrounded by four fluorine atoms in the same plane at the corners of a square.

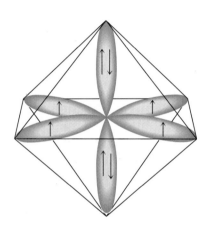

Figure 3-43
Orbital charge clouds of Xe in XeF₄.

Xenon Tetrafluoride

The first noble-gas compound, xenon tetrafluoride, was made by Neil Bartlett in 1962.

At a temperature of 400°C, xenon reacts with fluorine and produces xenon tetrafluoride (XeF_4). X-ray diffraction patterns show that this compound has a square planar geometry (Fig. 3-42). That is, a xenon atom is located in the centre of a square, and the four fluorine atoms occupy the vertices. To explain the bonding of xenon tetrafluoride, we begin with the ground-state electron configuration of xenon:

$$1s^2 2s^2 2p^6 3s^2 3p^6 3d^{10} 4s^2 4p^6 4d^{10} 5s^2 5p^6 5d^0 6s^0 6p^0$$

No singly occupied orbitals are available. However, the fifth shell has empty d orbitals to which electrons may be promoted when other atoms approach a xenon atom. Each of the four fluorine atoms can contribute one electron to a shared pair from its half-filled p orbital. This means that there must be four singly occupied orbitals in a xenon atom. These can be made available by the promotion of one s and three p electrons into two d orbitals. Hybridization produces six identical, octahedrally-directed sp^3d^2 hybrid orbitals that contain a total of eight electrons: four from the fluorine atoms and four promoted from the s and p orbitals to the d orbitals in xenon. Four of the sp^3d^2 hybrid orbitals contain one electron, and two contain a pair of electrons. The electrons are arranged at the vertices of a regular octahedron, as shown in the orbital charge-cloud diagram (Fig. 3-43). The octahedral electron arrangement is shown in an electron-dot structure (Fig. 3-44), and the spacing-filling model of XeF_4 is shown in Fig. 3-45.

With a background knowledge that enables us to predict shapes of simple molecules, we can now investigate the polarity of bonds and molecules.

POLARITY OF BONDS AND MOLECULES

The melting points, boiling points and other properties of pure substances are influenced by the shapes, sizes and polarities of their component molecules. The shapes and polarities of molecules are important only in relation to other molecules. For example, the melting point of a solid such as sulfur is influenced by the shape of the S_8 molecules that compose it. There are, of course, wide variations in the properties of individual molecular substances. We would expect the properties of substances made up

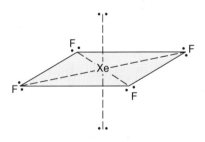

Figure 3-44
Electron-dot structure of XeF₄.

of polar covalent molecules to differ considerably from those made up of nonpolar covalent molecules. Properties such as melting and boiling points depend on attractions between molecules. Thus, the properties of a macroscopic sample depend on the polarity of the individual molecules. Molecular polarity, in turn, depends on the shape of the molecule and the polarity of the bonds between the atoms that compose the molecule.

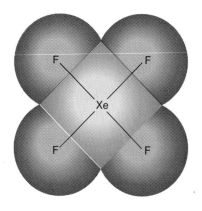

Figure 3-45
A space-filling model of the square planar XeF₄ molecule.

3-32

Bond Polarity

A chemical bond that does not share electrons equally can be polar.

The polarity of a bond is related to the difference in the electron affinities or electronegativities of the bonding atoms. A nonpolar bond is formed between atoms that have the same electronegativity. As the difference in electronegativity between the two atoms increases, the bond between them becomes more polar (see Fig. 3-46). The larger the difference in electronegativities, the greater the polarity. When the difference is great enough, it is assumed that the "shared" electrons become the "property" of the more electronegative atom. In other words, an electron is transferred from one atom to another. This results in the formation of a positive and a negative ion that carry charges equal to or multiples of the unit electron charge. Since electron transfer in polar molecules is not complete, the atoms behave as though they carry a partial charge. This partial charge, symbolized by the Greek letter delta (δ), represents the extent of electron transfer and can be used to calculate the percentage ionic character in a bond. Let us now go from bond polarity to molecular polarity.

Figure 3-46
A bond between two atoms becomes more polarized as the difference in electronegativity increases. When the atoms acquire a discrete charge, the bond is said to be ionic. The degree of distortion of an ion's electron cloud is affected by the relative size and charge of the two ions.

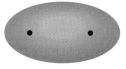

Nonpolar
covalent bond

Polar
covalent bond

Ions with distorted
electron clouds

Ions with symmetrical,
undistorted electron
clouds

3-33

Molecular Polarity

The polarity of a diatomic molecule depends on the electronegativity of the atoms. The polarity of a molecule with three or more atoms depends on the arrangement of the bonds.

We have already learned that a diatomic molecule is nonpolar if the atoms are identical in electronegativity and polar if the atoms

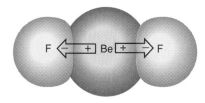

Figure 3-47
Nonpolar BeF_2 molecule. The polarities of the individual bonds are oriented at 180° from each other.

are different in electronegativity. When, however, two or more atoms are bonded to a third atom, the polarity of the molecule depends not only on bond distances but also on bond angles. Molecules in which the atoms attached to the central atom have the same electronegativity and are *symmetrically* arranged are nonpolar. This means that a molecule may be nonpolar even though all of the covalent bonds in the molecule are polar. For example, CH_4, BF_3 and BeF_2 are nonpolar even though all the covalent bonds in these molecules hold together dissimilar atoms and are polar.

The polarity of a molecule is equal to the geometric sum of the polarities of the individual bonds. Using the observed bonding angles (Table 3-6) and representing the relative polarity of each bond by the length of an arrow, we can show that the polar bonds in CH_4, BF_3 and BeF_2 cancel. Figure 3-47 shows that the two bonds in BeF_2 are equal in polarity and opposite in direction, giving the molecule a net polarity of zero.

On the other hand, the arrangement of atoms in water or in ammonia molecules is not symmetrical. As a result of the asymmetrical distribution, one end of the molecule is negative with respect to the other end. Thus, water and ammonia are dipoles (Fig. 3-48). The degree of molecular polarity has an important bearing on the behaviour of substances. We will see that the solubility of ionic and certain molecular compounds in water can be partially explained in terms of the high polarity of water molecules.

In this chapter, we developed a covalent-bond model that enables us to predict the characteristics and shapes of molecules. We concluded our discussion of covalent bonds by showing that all covalent bonds have a partial ionic character.

We will now extend our discussion of bonding to include the ionic bonds associated with ionic crystals. We will also discuss molecular aggregates, network solids and metallic crystals, and investigate the nature of intermolecular forces.

Figure 3-48
Water and ammonia both contain polar bonds oriented in such a way that the polarities do not cancel each other. The black arrows indicate the individual polar bonds; the red arrows indicate the net polarity of the molecules.

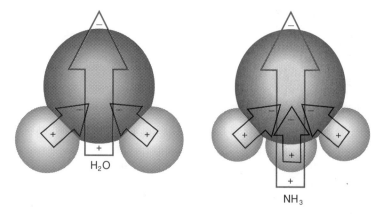

LASERS: A CHEMIST'S TOOL

From light shows at rock concerts to bar-code readers in supermarkets; from compact-disc players to sophisticated tools for eye surgery—lasers play an increasingly important role in our lives.

The first lasers, called masers, were built in the 1950s and generated electromagnetic radiation of microwaves. By 1960, optical lasers, capable of emitting beams of visible light of a specific wavelength, were being produced. In 1984, the first X-ray laser was constructed, producing photons of a very short wavelength. To understand the most recent developments in laser technology, it is important to understand the principles behind the workings of a conventional laser.

Lasers rely on a high-voltage current that excites, or pumps, an electron in an atom or molecule from its ground state to a higher energy level. When the electron decays to a lower level, it loses energy and emits a photon of energy (a quantum of light) equivalent to the energy difference between the two levels. Lasers have three requirements: an active medium, for example, a material with two energy levels; a means of exciting the electrons to higher energy levels while leaving the lower energy levels empty; and a means of resonant feedback to amplify the light emitted. Hence, the acronym *laser*, for *l*ight *a*mplification by *s*timulated *e*mission of *r*adiation.

Chemists use lasers in a variety of ways. Spectroscopic applications of lasers allow the study of solvation of free electrons, transition and decay processes of excited molecules and photoexcitation of complex molecules. Resonance-ionization spectroscopy uses a laser that has a set of specific wavelengths and is tuned to resonate with characteristic wavelengths of a particular atom or molecule. This causes the light to ionize or remove an outer-level electron of the atom or molecule. The ionized atom or molecule now has a net electric charge and can be separated from the mixture with the application of an electric field. Resonance-ionization spectroscopy can be used to analyse trace elements in natural materials such as seawater, to detect trace levels of impurities in "pure" elements and to study short-lived radioactive nuclei.

Laser photochemistry is another method of studying specific aspects of chemistry. In this method, the laser is used to excite one specific energy level in a molecule. This allows reactions between excited molecules to take place, resulting in different products than occur in reactions between unexcited molecules. Ultimately, laser photochemistry can selectively drive reactions, influence the course of chemical reactions, change the yield of products and cause the dissociation of molecular species.

As laser technology improves, the disciplines to which they can be applied expand. X-ray lasers may soon be used to construct holograms of chemical molecules and biological cells. Called *interferograms*, these three-dimensional maps of molecules may allow scientists to study, for example, the structure of DNA sequencing in order to improve medical diagnostic procedures. As well, lasers are already being used in surgical procedures. For example, in the treatment of angioplasty, high-powered lasers emit photons, which remove the plaque built up in human arteries.

In addition to improving the technology of lasers, scientists have investigated using the energy from chemical reactions in order to power lasers. With lasers being used to further the study of chemistry, great strides in the comprehension of certain chemical reactions can be expected to have important ramifications on various industries.

The study of lasers is a consistently exciting and changing discipline. We can expect to see the technology of lasers constantly improve as their influence on our lives continues to grow.

QUESTIONS

1. Identify two repulsive forces and two attractive forces that influence the formation of chemical bonds between two atoms.

2. Energetically speaking, which is the more stable, hydrogen atoms or a hydrogen molecule? Explain.

3. Where are the bonding electrons most likely to be found in a diatomic covalent molecule such as H_2 or Cl_2?

4. Describe qualitatively why two hydrogen atoms form an H_2 molecule while helium remains monatomic.

5. Explain why it is not possible to describe the bonding of compounds in terms of purely ionic or purely covalent bonds.

6. Explain what is meant by a *polar bond*.

7. Which of these bonds is most polar and which is least: S—O, Cl—Cl or Cl—O? Justify your arrangement.

8. Which has the greater degree of ionic character, an N—F bond or an Se—F bond? Explain.

9. Which bond is the more polar in each of the following pairs?
   a) H—O or S—O
   b) H—O or H—S
   c) B—O or C—O
   d) N—Cl or N—F
   e) Sn—Cl or P—Cl

10. Which of the bonds in question 9 has the smallest partial ionic character?

11. (a) What is meant by *octet structure*?
    (b) What evidence indicates that octet structures might be more stable than others?

12. Draw electron-dot structures of
    (a) SO_3^{2-}, (b) ClO_4^-, (c) ClO_3^-, (d) CCl_4,
    (e) N_2, (f) NCl_3, (g) BrCl, (h) BeO, (i) SeF_6,
    (j) OF_2, (k) HOCl, (l) HCN, (m) BrO_3^-,
    (n) SiO_2.

13. What reasons can you give for thinking that triple bonds are shorter and stronger than double or single bonds?

14. (a) In which is the bond distance the greater, C—N or C≡N? (b) In which is the bond energy (strength) the greater, C—N or C≡N?

15. Phosphorus forms PCl_3 and PCl_5. Nitrogen forms NCl_3 but not NCl_5. Explain why NCl_5 does not exist.

16. What is meant by *co-ordinate covalent bond*?

17. (a) Draw a Lewis structure for a hydronium ion (H_3O^+) and identify the co-ordinate bond. (b) In this ion, how does the strength of the co-ordinate bond differ from the other bonds?

18. (a) What is meant by *resonance*? (b) In what situations does the concept apply?

19. a) What experimental evidence indicates that the Lewis structure does not represent the structure of a nitrate ion accurately?
    b) Draw two Lewis stuctures for a nitrate ion.
    c) What are the structures called?
    d) What is a nitrate ion called in valence-bond terminology?
    e) Would a nitrate ion be more or less energetically stable than the structures represented in (b)?

20. Explain what is meant by a *polar molecule*.

21. Must a polar molecule contain a polar bond?

22. It is possible for a nonpolar molecule to contain polar bonds? Explain using examples.

23. How can you explain the fact that HF is polar while H_2 and F_2 are not?

24. a) Would you predict SiF_4 to be polar or nonpolar? Justify your answer.
b) Is the Si—F bond polar or nonpolar? Justify your answer.
c) Explain why your answers to (a) and (b) are consistent.

25. Since there is a difference in electronegativity between carbon and bromine, how can you explain the lack of polarity in the compound CBr_4?

26. What are the approximate bond angles in the following?
(a) NO_3^-, (b) SiF_4, (c) PH_3, (d) CO_3^{2-},
(e) SO_3^{2-}, (f) SO_3, (g) $Co(NH_3)_6^{2+}$

27. Explain why you would expect a BeF_2 molecule to be linear but an SF_2 molecule to be angular.

28. Predict the shapes of (a) PH_3, (b) PH_4^+,
(c) SeF_6, (d) SO_3^{2-}, (e) BrO_3^-, (f) CCl_4,
(g) CaH_2, (h) H_2S, (i) $Fe(CN)_6^{3-}$, (j) PO_4^{3-}.

29. Which of the neutral molecules in question 28 are dipoles?

30. a) How do you explain the existence of a Cl_2O molecule when both chlorine and oxygen have common negative oxidation states?
b) What is the shape of the molecule?
c) Is the molecule polar or nonpolar?
d) If polar, which end of the molecule has the partial negative charge?
e) What is the oxidation state of each atom in the molecule?

f) Draw the Lewis structure for the molecule.

31. (a) Do NH_3 and BF_3 have the same shape? Explain. (b) Can both NH_3 and BF_3 form co-ordinate covalent bonds? Explain any differences.

32. Aluminum(III) ions react with water molecules and form a species known as a *complex ion*. The formula of the ion is $Al(H_2O)_6^{3+}$.
a) How many water molecules are bonded to an Al^{3+} ion?
b) Draw a Lewis structure for the complex ion.
c) Which is the electron-pair acceptor—the Al^{3+} ion or the water molecules (H_2O)?
d) What is the shape of this ion?

33. What shapes are associated with the following hybrid orbitals?
(a) sp, (b) sp^2, (c) sp^3, (d) sp^3d^2

34. (a) How would you designate the hybrid orbitals formed by "mixing" one d, one s and two p orbitals? (b) How many of the hybrid orbitals would be formed by the mixing?

35. If nitrogen, carbon and oxygen all form sp^3 orbitals, what reason can you give for NH_3 and H_2O being polar while CH_4 is not?

36. The bond angles in NH_3, H_2O and CH_4 are 107°, 104.5° and 109.5°, respectively. How can these values be justified if sp^3 orbitals are involved in each case?

Ceramic tiles on the surface of the space shuttle prevent it from burning up like a meteor as it re-enters the earth's atmosphere at high speed.

AGGREGATES: BONDING AND PROPERTIES

Most of the pure substances used in laboratory experiments are either solids or liquids at ordinary room conditions. The smallest measurable quantity of a solid or liquid contains countless atoms, molecules or ions. Thus, when we describe the physical properties of a pure substance, we do not refer to those of individual particles but, rather, to those of an *aggregate* of particles (atoms, molecules or ions) that are held together by attractive forces (chemical bonds). For example, we cannot say that a sodium atom has a melting point of 97.5°C, that a sulfur atom is yellow or that a chlorine molecule has a density of 1560 kg/m³ at −30°C. It is true, however, that metallic crystals of sodium do melt at 97.5°C, that nonmetallic crystals of sulfur are yellow and that liquid chlorine at −30°C has a density of 1560 kg/m³.

One of the objectives of this chapter is to relate the physical properties of aggregates to the nature of the particles of which they are composed, and to the relative strength of the attractive forces that exist between the particles. We will develop models of aggregates that will help us explain the wide variation of physical properties exhibited by various pure substances. These models will allow us to qualitatively answer such questions as: Why is the

An aggregate is any solid or liquid made up of millions of atoms, molecules or ions chemically bonded in a repeating structure. Gases are not aggregates but consist of individual atoms or molecules.

melting point of helium less than $-272°C$ while that of tungsten is greater than $3400°C$? How is it that sodium (Na) conducts electricity in both the solid and liquid phases, chlorine (Cl_2) does not conduct electricity in any phase, but sodium chloride (NaCl) conducts electricity only in the liquid phase? How can we explain the waxiness of a candle, the brittleness of a salt crystal and the ductility of copper?

To develop generalizations that can be applied to large numbers of substances, we classify substances in terms of the structural units that make up the aggregates and the type of bond or force that exists between the units. The classification scheme is summarized as follows:

1. *Ionic substances*. Examples are NaCl, K_2SO_4, $Cu(NO_3)$ and BaO. The structural units that make up ionic solids are *oppositely charged ions*. The force of attraction between the ions is called an *ionic bond*.

2. *Molecular substances*. The structural units of molecular solids are either *nonpolar* or *polar molecules*. Examples of the former are sulfur (S_8) and methane (CH_4). Examples of the latter are water (H_2O) and sugar ($C_{12}H_{22}O_{11}$). The attractive forces between the molecules themselves are called *intermolecular forces*.

3. *Network, or macromolecular, solids*. These substances can be visualized as a gigantic network of atoms held together by *covalent bonds*. Examples are diamond, quartz and graphite.

4. *Metallic substances*. Examples are sodium (Na), iron (Fe) and copper (Cu). The structural units that make up metallic solids are atoms (positive ions). The atoms are held together by *metallic bonds*.

Let us first examine ionic substances and investigate their properties. We will then develop an ionic-bond model that will account for these properties.

IONIC SUBSTANCES

4-1
Identifying Ionic Substances

Ionic substances form most readily between Group IA elements (metals) and Group VIIA elements (nonmetals).

An ionic substance is formed when a positive ion (cation) and a negative ion (anion) attract each other. In our study of periodic properties, we found that all Group IA elements (metals) have relatively low ionization energies and high electron affinity, and are thus able to lose electrons and form cations. Group VIIA elements, on the other hand, have relatively high ionization energies and low electron affinity, and are thus able to gain electrons and form anions. We can predict, therefore, that the elements from these two groups would tend to react and form stable compounds in which the bonds have a high degree of ionic character. This is also true, to a lesser extent, for the elements in Groups IIA and VIA. In the binary ionic compounds containing elements from these groups, the ions have the characteristic octet structure of noble-gas atoms. It should be noted, however, that not all ions have this configuration. Notable exceptions are the ions formed by the atoms of the transition elements. These atoms may transfer their outer s electrons but, because of the presence of underlying d orbital electrons, form ions having as many as 18 electrons in the outer energy level.

Electron Affinity
Elements, other than noble gases, that have high ionization energies readily form negative ions. In doing so, they achieve the electron configuration of the noble gases. The exothermic processes that the elements (X^0) undergo can be represented as

$$X^0 + e^- \longrightarrow X^- + energy$$

The energy released when a neutral atom in the vapour state accepts an electron is called the *electron affinity*. The electron affinity determines how easily an atom forms a negative ion.

4-2
Properties of Ionic Substances

Ionic substances tend to have relatively high melting and boiling points, do not conduct electricity in the solid phase, are not very volatile, are brittle and are soluble in water.

The properties of sodium chloride (Fig. 4-1) and most other compounds known as salts cannot be explained in terms of molecules. The electrolysis of liquid sodium chloride provides indirect evidence that the liquid is composed of charged particles. X-ray diffraction provides additional evidence that the basic structural units of solid crystals are oppositely charged ions. Laboratory experiments reveal that, in general, ionic substances are characterized by the following properties:

1. In the solid phase at room temperature, they do not conduct an appreciable electric current.

2. In the liquid phase, they are relatively good conductors of an electric current.

3. They have relatively high melting and boiling points. There is a wide variation in the properties of different ionic compounds. For example, potassium iodide (KI) melts at 686°C and boils at 1330°C, while magnesium oxide (MgO) melts at 2800°C and boils at 3600°C. Both KI and MgO are ionic substances.

4. They have relatively low volatilities and low vapour pressures. In other words, they do not vaporize readily at room temperatures.

(a)

(b)

Figure 4-1
Sodium chloride. (a) Ordinary table salt processed and purified by industry. (b) Laboratory-grown cubic crystal of NaCl.

Stability is a relative term that applies to a specific process. Because a relatively large amount of heat energy is required to disrupt their lattice structure, most ionic crystals are said to be stable with respect to their conversion into the liquid or vapour phases.

It should be noted that certain ionic crystals containing polyatomic ions are relatively unstable with respect to their thermal decomposition into simpler pure substances.

5. They are brittle and easily broken when a stress is exerted on them.

6. Those that are soluble in water form electrolytic solutions, which are good conductors of electricity. There is, however, a wide range in the solubilities of ionic compounds. For example, at 25°C, 0.92 kg of sodium nitrate ($NaNO_3$) dissolves in 1.00 kg of water, while only 2×10^{-6} kg of $BaSO_4$ dissolves in the same mass of water.

These properties suggest that most ionic crystals are energetically stable and that the ionic bond is a relatively strong chemical bond. Let us examine a typical ionic substance for clues that will help us identify which atoms in the periodic table are most likely to be found in ionic substances, and also help us to explain the relatively high stabilities of the compounds.

4-3

Ionic Bonds

The forces of attraction between the positive and negative ions in an ionic crystal constitute ionic bonds.

Consider sodium chloride (NaCl). When metallic sodium is heated in an atmosphere of chlorine gas, a white crystalline solid consisting of positive sodium and negative chloride ions is formed. The existence of these ions in the crystal suggests that the net overall reaction involves the transfer of an electron from a neutral sodium atom to a neutral chlorine atom. We can use the concepts of ionization energy, electron affinity and electronegativity to interpret this observation. We would expect atoms with high electron affinities or high electronegativities to remove electrons from atoms with low ionization energies or low electronegativities. Thus, when chlorine atoms (electronegativity 3.0) collide with sodium atoms (electronegativity 0.9), there can be sufficient overlap of the electron clouds for the 3s electron of sodium to have a stronger attraction to the chlorine nucleus than to its own nucleus. Thus, in this reaction (Fig. 4-2), the single electron in the 3s orbital of a sodium atom is transferred to the half-filled 3p orbital of a chlorine atom.

Recall that *ionization energy* is the energy required to remove the most loosely held electron from an atom. *Electronegativity* is the relative power of an atom to attract shared electrons in a covalent bond.

Each ion formed in the reaction has an octet structure and represents an electrically charged particle surrounded by a non-directional electric field uniformly distributed about the ion. In our model, *an ion can be visualized as a spherical particle whose charge is concentrated at the centre of the sphere*.

It should be noted that in our model of the formation of sodium chloride, energy is absorbed to remove the 3s electron from a sodium atom to form a sodium ion, Na^+. Energy is released when a

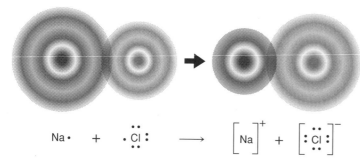

Figure 4-2
When sodium reacts with chlorine, ions are formed that have the same electron configuration as a noble gas. Note that an Na$^+$ ion is smaller than an Na atom, and a Cl$^-$ ion is larger than a Cl atom.

chlorine atom picks up this electron to form a chloride ion, Cl$^-$. Electrostatic attraction between the Na$^+$ and Cl$^-$ ions results in an ionic solid with relatively lower energy than the initial sodium metal and chlorine gas. Thus, the formation of an NaCl solid is an energy-releasing, or exothermic, process, and the compound is thermally stable. The coalescing of positive and negative ions leads to a lower-energy, more stable aggregation called an *ionic crystal*. The forces of attraction between the positive and negative ions in an ionic crystal constitute *ionic bonds*. This force of attraction between the ions accounts for the high stability of the crystal. This implies that ionic bonds are formed in response to the attractive forces between ions rather than in response to any tendency to form an octet or noble-gas structure.

4-4
The Lattice Structure of Crystals

Crystals consist of a pattern of repeating unit cells. The structures of various crystals are related to the types of bonds between atoms and the relationship between repeating units. Most solids, including ionic substances, have a crystalline shape (Fig. 4-3). A ***crystal*** is defined as a periodic arrangement of units, with the simplest repeating unit called the *unit cell*. Crystals are formed when the unit cells are arranged on top of each other. The positions of atoms or ions are represented by *lattice points* in the crystal. The three-dimensional array of lattice points is known as the *lattice structure*. In nature, crystals consist of unit cells with various lengths, but for our purposes we will consider only cubic unit cells that have equal lengths and angles of 90°.

There are three types of cubic unit cells: simple, face-centred and body-centred. All cubic unit cell types have six cube faces with eight identical atoms or ions in the corners of the cube. However, in both the face-centred and the body-centred unit cells, additional atoms or ions exist in the centre of the structure (Fig. 4-4). Note that these additional atoms or ions are identical to the atoms located in the corners.

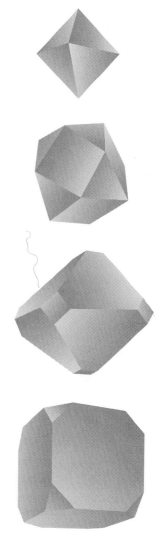

Figure 4-3
Shapes of some common crystals.

Figure 4-4
The three types of cubic unit cells, showing the arrangement of lattice points of atoms or ions. Note that all the atoms or ions are of the same kind; the second colour does not distinguish between atoms and ions.

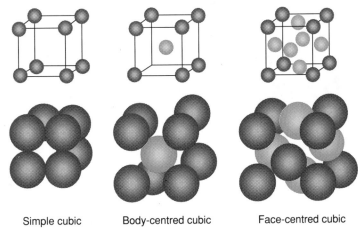

Simple cubic   Body-centred cubic   Face-centred cubic

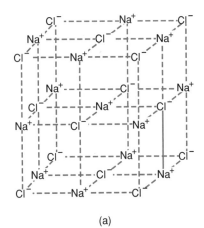

(a)

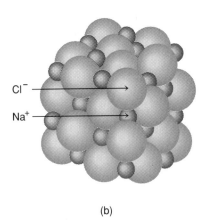

(b)

Figure 4-5
**(a) The lattice structure of a sodium chloride crystal. The symbols represent the location of the nuclei of the atoms in space. The lines that join lattice points do not represent bonds.
(b) Model showing how Na⁺ and Cl⁻ pack in a face-centred cubic crystal.**

The structure of an ionic crystalline solid is related to the structure of the unit cell. The distance between the nuclei of adjacent ions in a crystal (*interionic distance*) is determined by the tendency of the outer electrons to repel each other. The positions of the ions can be determined by X-ray diffraction. We can consider NaCl to be a crystal lattice with Cl⁻ ions defining the face-centred cubic cell and the Na⁺ ions surrounding them (Fig. 4-5). The attractive forces between the particles restrict the particles to a vibratory motion at these points.

The properties of ionic solids depend on the stability of the crystal. The stability of the crystal lattice is measured experimentally in terms of the **crystal-lattice energy**. This is the energy liberated when one mole of an ionic crystal is formed from gaseous ions. The crystal-lattice energy of NaCl is −761 kJ. The negative sign indicates that the process is exothermic and that the energy of the system decreases as the crystal forms. This relatively high value of the crystal energy of NaCl is the reason that NaCl is thermally stable and has a low vapour pressure.

There is a wide range in the physical properties of ionic substances, and these differences can sometimes be accounted for in terms of ionic radii and charge. Later, we will use these concepts to help us explain the differences in solubilities of certain ionic compounds. Let us now examine the role played by ionic radius and charge in determining bond strength and crystal stability.

4-5

Factors Affecting Bond Strength and Crystal Stability

Greater bond strength corresponds to larger crystal-lattice energies and more stable crystal structures.

We have indicated that ions tend to approach each other until the repulsion of their charge clouds causes the potential energy of the system to increase. In a crystal, the interionic distance is the distance between the nuclei of adjacent ions when the potential energy of the system is at a minimum (Fig. 4-6). This distance can be determined by X-ray measurements. By measuring the interionic distances in a number of different crystals formed by an element, and considering various other factors, scientists have been able to determine what fraction of the internuclear distance is occupied by each ion. Thus, values for the radii of most ions have been calculated and tabulated.

The force of attraction between ions is determined largely by the radii of and the charges on the ions. Since the charge of an ion acts as though it were concentrated at the centre of the ion, the force of attraction *(F)* between ions may be expressed by the inverse square law:

$$F = kq_1q_2/r^2$$

where k is a constant of proportionality, q_1 and q_2 are the charges of the ions and r is the sum of the radii of the positive and negative ions $(r^+ + r^-)$. One can see that the larger the ionic radius, the greater is the distance between the ions and the smaller is the force of attraction. The bond strength and the stability of the crystal are proportional to this force of attraction. *The greater the attraction, the stronger is the bond and the more stable is the crystal.*

We can illustrate the role played by the ionic radius by comparing sodium chloride with cesium chloride. A cesium ion is much larger than a sodium ion. The distance between the centres of the Cs^+ ions and Cl^- ions in CsCl is much greater than that between the Na^+ ions and Cl^- ions in NaCl. Consequently, the force of attraction between Cs^+ and Cl^- is much less than that between Na^+ and Cl^-. This suggests that the ionic bonds in CsCl are weaker than those in NaCl. *Weaker bonds correspond to smaller lattice energies and less stable structures.* We can conclude correctly that CsCl is less stable than NaCl, and that it is easier to separate a Cs^+ ion from Cl^- in a CsCl crystal than to separate Na^+ from Cl^- in NaCl. On this basis, we can predict that CsCl would have a lower melting point than NaCl.

The dissolving of an ionic substance also involves the separation of ions. Other factors being equal, therefore, the solubility of CsCl should be greater than that of NaCl. The data in Table 4-1 shows that this prediction is correct.

The role played by the charge on the ions in determining bond strength and crystal stability can be shown by comparing magnesium oxide (MgO) and sodium chloride (NaCl). Since the force of attraction between charged particles is proportional to the magnitude of the charges, the attraction between doubly charged

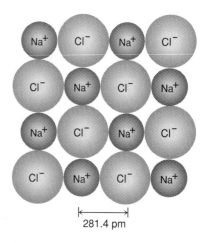

Figure 4-6
Sodium ions and chloride ions pack into a solid crystal in which each sodium ion is in contact with six chloride ions. The distance between the nucleus of any Na⁺ ion and that of any adjacent Cl⁻ ion (interionic distance) is 281.4 pm.

TABLE 4-1
MELTING POINTS AND SOLUBILITIES OF TWO IONIC COMPOUNDS

	Melting Point (°C)	Solubility (kg/kg H₂O, 0°C)
CsCl	646	1.61
NaCl	800	0.357

Experiments show that, in general, solutes composed of polar molecules or of ions are more soluble in polar solvents than in nonpolar solvents. Thus, sugar and salt dissolve in water but not appreciably in benzene. On the other hand, solutes composed of nonpolar molecules have a much greater tendency to dissolve in nonpolar solvents than in polar ones.

TABLE 4-2
MELTING POINTS AND SOLUBILITIES OF TWO IONIC COMPOUNDS

	Melting Point (°C)	Solubility (kg/kg H_2O, 0°C)
MgO	2800	6×10^{-5}
NaCl	800	0.357

magnesium ions and doubly charged oxide ions is greater than that between singly charged sodium and chloride ions. The large lattice energy of MgO is a reflection of this large attractive force and is the main reason that MgO crystals are more stable than NaCl crystals. The melting points and solubilities of the two crystals are shown in Table 4-2.

FOLLOW-UP PROBLEM

Which of the following substances has the higher melting point? Which would you expect to be more soluble in water? (a) NaBr (b) KBr

Answer:

The key difference is the larger ionic radius of the K^+ ions compared with the Na^+ ions. The solubility of KBr will be higher than NaBr, since KBr is less stable than NaBr. The lower stability is due to the greater distance between the centres of the ions in KBr than in NaBr.

4-6

Use of the Ionic-Bond Model to Interpret Properties of Ionic Substances

Certain properties of ionic compounds can be explained by the ionic-bond model.

We can now explain some of the general properties of ionic crystals in terms of their composition and the strong electrostatic forces of attraction between positive and negative ions.

1. *At room temperature, solid ionic crystals do not conduct an appreciable electric current.* The electrons are firmly held by the nuclei of the individual atoms, and the ions are bound together by strong electrostatic attractions. Even under the influence of an applied voltage, the ions are limited to vibratory motion, and both the ions and the electrons are unable to move about to any great extent; therefore, no current can flow.

2. *Melted ionic substances are moderate conductors of electric current.* When heated, the crystals reach a point where their ionic vibrations become so great that they break free from their fixed positions and begin to slide freely over each other, forming a liquid. The temperature at which this change occurs is the *melting point*. In the liquid phase, the mobile ions are free to move under the influence of an applied voltage, and thus an electric current (transfer of charge) results. As noted earlier,

ionic conduction differs in several ways from metallic conduction. In metals, the electric charge is transferred by electrons; because there is more resistance to the flow of ions than to the flow of electrons, metallic substances are much better electric conductors than ionic substances.

3. *Ionic crystals have relatively high melting and boiling points, low volatilities and low vapour pressures*. Ions that are tightly bound by strong attractive forces require relatively large amounts of energy in order to escape from the crystal lattice. In general, ionic crystals composed of small ions with high charges have the highest melting points and lowest vapour pressures. Thus, aluminum oxide (Al_2O_3) melts at 2045°C and has a vapour pressure of only 133 Pa when heated to 2148°C.

4. *Ionic crystals are brittle and easily broken when a stress is exerted on them*. Ionic crystals tend to be hard and brittle because of the nature of the packing. The oppositely charged ions surround each other in the crystal. A stress tending to distort the crystal brings similarly charged ions in contact with one another. The result is repulsion, instability and the breakdown of the crystal (Fig. 4-7).

  These crystals have definite boundaries or planes that intersect at certain precise angles. Thus, when a crystalline solid is split, it fractures (cleaves) along one of these planes, leaving the faces of the crystal at an angle that is characteristic of the given crystal. As an example, this angle is 90° in a sodium chloride crystal.

5. *Many ionic solids composed of polyatomic ions are thermally unstable*. It should be noted that ionic crystals containing a polyatomic ion sometimes decompose when heated. When heated, many salts containing carbonate ions (CO_3^{2-}), bicarbonate ions (HCO_3^-), hydroxide ions (OH^-) and ammonium ions (NH_4^+) can be decomposed to simpler compounds, one or more of which is a gas. The following are general rules that might help you in predicting products of decomposition reactions:
  – Metallic carbonates and bicarbonates usually decompose and form carbon dioxide and a metallic oxide.
  – The decomposition of hydroxides yields metallic oxide ions and water.
  – Ammonium compounds decompose and may produce ammonia gas (NH_3).
  – Metallic nitrates usually decompose and yield oxygen gas, an oxide of nitrogen and a metallic oxide.
  – Metallic chlorates usually decompose and form a metallic chloride and oxygen gas.

The melting point of NaCl is 800°C.

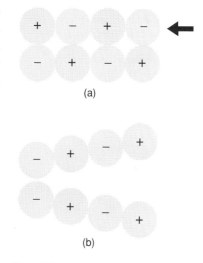

(a)

(b)

Figure 4-7
If a shearing force is applied to an ionic crystal (a), the ions shift in position, and the repulsive forces between similarly charged ions cause the crystal to shatter (b).

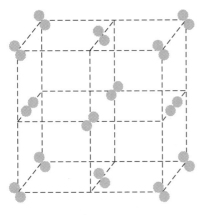

Figure 4-8
Orderly arrangement of I₂ molecules in a crystal of solid iodine. The above lattice structure shows the spatial arrangement of the molecules that occupy the lattice points but does not accurately show the size of the molecules.

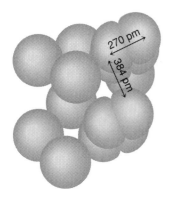

Figure 4-9
Section of crystal showing arrangement of I₂ molecules in iodine.

Intramolecular forces are the forces acting between the atoms of a molecule (covalent bonds). *Intermolecular forces* are the forces acting between molecules (van der Waals, hydrogen bonds).

The equations for the decomposition of several of these thermally unstable salts are given below:

$$CaCO_3(s) + heat \longrightarrow CaO(s) + CO_2(g)$$
$$2NaHCO_3(s) + heat \longrightarrow Na_2CO_3(s) + H_2O(g) + CO_2(g)$$
$$Ca(OH)_2(s) + heat \longrightarrow CaO(s) + H_2O(g)$$
$$NH_4HCO_3(s) + heat \longrightarrow NH_3(g) + H_2O(g) + CO_2(g)$$
$$2Cu(NO_3)_2(s) + heat \longrightarrow 2CuO(s) + 4NO_2(g) + O_2(g)$$
$$2KClO_3(s) + heat \longrightarrow 2KCl(s) + 3O_2(g)$$

FOLLOW-UP PROBLEM

Write equations for the thermal decomposition of
(a) $BaCO_3$, (b) $Ca(HCO_3)_2$, (c) NH_4Cl, (d) $Mg(OH)_2$
and (e) $Zn(NO_3)_2$.

Answers:
a) $BaCO_3(s) + heat \longrightarrow BaO(s) + CO_2(g)$
c) $NH_4Cl(s) + heat \longrightarrow NH_3(g) + HCl(g)$
e) $2Zn(NO_3)_2(s) + heat \longrightarrow 2ZnO(s) + 4NO_2(g) + O_2(g)$

In the last chapter we found that many common substances such as water (H_2O), carbon dioxide (CO_2), ammonia (NH_3), chlorine (Cl_2) and methane (CH_4) are composed of covalent molecules. In the solid phase, these substances are referred to as *molecular crystals*. The properties of these solids are related to the nature (polarity), shape and arrangement of the basic structural units (molecules) that compose the crystal. Let us now look at some general characteristics of these crystals and interpret them in terms of molecular characteristics and intermolecular forces.

MOLECULAR CRYSTALS

4-7

General Properties of Molecular Crystals and Liquids

The properties of molecular crystals suggest that their intramolecular forces are much greater than their intermolecular forces; that they are crystalline solids whose lattice points are occupied by neutral molecules; and that there is a wide variation in the properties of individual molecular substances. Experiments show that, in general, molecular crystals and liquids have the following properties:

1. Neither the solids nor the liquids conduct an appreciable electric current.

2. Many exist as gases at room temperature and atmospheric pressure, and many solids and liquids are relatively volatile.

3. The melting points of the crystals are relatively low.

4. The boiling points of the liquids are relatively low.

5. The solids are generally soft and may have a waxy consistency.

6. A large amount of energy is often required to decompose the substance chemically into simpler substances.

The first observation suggests that ***molecular crystals*** are crystalline solids whose lattice points are occupied by neutral molecules. If the points are occupied by polar molecules, we may call the solid a ***polar molecular crystal***. If the basic structural unit is a nonpolar molecule, then the crystal is called a ***nonpolar molecular crystal*** (Figs. 4-8 and 4-9).

The next four observations suggest that the intermolecular forces are relatively weak compared with the interionic forces in ionic substances (which are usually solids with relatively high melting and boiling points). Thus, the forces between the atoms of a molecule are not very strong.

The last observation indicates that the *intra*molecular forces (covalent bonds) are much greater than the *inter*molecular forces. For example, at a pressure of 101.3 kPa, water undergoes a phase change from liquid to gas at 100°C (the boiling point). However, liquid water does not appreciably decompose into H_2 and O_2 even at 2000°C.

As with ionic substances, there are also wide variations in the properties of individual molecular substances. For example, because of the intermolecular forces between such nonpolar molecules as methane (CH_4), dry ice (solid CO_2) (Fig. 4-10) or iodine (I_2), we would expect such solids to be much more volatile (that is, vaporize more readily) than a polar molecular solid such as ordinary ice (solid H_2O). This is because the attractive forces between nonpolar molecules are weaker than those between polar molecules such as water. It is apparent that properties such as melting and boiling points depend largely on attractions between the molecules and will, therefore, be influenced by the polarities of the individual molecules. As an example, consider solid ammonia (NH_3), an aggregate composed of polar covalent molecules, and methane (CH_4), an aggregate composed of nonpolar molecules. Although their molecular masses do not differ widely (17 u and 16 u respectively), the melting point of solid NH_3 is −77°C, while the melting point of CH_4 is −182°C.

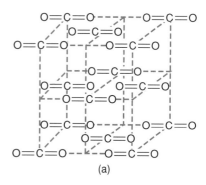

(a)

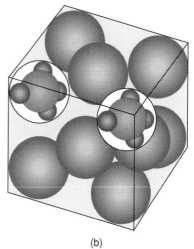

(b)

Figure 4-10
(a) Spatial arrangement of CO_2 molecules in solid CO_2 (dry ice). (b) Space-filling model of solid methane. Each section in the crystal lattice is occupied by a CH_4 molecule. For simplicity, all except two CH_4 molecules are represented by spheres.

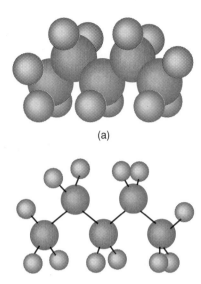

(a)

(b)

Figure 4-11
Two representations of normal pentane: (a) space-filling model, (b) ball-and-stick model.

The Effect of Molecular Shape on Properties

The shape of a molecule affects the physical properties of a molecular solid.

In the case of nonpolar molecular crystals and liquids, the shapes of the molecules play an important role in determining the properties of the substance. To determine the effect of shape we can compare the properties of two different substances composed of nonpolar molecules that differ only in shape. Consider normal pentane and neopentane. These substances, known as *isomers*, have identical molecular formulas (C_5H_{12}). However, they have different shapes and, thus, different properties. Because isomers are identical except in shape and physical properties, it is reasonable to assume that the difference in properties is related to the difference in shape.

Normal pentane boils at 36°C and melts at −130°C, while neopentane boils at 9°C and melts at −20°C. Normal pentane is a linear, chainlike molecule with a zigzag shape (Fig. 4-11). Because there can be a relatively large surface contact between the molecules in the liquid state, forces of attraction are large enough to give a relatively high boiling point. Because of its flexible, chainlike structure, however, it does not easily pack into a regular lattice, so the solid crystal has a relatively low melting point.

Neopentane is a compact, symmetrical, tetrahedral molecule (Fig. 4-12). Thus, it readily packs into a stable crystal lattice and has a relatively high melting point. In the liquid state, the compact molecules do not afford as much surface contact as the chainlike molecules of normal pentane. Hence, the forces of attraction between neopentane molecules are less than those between normal pentane molecules. Consequently, the boiling point of neopentane is lower than that of normal pentane. The characteristics of the two compounds are compared in Table 4-3.

Figure 4-12
Two representations of neopentane (tetramethyl methane): (a) space-filling model, (b) ball-and-stick model.

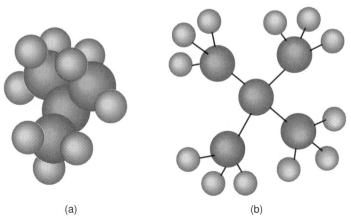

(a)   (b)

TABLE 4-3
CHARACTERISTICS AND PROPERTIES OF NEOPENTANE AND NORMAL PENTANE

Name	Molecular Shape	Surface Contact in Liquid	Crystal Packing in Solid	Melting Point (°C)	Boiling Point (°C)
Normal pentane, C_5H_{12}	zigzag, chainlike	large	noncompact, relatively irregular	−130	36
Neopentane, C_5H_{12}	compact, symmetrical, tetrahedral	small	compact, relatively regular	−20	9

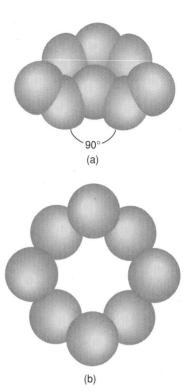

(a)

(b)

Figure 4-13
Two views of an S_8 molecule. Each lattice point in a sulfur crystal is occupied by an eight-membered ring of sulfur atoms. This puckered ring consists of atoms bonded to each other at 90° angles.

Another example of the importance of shape in determining the behaviour of a substance is found in sulfur. Ordinary sulfur, when heated, goes through a series of transformations that can be explained in terms of the puckered-ring structure of a sulfur molecule, whose molecular formula is S_8. This molecule is pictured in Fig. 4-13. At 120°C, sulfur melts, forming a clear, light-yellow, free-flowing liquid (low viscosity). As the temperature rises from 120°C to 200°C, the viscosity increases to the consistency of molasses. The sulfur becomes dark and opaque at the same time. From 200°C to the boiling point of 440°C, the viscosity again decreases. This behaviour is explained by assuming that just above the melting point, the S_8 rings gain enough kinetic energy to slip by and roll over each other easily. As the temperature continues to rise, the rings split into eight-atom chains that may then join and form long open-chain molecules of sulfur atoms; the half-filled orbitals at each end of the sulfur chain enable it to bond covalently to the ends of other chains (Fig. 4-14). The long chains easily become tangled and lose mobility; this represents the viscous stage. Above 200°C, the vibrational kinetic energy becomes sufficiently high so that the chains begin to break into smaller and smaller units, and liquid sulfur becomes lower in viscosity as the temperature continues to rise.

We have demonstrated that the melting and boiling points of molecular substances are influenced by the shape, size and polarity of the molecules and by the symmetry of the crystals. In general, *the melting and boiling points of molecular substances are much lower than those of ionic and metallic substances*. This implies that the forces of attraction between the molecules that occupy the lattice points of a molecular crystal are relatively weak. The weak forces between the molecules in molecular crystals and liquids are called *intermolecular forces*. Let us now examine the nature and origin of these intermolecular forces.

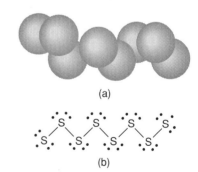

(a)

(b)

Figure 4-14
(a) When sulfur is heated above its melting point, the puckered ring opens and forms chains of sulfur atoms that link together and form large molecules. (b) Electron-dot formula for S_8.

TRIBOLUMINESCENCE, OR THE ELECTRIC LIFESAVER EFFECT

Most children are familiar with the "electric Lifesaver effect"—those bright flashes of light that result when they eat wintergreen-flavoured Lifesavers in the dark. Although such a phenomenon was first reported 400 years ago by Francis Bacon, it is only recently that scientists have been able to explain it.

Chemists discovered long ago that some crystals emit flashes of light when they are crushed. The explanation of this phenomenon, called *triboluminescence*, has come to light only in the 1980s as the result of research conducted by Linda Sweeting, a chemist at Towson State University in Baltimore.

Triboluminescence is the light emitted by the friction between two materials. It has long been known that sugar crystals emit light when crushed. These flashes of light are actually miniature dis-

charges of static electricity. Scientists have also known that wintergreen has its own triboluminescence. Sweeting's research revealed that the wintergreen absorbs the "lightning" given off by the sugar when it is crushed, and re-emits it.

For asymmetric crystals such as ordinary sugar, or for crystals with imperfect structures, a sudden smashing of the crystal results in an unequal distribution of electrons. The crystal cracks, creating pockets of opposite charge. In this unstable situation, the system tries to neutralize itself; the electrons jump across to the pockets of positive charge, just as electrons jump across the air during a thunderstorm. As in a thunderstorm, the electrons collide with nitrogen molecules in the air, exciting them and causing them to emit ultraviolet light (wavelength 300 nm). Sweeting referred to this discharge of energy as "sugar-lightning emissions."

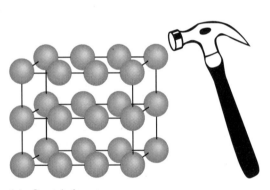

(a) Crystal of sugar

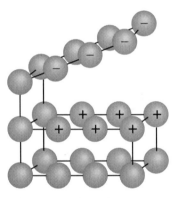

(b) Pockets of like charge, separated by a crack

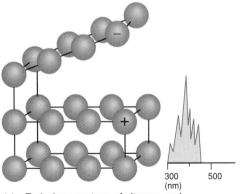

(c) Emission spectrum of nitrogen and absorption spectrum of wintergreen

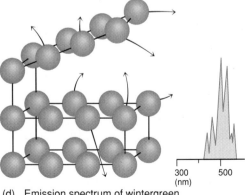

(d) Emission spectrum of wintergreen

Wintergreen, a flavouring obtained from a small plant of the same name, is a fluorescent material. However, wintergreen will not glow unless it absorbs light of a particular wavelength. Sweeting found that the light from the sugar-lightning emissions is at the wavelength required for the wintergreen molecules to fluoresce in the visible spectrum. The greater the proportion of wintergreen present, the greater the number of sugar-lightning emissions that are converted to visible sparks of light. It is obvious that wintergreen-flavoured candies contain a chemical mixture that shows off to advantage the triboluminescence of sugar.

Sweeting's discoveries have unravelled the mystery of a phenomenon that has delighted and perplexed us for years. Her research also paves the way for further investigations into the triboluminescence of other crystals.

INTERMOLECULAR FORCES OF ATTRACTION

Although it is technically proper to refer to all intermolecular forces as van der Waals forces, we will classify intermolecular forces into the following categories:
- dipole forces of attraction
- van der Waals forces
- hydrogen bonds

Hydrogen bonds and dipole forces exist between specific types of *polar molecules*. We will use the term *van der Waals forces* to represent intermolecular forces between *nonpolar molecules*.

4-9

Dipole Forces

Dipole forces are the forces of attraction between polar molecules, and are weak compared with interionic forces.

In Chapter 3 we found that polar molecules are characterized by an asymmetrical distribution of electron charge that leads to partial positive and negative charges within the molecule. These molecules, in which there is a separation of the centres of the positive and negative charges, are called *dipoles*. In polar molecular crystals, the dipoles line up so that the positive ends of the dipole of one molecule are adjacent to the negative ends of the dipole of another molecule; the positive ends are attracted to the negative ends of the dipole of another molecule (Fig. 4-15). This force of attraction between polar molecules is called a dipole-dipole attraction, or a *dipole force*. The forces of attraction between the partial positive and partial negative charges are relatively weak compared with those between the full charges carried by ions in ionic crystals. Thus, the melting points for polar molecular crystals are much lower than the melting points for ionic crystals. For example, solid phosphorus trichloride (PCl$_3$), a polar molecular crystal, melts at $-112°C$, and sodium chloride (NaCl), an ionic crystal, melts at $901°C$.

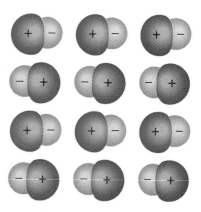

Figure 4-15
Dipole-dipole attraction. This type of intermolecular attraction occurs between molecules with separate centres of positive and negative charge; that is, between polar molecules. In a crystal, the polar molecules are packed so that the positive pole of one molecule is close to the negative pole of an adjacent molecule.

**JOHANNES D. VAN DER WAALS
1837–1923**

Johannes van der Waals was born in the Netherlands and attended the University of Leyden. He taught at Deventer, The Hague, before becoming a professor of physics at the University of Amsterdam.

Van der Waals was interested in the deviations from Boyle's law at higher pressures. His doctoral dissertation, "On the Continuity of the Gaseous and Liquid States," brought him immediate recognition. He introduced two factors in his *equation of state*, which accounted for the deviations in the behaviour of gases. These factors were: the volume occupied by gaseous molecules themselves and the attractive forces between the molecules. The attractive forces between the molecules in a gas are called *van der Waals forces*. Since many chemical phenomena involving solids, liquids and gases require the consideration of these intermolecular forces, the name of van der Waals appears frequently throughout every modern chemistry textbook.

Van der Waals's theoretical calculations and predictions stimulated others to attempt to achieve the liquefaction of the so-called "permanent gases" such as oxygen, nitrogen and nitric oxide. As a result of their investigations, van der Waals made the interesting prediction that the pressure inside a droplet of water is about 1.013×10^6 kPa.

In 1910, van der Waals received the Nobel Prize for physics.

4-10

Van der Waals Forces

Van der Waals forces do not involve ions and are caused by temporarily induced dipoles.

Van der Waals forces exist between nonpolar molecules and are the factors responsible for the existence of the liquid and solid phases of such substances as sulfur, iodine and hydrogen. The type of crystal formed by nonpolar molecular substances is largely a function of the shape of the molecules that make up the crystal. For example, sulfur molecules (S_8) tend to pack together so as to leave as little vacant space as possible, giving rise to *rhombic crystals*. The intramolecular forces (covalent bonds) between sulfur atoms are strong compared with the van der Waals forces between molecules. Thus, sulfur crystals are brittle and readily crushed.

There is no simple way to predict the structure of nonpolar molecular crystals. One-half the distance between nuclei in adjacent molecules in a molecular crystal is known as the *van der Waals radius* of the atom. For comparison, both the van der Waals and covalent radii of chlorine are illustrated in Fig. 4-16. It is evident that the van der Waals radius is almost twice the covalent radius. This supports the observation that covalent bonds between atoms are hundreds of times stronger than van der Waals forces of attraction between molecules.

Unlike dipole forces, van der Waals forces are difficult to visualize. They are caused, in part, by temporarily induced dipole effects created by fluctuations in the density of the electron cloud surrounding a molecule. An interaction with an adjacent molecule produces in it an induced dipole and causes an attractive force to operate between the two nonpolar molecules.

The regular rise in boiling points of closely related compounds such as CH_4, SiH_4 and GeH_4 (Table 4-4) suggests that the magnitude of the van der Waals force is largely determined by the number of electrons and the size and shape of the molecule. The greater the number of electrons and the larger the molecule, the stronger is the attractive force between the molecules. In large molecules, the electron cloud is farther from the nucleus and is more easily distorted by an adjacent dipole than in smaller molecules.

It should be emphasized that the relative melting points of ionic and molecular crystals do not reflect the relative strengths of ionic and covalent bonds. Melting an ionic crystal partially overcomes the ionic forces that constitute an ionic bond. Melting a molecular crystal separates the molecules in the crystal but does not break the covalent bonds between the atoms in the molecules. The lower melting points of molecular crystals simply mean that the force of attraction between molecules in a molecular crystal is less than that between ions in an ionic crystal.

Van der Waals forces or ordinary dipole forces are not strong enough to account for the properties of certain molecular crystals and liquids such as water (H_2O), ammonia (NH_3), hydrogen fluoride (HF) and other substances that contain hydrogen atoms bonded to these three highly electronegative atoms. In addition to ordinary van der Waals forces, molecules in these substances are bonded to one another by hydrogen bonds. We will now investigate the origin and nature of these highly important intermolecular bonds.

TABLE 4-4
BOILING POINTS OF RELATED MOLECULAR COMPOUNDS OF GROUP IVA

Formula	Number of Electrons	Boiling Point (°C)
CH_4	10	−161
SiH_4	18	−112
GeH_4	36	−90
SnH_4	54	−52

4-11
Hydrogen Bonds

Hydrogen bonds are strong intermolecular forces that result from the electrostatic interaction between a hydrogen atom of one molecule and a highly electronegative atom of a second molecule.

Consider the boiling points of the hydrides of the elements in Groups VA, VIA and VIIA, which are listed in Table 4-5 and graphed with those of the hydrides of Group IVA elements in Fig. 4-17. For example, in Group VA, the boiling points of PH_3, AsH_3 and SbH_3 increase with increasing molecular mass; however, NH_3, the lightest molecule in the family, has an unusually high boiling point of −33°C. Thus, NH_3 must not be subjected to the same intermolecular forces as the other molecules. Similarly, the boiling points of H_2O and HF do not conform to the expected trends in boiling points of their families.

The unusually high boiling points of NH_3, H_2O and HF lead us to believe that intermolecular forces in addition to van der Waals or ordinary dipole forces are operating between molecules in these substances. This additional force is explained by the attraction between the extra pair of electrons on the highly electronegative

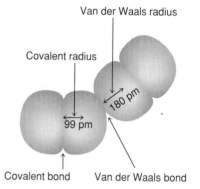

Figure 4-16
The van der Waals radius for chlorine is about twice the covalent radius. The shortest distance between the nuclei of two chlorine atoms in adjacent chlorine molecules is about 360 pm.

TABLE 4-5
BOILING POINTS OF BINARY HYDROGEN COMPOUNDS

Group VA			Group VIA			Group VIIA		
Formula	Number of Electrons	Boiling Point (°C)	Formula	Number of Electrons	Boiling Point (°C)	Formula	Number of Electrons	Boiling Point (°C)
NH_3	10	−33	H_2O	10	100	HF	10	19.4
PH_3	18	−85	H_2S	18	−59.6	HCl	18	−85
AsH_3	36	−55	H_2Se	36	−42	HBr	36	−67
SbH_3	54	−17	H_2Te	54	−1.8	HI	54	−35.5

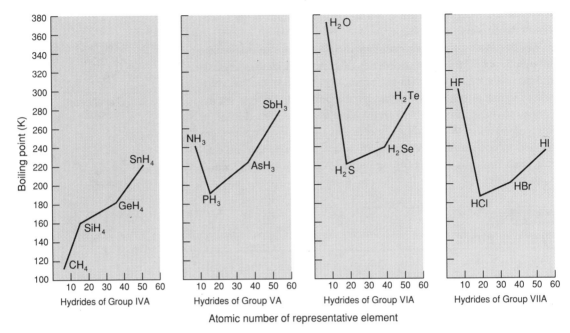

Hydrides of Group IVA   Hydrides of Group VA   Hydrides of Group VIA   Hydrides of Group VIIA

Atomic number of representative element

Figure 4-17
A graphical representation of the boiling points of various hydrides from four groups of elements.

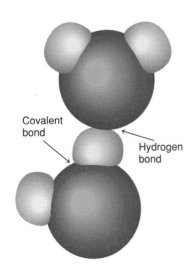

Figure 4-18
A hydrogen atom, covalently bonded to an oxygen atom, is attracted to the unbonded electron pair of the oxygen atom of a water molecule.

atom of one molecule and the hydrogen atom of an adjacent molecule. A highly electronegative atom, such as oxygen, fluorine or nitrogen, very strongly attracts the electrons bonding it to hydrogen atoms. In water, for example, the hydrogen atoms are almost like two exposed protons. Since the hydrogen atoms in these molecules are somewhat similar to positively charged particles, they exert an electrostatic force of attraction on electron pairs of highly electronegative atoms. In water molecules, the hydrogen atoms are joined by strong covalent bonds to an oxygen atom in one molecule and are held by electrostatic attractions to an adjacent molecule (Fig. 4-18). In effect, hydrogen acts as a bridge between two oxygen atoms. We can think of a **hydrogen bond** as an interaction between two molecules or two parts of a single molecule in which a polar hydrogen atom is unequally shared by two atoms. We will not be concerned at this point with intramolecular hydrogen bonds (formed between two parts of the same molecule). Because hydrogen bonds do not involve the sharing of electrons, they cannot be classified as covalent. They do not bind two ions together, so they are not ionic. They are too electrostatic in nature to be van der Waals or ordinary dipole forces. Therefore, they deserve a category of their own.

The energies of hydrogen bonds are, in general, about ten times those of van der Waals forces and approximately one-tenth those of ionic or covalent bonds. The energy needed to break hydrogen bonds, added to the energy required to overcome the van der Waals forces present in water and related compounds, is reflected in the high boiling points of hydrogen-bonded compounds (Fig. 4-19).

It is fortunate for life on earth that water is a polar molecule. If, for example, water were a nonpolar covalent molecule, the boiling point would be below −59°C, the boiling point of H_2S. Thus, no liquid water or ice could exist at the temperatures found on this planet.

Figure 4-19
A glass filled with water above the rim will not overflow because of the high surface tension and strong hydrogen bonding between water molecules.

4-12

Properties of Water and Other Compounds Containing Hydrogen

Hydrogen bonds affect a number of physical properties of molecular solids, including melting and boiling points, density and molar heat of vaporization.

The presence of hydrogen bonds accounts for many of the unique properties of water. For example, hydrogen bonds account for the density of ice being less than that of liquid water. Because of the shape and characteristics of water molecules, hydrogen bonds form at preferred angles. In ice, and partially in liquid water, the water molecules are tetrahedrally oriented to each other (Fig. 4-20). The hydrogen bonds joining adjacent molecules are weaker and longer than regular covalent bonds within a water molecule and give rise to the observed open, cagelike structure of ice. This open structure partially collapses when the ice melts, so that the molecules in the liquid are closer in water than in ice. Hence, the liquid has a greater density than the solid. Without hydrogen bonding, lakes would freeze from the bottom up; relatively shallow lakes would become solid blocks of ice in cold temperatures

Figure 4-20
Water molecules in ice are held together by hydrogen bonds. (a) Each oxygen atom is surrounded tetrahedrally by four hydrogen atoms—two covalently bonded and two hydrogen bonded. Water molecules are also tetrahedrally associated, as in (b). (c) Schematic showing the network of hexagonal corridors in ice crystals.

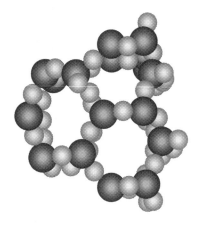

(a)

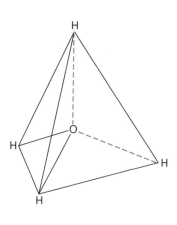

(b)

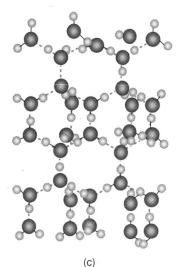

(c)

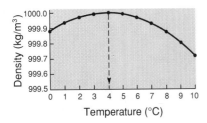

Figure 4-21
**Density-temperature plot for water.
Above 0°C, the open-cage structure
of ice collapses and the density
increases. Above 4°C, the increased
molecular motion causes the
molecules to move apart. Thus, the
density tends to decrease.**

The molar heat of vaporization is the
amount of heat required to vaporize a
mole of liquid already at its boiling
point.

Experimental data indicates that the
solubility of a substance is enhanced
when hydrogen bonding occurs
between the solute and solvent particles. Thus, ammonium compounds
tend to be quite soluble in water.

and, thus, would be unable to support any form of aquatic life. Fortunately, ice forms only on the surface of water, allowing aquatic life to survive during the winter.

The density of most substances decreases when they are warmed. When water at 0°C is warmed, however, the density increases as more hydrogen bonds are broken because the molecules continue to come closer together. Above 4°C, the expansion caused by heating more than compensates for the contraction caused by the breaking of hydrogen bonds. As the temperature rises above 4°C, the density of water gradually decreases. This behaviour is shown graphically in Fig. 4-21.

The strength of the hydrogen bond in ice is approximately 21 kJ/mol of water molecules. The heat required to melt ice at 0°C is only 5.9 kJ/mol. Therefore, less than 30% of the hydrogen bonds are broken when ice melts. This means that considerable hydrogen bonding remains in liquid water. Hydrogen bonding is responsible for the unusually high heat capacity of liquid water when compared with that of other molecular liquids. The high heat capacity means that a relatively large amount of heat must be added to raise the temperature of liquid water and, conversely, a large amount of heat is released when it cools. Thus, water prevents temperature extremes in the surroundings and acts as a modifier of the planet's climate. The unusually high heat of vaporization of water (40.5 kJ/mol) is further evidence of the strength of hydrogen bonds and of the many hydrogen-bonded molecules that remain even at temperatures just below the boiling point of 100°C.

There are many examples of the widespread occurrence and importance of hydrogen bonds. All living organisms contain hydrogen-bonded substances. Linus Pauling showed how hydrogen bonding partially accounts for the structure of proteins. The greater degree of hydrogen bonding in plants and wood makes their fibres more rigid than those of animal tissue. Hydrogen bonds in wood are oriented with the grain rather than across it. This means that a piece of wood is stronger if it is cut with the grain rather than against it. For example, a baseball bat is made by cutting with the grain of a tree, never across it.

Much of our clothing and food is made of hydrogen-bonded materials. Hydrogen bonds are responsible for the stickiness of honey. Both the water and sugar molecules in honey are hydrogen-bonded substances. Sugar molecules have many hydroxyl (—OH) groups protruding at various angles. The oxygen in the hydroxyl groups on one molecule is joined by hydrogen bonds to the hydrogen in neighbouring molecules. Considerable energy is required to break a large number of such bonds. The stickiness, or viscosity, of honey is a reflection of the large number of hydrogen bonds that resist being broken.

In view of the important materials whose properties are related to hydrogen bonding, it is apparent that this intermolecular force is in large measure responsible for the nature of life on earth. In Chapter 5 we will discuss hydrogen bonding in connection with the properties of many organic compounds.

We have learned that molecules are aggregates of a relatively few atoms bonded by covalent bonds. We called these aggregates of molecules *molecular crystals*. When a large number (in the magnitude of one mole) of atoms are bonded together in a crystal by a network of covalent bonds, the solid is called a *network*, or *macromolecular*, *solid*. A number of important and familiar substances fall into this category. For this reason, we will briefly examine the structure, bonding and properties related to this type of aggregate.

NETWORK, OR MACROMOLECULAR, SOLIDS

Network crystals, or macromolecules, consist of a one-, two- or three-dimensional network of atoms that may have the same or different elements joined by single covalent bonds. Examples of network solids include diamond, graphite and asbestos.

4-13
Three-Dimensional Network Solids

Three-dimensional solids are characterized by high melting points and extreme hardness resulting from strong bonds oriented to give the solid a rigid structure.

Examples of three-dimensional network solids are such pure substances as diamond, quartz and silicon carbide (Carborundum), which are highly stable, extremely hard, poor electric conductors and insoluble in most solvents. For example, diamond has the highest Mohs value and Knoop value, as shown in the margin on the next page. Furthermore, these solids have very high melting and boiling points. Diamond has a melting point greater than 3550°C, a boiling point of 4827°C and a density of 3500 kg/m³. These properties suggest that the atoms in a three-dimensional crystal are joined by very strong bonds oriented in such a way as to yield a very rigid structure.

Experimental data reveals that all C—C bond lengths in diamond equal 154 pm, all bond angles are 109°28′ and all carbon-to-carbon bond strengths are equal. Using this data, we can visualize a diamond crystal as a single macromolecule made up of a network of carbon atoms extending uniformly throughout the

DOROTHY CROWFOOT HODGKIN
1910–
Dorothy Crowfoot Hodgkin was born in Cairo, Egypt. As a child, she developed a life-long fascination with the shapes of crystals. This fascination led to her interest in the use of X-ray crystallography.

Hodgkin was educated at Oxford University in England. After graduation she joined the Cavendish Laboratory at Cambridge University from 1932 to 1934 where she developed the techniques of X-ray crystallography into a useful analytical tool. Together with C. H. Carlisle, she correctly analysed cholesterol iodide, the first complex organic molecule to be determined completely from X-ray crystallography. Working with fellow crystallographer, J. D. Bernal, Hodgkin also took the first X-ray diffraction photograph of the protein pepsin.

In 1934, Hodgkin returned to Oxford where she remained until 1970. During the 1940s, Hodgkin used X-ray crystallography to determine the structure of penicillin, an achievement that had an important effect on the development of other antibiotics.

In 1948, Hodgkin investigated the structure of vitamin B_{12} (cyanocobalamin) and in 1957, she announced to the world that she had determined its structure ($C_{63}H_{88}O_{14}N_{14}PCo$). For this work, Hodgkin received the 1964 Nobel Prize in chemistry.

In 1965, Hodgkin became the second woman, after Florence Nightingale, to be admitted to the Order of Merit.

The Mohs scale is a numerical scale from 1 through 10, used in mineralogy to indicate relative hardness. Knoop values of hardness are obtained by pressing a tiny, diamond, wedgelike chisel into the sample with a known force and measuring the length of the impression.

	Mohs Value	Knoop Value
Talc (3MgO·4SiO$_2$·H$_2$O)	1	
Gypsum (CaSO$_4$·2H$_2$O)	2	32
Calcite (CaCO$_3$)	3	135
Fluorite (CaF$_2$)	4	163
Apatite (CaF$_2$·3Ca$_3$(PO$_4$)$_2$)	5	430
Feldspar (K$_2$O·Al$_2$O$_3$·6SiO$_2$)	6	560
Quartz (SiO$_2$)	7	820
Topaz (AlF$_2$SiO$_4$)	8	1340
Silicon carbide (SiC)	9	2480
Diamond (C)	10	7000

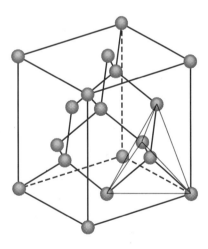

Figure 4-22
Carbon atoms in a diamond crystal. Each carbon atom is bonded covalently to four neighbouring atoms at the corners of a tetrahedron. The diamond structure is characterized by a three-dimensional network of atoms.

entire crystal. Each carbon atom must be at the centre of a tetrahedron whose vertices are occupied by other carbon atoms (Fig. 4-22). In this *three-dimensional network of atoms*, each carbon atom shares its four valence electrons with four other carbon atoms, thus filling all available sp^3 orbitals and providing a stable outer octet of electrons for each atom. The bonding electrons are tightly bound and highly localized. Thus, diamond crystals are poor electric conductors and are transparent. The network of atoms joined by strong, tetrahedrally oriented covalent bonds accounts for the extreme hardness of diamond crystals. The close packing of the small carbon atoms accounts for the high density compared with graphite. When the highly directional bonds in a diamond are distorted by stress, the crystal cleaves. This cleavage is related to the fact that new bonds cannot be formed easily with adjacent atoms, which have already formed bonds in certain preferred directions.

Pure silicon has the same outer-level electron configuration as carbon. Thus, both silicon and carbon form crystalline compounds with the rigid diamond structure. Silicon carbide (SiC), a common abrasive known as Carborundum, and quartz, a form of silicon dioxide (SiO$_2$)$_x$, are examples of three-dimensional covalent crystals. Because of their structural similarity to diamond, they are characterized by extreme hardness and high melting points.

4-14

Two-Dimensional Network Solids

The properties of two-dimensional solids suggest that there is more than one kind of bonding involved and that the bonding is very strong and covalent. Weak van der Waals forces act between the two-dimensional layers.

Graphite, another form of pure carbon, has properties entirely different from those of diamond. Graphite has a high melting and boiling point but is soft and a good conductor of electricity. These properties suggest that this crystal contains more than one kind of bonding. The high melting point reflects strong sigma covalent bonds, and the electric conductivity is characteristic of delocalized, mobile pi electrons. The softness, however, implies that there are some very weak bonds in the crystal. Visual observation of graphite reveals that it has a layered structure (Fig. 4-23). Apparently, the layers are a *two-dimensional network of atoms*. The atoms in the individual layers are bonded to each other by strong covalent bonds. Only weak bonds or forces join adjacent layers, so they move over each other easily. The softness of graphite is a reflection of this layered structure. When a film of gas such as oxygen, nitrogen or air is adsorbed between the layers, the slipperiness of graphite increases. As a result of this softness and slipperiness, graphite is used as a lubricant.

Studies of graphite crystals reveal that the atoms in the individual layers form a hexagonal pattern that involves 120° bond angles. Furthermore, it is found that the distance between the layers is 340 pm, while the distance between the atoms in a given layer is 142 pm. The average C—C single bond length is 154 pm and the average C═C double bond length is 134 pm. This data leads to the conclusion that there are rather weak bonds between the carbon atoms in adjacent layers. The bond distance between atoms within each layer is intermediate between a single and double bond length. This implies that the bonding within a layer involves resonance structures. The hexagonal pattern of carbon atoms in the layers and the delocalized electrons can be explained in terms of sp^2 hybridization similar to that observed in ethene. Within a layer, the overlap of singly occupied sp^2 orbitals yields strong sigma bonds between carbon atoms. Between adjacent layers, the unhybridized, parallel p orbitals overlap laterally and form pi bonds. The electrons forming the pi bonds are delocalized and spread out over the hexagons, where they are mobile and relatively free to move under the influence of electromagnetic radiation (light) or an externally applied electric voltage. In other words, the delocalized electrons account for the electric conductivity and the reflectivity (lustre) of graphite. Alternatively, the weak forces of attraction between the layers are sometimes interpreted as van der Waals attractions.

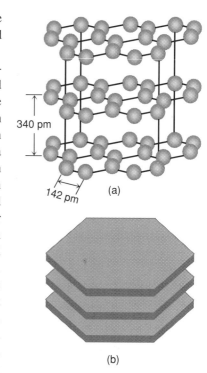

Figure 4-23
(a) Space-filling model of carbon atoms in a graphite crystal. (b) Layers of graphite, which can be obtained by cleaving a graphite crystal with a razor blade.

SILICON: ELEMENT OF THE ELECTRONIC AGE

K nowledge of silicon compounds is as old as civilization. Sand, quartz, clay—all the various forms of silica (SiO_2) and silicates—have been used for building materials and pottery for thousands of years. Silicon, contained in igneous rocks, is the second most abundant element (28%) in the earth's crust after oxygen (46%).

Chemical knowledge of silicon dates from 1824 when it was first identified as an element. Like carbon, silicon has four unpaired outer electrons; however, silicon is more electropositive than carbon and does not readily form the large molecules that are characteristic of organic compounds. The crystalline structure of silicon is similar to diamond, although silicon has some metallic properties. Substances such as silicon and germanium, and compounds such as cadmium sulfide and gallium arsenide, are known

as *semiconductors*; their properties are intermediate between metals and nonmetals.

The properties of silicon are most easily understood if we compare its structure with that of metals. Metals are good conductors of heat and electricity because the electrons are free to move about the atoms in a mobile sea. A crystal of silicon, however, is a poor conductor of electricity because the electrons are not mobile. This lack of mobility relates to the four covalent bonds formed by the valence electrons with neighbouring atoms. However, the addition of certain impurities such as boron or arsenic—in a process called *doping*—can increase the conductivity of silicon by providing it with extra electrons.

Doping silicon with an element such as arsenic or phosphorus, each of which contains five outer electrons, produces an *n-type semiconductor*. Because only four of the outer electrons are needed to bond to the silicon atoms, the "extra" electron is free to flow around the crystal. When silicon is doped with a trivalent element such as gallium or boron, the three valence electrons bond with the silicon to produce a *p-type semiconductor*. At the position of the fourth electron, there is an electron deficiency called a *positive hole*.

Both n-type and p-type semiconductors are good conductors of electricity. If an electric potential is applied to an n-type semiconductor, the mobile electrons move in the direction of the electric field. When a potential is applied to a p-type semiconductor, the electrons flow to fill the holes in the opposite direction of the electric field; that is, the holes provide a path for the electrons to move through the crystal.

When n-type and p-type semiconductors come into contact, they form a *junction*. Because silicon can be doped to produce n-type and p-type semiconductors in different areas on the same surface, these combinations of n-p junctions have had an important impact on the electronics industry. For example, in an n-p junction, the extra electrons in the n-type area are attracted to the positive holes in the p-type area and will move from one region to the other. Thus, the n-type area becomes positively charged from the loss of electrons, while the p-type area becomes negatively charged from the influx of electrons, until the buildup of charge prevents further migration of electrons between areas. At this point, the area near the boundary, called the *depletion region*, is devoid of extra electrons and holes and is similar to pure silicon. Thus, it is able to act as an insulator. If a potential is applied with the negative to the n-type semiconductor and the positive to the p-type semiconductor, the electrons will move out of the depletion region and continue to move from the n-type area to the p-type area. If a potential is applied in the opposite direction, both the extra electrons and the holes are pulled to the opposite ends of the crystal. Consequently, the size of the depletion region increases and the current does not flow. Thus, an n-p junction is a conductor in one direction and an insulator in the other.

In the early part of the twentieth century, this control of the flow of electric current was accomplished by the use of vacuum tubes. Recently, components made from silicon have almost completely replaced those large, expensive, power-hungry devices. The n-p junctions are used in diodes, transistors, rectifiers and microchips. Silicon is essential in modern information storage and data processing. As the technology of doping has advanced, smaller and smaller chips have been produced.

Silicon can be doped with a variety of different substances to produce crystals with countless properties. Photosensors used in thermographs and infrared cameras contain crystals whose electric properties change in the presence of a particular wavelength of light. Solar cells in watches and calculators use silicon crystals to generate small amounts of electric power. At different temperatures, specially designed crystals radiate light of a specific wavelength, and can thus be used in temperature indicators. Changes in pressure can cause changes in the electric properties of crystals, making them a useful component in pressure-measuring devices.

New uses for silicon will continue to appear as technology advances. Because of its unique position between metals and nonmetals, conductors and insulators, small-sized atoms and large-sized atoms, silicon has become the wonder element of the electronic age.

Si crystal

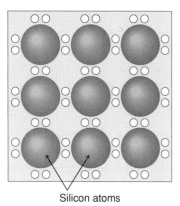

Silicon atoms

n-type semiconductor

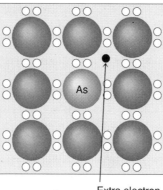

Extra electron

p-type semiconductor

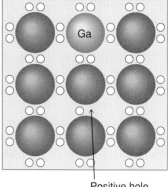

Positive hole

(a)

4-15
One-Dimensional Network Solids

One-dimensional solids include asbestos and are fibrous in character.

The analysis of asbestos and asbestos-type minerals reveals that they are composed of silicon, oxygen and certain metallic elements such as magnesium and calcium. The fibrous nature and other properties of these minerals lead us to conclude that they consist of a one-dimensional network of atoms. In these crystals, the silicon and oxygen atoms form long chains with metal atoms associated with the chains (Fig. 4-24). The atoms within the chain are held together by strong covalent bonds. The forces between the adjacent parallel chains are relatively weak, resulting in a substance with a threadlike structure.

We have now discussed ionic bonds, covalent bonds and intermolecular bonds. As a result of our study we can make the following generalizations:

1. Ionic bonds exist between atoms with low electronegativities (metals) and those with high electronegativities (nonmetals).

2. Polar covalent bonds exist between dissimilar atoms with different electronegativities.

3. Nonpolar covalent bonds exist between identical nonmetallic atoms.

4. Dipole forces exist between most polar molecules.

5. Hydrogen bonds exist between those polar molecules containing a hydrogen atom covalently bonded to a highly electronegative atom such as fluorine, oxygen or nitrogen.

6. Van der Waals forces exist between all molecules but are the only forces that exist between nonpolar molecules.

Examination of the list above reveals that we have not accounted for the bonds that exist between metallic atoms. We will now discuss the properties and bonding related to an aggregate of metallic atoms. Such an aggregate is called a *metallic crystal*.

METALLIC CRYSTALS AND METALLIC BONDS

Approximately 80% of all the elements are metals. The properties of individual metals vary to a great extent. Because of this, they serve many useful purposes. Gold, silver, platinum and iridium are

(b)

(c)

Figure 4-24
(a) Asbestos is a fibrous mineral consisting of chains of alternating silicon and oxygen atoms. Calcium or magnesium atoms are associated with the chains. (b) Asbestos fibres. (c) Asbestos is widely used in building construction as a fire retardant and insulator. Recent concerns about asbestos-related diseases have led to a U.S. ban on asbestos, most of which is manufactured in Quebec. Airborne asbestos particles can accumulate in human lungs because they are not expelled and do not dissolve. Long-term exposure to high concentrations of asbestos dust can cause the lung disease *asbestosis*. There is no evidence that exposure to asbestos poses any danger to the general public.

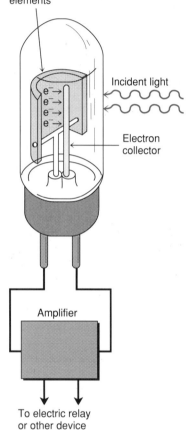

Curved plate coated
with Cs, Rb or a
compound of these
elements

Incident light

Electron
collector

Amplifier

To electric relay
or other device

Figure 4-25
**A photoelectric cell. Because they
have very low first-ionization energies, rubidium and cesium are used in
photoelectric cells, commonly called
"electric eyes." In such a cell, an
evacuated tube is covered on one
side with cesium metal or with certain
compounds of rubidium or cesium.
When light strikes the coating, electrons are ejected and give rise to an
electric current, which activates
mechanical devices.**

used in valuable jewellery. Copper and aluminum are used in electric wire, and iron is used as the structural backbone of our buildings and bridges. Although some of these metals have been known and used for thousands of years, it has only been in the last 100 years that scientists have developed theories that help explain many of their properties.

4-16
Properties of Metals

Metals have a characteristic set of properties that cannot be accounted for by pure covalent bonds, ionic bonds or van der Waals forces.

Most metals are characterized by the following properties:

1. *Lustre, or reflectivity.* Freshly cleaned metallic surfaces are good reflectors of light. Most metals reflect all frequencies of visible light and appear silvery white under white light.

2. *High electric conductivity.* Metals such as copper and alumi- num are used in electric cables because of their outstanding ability to conduct an electric current. When a small difference in voltage is maintained in a metal, a relatively large current flows through the metal. This flow of current represents the passage of electrons through the metal. The passage of current does not cause any change in the composition of the metal as it does when it passes through melted ionic substances or solutions.

3. *High heat conductivity.* Aluminum cookware and copper-plated pans have long been used as cooking utensils because of their outstanding ability to conduct heat. In contrast, most nonmetals (such as sulfur) and compounds (such as water) are poor con- ductors of heat and electricity. *The best electric conductors are the best heat conductors.* This implies that the two properties may be related to a common factor.

4. *Workability.* Most metals can be hammered into sheets (mallea- bility), drawn into wires (ductility) or formed into various shapes without shattering. This is not true of most other pure substances.

5. *Electron emission caused by heat or light.* When metals are heated or when their surfaces are exposed to sufficiently short wavelengths of light, they emit electrons. Vacuum tubes and photoelectric cells used in automatic door-openers and other electronic devices use this property of metals (Fig. 4-25).

These properties cannot be accounted for in terms of pure covalent bonds, ionic bonds or van der Waals forces. The existence of such bonds in metallic crystals can be discounted on the basis of the following observations:

1. *Covalent bonds are directional with fixed lengths*. Such bonds would resist the deformation that takes place when a stress is applied during the working of metals. Because the electrons in covalent bonds are tightly bound and highly localized, they do not readily conduct electricity or heat or reflect light.

2. *Ionic bonds, although non-directional, resist deformation, while metallic bonds do not*. When stress is applied to an ionic substance, ions of like charge come into contact, causing a high-energy, unstable situation that causes the shattering of the crystal. Substances containing ionic bonds do not conduct an appreciable electric current, nor do they reflect much light. The electrons are strongly attracted by the nuclei of the respective ions and are not free to move throughout the crystal under the influence of applied voltage or light energy.

3. *Van der Waals forces can be discounted as a significant factor because of the relatively weak nature of these forces*. The melting points of most metals are far too high to be explained in terms of the relatively weak van der Waals attractions.

4-17
Metallic Bonds

The bonds in metals are characterized by the electrostatic attraction between mobile electrons and atomic kernels.

Most observable properties of substances can be interpreted in terms of three atomic characteristics: outer-level electron configurations, ionization energies and atomic radii. These characteristics are related to the nature of the bond between the atoms of the aggregate. Let us first look for features common to all metallic atoms. Then we will determine the manner in which these characteristics can be used to develop a model of metallic bonding that will explain the observed properties of metals. Examination of the electron configurations and the ionization energies of atoms of substances with metallic properties reveals two common features: a number of vacant orbitals and low ionization energies.

Consider the element sodium, whose atoms meet these requirements. A sodium atom has only one electron in its outer energy level and a low ionization energy, indicating that the $3s$ electron is rather loosely bound. X-ray diffraction shows that each sodium atom in the solid crystal is surrounded by eight other sodium atoms. Each has one electron and several vacant orbitals in the third energy level.

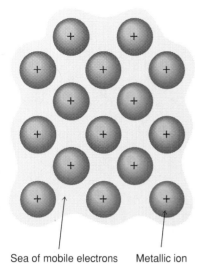

Sea of mobile electrons   Metallic ion

Figure 4-26
A metal consists of positive metallic ions arranged in a "sea" of highly mobile electrons. The metallic bond is the result of the attraction between the positively charged kernels and the surrounding electrons.

There are not enough valence electrons for each sodium atom to form a covalent bond with all of its neighbours—each atom would need eight electrons to form covalent bonds with each of its eight neighbours. Therefore, the single, loosely held electron from each atom remains delocalized in the region between the atoms. The space about each of the atoms is subject to the same positive nuclear charge. The space between the atoms, therefore, represents a region of uniformly low potential energy for the negative electrons. Any 3s electron in the crystal can move easily through this region of low potential energy, which extends throughout the crystal. In other words, the outer, loosely bound electrons of atoms in a metallic crystal are not localized but are free to move throughout the crystal.

In a metallic crystal, each atom contributes its outer electrons to the common pool of electrons that extends uniformly throughout the crystal. The contribution of the outer-shell electrons by each atom leaves a positive ion, or positive atomic kernel, occupying a latttice point of the crystal. The electrostatic attraction between the mobile electrons and the atomic kernels gives rise to the ***metallic bond***. The structure of a metallic crystal and the nature of the metallic bond are shown in Fig. 4-26 and summarized below.

1. Metallic crystals consist of a three-dimensional, closely-packed latticework of atomic kernels surrounded by a sea of delocalized, mobile valence electrons.

2. The electrons can move throughout the crystal rather like gas molecules confined in a container. The electrons are held within the metal by the attraction of the positive atomic kernels.

3. The atomic kernels are held together by the electrostatic attraction of the electrons that move between them. It is this force of attraction that results in a metallic bond between the atoms of a metal.

4. The strength of a metallic bond depends on the nuclear charge and the number of electrons in the outer energy levels. As the number of outer electrons increases, the strength of the metallic bond increases. This trend is to be expected, since a greater number of electrons would give each atomic kernel a higher charge and a greater share of bonding electrons. In general, *as the strength of the metallic bond increases, the melting and boiling points and the hardness of the metal increase*. Thus, we find that metals in the first transition series from scandium to copper, which have partially filled 3d and 4s orbitals, have more delocalized electrons. These metals are harder and have higher melting points than sodium and other metals of the representative elements.

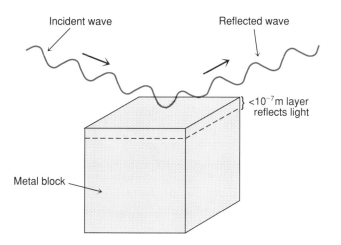

Incident wave

Reflected wave

} <10^{-7}m layer reflects light

Metal block

Figure 4-27
Reflection of light from a metal sur-face. Only the "free-moving" conduc-tion electrons located in a small vol-ume (thin layer) of the surface of a metal reradiate and reflect visible light that strikes the metal. Almost all the energy of the incident light goes into the reflected light. Therefore, uncorroded, smooth surfaces of many metals are shiny and can be used as mirrors.

4-18
Using the Metallic-Bond Model to Interpret the Properties of Metals

The properties of metals can be explained by a metallic-bond model that involves non-localized, mobile electrons.
Let us now use the metallic-bond model to explain observed properties of metals.

1. *Lustre, or reflectivity*. Non-localized, mobile electrons account for this and other properties (Fig. 4-27). Light energy causes the outer electrons of metals to move back and forth with the same frequency as the light that strikes the metal. Oscillation of a charged particle involves acceleration, which results in radia-tion of electromagnetic energy. Since the radiated energy is the same frequency as the incident light, we see it as a reflection of the original light beam.

2. *Electric conductivity*. Mobile electrons account for the high electric conductivity of metals. The tiny electrons can move rapidly from one position to another under the influence of an applied voltage. At higher temperatures, the conductivity in general decreases because the increased vibration of the atomic kernels interferes with the motion of the electrons.

3. *Heat conductivity*. Metals conduct heat well, a fact that is also explained in terms of highly mobile electrons. These electrons can move rapidly from regions of high temperature, where they attain high kinetic energy, to cooler regions, where they transfer some of this kinetic energy to the crystal lattice. Heat is slowly transported throughout a crystal lattice by the vibrational motion of the atoms, molecules or ions that occupy the lattice sites. Covalent and other crystals have tightly bound, localized

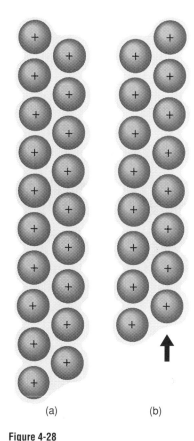

(a)   (b)

Figure 4-28
Unlike an ionic crystal, a metallic crystal can be "worked" into thin sheets or drawn into wires. This is because the positively charged atomic kernels can be moved within the "sea" of electrons without funda-mentally altering their environment. Thus, crystal (a) may be converted into crystal (b) without cracking or shattering.

bonding electrons. Heat conduction through such substances must depend solely on the vibration of atoms or molecules about fixed positions in the crystal lattice colliding with adjacent atoms, with a resultant transfer of energy. They are, therefore, poor conductors.

4. *Workability*. Since metallic bonds are non-directional, metal lattices can easily be deformed. Unlike ionic crystals, they do not shatter when a stress is applied. In metallic crystals, as one plane of atoms slides over another, there is no increase in electrostatic repulsion. The environment of each atom remains essentially unchanged, and the bonding electrons continue to exert uniform attractive force on the atomic kernels (Fig. 4-28).

5. *Electron emission caused by heat or light*. When enough heat energy is applied to a metal to overcome the attractive force between the atomic kernels and an outer electron, the electron is emitted from the metallic atom. When the frequency and, hence, the energy of the light that strikes the metal is great enough to overcome the attractive forces, the electron escapes from the metal with a resultant decrease in the energy of the incident photon. This is called the *photoelectric effect*.

CERAMICS: THE MADE-TO-ORDER MATERIAL

Ceramics—the word evokes images of shards of ancient pottery dug up by archaeologists or exquisite vases displayed in museums as works of art. Today, however, ceramics are being heralded as one of the most important materials used in the field of high technology. Ceramic materials have found widespread use in a variety of objects: from computers to telecommunication networks; from false teeth to space shuttles.

A ceramic material is any product made from a nonmetallic mineral compound and then fired at high temperatures. Ceramics are composed of three basic silicate materials: clay, sand and aluminosilicate. Clay contains a mixture of chemical compounds produced by the weathering of granite rocks. Aluminosilicates have a tetrahedral structure containing potassium, sodium and other ions in addition to aluminum, oxygen and silicon. When heated and mixed with clay and silica, the aluminosilicate tetrahedrons produce a mixture of crystals held together in a silica glass (SiO_2) matrix.

Ceramic technology began with the shaping and firing of clay pots in the prehistoric era, and advanced to include the production of brick, cement, glass and porcelain. However, ceramic materials have chemical and physical properties that make them very useful in many high-tech applications as well. Ceramics are chemically non-reactive and are able to withstand very high temperatures. They are also good electric conductors and insulators. These properties are related to their crystalline shape, that is, their three-dimensional bonding structure.

It is difficult to attribute the various properties of ceramics to one particular component, since there are so many different types of ceramics, all containing a different chemical composition. For example, alumina (Al_2O_3) and zirconia (ZrO_2) are used as bases for ceramic insulators. Ceramics containing iron compounds are known for their magnetic properties and are used in computer microchips. As well, the procedure for making ceramics can affect their physical properties. For example, if silica is cooled slowly, it will form quartz crystals; if it is cooled quickly, it will form non-crystalline glass.

As anyone who has ever dropped a porcelain vase on the floor can attest, ceramics are easily cracked or broken. This property is related to the degree of bond strength between their atoms, which, unlike the bonds in metals, does not permit atoms to slide over one another. Thus, ceramics can bear a load up to a certain point and then suddenly give way. Although various methods have been developed to increase this resistance to cracking, the most popular method involves incorporating synthetic fibres into the ceramic material to make it more resilient.

Today, ceramics can be found in computers, as glass optic fibres in telecommunications systems and as dental crowns, caps and dentures. Ceramic tiles are used on the exteriors of space shuttles because of their high heat resistance. This property allows the shuttle to re-enter the earth's atmosphere without burning up. In the future, ceramics may be used for car engines because they are lighter than metals, more durable and heat resistant. Ceramic materials may one day be used in orthopedics as bond and joint replacements.

The raw materials of ceramics are abundant and inexpensive. As more is learned about them and as scientists are able to tailor

them to meet the needs of developing technologies, ceramics may indeed become the made-to-order material of the future.

4-19
Comparison of Crystalline Solids

The different types of crystalline solids are related to the types of bonds or forces that bind together the particles in the crystal. The properties of these solids are also related to the bond type.

We have seen that the types of crystalline solids formed by various molecules relate to the intermolecular forces between the molecules. Table 4-6 shows the relationship between the type of crystal, the bonds and the physical properties.

TABLE 4-6
PROPERTIES OF CRYSTALLINE SOLIDS

	Solid Ionic Crystals	Solid Molecular Crystals	Solid Covalent Crystals	Solid Metallic Crystals
Examples	NaCl CsF MgO	Cl_2 H_2O CH_4	diamond (C) quartz (SiO_2) silicon carbide (SiC)	sodium iron copper
Particles occupying lattice points of crystal	positive or negative ions	molecules	atoms	positive atomic kernels
Type of bond or force between units occupying lattice points	ionic bonds (electrostatic)	van der Waals, dipole and sometimes hydrogen bonds	covalent bonds	metallic bonds

TABLE 4-6 (continued)
PROPERTIES OF CRYSTALLINE SOLIDS

	Solid Ionic Crystals	Solid Molecular Crystals	Solid Covalent Crystals	Solid Metallic Crystals
Relative melting point	high	low	very high	moderate to high
Electric conductivity in solid state	poor	poor	poor	good
Electric conductivity in liquid state	moderate	poor	poor	good
Heat conductivity	poor	poor	poor	good
Workability or hardnesss	hard and brittle	usually soft	hard	soft to hard, workable
Reflectivity or transparency	transparent	translucent, transparent	transparent	opaque, good reflectors

If we look at the periodic table, we see that the properties of the elements change from left to right. These differences reflect the changes in types of chemical bonds that can be formed, which, in turn, affect the type of crystal formed (Fig. 4-29). Note that when looking at a horizontal row in the periodic table, we see a range of dissimilar properties. In contrast, when we look at a vertical group of elements, we see a range of similar properties. As we move from left to right in a row of elements, properties such as electric conductivity, melting points, boiling points, molar heats of fusion and molar heats of vaporization undergo sharp increases and decreases. These abrupt changes in properties reflect the differences in the type of bonding that we find as the atomic number increases by one unit. Table 4-7 shows some of the properties of the period 3 elements.

Figure 4-29
Types of crystals formed by elements in the periodic table. What types of forces bind together the atoms in elemental molecular crystals?

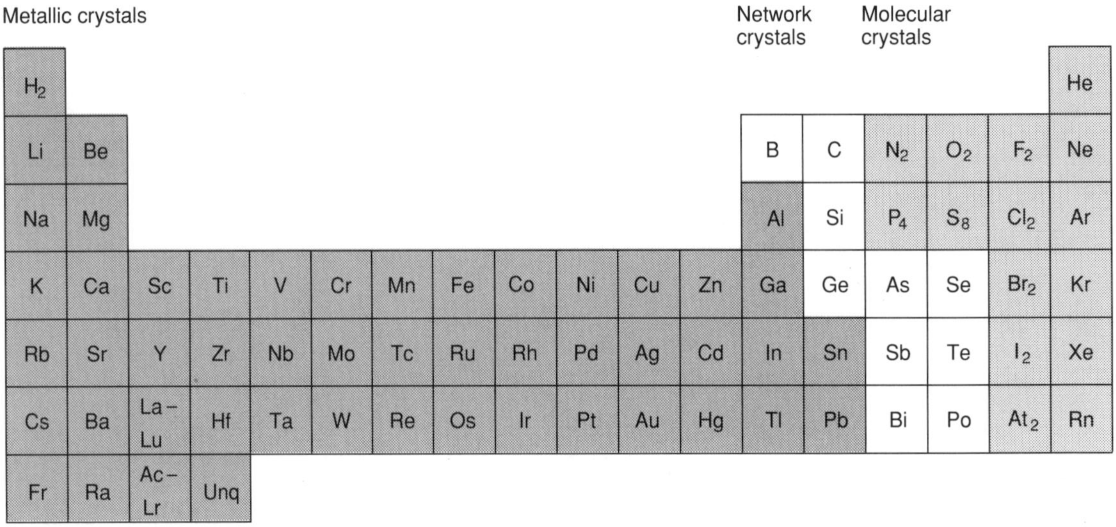

Metallic crystals

Network crystals

Molecular crystals

TABLE 4-7
PROPERTIES OF ELEMENTS IN PERIOD 3 OF THE PERIODIC TABLE

	Na	Mg	Al	Si	P_4 (yellow)	S_8 (rhombic)	Cl_2	Ar
Melting point (°C)	97.5	651	659.7	1420	44.1	112	−103	−189
Heat of fusion (kJ/mol)	2.98	8.95	8.65	46.4	0.648	1.42	3.22	1.12
Boiling point (°C)	889	1120	2357	2355	280	445	−34.1	−186
Heat of vaporization (kJ/mol)	96.6	132	284	439	12.5	10.5	20.5	6.69
Metallic properties				(diminishing)				
Conductivity	+	+	+	s	−	−	−	−

(+ conducting, s semiconducting, − nonconducting)

Let us examine more closely the bonding in each of the elements in Table 4-7 and relate the type of bonding to some of the observed properties. Sodium, magnesium and aluminum all form metallic crystals in which the atoms are held together by metallic bonds. We can attribute the respective increases in melting point, boiling point, heat of fusion and heat of vaporization partially to the increase in strength of the metallic bond as we go from sodium to aluminum.

The sudden rise in the melting point of silicon is a reflection of a complete change in the type of bond found in silicon crystals (Fig. 4-30). Evidence from a variety of sources indicates that silicon crystals are covalent crystals in which the silicon atoms are covalently bonded and arranged in a rigid, three-dimensional network.

The sharp drop in the melting point, boiling point, heat of fusion and heat of vaporization that occurs from silicon to phosphorus reflects another change in bonding. Phosphorus forms molecular crystals. The van der Waals attractions between the molecules that occupy the lattice points of the crystal are small compared with the strong covalent bonds between the silicon atoms that occupy the lattice points of the covalent crystal. The covalent bonds between the phosphorus atoms in the P_4 molecules are not ruptured during melting. Therefore, individual phosphorus atoms are not present in the liquid state.

The nature of the bonding in sulfur crystals is essentially the same as that in phosphorus crystals. Sulfur forms molecular crystals containing S_8 molecules. The S_8 molecules are much larger and contain many more electrons than P_4 molecules. Therefore, we would expect the van der Waals forces to be greater and predict that sulfur would have a higher melting point than phosphorus.

Both chlorine molecules and argon atoms are small and symmetrical, with filled outer orbitals. Thus, we can predict that the

The molar heat of fusion is the amount of heat required to liquefy one mole of solid already at its melting point.

Figure 4-30
Various forms of silica crystals: sand, rock crystal quartz, picture jasper, smoky quartz, amethyst, citrine and rose quartz.

melting points of these elements would be low, a consequence of the small intermolecular forces of attraction between the chlorine molecules and argon atoms.

In this chapter, we have examined the general structure of aggregates, the nature of the bonds that exist within various types of aggregates and the relationship between the type of bonds or forces and the physical properties of the aggregate.

In the next chapter, we will examine the nature of bonding within and the structure and physical properties of carbon-containing compounds. The ability of carbon to bond with other carbon atoms, hydrogen atoms or atoms of other elements in a wide variety of combinations is largely responsible for the vast number of different carbon-containing compounds, called *organic compounds*. Organic chemistry is closely related to the chemistry of living organisms and is responsible for many of the natural and synthetic products essential to our existence.

SUPERCONDUCTORS: A TECHNOLOGICAL REVOLUTION IN THE MAKING

In 1911, a Dutch physicist made a curious and remarkable discovery—certain metals bathed in liquid helium (boiling point 4.2 K, or −269°C) lost almost all resistance to the flow of electric current. The physicist's name was Heike Kamerlingh Onnes, and the phenomenon he discovered became known as superconductivity.

Excitement rippled through the scientific world. Until this discovery, all conductors, such as copper, aluminum and silver, were known to present minor but important levels of resistance to electron flow. This resistance meant that some of the electric energy was converted to heat. Not only does this generated heat represent a waste of energy but it requires the use of extremely dangerous voltages in overhead cables. Resistance also limits the capacity of computer microcircuit chips, since the heat generated by thousands of chips crowded together on a circuit board can destroy the computer. If superconductivity could work closer to or at room temperature, electric current could be transmitted tremendous distances without resistance or the need to guard against the heat generated.

High-temperature or room-temperature superconductivity has, however, proved elusive. Thirty years after Kamerlingh Onnes's discovery, scientists had only managed to cause niobium alloys to become superconducting at the frigid level of 15 K (−258°C). By 1975, research had shifted from metals and alloys to mixed oxides. In January 1986, K. Alex Müller and J. Georg Bednorz of IBM's Zurich Research Laboratory announced that they had achieved a decades-awaited breakthrough: superconductivity at 35 K (−238°C) using a ceramic oxide of lanthanum, barium and copper. Their work was considered of such importance that they were awarded the Nobel Prize for physics in 1987.

Stimulated by the news of the Müller-Bednorz discovery, scientists raced to develop and test a variety of oxides. In March 1987, Paul Chu and his colleagues at the University of Houston, Texas, reported that they had discovered an yttrium–barium–copper oxide that became superconducting at 94 K (−179°C). A typical, nonstoichiometric formula for such a superconductor is $YBa_2Cu_3O_x$, where x equals between 6.5 and 7.2 oxygen atoms.

The 94 K temperature level meant that liquid nitrogen, which boils at 77 K (−196°C), could be used to replace liquid helium. While liquid helium is both costly and rare, liquid nitrogen can readily be produced at a price hardly more expensive than milk. The technology to produce and handle liquid nitrogen is also straightforward and well known. Breaking the liquid nitrogen barrier was thus the first step toward practical applications for superconductivity.

Some of the most exciting of these applications involve the unique magnetic properties of superconductors. It is well known, for example, that an external magnetic field will induce current to flow in a conductor, and that current flowing through a conductor produces a magnetic field around it. The same phenomena occur with superconductors, but with important differences. If an external magnet is brought close to a superconductor, it will induce a current to flow in the superconducting material. However, the superconductor immediately produces and sustains an equally powerful magnetic field around itself; it becomes the mirror image of the magnet, or a diamagnet. This creates a repulsive force that is able to float the superconductor over the magnet or levitate the magnet over the superconductor. This phenomenon is known as the *Meissner effect*.

The Meissner effect can potentially be used to develop motors and generators with no touching parts and therefore no frictional load. Such a prototype motor has already been developed at the Argonne National Laboratory in Illinois. Entire trains could be levitated above superconducting tracks, their only frictional contact being with the air through which they would rush at speeds up to 500 km/h; Japan has developed such a magnetically levitated train. Other devices already in use that rely on the unique magnetic properties of superconductors include nuclear magnetic resonance imagers, particle accelerator magnets, astronomical sensors and sophisticated scientific instruments.

How do the ceramic oxide superconductors work? Although several theories exist, there is no consensus. Ceramic oxides can be made by mixing the oxides and/or carbonates of the appropriate metals together and firing them at around 1000°C, after which they are annealed at 500°C in an oxygenated atmosphere. During this process, the ceramic oxide crystallizes to produce electrically conducting chains, many of which are one-dimensional. In the $YBa_2Cu_3O_x$ superconductor, the one-dimensional chains are made up of alternating atoms of copper and oxygen. It is along such one-dimensional chain paths that superconductivity appears to occur. During any flow of electricity, it is the conduction electrons and not the valence electrons, which are tied up in chemical bonding, that cause electric current. For superconductivity to occur, the conduction electrons apparently must be paired. Normally, this is impossible, as heat and electrostatic repulsion keep the electrons apart. One theory proposes that as a superconducting material reaches a critical temperature, the valence electrons begin to resonate back and forth. This creates distortions in electrostatic forces that allow conduction electrons to form pairs.

Today, scientists around the world are vying to unlock the puzzle of room-temperature superconductivity. A team at the University of Arkansas has succeeded in developing a thallium–calcium–barium oxide compound that becomes superconducting at 123 K (−150°C). Several researchers have also reported drops in resistance through various compounds near or above room temperature. To date, however, none of these drops can yet be associated with true superconductivity.

The ramifications of room-temperature superconductivity are significant. The higher the temperature at which a material becomes a superconductor, the more widespread the applications. Superconducting electrical distribution systems could become reality; thin films of superconducting material could be used to develop new computer chips that would be a thousand times faster than any in existence today; electric generators and motors without touching parts would take decades to wear out and would be significantly cheaper to operate.

Even if room-temperature superconductivity is achieved, however, there are still many technical problems to overcome. Most of the superconducting ceramics tend to be brittle and extremely difficult to form into workable shapes. Several of the lanthanon compounds appear to be unstable and slowly deteriorate when exposed to moisture. Maximum current densities in ceramic superconductors are still too low to allow their use in most applications. The ceramics' superconducting properties can also be destroyed by too much current or heat, or by exposure to too strong a magnetic field. New, low-resistance contacts must be engineered before thin films can ever become a practical reality.

With all these challenges, scientists nevertheless remain confident that the next century may well mark the dawn of the superconductivity revolution.

QUESTIONS

1. What factors determine which of two reacting atoms donates electrons and which accepts electrons?

2. List four characteristics of ionically bonded crystals.

3. Consider the following data:

	Solubility in Water (kg/kg H_2O, 25°C)	Melting Point (°C)
NaF	0.042	988
NaCl	0.357	801
NaBr	1.16	755
NaI	1.84	651

a) Explain the decreasing melting point from NaF to NaI.
b) Explain the increasing solubility in the same order.
c) Cesium fluoride has a melting point of 682°C and a solubility of 3.67 kg/kg H_2O at 25°C. Explain the difference between the properties of CsF and NaF.

4. Lattice energy is related to melting point. What factors explain that sodium sulfide melts at 1180°C, while magnesium sulfide melts at a temperature over 2000°C?

5. Arrange the following aggregates in order of decreasing percentage ionic character:
LiI   BaO $AlCl_3$ CsF   RbBr
K_2S CaO   ClF P_2S_3 F_2

6. What tests would determine whether a solid substance contains ionic bonds?

7. Explain the poor conductivity of heat and electricity exhibited by covalently bonded substances.

8. What is the reason for the generally low melting points of molecular solids?

9. (a) What are van der Waals forces? (b) What are the structural features of substances in which only van der Waals forces are important in their interparticle bonding?

10. Why do NH_3, H_2O and HF have abnormally high boiling points when compared with their analogs, PH_3, H_2S and HCl?

11. The following compounds are fairly similar, and we might expect them to have similar boiling points. Explain the increase in boiling points of the compounds.

Formula	Common Name	Chemical Name	Boiling Point (°C)
C_3H_7OH	rubbing alcohol	propanol	82
$C_2H_4(OH)_2$	antifreeze	1,2-ethanediol	189
$C_3H_5(OH)_3$	glycerin	1,2,3-propanetriol	290

12. (a) Which compound in question 11 is the most viscous (has the least ability to flow)? (b) Which is the most fluid (least viscous)?

13. Explain why life on earth would not be possible if water did not expand when cooling from 4°C to 0°C and also when freezing.

14. How do network crystals differ from molecular crystals (a) in structure, (b) in hardness and (c) in melting point?

15. What property of graphite is the result of the presence of delocalized electrons?

16. A metal is sometimes said to be composed of atoms in which there are more vacant orbitals than occupied orbitals in the outer energy level. Show how this applies for Li, Mg and Al.

17. Show how the idea that a metal is composed of the kernels of atoms in a sea of mobile electrons helps explain a metal's (a) lustre, (b) electric conductivity, (c) heat conductivity, (d) photoelectric effect, (e) thermoelectric effect, (f) malleability.

18. What is the reason for the generally low melting points of the Group IA metals as compared with the high melting points of metals in the centre of the transition series?

19. Classify the following substances as ionic, solid molecular, solid covalent or solid metallic crystals:
a) lattice composed of positive ions sharing electrons with neighbouring positive ions
b) lattice composed of atoms bonded covalently to neighbouring atoms
c) a solid only at extremely low temperatures
d) a good conductor of heat and electricity
e) extremely hard, yet very soluble in polar liquids
f) extremely hard, not workable and a poor conductor of heat and electricity
g) a good electric conductor only when melted

20. Classify the following materials according to the type of bonds between particles: (a) paraffin, (b) wood, (c) sugar, (d) liquid nitrogen, (e) gasoline, (f) liquid ammonia. Explain each answer.

21. (a) Explain how a nonpolar covalent molecule such as BeH_2 can be held together by electrostatic forces. (b) Explain how a steel cable can be strong even though it consists of neutral atoms adjacent to each other.

22. Explain why $C_{20}H_{40}$ is a solid at 25°C, while C_4H_8 is a gas at 25°C.

23. Germanium (Ge) is a solid whose atoms are all covalently bonded to each other, much like those of carbon atoms in a diamond crystal. 1,2,3-propanetriol (glycerol, $C_3H_5(OH)_3$) is an alcohol. Potassium chloride (KCl) is a white crystalline solid. Methane (CH_4) is a gas that is liquefied only under high pressures and low temperatures. Rubidium metal is very malleable and an excellent conductor of electricity. Which has (a) hydrogen bonding? (b) the greatest hardness in the solid phase? (c) the highest melting point? (d) conductivity of electricity when melted? (e) the lowest molar heat of vaporization? (f) particles held together by van der Waals forces? (g) non-directional bonds?

24. (a) Explain why graphite is soft and has a high melting point. (b) Explain why diamond is hard and has a high melting point. (c) Why is diamond a poor conductor of an electric current and graphite a good conductor?

25. Account for the sharp drop in melting point as you move in the periodic table from element 14, silicon, to element 15, phosphorus.

26. Explain why the electric conductivity changes as you move from left to right across a row of the periodic table.

27. Is the melting point of element 32, which is directly below silicon in the periodic table, low or high? Explain.

28. The boiling point of sulfur (S_8) is very high compared with that of chlorine (Cl_2). Explain this difference.

29. Which compound in each of the following pairs has the higher boiling point? Explain your choice. (a) NH_3 or PH_3, (b) C_2H_6 or C_4H_{10}, (c) sulfur (S_8) or chlorine (Cl_2)

30. Which compound in each of the following pairs has the higher melting point? (a) CaO or KI, (b) KCl or KI, (c) RbCl or ICl

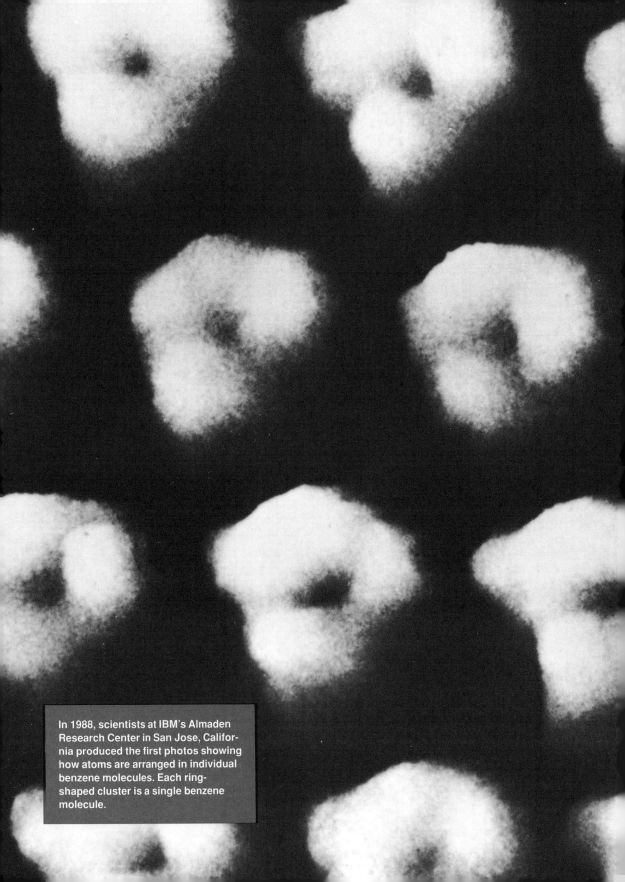

In 1988, scientists at IBM's Almaden Research Center in San Jose, California produced the first photos showing how atoms are arranged in individual benzene molecules. Each ring-shaped cluster is a single benzene molecule.

ORGANIC CHEMISTRY: AN INTRODUCTION TO ORGANIC COMPOUNDS

"Organic chemistry just now is enough to drive one mad. To me it appears like a primeval tropical forest full of the most remarkable things, a dreadful endless jungle into which one does not dare enter, for there seems no way out."
Friedrich Wöhler

A ccording to the periodic table, there are just over 100 different chemical elements. However, more than 10 million compounds exist. Since carbon occurs in well over 90% of all compounds, it is convenient to study most carbon compounds as a separate part of chemistry, called organic chemistry.

We would find it difficult to get by in a modern society without the diversity of synthetic carbon compounds that we have come to depend on. These compounds go into making the plastics for the countertops, food containers, paints, refrigerators and floor coverings in our homes. We wear clothing made of natural organic fibres such as wool, cotton and silk, as well as synthetic polymers such as nylons, acrylics and polyesters. Although dyes can be extracted from plants, the chemist can make better dyes using synthetic organic chemistry. Many of the drugs and medicines we use today have been synthesized in the last 100 years. Study and research in many fields such as medicine, pharmacology and molecular genetics depend on a knowledge of organic compounds and their reactions.

Apart from this large number of synthetic carbon compounds, a wide range of organic substances such as oils, fats, carbohydrates,

FRIEDRICH WÖHLER
1800–1882
Wöhler, a German chemist, was always fascinated with chemical experiments. Although he received his medical degree from the museum of Marburg in 1823, he studied chemistry for one year with Europe's leading chemist, Jöns Jakob Berzelius, in Stockholm.

While studying under Berzelius, Wöhler learned much about investigative techniques in chemistry and the chemistry of the elements. When Wöhler returned to Berlin, he taught chemistry in a technical school until 1831. In 1836 he was appointed professor of chemistry at the University of Göttingen, where he continued his studies in chemistry, isolating several elements and investigating the physiological importance of uric acid and cocaine.

Wöhler is most remembered for his synthesis of urea from ammonium cyanate in 1828. A prevalent idea at that time was that naturally occurring compounds from plants or animals were produced mysteriously by something called the *vital force*. When, upon heating ammonium cyanate, Wöhler produced urea crystals, he was astounded. After repeating the experiment and analysing the crystals, he wrote to Berzelius: "I must tell you that I can prepare urea without requiring a kidney of an animal, either man or dog."

proteins and nucleic acids are found naturally in our bodies. Even the simplest living organisms contain complex carbon molecules.

Many of the environmental concerns that are increasingly being reported in the media are related to organic substances. For example, the freons used in refrigerants and aerosol propellants are known to destroy the earth's protective ozone layer. The combustion of coal generates sulfur dioxide—a source of acid rain. By reducing the mosquito population, the insecticide DDT has saved millions of people from death by malaria, but it has also caused major environmental problems in food chains. Plastics such as polyethylene and polystyrene form an increasing part of the garbage that is accumulating on our planet. As we proceed through our study of organic chemistry in this book, we will consider in more detail both the positive and negative aspects of organic compounds.

This chapter will focus on the nature of organic compounds, their structures and classification into families, as well as the naming and properties of these compounds. We will first look at the origins of modern organic chemistry.

GENERAL CHARACTERISTICS AND CLASSIFICATION OF ORGANIC COMPOUNDS

Until 1828, chemists believed that certain materials such as sugar, silk, vinegar and oil could be produced only by living organisms. Such materials were called *organic*. Alchemists knew that organic substances were easily decomposed by heat and that sometimes inorganic residues remained, but no scientist had been able to convert inorganic substances into organic substances. Synthetic organic chemistry began in 1828 when Friedrich Wöhler converted an inorganic chemical called ammonium cyanate into urea, an organic compound:

$$\text{NH}_4\text{OCN}(aq) + \text{heat} \longrightarrow \text{NH}_2-\overset{\displaystyle \overset{O}{\|}}{\text{C}}-\text{NH}_2(aq)$$

ammonium cyanate (an inorganic salt made of ions) urea (a covalently bonded organic molecule)

As a medical student, Wöhler had experimented with the waste products in urine. He had often seen the long crystals of urea and recognized it as the product of his synthesis. At that time, chemists accepted the *vital force theory*, which stated that organic compounds could not be made in the laboratory because living organisms had a hidden, controlling force directing the organism's growth and the formation of organic compounds within it. Wöhler's urea synthesis did not lead to a speedy downfall of the vital force theory. Throughout the history of science there have been many instances in which new theories were not readily accepted. The belief in vitalism was no exception; it took about 20 years for the theory to disappear. The work of other chemists led to the gradual acceptance that organic compounds could, in fact, be synthesized outside a living system. Hermann Kolbe (1818–1884) of Germany was one such chemist who helped provide evidence to dispute the vitalism theory. He believed in the vital force theory, but in 1845 he successfully synthesized the common organic compound, acetic acid, by a series of chemical reactions, starting with the element carbon itself.

Later in the 19th century, the synthetic organic chemical industry received a strong impetus from a 17-year-old English chemistry student, Sir William Henry Perkin (1838–1907). While trying to synthesize the antimalarial drug quinine, Perkin accidentally produced the first synthetic dye—mauve—from aniline extracted from coal tar. After Perkin's discovery, more and more organic compounds, including other dyes, drugs, explosives and photographic chemicals, were derived from compounds isolated from coal tar.

Although we still obtain organic chemicals from organic sources such as plants, the modern definition of organic chemistry is *the chemistry of carbon compounds*. Note that a few carbon compounds such as carbon monoxide, carbon dioxide, carbonates, bicarbonates and cyanides are classified as inorganic because they have properties that are generally associated with inorganic compounds. The chemical and physical properties of organic and inorganic compounds differ because of the nature of the bonding found in each of these categories. In general, inorganic compounds form ionic bonds through the transfer of electrons, while organic compounds form covalent bonds through the sharing of electrons. Although there is no sharp boundary between ionic and covalent bonds, covalent bonds have characteristics that result in properties quite distinct from those of the ionic bonds of inorganic salts. Table 5-1 on the next page outlines some properties of organic compounds compared with inorganic salts. It should be kept in mind, however, that exceptions to these properties do exist.

Because most organic bonds are covalent rather than ionic in nature, the physical properties of organic substances can be interpreted in terms of van der Waals forces, dipole interactions and hydrogen bonding. Another factor that affects the physical properties of organic compounds is their shape. The large, bulky shape of organic molecules also affects the rate of most organic reactions.

Because of the nature of the intramolecular bonding and the complexity of organic molecules, organic reactions are usually slower than inorganic ones. The reason for this is that the barriers to making and breaking covalent bonds are greater than those associated with ionic bonds. In addition, organic reactions may involve a number of side reactions that yield unwanted products. This gives chemists the additional task of separating and purifying the various products that may be present in the final, complex reaction mixture.

TABLE 5-1
COMPARISON OF ORGANIC COMPOUNDS AND INORGANIC SALTS

Organic Compounds	Inorganic Salts
– Contain carbon.	– Contain elements other than carbon, although a few do contain carbon.
– Over 10 million exist, and more than 300 000 new ones are synthesized each year.	– A few hundred thousand are known and only a few new ones are synthesized each year.
– Are formed through covalent bonds.	– Are formed through ionic bonds.
– Most are non-electrolytes incapable of conducting electricity, as they do not form ions in solution.	– Most are electrolytes capable of conducting an electric current, as they dissociate in solution to give free ions.
– Can frequently be distilled.	– Can be vaporized only at extremely high temperatures.
– Have relatively low melting points.	– Generally have high melting points.
– Many are sparingly soluble or insoluble in water but are soluble in non-aqueous solvents.	– Many are soluble in water, but only sparingly soluble or insoluble in non-aqueous solvents.

5-1

What Makes Carbon Compounds Different?

Carbon compounds are unusual in that they can form extended chains and rings of carbon atoms.

In all but a very few carbon compounds, carbon is tetravalent; that is, the large number of organic compounds can be attributed to the ability of a carbon atom to form four strong covalent bonds with other carbon atoms. This leads to the formation of chainlike molecules, which may contain thousands of carbon atoms. When the ends of a chain are joined, cyclic or ring structures are obtained. Because the electronegativity of carbon (2.5) is near that of hydrogen, oxygen, nitrogen and sulfur, carbon also forms covalent bonds with these elements.

It is convenient to represent organic compounds by Lewis structures. The simplest organic compound, methane, is represented by the Lewis structure below. Recall from Chapter 3 that the inner, lower-energy-level electrons as well as the nucleus are represented by the symbol of the element. An alternative method of representing methane, using lines to represent single covalent bonds, is also shown.

$$
\begin{array}{ccc}
& & H \\
H & & | \\
H\!:\!\overset{\cdot\cdot}{\underset{\cdot\cdot}{C}}\!:\!H & & H-C-H \\
H & & | \\
& & H
\end{array}
$$

methane

You should always carefully check that a carbon atom has exactly four bonds to other atoms in a Lewis structure.

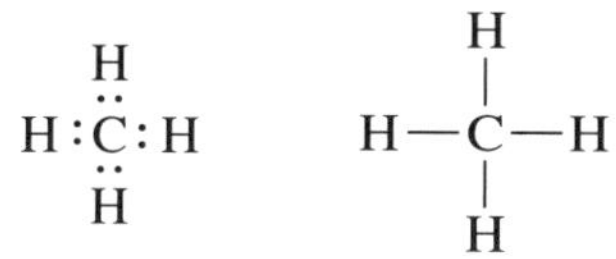

5-2

The Shapes of Hydrocarbons

In hydrocarbons containing only single bonds, the H—C—H bond angle is equal to 109.5°.

If we could examine the methane molecule, we would find that it has the shape of a tetrahedron, with a carbon atom in the centre and a hydrogen atom at each apex. The valence shell electron-pair repulsion (VSEPR) theory explains the tetrahedral shape of methane molecules. Mutual repulsion of the four C—H bonds drives the bonding pairs as far apart as possible to minimize repulsion, thus resulting in a tetrahedral shape. Similarly, VSEPR theory justifies the shapes of other organic molecules in which there are chains of bonded carbon atoms.

Another model used to explain the covalent bonding of carbon in organic compounds is that of *orbital hybridization*. An isolated carbon in its ground state has an electron configuration of $1s^2, 2s^2, 2p^2$. By applying the concept of orbital hybridization, we can explain the ability of carbon atoms to form four covalent bonds.

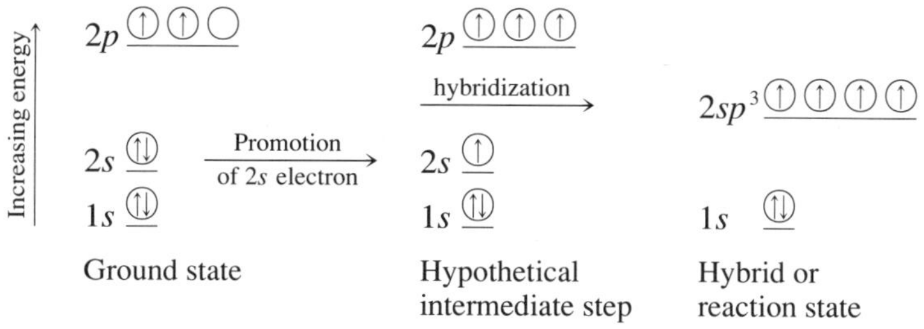

Increasing energy →

| Ground state | Hypothetical intermediate step | Hybrid or reaction state |

When undergoing a reaction, the ground-state electron configuration of carbon can be altered by the promotion of a $2s$ electron to

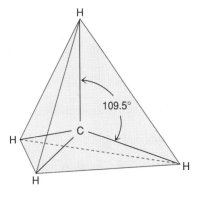

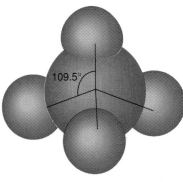

Figure 5-1
In methane, the *sp*³ bonding orbitals of a carbon atom are directed toward the corners of a tetrahedron. In the space-filling model, all H—C—H bond angles are equal to 109.5°.

the empty $2p$ energy state to form four equivalent sp^3 orbitals. The four sp^3 orbitals are the result of the mixing or hybridizing of the s orbital and three p orbitals. Each of the hybrid sp^3 orbitals of the carbon atom is directed in space tetrahedrally.

Because sp^3 hybridization is assumed to be involved in the formation of a large number of organic molecules, the shapes of many of these molecules are related to the tetrahedral bond angle of 109.5°. Although it is convenient to represent the structure of methane by a Lewis structure or line formula, these formulas can be misleading because they imply that all five atoms are in the same plane. Three-dimensional models and diagrams, such as those shown in Fig. 5-1, suggest the correct spatial orientation of the atoms and the shapes of the molecules.

As we have discussed, carbon can form stable chains of carbon atoms. This explains why there is no theoretical limit to the number of carbon compounds. How can anyone cope with the study of organic chemistry when such a large number of molecules are involved? We will see that their study can be greatly simplified. The strength of the C—C bond is so great that, during many reactions, the carbon skeleton of the molecule remains intact, even though other groups (—Cl, —OH, —NO₂) attached to the molecule may be changed. This makes it convenient to classify carbon compounds in terms of their skeletal carbon structure and *reactive groups (functional groups)* located within the molecule.

Organic substances containing the same functional group are classified into families because they have very similar chemical properties. Within each family there are regular trends in physical properties, such as melting and boiling points. We will see that members of different families can undergo the same kinds of chemical changes. Let us start by looking at the different types of skeletal carbon structures.

5-3
Hydrocarbons: The Skeletal Structures of Organic Compounds

Hydrocarbons are compounds that contain only carbon and hydrogen. They are classified into two general categories— aliphatics and aromatics.

Hydrocarbons are the skeletal structures of organic compounds. If the compound contains single covalent bonds, double bonds or triple bonds between carbon atoms, the hydrocarbon is called **aliphatic**. Other hydrocarbons, called **aromatic**, have bond lengths and strengths that fall somewhere between the values for C—C and C=C bonds.

Aliphatic hydrocarbons occur as open-chain compounds or as structures with closed rings of carbon atoms (alicyclics). Compounds that have only C—C bonds are called *alkanes*. Those with one or more C=C bonds are *alkenes*; those with one or more carbon-to-carbon triple bonds (C≡C) are called *alkynes*. The word aliphatic is from the Greek word for oil. Many natural food oils and fats contain C—C and C=C bonds in their hydrocarbon chains. Figure 5-2 shows a detailed classification of the hydrocarbons.

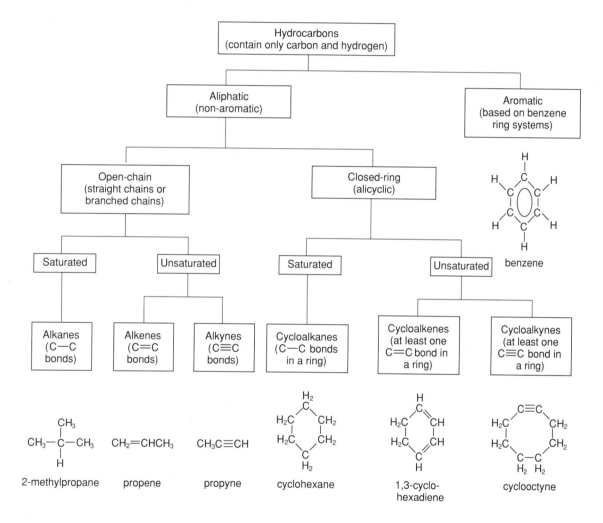

If a hydrocarbon is said to be **saturated**, it means that each carbon atom is bonded to the maximum number of four other atoms; that is, all carbon-to-carbon bonds are single bonds. The presence of one or more C=C or C≡C bonds in the molecule makes it **unsaturated**. We will find that unsaturated and saturated hydrocarbons have quite different chemical properties.

The unsaturated hydrocarbons can become saturated in a pro-

Figure 5-2
Classification of hydrocarbons.

cess called *hydrogenation*. The C=C bonds and C≡C bonds are broken, and hydrogen atoms are added, resulting in a saturated hydrocarbon. For example, hydrogen added to the C≡C bond in ethyne converts it to a C=C bond, producing ethene. The process is repeated, and the C=C bond is hydrogenated to a C—C bond, forming ethane:

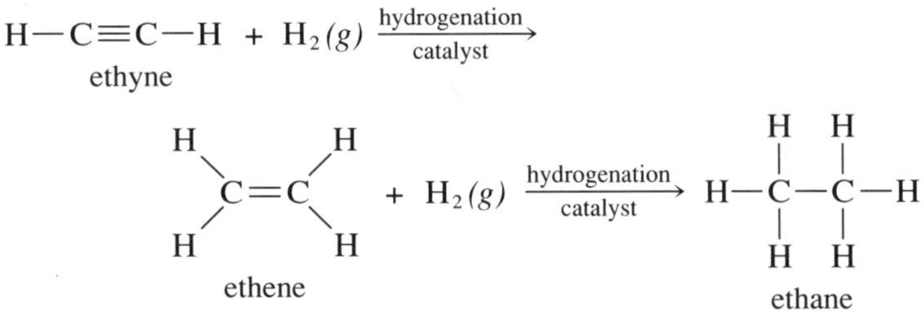

$$H-C{\equiv}C-H \ + \ H_2(g) \xrightarrow[\text{catalyst}]{\text{hydrogenation}}$$

ethyne

ethene

ethane

Aromatic hydrocarbons have properties that are very different from aliphatic hydrocarbons. These compounds derive their name from the fact that some of them have a pronounced odour. An example of a familiar aromatic hydrocarbon is naphthalene ($C_{10}H_8$), which is used to make mothballs. Aromatic compounds include benzene (C_6H_6) and its structurally related compounds. Early attempts to deduce a benzene structure were unsuccessful until 1866, when August Kekulé suggested a cyclic structure with alternating single and double bonds. However, the Kekulé formula was unsatisfactory, since benzene did not show the typical reactions of unsaturated hydrocarbons. Kekulé then proposed that the double bonds were not fixed, but could be arranged in two ways. He also suggested that the two structures could rapidly interconvert. In fact, benzene has only one structure with a delocalized electron system and six identical carbon-to-carbon bonds. Many organic-chemistry books still show benzene and other aromatic compounds with the alternating arrangement of C—C and C=C bonds of the Kekulé structures, as shown in the margin. Another representation of benzene depicts the delocalized pi electrons, which belong equally to all six carbons, with a circle inside the hexagonal ring:

"Atoms were gamboling before my eyes, twisting and twining in snake-like motion. Then one of the snakes seized its own tail."
Description by August Kekulé (1829–1896) of a dream that led to his hypothesis of the ring structure of benzene.

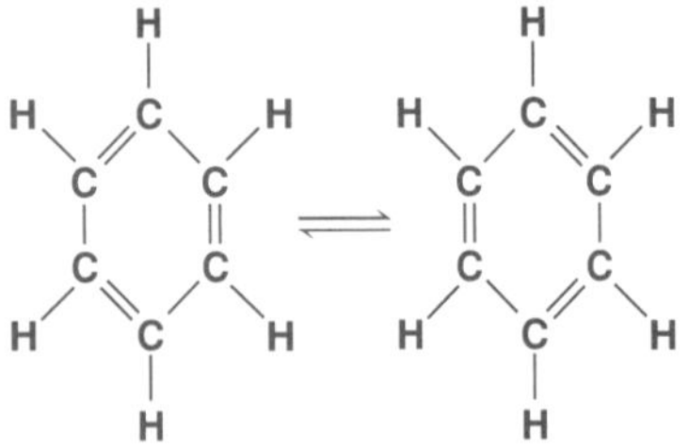

Kekulé structures

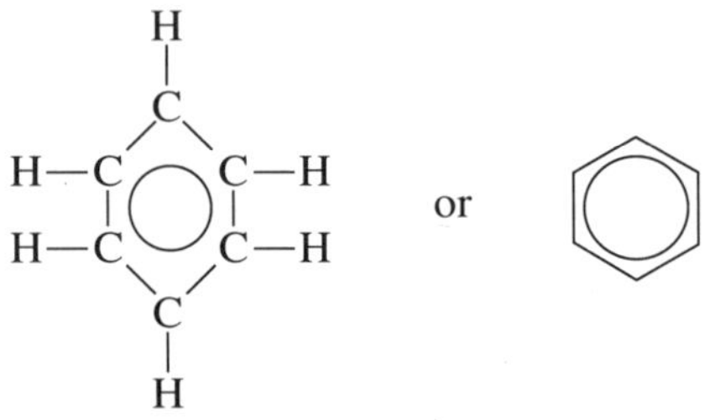

or

Although we are considering only hydrocarbons at this stage, we should note another category of ring compounds, the *heterocyclic compounds*. The prefix *hetero-* means "different" or "other." In heterocyclic compounds, therefore, not only carbon atoms are present in the ring, but another atom such as oxygen, nitrogen or sulfur as well. Two examples of heterocyclic rings are shown in Fig. 5-3.

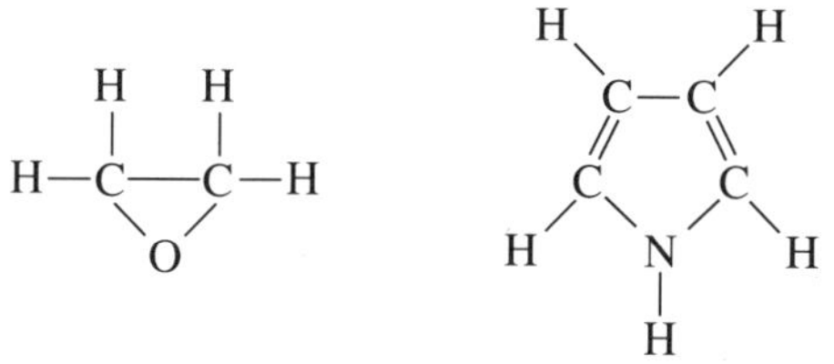

ethylene oxide   pyrrole

Figure 5-3
Heterocyclic compounds, ethylene oxide and pyrrole, incorporate oxygen and nitrogen, respectively, into the ring structure. Ethylene oxide is a cyclic ether (epoxide) and pyrrole is an amine.

5-4

Representations of Hydrocarbon Compounds

Chemists frequently represent organic compounds by molecular and structural formulas.

In chemistry, the *molecular formula* is used to indicate the number and type of atoms present in a compound. However, because the properties of an organic compound depend on its structure, chemists frequently use *structural formulas* to represent hydrocarbons. As well, *isomers*, which are two different compounds with the same molecular formula, can only be differentiated by structural formulas. For example, the following structural formulas represent two different compounds with the same molecular formula, C_4H_{10}:

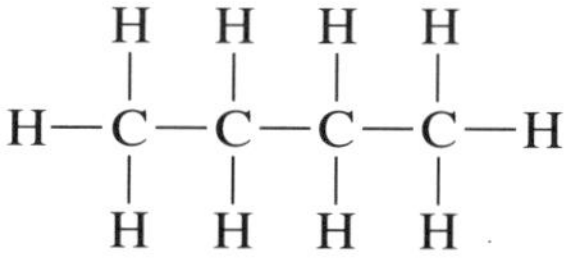

butane   2-methylpropane

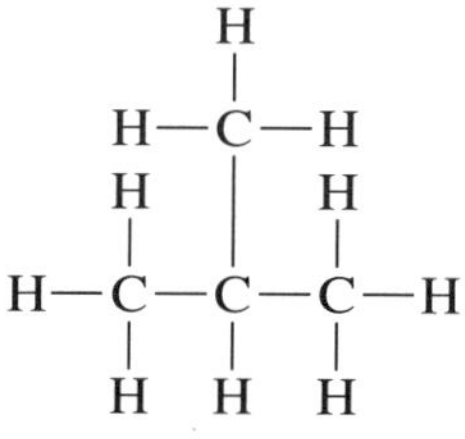

A convenient simplification of a structural formula is the *condensed formula*, where

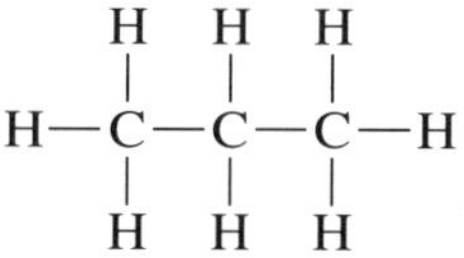

$= CH_3CH_2CH_3$

propane

As you can see, the lines representing single bonds between atoms are omitted. When branching occurs off the main chain, this is indicated by parentheses. For example,

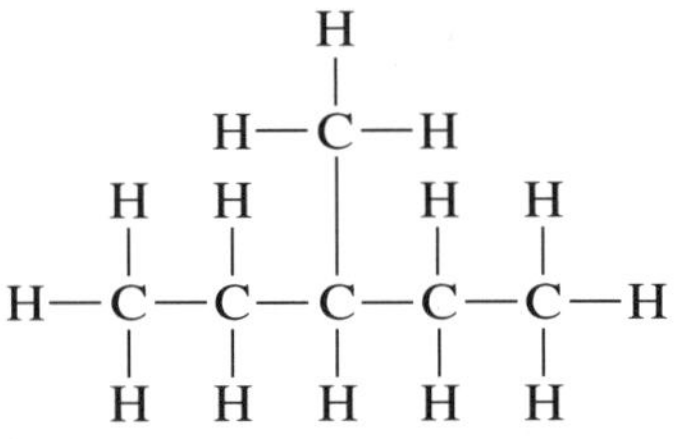

3-methylpentane

$$= CH_3CH_2CH(CH_3)CH_2CH_3$$

As the structures of organic compounds become more complex, chemists use *stick formulas*, which take into account the angles between carbon atoms. Thus,

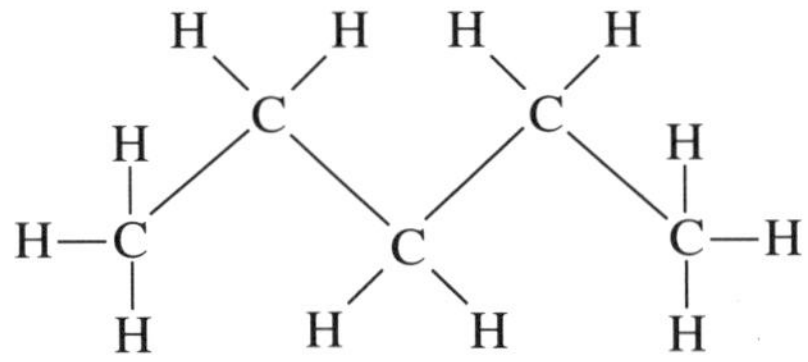

pentane

A carbon is implied at each end of the line, as well as at each bend. The hydrogen atoms are omitted. Stick formulas are also used to represent cyclic structures:

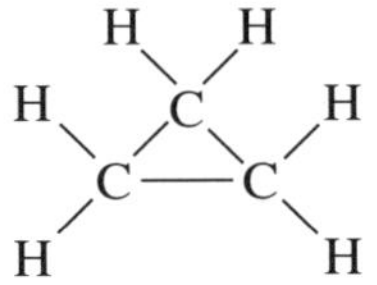

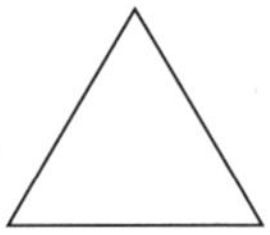

cyclopropane 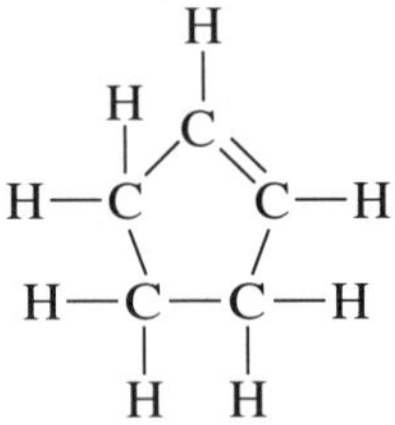   is written

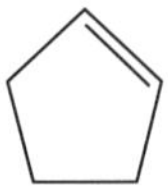

cyclopentene   is written

FOLLOW-UP PROBLEMS

1. Which of the following compounds are organic?
   (a) C_3H_6, (b) $Ca(OH)_2$, (c) $C_{10}H_8$,
   (d) $C_2H_4(OH)_2$, (e) H_2SO_4

2. Select the unsaturated hydrocarbons:

(a) $CH_3CH_2CH_2CH_3$ (b) $CH_3CH=CH_2$

(c) $CH_3CH_2C\equiv CH$ (d) $\quad\quad CH_3$
$\quad\quad\quad\quad\quad\quad\quad\quad\quad | $
$\quad\quad\quad\quad\quad\quad\quad CH_3CH_2CH_2CH_3$

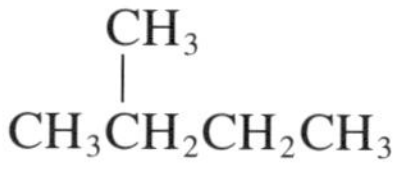

(e)

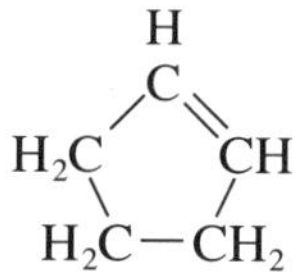

3. Which of the following compounds are heterocyclic?
   Which are aromatic?

(a) (b) 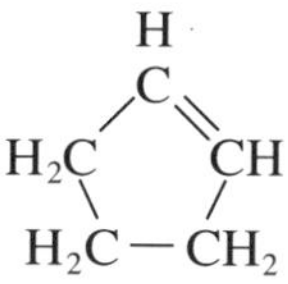 (c)

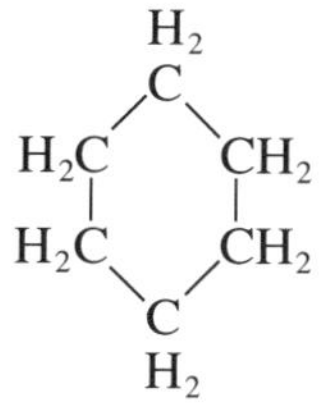

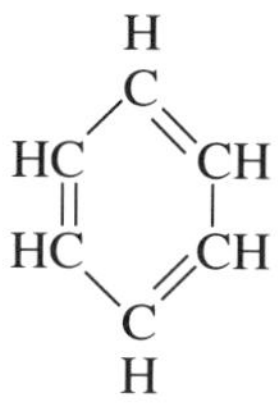

(d) 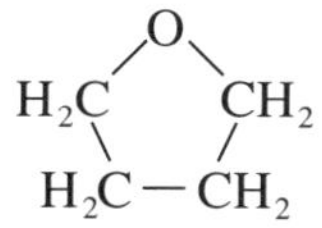 (e)

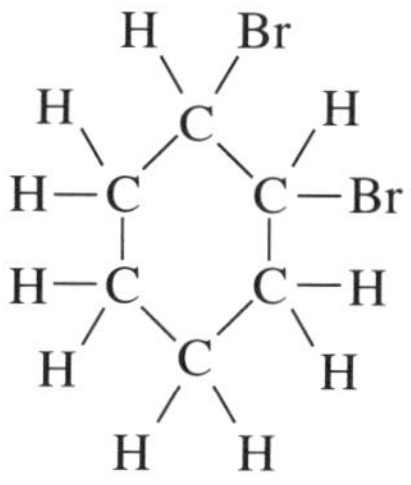

4. Represent decane by a condensed formula.

Answers:
1. a, c, d
2. b, c, e
3. (d) heterocyclic, (c) aromatic
4. $CH_3(CH_2)_8CH_3$

As we mentioned earlier, there are millions of carbon compounds. Their study can be simplified if we group them into families according to their *functional groups.* A functional group is the site that undergoes chemical reactions. In the next section, we will examine the different functional groups that constitute different families.

Functional Groups

The specific, unique chemical reactivity of any family of organic compounds is determined by a characteristic structure called a functional group.

The chemical properties of organic compounds are determined by an atom or a group of atoms that substitute for a hydrogen atom on the hydrocarbon chain. These atoms are referred to as functional groups. For example, compounds that have one or more carbon-to-carbon double bonds ($C=C$), which is the functional group, belong to the alkene family. Alcohols make up a family that has a

TABLE 5-2
ORGANIC COMPOUNDS AND THEIR FUNCTIONAL GROUPS

Family Name	Functional Group	Formula	IUPAC Suffix or Prefix	Example
Alkane	–	$R-H$	-ane	CH_3-CH_3 ethane
Alkene	$C=C$ double bond		-ene	ethene
Alkyne	$C\equiv C$ triple bond	$R_1-C\equiv C-R_2$	-yne	$H-C\equiv C-H$ ethyne
Aromatic			-benz phenyl-	ethylbenzene 2-phenylpropane
Alcohol	$-OH$ hydroxyl	$R-OH$	-ol	CH_3-CH_2-OH ethanol
Ether	$-O-$ ether	$R-O-R'$	alkoxy-	CH_3-O-CH_3 methoxymethane
Aldehyde	carbonyl		-al	methanal

hydroxyl group (—OH) bonded to a hydrocarbon chain.

Table 5-2 lists twelve of the more important functional groups. As you proceed with your study of organic chemistry, you will find it convenient to refer to this table. In the rest of this chapter we will note the names, structures and physical properties associated with each functional group and also look briefly at their chemical properties.

ALKANES

Alkanes are saturated hydrocarbons that contain only carbon-to-carbon and carbon-to-hydrogen single bonds. Methane (CH_4), the

TABLE 5-2 (continued)

Family Name	Functional Group	Formula	IUPAC Suffix or Prefix	Example
Ketone	$$\overset{\displaystyle O}{\overset{\displaystyle \|}{-C-}}$$ carbonyl	$$\overset{\displaystyle O}{\overset{\displaystyle \|}{R-C-R'}}$$	-one	$$\overset{\displaystyle O}{\overset{\displaystyle \|}{CH_3-C-CH_3}}$$ propanone
Carboxylic acid	$$\overset{\displaystyle O}{\overset{\displaystyle \|}{-C-OH}}$$ carboxyl	$$\overset{\displaystyle O}{\overset{\displaystyle \|}{R_1-C-OH}}$$	-oic acid	$$\overset{\displaystyle O}{\overset{\displaystyle \|}{CH_3-C-OH}}$$ ethanoic acid
Ester	$$\overset{\displaystyle O}{\overset{\displaystyle \|}{-C-OR}}$$ ester	$$\overset{\displaystyle O}{\overset{\displaystyle \|}{R_1-C-OR}}$$	-oate	$$\overset{\displaystyle O}{\overset{\displaystyle \|}{CH_3-C-O-CH_3}}$$ methyl ethanoate
Amine	—NH_2 amino		amino-	
- primary		$R-NH_2$		CH_3-NH_2 aminomethane
- secondary		$R-NH-R'$		$CH_3-NH-CH_3$ N-methylaminomethane
- tertiary		$$R-\overset{\displaystyle}{\underset{\displaystyle \underset{R''}{\|}}{NH}}-R'$$		$$CH_3-\overset{\displaystyle}{\underset{\displaystyle \underset{CH_3}{\|}}{NH}}-CH_3$$ N,N-dimethylaminomethane
Amide	$$\overset{\displaystyle O}{\overset{\displaystyle \|}{-C-NH}}$$ amide	$$\overset{\displaystyle O}{\overset{\displaystyle \|}{R_1-C-NH}}$$	-amide	$$\overset{\displaystyle O}{\overset{\displaystyle \|}{CH_3-C-NH_2}}$$ ethanamide
Nitrile	$-C\equiv N$ nitrile	$R-C\equiv N$	-onitrile	$CH_3-C\equiv N$ ethanonitrile

R, R' and R'' represent alkyl groups. Examples of alkyl groups can be found in Table 5-3.
R_1, R_2 and so on represent alkyl groups or hydrogen atoms.

Figure 5-4
Liquid butane is used as a fuel in some cigarette lighters. The butane vaporizes and is ignited by a spark from the flint. Fatal accidents have happened to people cutting or welding metal while carrying such a lighter in their pocket. Stray sparks have landed on the cigarette lighter, causing the fuel to ignite and explode.

first member of the alkane family, is the major component of natural gas. Other examples of alkanes include automobile fuel (octane, C_8H_{18}) and candle wax (a mixture of alkanes). All alkanes, whether open-chain or cyclic in structure, are saturated, aliphatic hydrocarbons.

5-6
Naming Alkanes

Table 5-3 gives the names and formulas for the first ten unbranched, open-chain alkanes. Each name ends in -ane, as in methane. The prefix of the alkane name indicates the number of carbon atoms in the molecule: meth- for one carbon atom, eth- for two carbons and so on. Starting with pentane, the prefix of each alkane name is derived from Greek numbers: penta- for five, hexa- for six and so on. The reason for this variation in prefixes is that the names of the first four members of this series were in widespread use before any attempts were made to systematize the names of organic compounds. The International Union of Pure and Applied Chemistry (IUPAC) is the organization responsible for establishing universal rules for naming organic compounds. We will discuss these rules in Section 5-11.

TABLE 5-3
REPRESENTATIVE ALKANES AND THEIR CORRESPONDING ALKYL GROUPS

Alkane	Molecular Formula	Number of Carbon Atoms	Prefix	Alkyl Group	Alkyl Formula
Methane	CH_4	1	meth-	methyl	CH_3-
Ethane	C_2H_6	2	eth-	ethyl	C_2H_5-
Propane	C_3H_8	3	prop-	propyl	C_3H_7-
Butane	C_4H_{10}	4	but-	butyl	C_4H_9-
Pentane	C_5H_{12}	5	pent-	pentyl	$C_5H_{11}-$
Hexane	C_6H_{14}	6	hex-	hexyl	$C_6H_{13}-$
Heptane	C_7H_{16}	7	hept-	heptyl	$C_7H_{15}-$
Octane	C_8H_{18}	8	oct-	octyl	$C_8H_{17}-$
Nonane	C_9H_{20}	9	non-	nonyl	$C_9H_{19}-$
Decane	$C_{10}H_{22}$	10	dec-	decyl	$C_{10}H_{21}-$

5-7
Physical Properties of Alkanes

Alkanes show trends in their physical properties that can be explained in terms of the shape of their molecules and the forces of attraction between them.

TABLE 5-4
PHYSICAL PROPERTIES OF SELECTED STRAIGHT-CHAIN ALKANES

Alkane	Condensed Formula	Melting Point (°C)	Boiling Point (°C)	Density (g/mL at 20°C)
Methane	CH_4	−182	−164	gas
Ethane	CH_3CH_3	−183.3	−88.6	gas
Propane	$CH_3CH_2CH_3$	−189.7	−42.1	gas
Butane	$CH_3CH_2CH_2CH_3$	−138.4	−0.5	gas
Pentane	$CH_3CH_2CH_2CH_2CH_3$	−130	36.1	0.63
Hexane	$CH_3CH_2CH_2CH_2CH_2CH_3$	−95	69	0.66
Heptane	$CH_3CH_2CH_2CH_2CH_2CH_2CH_3$	−90.6	98.4	0.68
Octane	$CH_3CH_2CH_2CH_2CH_2CH_2CH_2CH_3$	−56.8	125.7	0.70
Nonane	$CH_3CH_2CH_2CH_2CH_2CH_2CH_2CH_2CH_3$	−51	150.8	0.72
Decane	$CH_3CH_2CH_2CH_2CH_2CH_2CH_2CH_2CH_2CH_3$	−29.7	174.1	0.73

The alkanes have low melting and boiling points relative to other families of organic compounds. Table 5-4 lists some of the physical properties of the first ten alkanes. Note that the first four alkanes—methane to butane—are gases at room temperature. Members from pentane to hexadecane are liquids, and straight-chain alkanes having more than sixteen carbon atoms are waxy solids.

Triacontane ($C_{30}H_{62}$) is one of the alkanes found in candle wax.

We can use the bonding forces between the atoms and the shapes of the alkane molecules to explain the trends in physical properties. For example, methane has a melting point of −182°C and boils at −164°C. Previously, we noted that methane is a tetrahedral molecule. Each of the C—H bonds is slightly polar but, because of the tetrahedral shape, the molecule as a whole is nonpolar. Thus, the only bonding forces between the molecules are weak van der Waals attractions. This explains the low melting and boiling points of methane and other alkanes of low mass. In general, we see that melting and boiling points increase with increasing molecular mass. As molecules increase in mass, the surface area of the molecules also increases, providing more opportunity for van der Waals forces to act.

We see from Table 5-4 that the first three alkanes have melting points out of line with the general trend. This is explained by the fact that melting points depend not only on molecular mass, but also on the shape of the molecules and how well they pack into a regular crystal lattice. For example, although ethane has a relative mass of 30 and is longer than methane (relative mass 16), it has a lower melting point. This is because the symmetrical methane molecules pack readily into a crystal structure, while the rod-shaped ethane molecules do not pack so neatly. Although propane has an even larger surface area over which van der Waals forces

The protective wax on cabbage leaves is made of unbranched alkanes: 95% $C_{29}H_{60}$ and 5% $C_{31}H_{64}$.

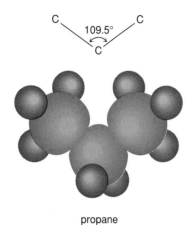

propane

Figure 5-5
A space-filling model of propane
(C_3H_8) showing the 109.5° bond angle
between alternate carbon atoms.

can act, it has a lower melting point. This is because the alternate carbon atoms of propane have a bond angle of 109.5° (Fig. 5-5), resulting in a bent structure that packs with even less efficiency than ethane. We see no discrepancy in the trend of boiling points increasing in successively heavier alkane molecules.

The nonpolarity of alkanes also affects their solubility in water. As discussed in Chapter 4, water is a polar solvent that dissolves polar molecules. Because alkanes are nonpolar, they are not water soluble. They do, however, dissolve in nonpolar solvents.

5-8
Homologous Series

The members of the alkane family demonstrate regularities in structure and physical properties and are said to form a homologous series.

In any homologous series, a general formula applies to the molecular structure of the compounds, and there are regular trends in both physical properties and chemical behaviour. Each member of a homologous series is called a *homolog*.

The alkanes can be used to illustrate features of a homologous series having the general formula C_nH_{2n+2}. We can derive this general formula from the structure of pentane:

$$
\begin{array}{ccccc}
& H & H & H & H & H \\
& | & | & | & | & | \\
H- & C- & C- & C- & C- & C-H \\
& | & | & | & | & | \\
& H & H & H & H & H \\
\end{array}
$$

We see that each carbon atom has two hydrogen atoms attached except for the two end carbons. Hence, C_nH_{2n} forms part of the formula. But to fulfil carbon's capacity of four single bonds, an additional hydrogen atom must be present at each end of the carbon chain to give C_nH_{2n+2}.

Each functional group family is a homologous series. For instance, the alcohols are represented by the general formula $C_nH_{2n+1}OH$, and the series proceeds as CH_3OH, CH_3CH_2OH, $CH_3(CH_2)_2OH$ and so on. Similarly, the alkyne family has the general formula C_nH_{2n-2}, and the family of homologs is C_2H_2, C_3H_4, C_4H_6 and so on.

In summary, all homologous series show the following characteristics:

1. Each successive member has an additional CH_2 unit.
2. The family is represented by a general formula.
3. The melting and boiling points generally increase as the mass of the molecule increases.

4. Each member of a homologous series exhibits similar chemical behaviour.

By studying the chemical properties of one member of an organic family, we can predict the possible behaviour of all the others.

5-9

Chemical Properties of Alkanes

Alkanes exhibit low chemical reactivity compared with other organic families.

The old name for the alkanes was *paraffin hydrocarbons*. Paraffin, from the Latin *parum* and *affinis*, means "little affinity" and refers to the low reactive tendency of the alkanes. At ordinary temperatures and pressures, alkanes remain chemically unchanged. Candles, for example, are composed of mixtures of solid alkanes that can be kept at room temperature for years with virtually no sign of decomposition or change. Table 3-14 lists the values of bond strengths for many covalent bonds and indicates that the C—C and C—H bond strengths are relatively high compared with the other single-bond values given. This explains the low chemical reactivity of alkanes at ordinary temperatures and pressures.

Despite their low reactivity, alkanes can undergo chemical reactions under certain conditions. Their main reactions fall into three groups: combustion reactions, which provide heat and energy; substitution reactions, which involve replacing hydrogen atoms in alkanes with other atoms such as chlorine and bromine; and thermal and catalytic cracking of longer-chain alkanes into smaller fragments, some of which are unsaturated. These reactions will be discussed in more detail in Chapter 6.

As the carbon chain length of the alkanes increases beyond the three carbon atoms in propane (C_3H_8), we find that a given molecular formula represents different structures with branches off the main chain. These are called *structural isomers*.

5-10

Structural Isomers

Structural isomers are molecules that have the same molecular formula but different spatial arrangements of the atoms.

Earlier, we noted Wöhler's contribution to chemistry in the synthesis of urea ($CO(NH_2)_2$) from ammonium cyanate (NH_4OCN). Although both of these molecules can be represented by the molecular formula, H_4CN_2O, they have different structures, and are known as structural isomers.

Alkanes, excluding methane, ethane and propane, show struc-

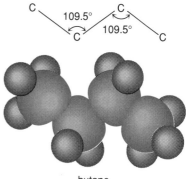

butane
m.p. −138.4°C
b.p.   −0.5°C

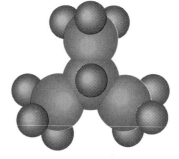

isobutane
m.p. −159.6°C
b.p.   −11.7°C

Figure 5-6
Butane and isobutane are structural isomers. Their molecular formulas are the same, but the spatial arrangement of their atoms is different. In isobutane, the central carbon atom is bonded to three other carbon atoms.

tural isomerism because the molecules are either unbranched or have side chains of different lengths and in different locations along the main chain. The number of possible isomers greatly increases with the number of carbon atoms, as shown in Table 5-5.

TABLE 5-5
ALKANES AND ISOMERS

Alkane	Molecular Formula	Number of Isomers
Methane	CH_4	–
Ethane	C_2H_6	–
Propane	C_3H_8	–
Butane	C_4H_{10}	2
Pentane	C_5H_{12}	3
Octane	C_8H_{18}	18
Decane	$C_{10}H_{22}$	75
Eicosane	$C_{20}H_{42}$	366 319
Triacontane	$C_{30}H_{62}$	4 111 846 763

Two possible butane structures exist—butane and isobutane—as shown in Fig. 5-6. The old name for butane is *n-butane*, with the *n* signifying "normal" to indicate that the structure is unbranched. The prefix *iso-* in the name *isobutane* indicates that there is a CH_3 branch off the second carbon atom of the main chain. Isomeric molecules differ in shape and therefore have different melting and boiling points, as indicated in Fig. 5-6. Because *n*-butane has a regular zigzag shape compared with isobutane, it packs into a crystal lattice more efficiently, allowing far more surface contact and stronger van der Waals forces. Consequently, butane has a higher melting point than isobutane.

Pentane can occur as three isomers—pentane, isopentane and neopentane—as shown by the structures in Fig. 5-7. Again we see that melting and boiling points differ for each isomer.

Figure 5-7
The three structural isomers of pentane. The prefix *iso-* identifies the isomer with the greatest similarity to isobutane. The prefix *neo-* comes from the Greek word for new.

pentane
m.p. −130°C
b.p.   36°C

2-methylbutane
(isopentane)
m.p. −160°C
b.p.   28°C

2,2-dimethylpropane
(neopentane)
m.p. −17°C
b.p.   10°C

FOLLOW-UP PROBLEM

Which of the following structures are isomers?

(a) 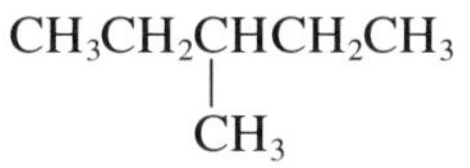 $CH_3CH_2CHCH_2CH_3$
                  |
                 CH_3

(b) 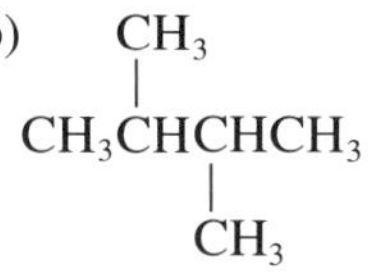 CH_3
         |
   $CH_3CHCHCH_3$
           |
         CH_3

(c) 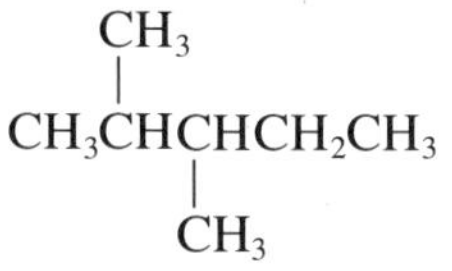 CH_3
         |
  $CH_3CHCHCH_2CH_3$
           |
       CH_3

(d) 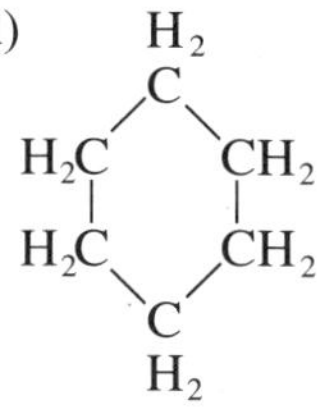 H_2
      C
 H_2C CH_2
 H_2C CH_2
      C
     H_2

(e) 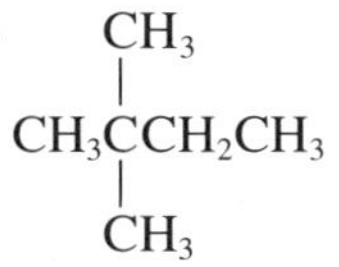 CH_3
         |
  $CH_3CCH_2CH_3$
         |
      CH_3

Answer: a, b and e are all structural isomers having the molecular formula C_6H_{14}.

The number of possible isomers can be determined mathematically. Many, if ever isolated or synthesized, would prove to be uninteresting because they are so alike chemically. Because there can be numerous organic structures for one molecular formula, chemists have developed a systematic set of rules for naming compounds.

5-11

Systematic Naming of Alkanes

The International Union of Pure and Applied Chemistry (IUPAC) has established rules for the systematic naming of chemical compounds to prevent confusion created by giving randomly selected names to isomers and to allow the chemist to readily identify the structure of any compound.

In the early beginnings of organic chemistry, compounds were named according to associations with their origin or on the basis of a property they exhibited. These are called *trivial*, or *common*, *names* and are still in use today. For example, the name of the sour-tasting compound, acetic acid, is derived from *acetum*, the Latin word for vinegar. Acetic acid also has a *systematic name*, ethanoic acid, which indicates structure. Generally, a chemist knows both the trivial and systematic names for the more common organic compounds.

Table 5-3 lists the systematic names for the first ten unbranched alkanes. Since it would be exceedingly difficult to memorize, for example, 75 different trivial names for the possible decane isomers, IUPAC has developed a system for naming and numbering the main chain and branches. To correctly name isomers, whether of alkanes or other organic families, the names of the simpler side chains must first be considered. The side chains in branched isomers are groups of atoms such as CH_3, C_2H_5, C_3H_7 and so on, called **alkyl groups**, or **radicals**. These alkyl groups can be related to corresponding alkanes (see Table 5-3). Alkyl radicals are simply the neutral species formed when one hydrogen atom is removed from the parent hydrocarbon. For example, the removal of one hydrogen atom from methane (CH_4) produces the methyl radical, or group, CH_3. Similarly, the ethyl group (C_2H_5) is derived by removing one hydrogen atom from ethane (C_2H_6). We should note that any alkyl radical is a group of atoms and not a charged species or ion.

Two different alkyl groups can be obtained from propane:

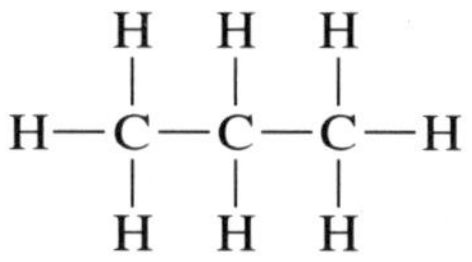

$$\begin{array}{ccccccc} & H & & H & & H & \\ & | & & | & & | & \\ H- & C & - & C & - & C & -H \\ & | & & | & & | & \\ & H & & H & & H & \end{array}$$

propane

If an end hydrogen is removed, then the propyl radical is obtained:

$$\begin{array}{ccccccc} & H & & H & & H & \\ & | & & | & & | & \\ H- & C & - & C & - & C & - \\ & | & & | & & | & \\ & H & & H & & H & \end{array}$$

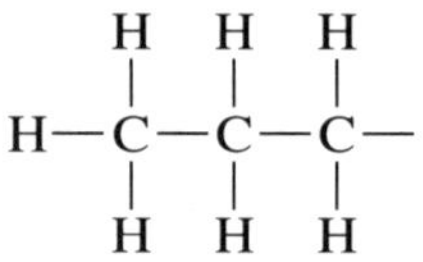

propyl

If a hydrogen is removed from the middle carbon, then the isopropyl radical is obtained:

$$\begin{array}{ccccccc} & H & & H & & H & \\ & | & & | & & | & \\ H- & C & - & C & - & C & -H \\ & | & & | & & | & \\ & H & & & & H & \end{array}$$

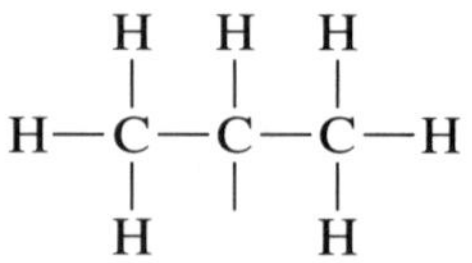

isopropyl

We previously noted that alkanes have the general formula C_nH_{2n+2}. By analogy, we find that the alkyl radical can be represented by C_nH_{2n+1}. Often, an alkyl group is denoted as R; for example, the general formula of an alcohol can be represented by ROH.

The names of many organic compounds are based on the names of the first ten members of alkanes and their corresponding alkyl groups. The structures shown in the margin are accompanied by their systematic names. To explain such names we will first apply the IUPAC rules of nomenclature to molecules that have only one kind of side branch, such as a methyl group.

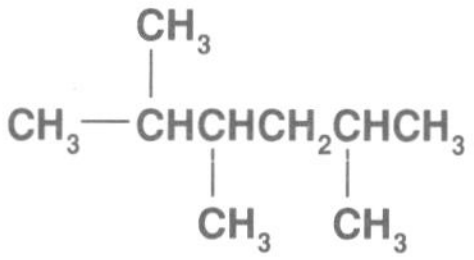

$$CH_3$$
$$|$$
$$CH_3-CHCHCH_2CHCH_3$$
$$|\qquad\quad|$$
$$CH_3\quad CH_3$$
2,3,5-trimethylhexane

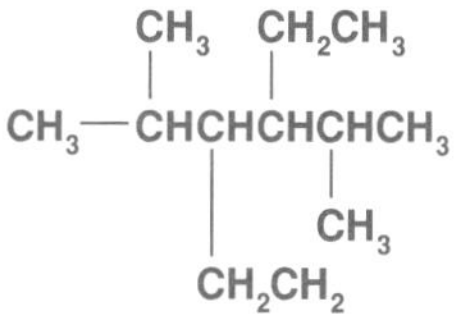

$$CH_3\quad CH_2CH_3$$
$$|\qquad\quad|$$
$$CH_3-CHCHCHCHCH_3$$
$$|$$
$$CH_3$$
$$CH_2CH_2$$
3,4-diethyl-2,5-dimethylhexane

EXAMPLE 5-1
Naming Alkanes With Only One Kind of Side Chain
What is the IUPAC name for the following compound?

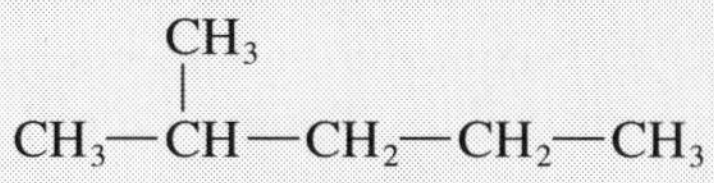

$$CH_3$$
$$|$$
$$CH_3-CH-CH_2-CH_2-CH_3$$
isohexane
(trivial name)

SOLUTION
1. Select the longest, continuous chain of carbon atoms as the parent, or main, chain. In our example, the longest, continuous chain has five carbon atoms.

2. Number the carbon atoms of the parent chain, starting from the end that has the branch nearest it:

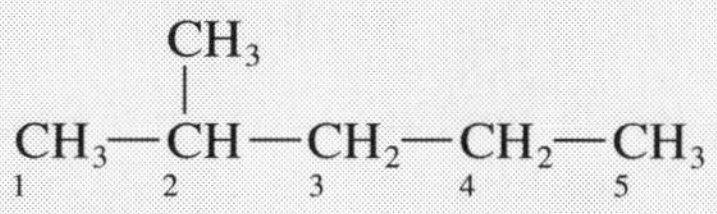

$$CH_3$$
$$|$$
$$CH_3-CH-CH_2-CH_2-CH_3$$
$$\small 1\quad\ \ 2\quad\ \ 3\quad\ \ 4\quad\ \ 5$$

3. Name the main chain in accordance with the alkane names. The structure shown has a five-carbon main chain, which gives us *pentane* as the root of the systematic name.

4. Name the branched chain according to the name of the corresponding group, and locate its position along the main chain. In our example, the branched chain is a methyl group at carbon number two of the main chain. Therefore, the IUPAC name for isohexane is *2-methylpentane*.

The molecular formula of the alkane in Example 5-1 is C_6H_{14}, and the substance is a hexane isomer. However, the compound is named as if a methyl group had taken the place of a hydrogen atom bonded to carbon number two of a pentane molecule. The actual hexane isomer cannot be made directly from pentane in such a simple manner.

What if we were to number the main chain from the other end, as follows?

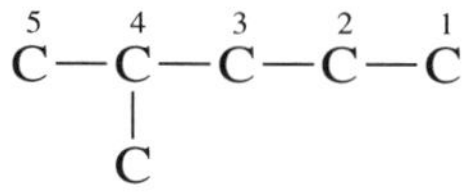

$$\overset{5}{C}-\overset{4}{C}-\overset{3}{C}-\overset{2}{C}-\overset{1}{C}$$
$$\vert$$
$$C$$

The apparent name would be 4-methylpentane, which is not acceptable according to IUPAC rules. *The number of the carbon atom with the side chain is always kept as low as possible.*

Shown below is an alkane that appears to have a main chain of six carbon atoms and a methyl group branching from carbon number one of the main chain. Should we call the substance 1-methylhexane? The answer is no. There is freedom of rotation about a C—C single bond, and therefore the longest, continuous chain has seven carbon atoms and no branch. *We can never have a branch off the end carbon of a main chain.*

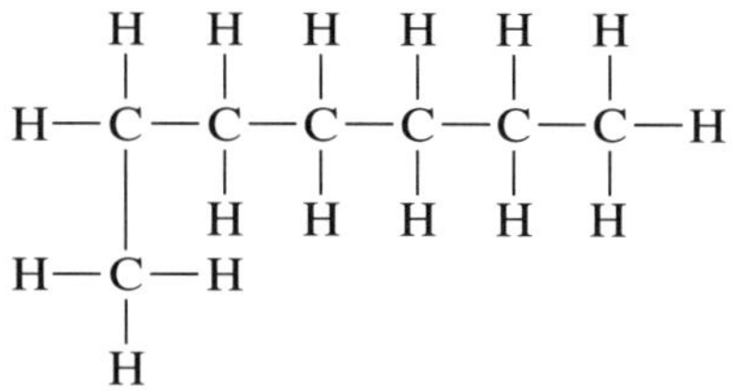

$$
\begin{array}{ccccccc}
 & H & H & H & H & H & H \\
 & | & | & | & | & | & | \\
H- & C- & C- & C- & C- & C- & C-H \\
 & | & | & | & | & | & \\
 & H & H & H & H & H & \\
H- & C-H & & & & & \\
 & | & & & & & \\
 & H & & & & & \\
\end{array}
$$

heptane

Prefix	Number
Mono-	1
Di-	2
Tri-	3
Tetra-	4
Penta-	5
Hexa-	6

Because a molecule can have two or more side chains, suitable rules for nomenclature have been developed to accommodate such structures. The location of every side branch is numbered, and the total number of that particular alkyl group is indicated by the prefixes *di-*, *tri-* and so on. Some prefixes and the numbers they represent are given in the margin.

In the following example, we will consider a more complex alkane with four methyl side branches.

EXAMPLE 5-2
Naming Alkanes With Multiple Side Chains
What is the IUPAC name for the structure shown?

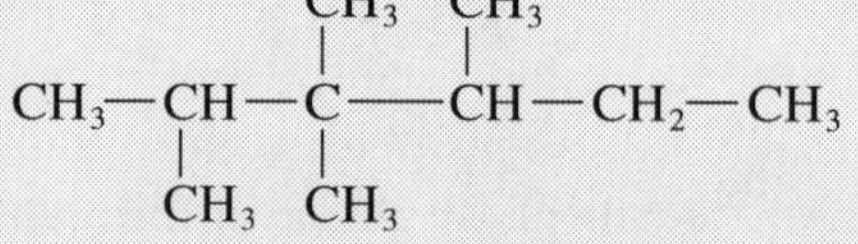

$$
\begin{array}{c}
\qquad\quad CH_3 \quad CH_3 \\
\qquad\quad | \qquad\; | \\
CH_3-CH-C\!-\!\!-\!\!-CH-CH_2-CH_3 \\
\qquad\quad | \qquad\; | \\
\qquad\quad CH_3 \quad CH_3
\end{array}
$$

SOLUTION
1. Select the longest, continuous chain of carbon atoms as the parent chain. It has six carbon atoms.

2. Number the carbon atoms of the main chain, starting from the end that has a branch closest to it. In this example, we would begin counting from the left:

$$
\begin{array}{c}
\quad\;\; \text{C} \quad\; \text{C} \\
\quad\;\; | \quad\;\; | \\
\text{C}-\text{C}-\text{C}-\text{C}-\text{C}-\text{C} \\
{\scriptstyle 1 \quad |2 \quad |3 \quad 4 \quad 5 \quad 6} \\
\quad\;\; \text{C} \quad\; \text{C}
\end{array}
$$

3. Name the parent chain in accordance with the root of the IUPAC name of the alkane that has a six-carbon unbranched chain, which is *hexane*.

4. Locate the branches and name them according to the corresponding alkyl groups. In our example, there is one methyl branch at carbon number two, two methyl groups at carbon number three and one at carbon number four.

5. Indicate the number of side branches by adding the corresponding prefix to the name of the side chain. In this example, there are four methyl groups; therefore, *tetra-* is the prefix, as in tetramethylhexane. The number locating each branch is written first, for example, *2,3,3,4-tetramethylhexane*. Note that we use four numbers because there are four side chains, and we repeat the number three because there are two distinct methyl branches off carbon number three.

Some alkanes have more than one type of side chain. In such instances, the IUPAC rules state that the names of the side branches be written in alphabetical order, and the number of the side chains indicated by numbers, as before.

EXAMPLE 5-3
Naming Alkanes With More Than One Type of Side Chain
What is the IUPAC name for the following alkane?

$$
\begin{array}{c}
\quad\;\; \text{CH}_3 \quad\quad\quad\; \text{CH}_3 \\
\quad\;\; | \quad\quad\quad\quad\;\; | \\
\text{CH}_3-\text{CH}-\text{CH}-\text{C}-\text{CH}_2-\text{CH}_3 \\
\quad\quad\quad\;\; | \quad\quad\; | \\
\quad\quad\quad\; \text{CH}_3 \quad \text{CH}_2-\text{CH}_3
\end{array}
$$

SOLUTION

1. Look for the longest, continuous carbon chain to obtain the root of the systematic name. It is a six-carbon chain, which gives us *hexane*.

2. Branching starts closest to the left side, so we number the carbons of the main chain from left to right.

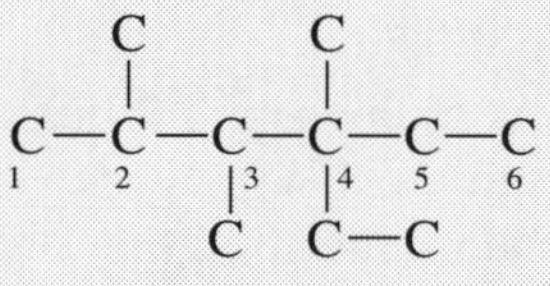

3. There is one methyl branch off carbon number two, a methyl branch from carbon number three and another methyl branch off carbon number four. This gives us *2,3,4-trimethyl*, with the *tri-* indicating the number of methyl branches.

4. There is an ethyl branch off carbon number four of the main chain. This gives us *4-ethyl* as part of the name.

5. Finally, we apply the rule of alphabetical order and put ethyl ahead of methyl. Therefore, the name is *4-ethyl-2,3,4-trimethylhexane*.

Given the correct systematic name of a branched alkane, we will find it relatively simple to draw the structure. Let us look at an example.

EXAMPLE 5-4
Drawing Structural Formulas From IUPAC Names
Draw the structural formula for the alkane 2,3,4,4,5-pentamethyloctane.

SOLUTION

1. The root *octane* indicates that the longest, continuous chain has eight carbon atoms.

2. *Pentamethyl* tells us that there are five methyl side branches off the main chain, and the numbers 2,3,4,4,5 indicate the locations of the side branches.

3. Finally, the hydrogens should be added to give a complete structural formula:

$$CH_3-\underset{\underset{\displaystyle CH_3}{|}}{\overset{\overset{\displaystyle CH_3}{|}}{CH}}-\underset{\underset{\displaystyle CH_3}{|}}{CH}-\underset{\underset{\displaystyle CH_3}{|}}{\overset{\overset{\displaystyle CH_3}{|}}{C}}-\underset{\underset{\displaystyle CH_3}{|}}{\overset{\overset{\displaystyle CH_3}{|}}{CH}}-CH_2-CH_2-CH_3$$

Before determining the systematic names of alkanes, be sure to pick the longest possible main chain. This may not always be obvious. Consider the structure given in the margin. As written, it appears to have a five-carbon main chain, with two ethyl branches located at positions two and four of the main chain. However, the longest chain has seven carbons and runs from the end of one apparent ethyl side chain to the carbon end of the other ethyl side chain. *No correct structure for an alkane can have ethyl branches at carbon number two at either end of the main chain.*

As hydrocarbons and other organic compounds increase in complexity, other rules for nomenclature have been introduced by IUPAC. As we discussed previously, there are two possible propyl radicals—propyl and isopropyl—shown as side chains in the alkane below. Note that the name of this compound adheres to the rule of alphabetical order.

$$CH_3-\underset{\underset{\displaystyle CH_2-CH_3}{|}}{CH}-CH_2-\underset{\underset{\displaystyle CH_2-CH_3}{|}}{CH}-CH_3$$

$$CH_3-CH_2-CH_2-\underset{\underset{\displaystyle \underset{\underset{\displaystyle CH_2-CH_2-CH_3}{|}}{|}}{}}{CH}-\underset{\overset{\displaystyle CH_3-CH-CH_3}{|}}{CH}-CH_2-CH_2-CH_3$$

isopropyl side chain

propyl side chain

4-isopropyl-5-propyloctane

FOLLOW-UP PROBLEM

Name the following alkanes using IUPAC rules.

a)
$$CH_3-CH_2-\underset{\underset{\displaystyle CH_3}{|}}{\overset{\overset{\displaystyle CH_3}{|}}{CH}}-CH_2-CH_3$$

b)
$$CH_3-CH_2-\underset{\underset{\displaystyle CH_3}{|}}{\overset{\overset{\displaystyle CH_3}{|}}{C}}-CH_2-CH_3$$

c)
$$CH_3-CH_2-\underset{\underset{\displaystyle CH_3}{|}}{\overset{\overset{\displaystyle CH_2-CH_3}{|}}{CH}}-CH_2-\underset{\underset{\displaystyle CH_3}{|}}{CH}-CH_3$$

d)
$$CH_3—CH_2—\underset{\underset{CH_2—CH_3}{|}}{\overset{\overset{CH_2—CH_3}{|}}{C}}—CH_2—CH_3$$

e)
$$CH_3—CH_2—\underset{}{\overset{\overset{CH_2—CH_2—CH_3}{|}}{CH}}—CH_2—CH_2—CH_3$$

f)
$$CH_3—CH_2—CH_2—\underset{\underset{CH_3—CH—CH_3}{|}}{CH}—CH_2—CH_2—CH_3$$

Answers:
a) **3-methylpentane**
b) **3,3-dimethylpentane**
c) **4-ethyl-2-methylhexane**
d) **3,3-diethylpentane**
e) **4-ethylheptane**
f) **4-isopropylheptane**

As mentioned earlier, alkanes are relatively unreactive because of their strong C—C and C—H bonds. However, there are other hydrocarbons that are more reactive than alkanes. For example, members of the alkene family have a number of reactions taking place at the unsaturated carbon-to-carbon double bond, leading to the production of many synthetic polymers.

ALKENES

The alkenes are unsaturated hydrocarbon molecules that contain one or more double bonds between carbon atoms. The simplest alkene is ethene (C_2H_4), commonly called ethylene. The demand for ethylene in the chemical industry consistently exceeds the supply, since it is the most popular alkene for making synthetic polymers. Polyethylene, for example, is commonly used in milk bags, garbage bags and food storage containers. Propene (propylene, C_3H_6), the second member of the alkene family, is used in making polypropylene, the material of indoor-outdoor carpeting and plastic ropes.

Both natural and synthetic rubbers are composed of alkene units joined together in long-chain molecules. Table 5-6 gives the systematic names, common names, molecular and structural formulas, and the physical properties of some alkenes.

Figure 5-8
In August 1979, a world-scale ethylene plant went into production in Red Deer, Alberta, at an estimated cost of $355 million. The plant produces 5.5 million kg of ethylene yearly, valued at approximately $200 million.
  The ethylene is made using ethane extracted from natural gas. Prospective derivatives from ethylene include ethylene glycol and ethylene oxide, which are used in the manufacture of antifreeze and polyester fibres.

TABLE 5-6
REPRESENTATIVE ALKENES

Systematic Name	Common Name	Molecular Formula	Structural Formula	Melting Point (°C)	Boiling Point (°C)
Ethene	ethylene	C_2H_4		−169	−103.7
Propene	propylene	C_3H_6		−185.2	−47.4
1-Butene	butylene	C_4H_8		−185.3	−6.3
1-Pentene	–	C_5H_{10}		−138	30

By looking at the molecular formulas of the alkenes in Table 5-6, we can see that the general formula is C_nH_{2n}, and that it applies to structures with only one double bond. Alkenes with two or more C=C bonds in the molecule, such as 1,3-butadiene, shown in the margin, do not fit this general formula.

$$CH_2=CHCH=CH_2$$
1,3-butadiene

5-12
Naming Alkenes

In naming alkenes, we give the location of the C=C bond in the chain the lowest number possible.
To name an alkene we retain the first part of the alkane name that indicates the number of carbon atoms and change the end of the name to *-ene*. For example, the alkene with five carbon atoms and one C=C bond in the carbon chain is *pentene*.

The physical and chemical properties of the alkenes are a function of the position of the carbon-to-carbon double bond. For this reason, IUPAC rules for naming alkenes give the location of the C=C bond the lowest number possible.

EXAMPLE 5-5
Naming an Alkene Using IUPAC Rules
Give the IUPAC name for the following alkene:

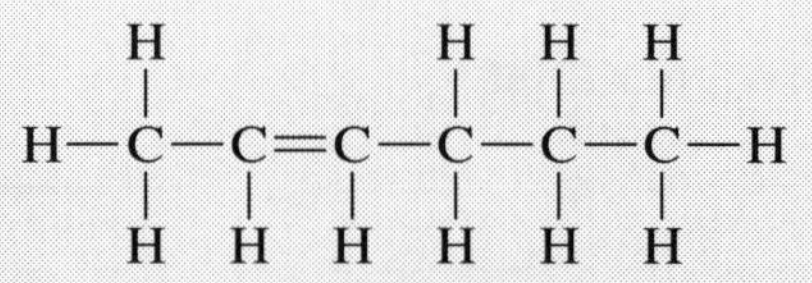

$$
\begin{array}{ccccccc}
& H & & & H & H & H \\
& | & & & | & | & | \\
H\!-\!C\!-\!C\!=\!C\!-\!C\!-\!C\!-\!C\!-\!H \\
& | & | & | & | & | & | \\
& H & H & H & H & H & H
\end{array}
$$

SOLUTION

1. Select the longest carbon chain containing the C=C bond. Since it has six carbon atoms, the root of the IUPAC name is *hexene*.

2. Give the location of the C=C bond the lowest possible number. The double bond is between carbons two and three. Therefore, the name is *2-hexene*.

What if an alkene has side branches? The systematic naming of such alkenes is illustrated in the following example.

EXAMPLE 5-6
Naming Alkenes With Side Branches

Name the following alkene using IUPAC rules.

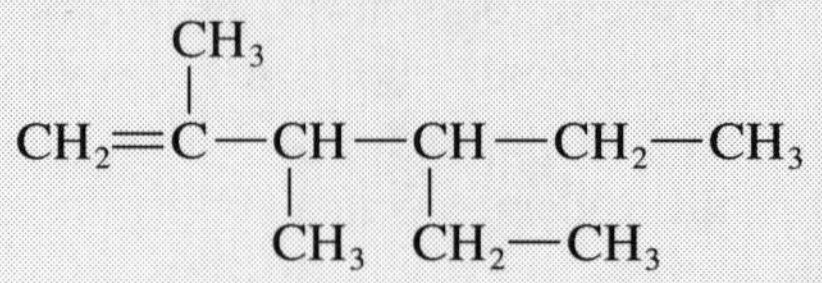

$$
\begin{array}{c}
CH_3 \\
| \\
CH_2\!=\!C\!-\!CH\!-\!CH\!-\!CH_2\!-\!CH_3 \\
| \quad\;\; | \\
CH_3 \;\; CH_2\!-\!CH_3
\end{array}
$$

SOLUTION

1. Selecting the longest, continuous chain containing the C=C bond as the parent chain, we find it has six carbon atoms. Thus, the root of the name is *hexene*.

2. Numbering the chain from the end that has the C=C bond closest gives *1-hexene*.

3. There is one ethyl side chain off carbon number four of the main chain, so we call it *4-ethyl*.

4. Two methyl branches are at carbons two and three of the main chain, so we write *2,3-dimethyl*.

5. Finally, we apply the rule of alphabetical order previously stated for branched alkanes and name the compound *4-ethyl-2,3-dimethyl-1-hexene*.

The name 2-hexene derived in Example 5-5 is incomplete

because the presence of one or more C=C bonds in a chain leads to the possibility of a new kind of isomerism, called *geometric isomerism*.

5-13

Shapes of Alkenes (Geometric Isomerism)

The C=C bond of an alkene is a rigid structure that produces geometric isomers.

The shape of ethene and other members of the alkene family can be determined by applying the VSEPR theory. Figure 5-9 shows that each of the two carbon atoms of ethene has two single bonds and one double bond. In VSEPR theory, the C=C double bond is assumed to behave like a single bond in terms of electron-pair repulsions. Thus, each of the two carbon atoms effectively has three single bonding pairs around it. Mutual repulsion of the three bonding electron pairs results in a flat, triangular distribution of the bonds around each of the carbons. Therefore, the ethene molecule is a flat, or planar, structure whose bond angles are approximately 120°.

In Chapter 3 we saw that ethene has a strong sigma (σ) bond formed by the overlap of two sp^2 orbitals, and a weaker pi (π) bond formed by the overlap of two p orbitals. Because of the double bond, alkenes have a much more rigid structure than alkanes. For example, the two CH_3 groups in ethane can be rotated in opposite directions. However, the CH_2 groups in ethene cannot. This rotation would destroy the pi bond and require a significant input of energy. Consequently, the alkenes from butene on can exist in geometrically distinct structures, called **geometric isomers**. These are structures that, regardless of how you twist and turn them, cannot be laid down over one another in a way that allows the side chains to coincide. For example, there are two possible isomers of 2-butene (also shown in the margin):

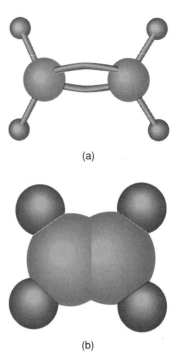

(a)

(b)

Figure 5-9
Structure of ethene in (a) a ball-and-stick model and (b) a space-filling model.

$$H_3C\diagdown\qquad\diagup CH_3 \qquad H_3C\diagdown\qquad\diagup H$$
$$C\!=\!C \qquad\qquad C\!=\!C$$
$$H\diagup\qquad\diagdown H \qquad\quad H\diagup\qquad\diagdown CH_3$$

    cis-2-butene   *trans*-2-butene

The *cis isomer* of 2-butene, *cis*-2-butene, has the two methyl groups on the same side of the plane of the double bond (*cis* meaning "on the same side"). In the *trans isomer*, *trans*-2-butene, the methyl groups are on opposite sides of the C=C plane (*trans* meaning "on opposite sides"). Thus, when naming geometric isomers, we must indicate the location of the C=C bond and whether the attached groups are on the same side or on opposite sides of the plane of the double bond.

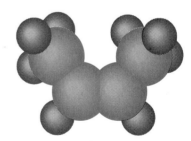

cis-2-butene

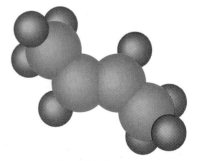

trans-2-butene

Some alkenes have two or more double bonds. A *diene* has two C=C bonds, and a *triene* has three C=C bonds, as shown below. The names of dienes, trienes and so on are formed by replacing the *-ne* ending of the corresponding alkane name by *-diene*, *-triene* and so on.

$$H_2C=CH—CH=CH_2$$
1,3-butadiene

$$H_2C=CH—CH=CH—CH=CH—CH_3$$
1,3,5-heptatriene

Some molecules have an alternating system of C—C and C=C bonds, as in C—C=C—C=C—C=C—C=C; this is called a *conjugated double-bond system*. The electrons occupying the *p* orbitals of a C=C bond can absorb light energy and move to an excited state. As the number of conjugated double bonds in a molecule increases, pi-cloud electrons require less energy to move to an excited state. Thus, we find that most C=C conjugated systems, such as those in β-carotene and lycopene (Fig. 5-10), absorb visible wavelengths of light and are, consequently, coloured. For example, β-carotene absorbs light of wavelengths 483 nm and 453 nm, which correspond to blue and blue-green in the spectrum. As the light of these colours is absorbed, the β-carotene appears yellow to orange.

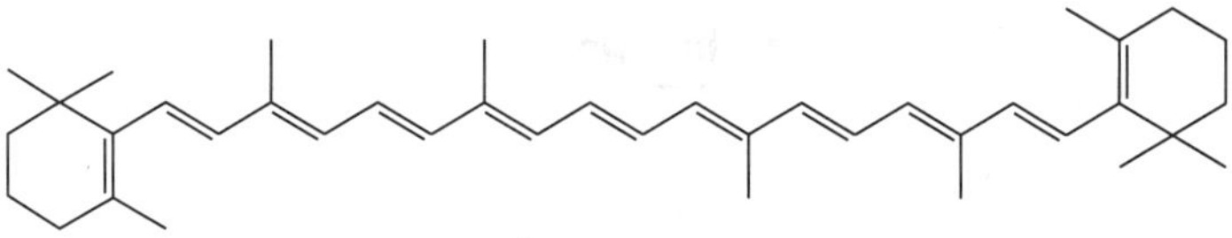

Figure 5-10
Examples of a conjugated double-bond system. β-carotene is the precursor of vitamin A and gives carrots their colour; it is also used to colour margarine. Lycopene occurs in tomatoes and other red fruits.

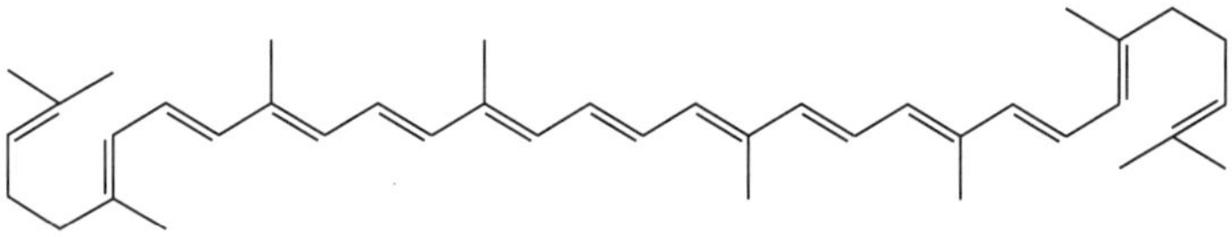

β-carotene

lycopene

We will see in the next two sections that the physical and chemical properties of the alkene family depend on the presence of C=C double bonds.

FOLLOW-UP PROBLEMS

1. Give systematic names for the following alkenes:

a)

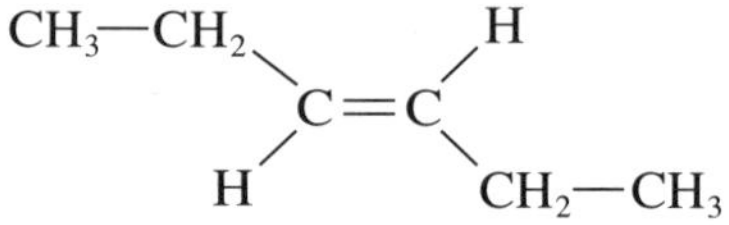

b) 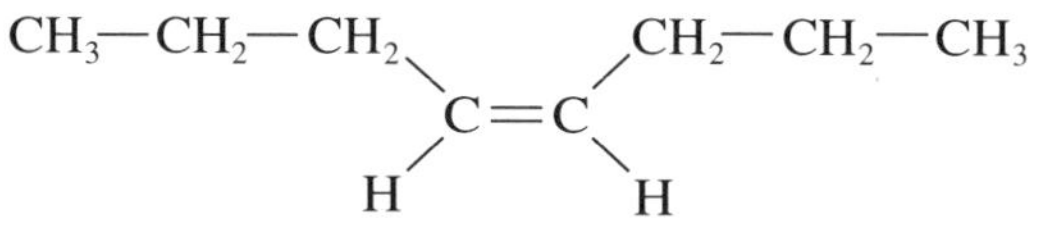 CH_3—CH_2—CH_2 $\diagdown$ CH_2—CH_2—CH_3
$C=C$
H H

2. Draw structures for (a) *cis*-3-octene and (b) 5-ethyl-6-methyl-*trans*-3-heptene.

Answers:

1. (a) *trans*-3-hexene, (b) *cis*-4-octene

2. a) 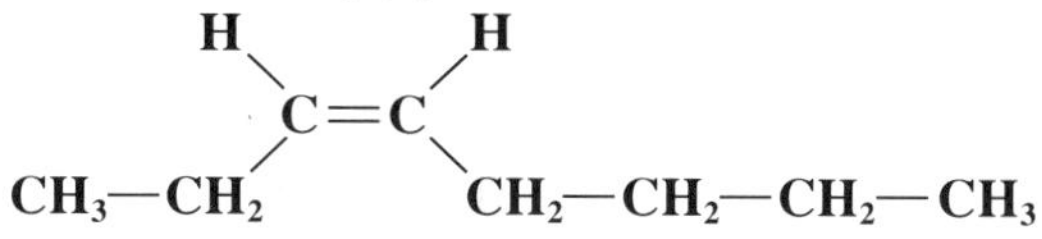
H H
$C=C$
CH_3—CH_2 CH_2—CH_2—CH_2—CH_3

b) 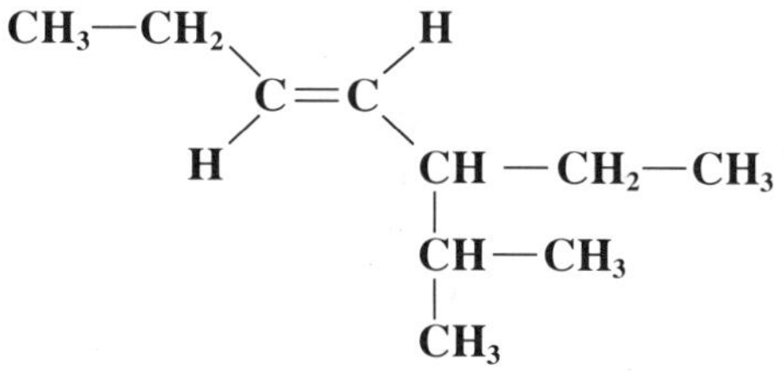 CH_3—CH_2 $\diagdown$ H
$C=C$
H CH — CH_2—CH_3
CH—CH_3
CH_3

5-14
Physical Properties of Alkenes

Melting points of alkenes do not increase in a regular manner, although they tend to rise as the molecular mass increases. Boiling points increase with an increase in molecular mass. Table 5-6 gives the melting and boiling points of the first four unbranched alkenes that have the C=C bond between carbons one and two. From 1-butene on, the irregularity of melting points is explained by the freedom of rotation about the single bonds. Because these alkenes are not rigid throughout their length, they do not pack neatly into a crystal lattice. However, the boiling points of the alkenes are not significantly affected by the orientations of the atoms, and they tend to increase with an increase in molecular mass.

5-15
Chemical Properties of Alkenes

Alkenes are very reactive compared with alkanes because of the C=C unsaturated bond.
The carbon-to-carbon double bonds of the alkenes are very reactive sites in which the pi-bond electron clouds are spread out over

the upper and lower part of the molecules, and are thus easily affected by polar molecules or molecules that will react with the accessible electrons. For example, when halogens such as chlorine and bromine add across the double bond, they form halogenated alkanes; the addition of hydrogen converts alkenes into alkanes; and water, under certain conditions, can be added to produce alcohols. We will look at these reactions in the next chapter. In industry, the most important reaction of alkenes is *polymerization*, in which alkenes link across the double bonds to themselves or to other unsaturated molecules.

ETHYLENE AS A PLANT HORMONE

"I t takes only one rotten apple to spoil the barrel" is an old adage based on scientific fact: When one apple in a barrel begins to rot, it stimulates the production of a gas, causing the rest of the apples in the barrel to go bad as well. Scientists have identified this gas as ethene (ethylene), a plant hormone that affects various stages in a plant's life.

The effect of ethylene on plants was first noted around 1900 in Germany, where "illuminating gas" was burned in street lamps. Wherever leaks appeared in the gas lines, the nearby trees lost their leaves. Similarly, mango and pineapple growers would light fires near their crops because they knew that some component in the smoke caused the fruits to all flower and, thus, ripen at the same time. By 1910, the active ingredient, ethylene, had been identified, and scientists began to study its effects on plant growth.

Ethylene has profound effects on the metabolism of plants. The production of ethylene within different plant tissues is activated by other plant hormones, primarily the *auxins*. Auxins stimulate root formation, stem elongation and fruit development. When the auxin concentration reaches a certain level, it causes the production and release of ethylene. Ethylene inhibits the growth of roots and stems and encourages leaf fall and flower development. It also plays an important role in the aging process (senescence) of plants and in the ripening of fruits.

Although auxins initiate the development of fruit, ethylene stimulates the ripening process. Ethylene helps fruits release *pectinase*, an enzyme that breaks down pectins in the cell wall to soften fruit, and other enzymes that convert starch to sugars. The production of ethylene relies on a positive feedback system in which the ethylene produced by the fruit stimulates the fruit to produce more ethylene.

In Canada, ethylene is used commercially to promote natural colouring in locally grown fruits such as blueberries and apples, and to loosen cherries for easier harvesting. Ethylene is also used to ripen many imported fruits. Fruits such as bananas, pineapples and citrus fruits are picked while they are still green and stored in atmospherically controlled containers. The concentration of ethylene in these containers is regulated to control the speed of ripening before or during transportation to markets. Recently, compounds that release ethylene gradually have been developed for use on plants in the open air as well as in closed containers. In tropical areas, ethylene is widely used to promote the flowering of pineapples and to increase the yield of latex from rubber trees.

Ethylene has proved to be a relatively safe agricultural compound—any leaks disperse rapidly; there is no known toxicity; and it does not contaminate the food chain.

Because ethylene is a gas, it not only travels within the plant to reach target tissues, but can also travel through the air to reach the tissues of other plants. Therefore, ripening is contagious and can be initiated by one single fruit.

ALKYNES

Another homologous series with pi electrons available for addition and polymerization reactions are alkynes. As with the double bonds of alkenes, the triple bonds of alkynes play an important role in determining their properties and reactions.

Alkynes are unsaturated hydrocarbons that contain at least one C≡C bond as the functional group. The simplest alkyne—ethyne (C_2H_2), commonly called acetylene—is the fuel for the oxyacetylene torch used extensively in industry for cutting metals. The reaction of hydrogen chloride with acetylene forms vinyl chloride (CH_2=CHCl), a compound commonly used in making plastics.

The names, physical properties and molecular and structural formulas of some alkynes are listed in Table 5-7.

TABLE 5-7
REPRESENTATIVE ALKYNES

Systematic Name	Common Name	Molecular Formula	Structural Formula	Melting Point (°C)	Boiling Point (°C)
Ethyne	acetylene	C_2H_2	H—C≡C—H	−80.8	−84.0
Propyne	methylacetylene	C_3H_4	H—C≡C—C—H (with H above and below middle C)	−101.5	−23.2
1-Butyne	ethylacetylene	C_4H_6	H—C≡C—C—C—H (with H's)	−125.7	8.1
1-Pentyne	–	C_5H_8	H—C≡C—C—C—C—H (with H's)	−90	40.2

5-16

Naming Alkynes

As in the alkene family, the location of the functional group is given precedence and is assigned the lowest possible number. The general formula for alkynes with one C≡C bond is C_nH_{2n-2}. The systematic names are obtained by replacing the *-ane* ending of the corresponding alkane name with the suffix *-yne*. Structural isomers begin with butyne, where the triple bond can lie between carbons one and two, or two and three. Therefore, from butyne on, the position of the triple bond is indicated with the lowest number possible. For example, $HC{\equiv}CCH_2CH_2CH_3$ is 1-pentyne, while $CH_3CH_2CH_2C{\equiv}CCH_2CH_3$ is 3-heptyne, the $C{\equiv}C$ bond of which lies between carbons three and four.

The trivial names of alkynes were assigned on the basis that an alkyl group replaced a hydrogen atom of acetylene. For example, propyne is commonly called methylacetylene because a hydrogen atom of acetylene has been replaced by a methyl group. Similarly, 1-butyne has the trivial name ethylacetylene, which shows that a hydrogen atom of acetylene has been replaced by an ethyl group.

5-17
Shapes and Physical Properties of Alkynes

The simplest member of the alkyne family, ethyne, has a linear structure. However, as the molecular size of the homolog increases, the shape of the molecule changes, resulting in an irregular change in melting points.

The linear geometry of ethyne, $H{-}C{\equiv}C{-}H$, can be explained by VSEPR theory: The $C{\equiv}C$ triple bond behaves like a $C{-}C$ bond in terms of electron-pair repulsions, and thus each carbon atom in ethyne can be viewed as having two single bonds. To minimize repulsion, the bonding electrons locate themselves as far apart as possible, that is, 180° apart on either side of the carbon atoms. Although the $H{-}C{\equiv}C{-}H$ molecule is linear (Fig. 5-11), it changes its shape when an alkyl group is attached to the triple-bonded carbon, as in $H{-}C{\equiv}C{-}CH_3$, $H{-}C{\equiv}C{-}C_2H_5$ and $H{-}C{\equiv}C{-}C_3H_7$.

The freedom of rotation about the $C{-}C$ single bonds of the alkyl groups results in an irregular packing arrangement of molecules in those alkynes from propyne on. Therefore, as is the case with the alkenes, melting points do not increase in a regular manner. Table 5-7 shows that the first four unbranched alkynes with a triple bond between carbons one and two show no systematic increase in melting points. Boiling points, however, show a systematic increase in the homologous series.

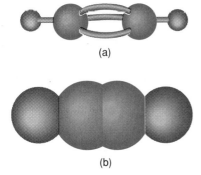

(a)

(b)

Figure 5-11
Structure of ethyne in (a) a ball-and-stick model and (b) a space-filling model.

5-18
Chemical Properties of Alkynes

Alkynes are more unsaturated than alkenes and, therefore, are more chemically reactive.

Among the hydrocarbons, the alkynes have the least number of attached hydrogen atoms and, therefore, are the most unsaturated.

Experiments show that alkenes and alkynes are reactive compounds compared with the alkanes, which are saturated hydrocarbons. Many of the reactions of alkynes are similar to those of the alkenes.

How does the bonding theory explain the differences in chemical reactivity between hydrocarbons? The C≡C bond is stronger than the C=C bond, which in turn is stronger than the C—C bond. In an alkene, the C=C bond consists of a sigma bond and a pi bond, whereas in an alkyne, the C≡C bond has one sigma and two pi bonds between the unsaturated carbon atoms. Both alkenes and alkynes undergo addition reactions in which an atom or group is added to the carbon atoms. The presence of molecules such as Cl_2 and Br_2 disturbs the pi cloud, breaking open the C≡C or C=C bonds in a way that allows the addition of the atoms to the previously unsaturated linkage. Because the alkynes are more unsaturated than alkenes, they can undergo more addition reactions.

Before moving on to the next class of organic hydrocarbons, we should note that, in general, cyclic hydrocarbons that have C—C, C=C or C≡C bonds show the same reactivity as their open-chain counterparts. Let us look at the cycloalkanes as an example. The simplest cycloalkane is cyclopropane, whose structure is shown below. The C—C bonds are strained, making the compound reactive even though it is saturated. Typically, C—C bonds in open-chain structures have a bond angle of 109.5°. In cyclopropane, the bond angle is 60°, which results in increased repulsive forces between the C—C bonds and high bond strain in the ring. As the number of carbons in the cycloalkanes increases, the bond angle increases and the bond strain decreases. Compounds such as cyclopentane and cyclohexane have about the same reactivity as their open-chain counterparts.

Geometric isomerism cannot occur in alkynes.

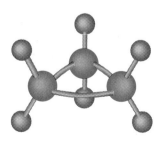

.cyclopropane
m.p. −127.6°C
b.p.   −32.7°C

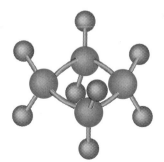

cyclobutane
m.p. −93.9°C
b.p.   49.2°C

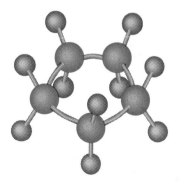

cyclopentane
m.p.   6.5°C
b.p.   80.7°C

AROMATIC COMPOUNDS

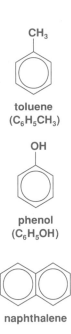

toluene
($C_6H_5CH_3$)

phenol
(C_6H_5OH)

naphthalene

Aromatic compounds include benzene (C_6H_6) and those compounds that contain a benzene ring or a related structure. Benzene is a very useful industrial solvent and is used to derive many other organic substances. In these synthesis reactions, the hydrogen atoms of the benzene ring are replaced with other atoms or groups. Some examples are shown in the margin. The other major feature of benzene is its ability to form aromatic hydrocarbons composed of two or more joined benzene molecules, as in naphthalene (shown in the margin). Although benzene and other aromatic compounds are unsaturated, *they do not undergo the addition reactions typical of the aliphatic unsaturated compounds and are not as reactive*. To explain these differences, we will first examine the benzene molecule in more detail.

X-ray diffraction and infrared spectroscopy reveal that the six carbon atoms in benzene form a *regular hexagon*. The benzene molecule is planar, all carbon-to-carbon bonds are identical and all bond angles are 120°. Recall from Chapter 3 that since no single electron-dot formula can be drawn that is consistent with this data, we must consider the benzene molecule to be a *resonance hybrid*. The two most important resonance structures are shown below:

Michael Faraday (1791–1867) was the first person to isolate benzene from gas oils in 1825. However, its structure remained unknown until 1866, when August Kekulé proposed that benzene had a ring structure.

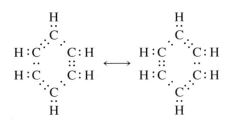

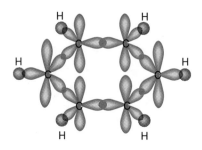

Figure 5-12
Schematic diagram for benzene, showing sigma bonds between adjacent carbon atoms and between each carbon and hydrogen atom.

Because all four bonding electrons of each carbon atom are involved in either C—C or C—H bonds, we can assume that sp^2 hybrid orbitals, each containing an electron, are involved. Two of the sp^2 orbitals of each carbon atom take part in carbon-to-carbon bond formation and each overlaps (endways) an sp^2 orbital from an adjacent carbon atom. This results in the formation of a strong, single, covalent sigma bond between both carbon atoms. The unhybridized p_y orbital of each carbon atom containing a single electron is perpendicular to the plane of the sp^2 hybrid orbitals and is parallel to the other five unhybridized p_y orbitals (Fig. 5-12). The lateral overlap of p_y orbitals produces pi bonds. The electrons involved in pi bonds are delocalized and spread out over the entire molecule and form the doughnut-shaped lobes illustrated in Fig.

5-13. The resonance-hybrid model for benzene is partially explained in terms of the six delocalized electrons and justified on the basis of experimentally derived bond energies.

Unsaturated aromatic hydrocarbons are less reactive than unsaturated aliphatic hydrocarbons. We can use the delocalization of the pi electrons and the concept of resonance to account for the extra stability of the benzene molecule. The experimentally derived bond strength in benzene is actually much greater than that calculated by assuming the presence of three double bonds. The difference between actual and calculated bond energies is called **resonance energy**. It is the stabilizing effect of this resonance energy that causes unsaturated aromatic rings to be less reactive than unsaturated aliphatic molecules, which have true double bonds. The six equivalent carbon-to-carbon bonds in benzene are intermediate in nature between a single and a double bond.

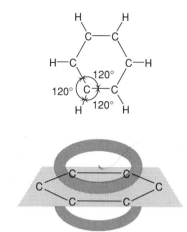

Figure 5-13
Bonding in benzene shows that the charge cloud formed by the electrons of the laterally overlapping p_y orbitals consists of doughnut-shaped lobes above and below the plane of the carbon ring.

5-19
Naming Aromatic Compounds

Aromatic compounds are often named using benzene or derivatives of benzene as a root of the name.

The carbon atoms of the benzene ring are numbered one to six in a clockwise direction, starting from the top of the ring. One or more hydrogen atoms of the benzene molecule may be replaced by different groups whose locations are indicated by numbers. These numbers are kept as low as possible. For example, two alkyl groups in the 1,6- positions are actually in the 1,2- locations, because the ring can be turned over like the page of a book so that the alkyl groups are numbered as if in the 1,2- locations. Similarly, the 1,5- positions are really the 1,3- locations.

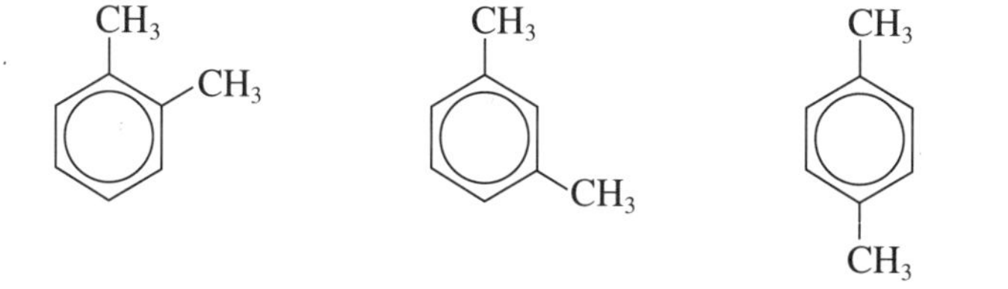

Figure 5-14
The three structural isomers of dimethylbenzene (xylene).

1,2-dimethylbenzene
(*o*-xylene)

1,3-dimethylbenzene
(*m*-xylene)

1,4-dimethylbenzene
(*p*-xylene)

Trivial names of substituted benzene compounds are based on prefixes: *o*- (or *ortho*) indicates that two substituted groups are on adjacent carbons of the benzene ring; *m*- (or *meta*) indicates that they are in the 1,3- positions; and *p*- (or *para*, which means "opposite") is used when the groups are in the 1,4- positions. We can use the family of dimethylbenzenes (xylenes) to explain the systematic and trivial names. As the systematic name reveals,

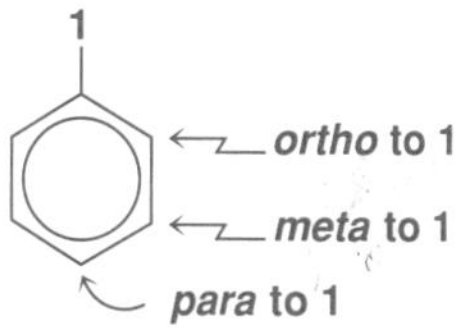

ortho to 1

meta to 1

para to 1

DAME KATHLEEN LONSDALE
1903–1971

Kathleen Lonsdale was born Kathleen Yardley in Newbridge, Ireland, the youngest of ten children. In 1908 the family moved to Essex County, in England, where Lonsdale won a scholarship to the County High School for Girls. Because of her abilities in science, she took classes in chemistry and physics at the local boys' school.

At age 16, Lonsdale went to London's Bedford College for Women, where she graduated as top student in 1922. English physicist, Sir William Henry Bragg, offered her a research position at University College, London, and then later at the Royal Institution.

In 1927, she worked in the physics department of Leeds University. She moved back to London in 1931 and continued her research for 15 years at the Royal Institution. In 1945, Lonsdale was the first woman to be elected to the Royal Society. She became Professor of Chemistry at University College, London, in 1946.

Lonsdale is noted for her use of X-ray crystallography to determine the structure of organic compounds. In 1929, she established the regular hexagonal arrangement of carbon atoms in benzene compounds. She was also able to accurately measure the distance between carbon atoms in diamond.

dimethylbenzene has two methyl groups in place of two hydrogen atoms of the benzene ring. Three isomers are possible, as shown in Fig. 5-14. Although the xylenes have the general formula C_nH_{2n-6}, there is no general formula for more complicated, substituted benzene molecules or for other aromatic compounds.

Removal of any one of the hydrogen atoms of the benzene molecule gives a neutral group, or radical, called the *phenyl group* (C_6H_5). Some organic structures containing the C_6H_5 group are named as though the phenyl group replaced a hydrogen atom of a hydrocarbon chain. For example, the structure

$$C\equiv CH$$

has the trivial name phenylacetylene.

An aromatic compound with one hydrogen removed is given the generic name *aryl*. Just as R was used as a general abbreviation for an alkyl group, Ar is used to represent an aryl group. Consequently, benzene and other aromatic compounds are often represented by ArH. The groups represented by R, R′ and R″ in Table 5-2 can also be aryl groups. For example, the formula ArOH is used to represent an aromatic compound with the hydroxyl group (—OH) as the functional group.

Aromatic compounds constitute a large class of compounds with different structures and properties. In the next section, we will look at the physical and chemical properties of aromatic hydrocarbons.

5-20

Physical and Chemical Properties of Aromatic Hydrocarbons

The properties of aromatic hydrocarbons differ from those of the aliphatic hydrocarbons because of the stability of the aromatic ring.

Many aromatic hydrocarbons are derived from petroleum. The simpler aromatic compounds, listed in Table 5-8, are good solvents for a number of organic compounds. Benzene, for example, is used as a solvent in which other organic reactions take place, and toluene is used as a solvent for lacquers. However, these compounds are toxic liquids that produce poisonous vapours when exposed to air and must be handled with caution. Reactions involving these liquids must be performed in well-ventilated areas or under fume hoods.

TABLE 5-8
**SOME SIMPLE AROMATIC HYDROCARBONS AND
THEIR PROPERTIES**

Systematic Name	Common Name	Condensed Formula	Boiling Point (°C)	Melting Point (°C)
Benzene	benzene	C_6H_6	80.1	5.5
Methylbenzene	toluene	$C_6H_5CH_3$	110.6	−95
1,2-Dimethyl-benzene	o-xylene	$(CH_3)_2C_6H_5$	144.4	−25
1,3-Dimethyl-benzene	m-xylene	$(CH_3)_2C_6H_5$	139.1	48
1,4-Dimethyl benzene	p-xylene	$(CH_3)_2C_6H_5$	138.4	13

Like many scientists in the twentieth century, Kathleen Lonsdale had a strong sense of social responsibility. She refused to register for employment at the outbreak of World War II, considering all wars immoral. She refused to pay the fine and was sent to prison for one month. For the rest of her life she remained a committed pacifist.

In 1956, Kathleen Lonsdale was created Dame of the British Empire and, in 1968, became the first woman President of the British Association for the Advancement of Science.

Aromatic compounds are not as reactive as the aliphatic compounds due to the extra stability associated with the delocalizing electrons in the aromatic ring. In fact, aromatic compounds do not readily participate in addition reactions because of this stability. Aromatic compounds, however, do undergo substitution reactions in which one or more hydrogen atoms from the aromatic ring are replaced by another group. We will look at the chemical reactions of aromatic compounds in Chapter 6.

benzopyrene

ALCOHOLS

Alcohols are characterized by a hydroxyl group (—OH) attached to a hydrocarbon chain. The simpler alcohols have many applications in our lives (Fig. 5-15). For example, methanol (CH_3OH) is used in lacquer solvents and antifreeze liquids. Ethanol (C_2H_5OH) is the alcohol in wines, beers and liquors, and is also found in the fuel gasohol. A common bactericide is isopropyl alcohol, or 2-propanol ($CH_3CH(OH)CH_3$).

5-21

Naming Alcohols

When naming an alcohol, replace the -e ending of the corresponding alkane name with -ol.
Each alcohol containing one —OH group attached to an alkyl group has the general formula $C_nH_{2n+1}OH$, or ROH. The physical and chemical properties of alcohols depend on the functional group, —OH. As with the systematic naming of alkenes and alkynes, the position of the functional group is given the lowest

Figure 5-15
Personal-care products such as perfumes, creams and lotions contain alcohols as well as aldehydes, ketones and esters.

number in the longest, continuous carbon chain. Two examples are shown below:

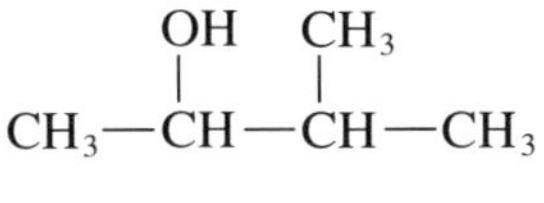

$$\begin{array}{ccc} & OH & CH_3 \\ & | & | \\ CH_3{-}CH{-}CH{-}CH_3 \end{array}$$

$$\begin{array}{cccc} & CH_3 & OH & \\ & | & | & \\ CH_3{-}CH{-}C{-}CH_2{-}CH_3 \\ & | & \\ & CH_2{-}CH_3 \end{array}$$

3-methyl-2-butanol 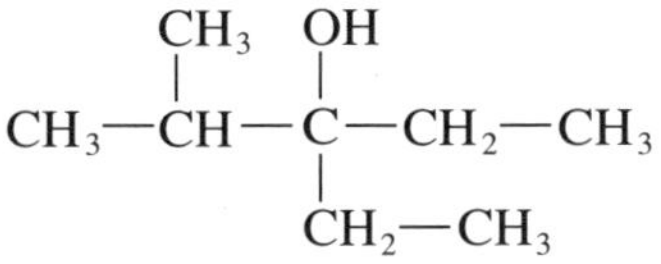   3-ethyl-2-methyl-3-pentanol

From the C_3 alcohols on, structural isomerism occurs. Table 5-9 includes the formulas for two propyl alcohols: 1-propanol and 2-propanol. As expected, these isomers have different odours, different melting and boiling points, and show differences in chemical behaviour. Commonly available as a germicide, 2-propanol is sold under the name "rubbing alcohol."

TABLE 5-9
REPRESENTATIVE ALCOHOLS

Systematic Name	Common Name	Condensed Formula	Structural Formula	Melting Point (°C)	Boiling Point (°C)
Methanol	methyl alcohol	CH_3OH	$\begin{array}{c} H \\ | \\ H{-}C{-}OH \\ | \\ H \end{array}$	−94	65
Ethanol	ethyl alcohol	C_2H_5OH	$\begin{array}{c} H \quad H \\ | \quad | \\ H{-}C{-}C{-}OH \\ | \quad | \\ H \quad H \end{array}$	−117.3	78.5
1-Propanol	propyl alcohol	C_3H_7OH	$\begin{array}{c} H \quad H \quad H \\ | \quad | \quad | \\ H{-}C{-}C{-}C{-}OH \\ | \quad | \quad | \\ H \quad H \quad H \end{array}$	−126.5	97.4
2-Propanol	isopropyl alcohol	$CH_3CH(OH)CH_3$	$\begin{array}{c} H \quad H \quad H \\ | \quad | \quad | \\ H{-}C{-}C{-}C{-}H \\ | \quad | \quad | \\ H \quad O \quad H \\ \quad | \\ \quad H \end{array}$	−89.5	82.4

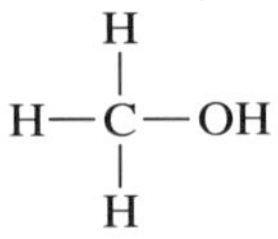

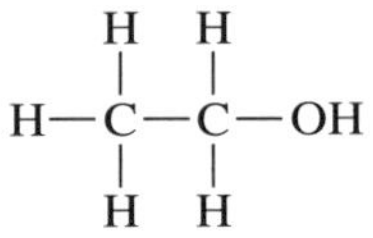

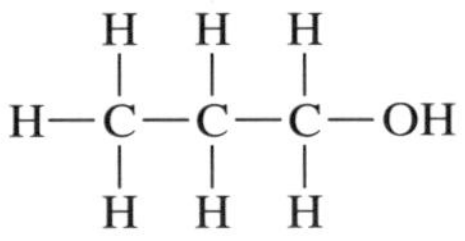

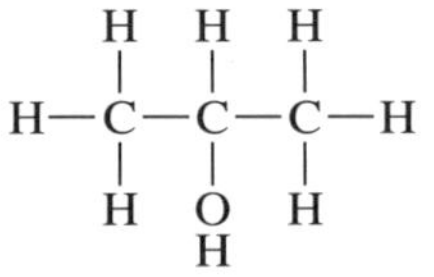

Because of isomerism, another classification of alcohols has been developed, based on the number of carbons bonded to the carbon that has the hydroxyl group attached. If this carbon has one other carbon and two hydrogens attached, the structure is said to be a *primary alcohol*, for example, 1-butanol:

$$CH_3{-}CH_2{-}CH_2{-}CH_2{-}OH$$
1-butanol
(butyl alcohol)

If there are two other carbons attached to the carbon bearing the hydroxyl group, it is said to be a *secondary alcohol*:

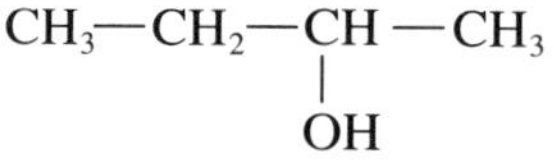

$$CH_3-CH_2-\underset{\underset{OH}{|}}{CH}-CH_3$$

2-butanol
(*sec*-butyl alcohol)

If there are three other carbons, it is a *tertiary alcohol*:

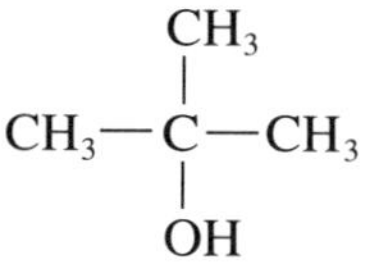

$$CH_3-\underset{\underset{OH}{|}}{\overset{\overset{CH_3}{|}}{C}}-CH_3$$

2-methyl-2-propanol
(*tert*-butyl alcohol)

The trivial names of alcohols are based on the name of the alkyl radical, followed by the word *alcohol*. For example, CH_3OH is commonly called methyl alcohol. We noted earlier that there are two distinct propyl radicals: propyl ($CH_3CH_2CH_2$) and isopropyl (CH_3CHCH_3). These are used in the trivial names of alcohols to indicate if the structure is a primary or a secondary alcohol. For example,

$$CH_3-CH_2-CH_2-OH$$

is a primary alcohol, called propyl alcohol. The structure

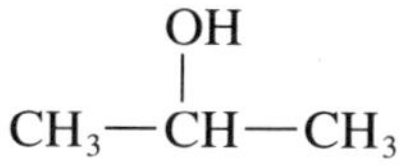

$$\underset{CH_3-\underset{\underset{}{|}}{CH}-CH_3}{\overset{\overset{OH}{|}}{}}$$

is a secondary alcohol, called isopropyl alcohol.

As in the water molecule, the —OH group of alcohol molecules is slightly polar and thus influences the properties of simpler alcohols in which the —OH group forms a larger part of the chain length.

Methanol is commonly called methyl alcohol, methyl hydrate and wood alcohol.

FOLLOW-UP PROBLEMS

1. Give the systematic names of the following alcohols.

a)
$$CH_3-CH_2-CH_2-\underset{\underset{}{|}}{\overset{\overset{OH}{|}}{CH}}-CH_3$$

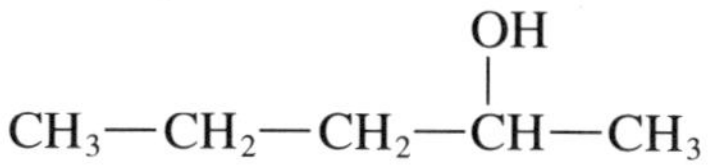

b) $CH_3-\underset{\underset{CH_3}{|}}{CH}-CH_2-\underset{\underset{OH}{|}}{CH}-CH_2-CH_3$

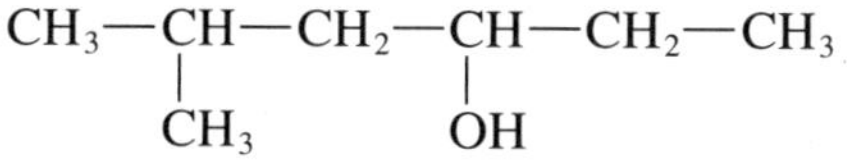

c)

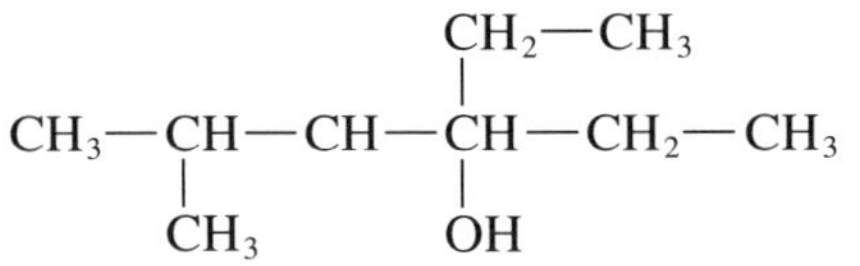

$$CH_3-CH-CH-CH-CH_2-CH_3$$

with CH_2-CH_3 branch above the fourth carbon, CH_3 below the second carbon, and OH below the fourth carbon.

2. Draw structures for (a) 1-pentanol and (b) 2-methyl-3-hexanol.

Answers:

1. (a) **2-pentanol**, (b) **5-methyl-3-hexanol**, (c) **3-ethyl-5-methyl-3-hexanol**

2. a)

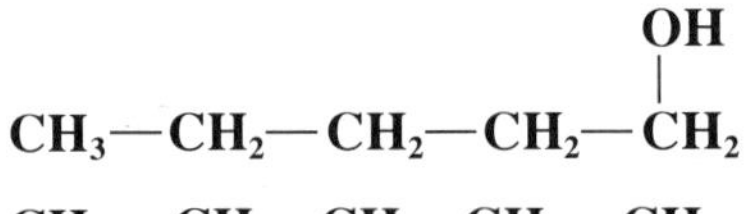

$$CH_3-CH_2-CH_2-CH_2-CH_2$$

with OH above the last carbon.

b) $$CH_3-CH-CH-CH_2-CH_2-CH_3$$

with CH_3 below the second carbon and OH below the third carbon.

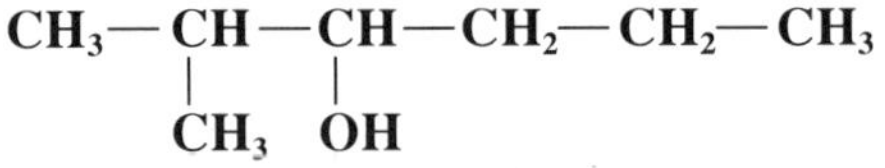

5-22

Physical Properties of Alcohols

The physical properties of the simpler alcohols are determined by the hydroxyl group, which is capable of hydrogen bonding. Liquids that dissolve completely in one another to form a homogeneous solution are said to be *miscible*. The simpler alcohols dissolve in water as the strongly negative oxygen ends of H_2O molecules are attracted to the positive hydrogens of the alcohol molecules, and vice versa, forming hydrogen bonds. Any ratio of water and methanol can be mixed because each liquid is soluble in the other without limit.

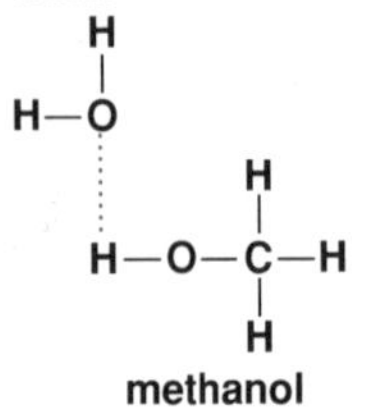

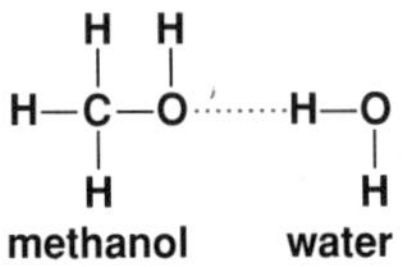

Methanol, the simplest alcohol, forms hydrogen bonds with water, as shown in the margin. The strong influence of the polar hydroxyl group in the simple alcohols can be seen by comparing the physical properties of these alcohols with alkanes of about the same mass. Table 5-10 shows that the nonpolar hydrocarbons have much lower melting and boiling points than the alcohols with similar molecular mass.

As the hydrocarbon part of the chain lengthens, the influence of the polar —OH group of the alcohol lessens and becomes minor. The longer-chain alcohols have physical properties resembling those of long-chain alkanes. Table 5-11 shows the trend in solubilities of the unbranched-chain primary alcohols.

water

$$H-O-H$$

$$H-O-C-H$$

methanol

$$H-C-O\cdots H-O$$

methanol   water

TABLE 5-10
COMPARISON OF ALCOHOLS AND ALKANES

Systematic Name	Condensed Formula	Molar Mass (g/mol)	Melting Point (°C)	Boiling Point (°C)
Ethane	C_2H_6	30.0	−183	−88
Methanol	CH_3OH	32.0	−94	65
Propane	C_3H_8	44.0	−190	−42
Ethanol	C_2H_5OH	46.0	−117	78

TABLE 5-11
SOLUBILITIES OF ALCOHOLS

Systematic Name	Condensed Formula	Solubility in Water
Methanol	CH_3OH	fully miscible
Ethanol	C_2H_5OH	fully miscible
Propanol	C_3H_7OH	fully miscible
1-Butanol	C_4H_9OH	9.0%
1-Pentanol	$C_5H_{11}OH$	2.7%
1-Hexanol	$C_6H_{13}OH$	0.6%

5-23
Chemical Properties of Alcohols

The hydroxyl groups are the reactive sites of alcohols where many reactions take place, converting alcohols into other families of organic compounds.

The simplest alcohols—methanol and ethanol—are efficient, clean-burning fuels. Primary alcohols can be converted into another family of organic substances—the *aldehydes*. Secondary alcohols can be changed to *ketones* in a similar way. Alcohols can be dehydrated to produce alkenes, and the reaction of alcohols with organic acids produces *esters*. The hydroxyl group of an alcohol can be readily replaced by a halogen.

5-24
Polyhydroxy Alcohols

Polyhydroxy alcohols have two or more hydroxyl groups attached to different carbon atoms of the chain.

Polyhydroxy alcohols contain two or more hydroxyl groups and are named systematically by adding the suffix *-diol*, *-triol* and so on (indicating the number of hydroxyl groups) to the parent alkane name. The locations of the hydroxyl groups are indicated by numbers, as in the following examples:

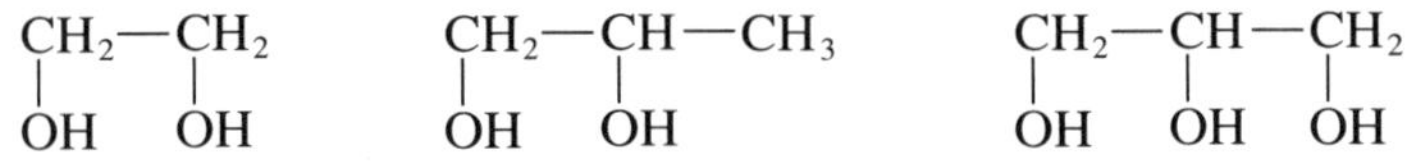

$$CH_2 \!-\! CH_2$$
$$|\qquad|$$
$$OH \quad OH$$
1,2-ethanediol
(ethylene glycol)

$$CH_2 \!-\! CH \!-\! CH_3$$
$$|\qquad|$$
$$OH \quad OH$$
1,2-propanediol
(propylene glycol)

$$CH_2 \!-\! CH \!-\! CH_2$$
$$|\qquad|\qquad|$$
$$OH \quad OH \quad OH$$
1,2,3-propanetriol
(glycerol)

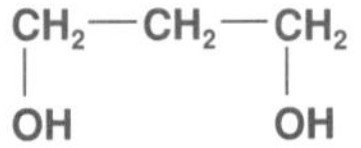

$$CH_2 \!-\! CH_2 \!-\! CH_2$$
$$|\qquad\qquad|$$
$$OH \qquad\quad OH$$
1,3-propanediol

As shown in the margin, 1,2-propanediol has an isomer, 1,3-propanediol.

In the trivial naming system, the term *glycol* is restricted to dihydroxy alcohols that have two —OH groups attached to neighbouring carbon atoms. Ethylene glycol ($C_2H_4(OH)_2$) is a polyhydroxy alcohol that is used mainly as an antifreeze in automobiles. Glycerol ($C_3H_5(OH)_3$) is used in the preparation of skin lotions and cough syrups.

It seems reasonable to predict that ethylene glycol, with two hydroxyl groups per molecule, will show more ability to form hydrogen bonds than ethanol (C_2H_5OH), which has only one polar hydroxyl group per molecule. The syrupy consistency of ethylene glycol indicates the strong hydrogen bonding that occurs between the molecules. Its high boiling point (198.93°C) is due to the large number of hydrogen bonds that must be broken before the liquid can vaporize. As predicted, ethylene glycol is completely miscible with water.

Glycerol, with three hydroxyl groups in the molecule, has more intermolecular hydrogen bonding than ethylene glycol and, as a result, is more viscous and has a higher boiling point (290°C). Glycerol is not used as an antifreeze because of its slow rate of flow through an engine's cooling system. While alcohols with two or more hydroxyl groups taste sweet, ethylene glycol is poisonous. Propylene glycol, on the other hand, is nontoxic and is used as a syrupy sweet component of synthetic additives in pies and other confectionary items.

A hydroxyl group can also be attached to a benzene ring to form the aromatic compound, phenol (C_6H_5OH). Phenol does not react like an aliphatic alcohol; rather, it behaves like a weak acid in water solution by the release of hydrogen ions, as shown below.

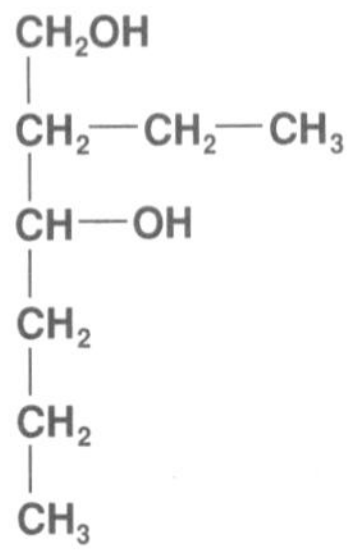

Disposal of Waste Antifreeze
1,2-Ethanediol (ethylene glycol) is the most commonly used automobile antifreeze. A 58% solution of ethylene glycol in water freezes at −48°C. When a car radiator is flushed out to remove the antifreeze solution, the waste liquid is dumped down the drains, where it may be carried to the water table. Thus, toxic ethylene glycol, being water soluble, poses a serious threat to the water supply of communities that depend on well water.

CoolWhip contains propylene glycol.

$$CH_2OH$$
$$|$$
$$CH_2 \!-\! CH_2 \!-\! CH_3$$
$$|$$
$$CH \!-\! OH$$
$$|$$
$$CH_2$$
$$|$$
$$CH_2$$
$$|$$
$$CH_3$$

2-Ethyl-1,3-hexanediol is an insect repellent sold under the name "6-12."

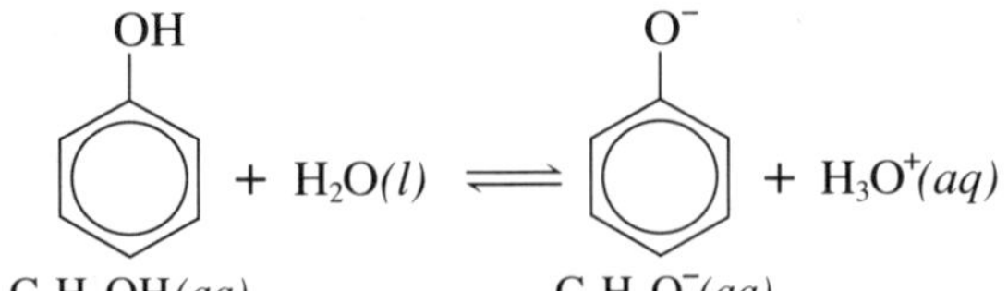

$C_6H_5OH(aq)$ + $H_2O(l)$ ⇌ $C_6H_5O^-(aq)$ + $H_3O^+(aq)$
phenol ⟶ phenoxide ion

The acidic characteristic of phenol is attributed to the stabilization of the ion by the delocalization of the negative charge into the benzene ring.

Phenol is a highly toxic and potentially fatal substance, used to sterilize surgical instruments. When exposed to phenol, skin must be washed immediately with ethyl alcohol or warm water. Because phenol acts as a local anesthetic, contact may not be detected immediately, despite its burning action.

Although the physical and chemical behaviour of alcohols are related to the hydroxyl group, there is a group of isomers of the alcohol family that does not have the hydroxyl group as the functional group and therefore has properties very different from alcohols. These are the *ethers*. Because ethers have a specific structure that characterizes their properties and reactions, they constitute a separate homologous series.

ETHERS

Ethers contain the C—O—C functional group and are isomers of alcohols. Isomers of alchols such as 1-propanol and 2-propanol have similar properties because they contain the same functional group, —OH. However, isomers do exist that have different functional groups and, hence, different chemical behaviour. Such substances are called *fuctional group isomers*. For example, ethanol and dimethyl ether (shown below) have the same molecular formula (C_2H_6O), but the former is a typical alchol and the latter is the simplest ether. Note that the oxygen of any ether is always between two alkyl groups.

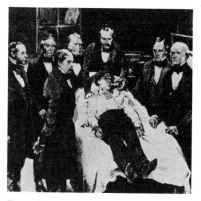

Figure 5-16
On October 16, 1846, the first anesthetic was used—diethyl ether. This ether depresses the activity of the central nervous system, causing unconsciousness. However, because of its side effects, which included irritation of the respiratory tract, nausea and vomiting, diethyl ether was replaced by methyl propyl ether ($CH_3OCH_2CH_2CH_3$).

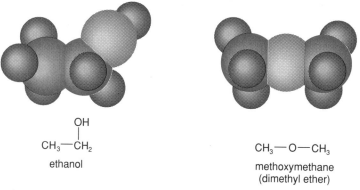

$$CH_3—\overset{\overset{\displaystyle OH}{|}}{C}H_2$$
ethanol

$$CH_3—O—CH_3$$
methoxymethane
(dimethyl ether)

Naming Ethers

The trivial names of ethers, which are based on the names of the alkyl groups with the word *ether* added, are more commonly used than the systematic names.

In 1987 the Canadian Armed Forces tested a nerve-gas "simulator" called 1-methoxyheptatriene. This ether can cause discomfort in people wearing gas masks improperly.

The trivial names of ethers are derived by naming the two alkyl groups and adding the word *ether*; for example, $CH_3OCH_2CH_3$ is called ethyl methyl ether. If the same alkyl group appears on both sides of the oxygen, the prefix *di-* is used; for example, $CH_3CH_2OCH_2CH_3$ is called diethyl ether. Note that the names of the alkyl groups appear in alphabetical order.

The systematic names of ethers are based on the longest alkyl group. The shorter alkyl group and the oxygen together is called an *alkoxy group*; for example, $CH_3OCH_2CH_3$ is called methoxyethane. The systematic names, however, are not in wide use, and in most texts you will encounter the trivial names. Table 5-12 gives both the systematic and trivial names for some of the simpler ethers.

TABLE 5-12
REPRESENTATIVE ETHERS

Systematic Name	Common Name	Condensed Formula	Structural Formula	Melting Point (°C)	Boiling Point (°C)
Methoxymethane	dimethyl ether	CH_3OCH_3		−141.5	−24.9
Methoxyethane	ethyl methyl ether	$CH_3OCH_2CH_3$		–	11
Ethoxyethane	diethyl ether	$(CH_3CH_2)_2O$		−116.3	34.6

5-26

Physical and Chemical Properties of Ethers

The inability of ethers to form hydrogen bonds and the low reactivity of their C—O—C functional group explain the difference in properties between ethers and their corresponding alcohols.

The simplest ether, commonly called dimethyl ether, dissolves in water, but as the number of carbon atoms in the ether series increases, they become insoluble. Diethyl ether, for example, is only partly miscible with water. This characteristic, combined with the fact that many organic compounds are more soluble in ether than in water, makes diethyl ether a very useful extracting agent (Fig. 5-17).

When an aqueous solution of an organic compound is shaken with ether, most of the compound transfers to the ether, which, having the lower density, forms a layer on top of the water. Because ethers lack the ability to form hydrogen bonds, they have low boiling points and can be distilled off the dissolved organic compound at temperatures low enough to prevent decomposition of the solute.

The ethers' low reactivity compared with other organic structures contributes to their favourable solvent properties. However, ethers are highly flammable and must be used with caution; explosive mixtures of ethers and air have resulted in industrial accidents. At one time, diethyl ether was used as an anesthetic, but because of its flammability, it was replaced by safer substances. A practical application of the flammable nature of ethers is the use of diethyl ether in "Quickstart" spray in automobile carburetors.

In the late 1980s, methyl *tert*-butyl ether, whose structure is shown in the margin below, was listed in the top 100 list of chemicals most widely used in industry. Its primary use is as an additive to improve the octane rating of gasoline.

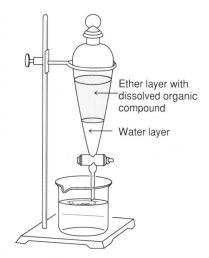

Ether layer with dissolved organic compound

Water layer

Figure 5-17
Extraction of a compound from an aqueous solution is often achieved by means of a separatory funnel. Ether is added to the aqueous solution in the funnel and then shaken. The preferred solubility of the organic compound in ether causes most of it to transfer to the ether phase. The water phase is then drained, and the ether can be distilled off the dissolved organic compound.

$$CH_3-O-\overset{\displaystyle CH_3}{\underset{\displaystyle CH_3}{\overset{|}{\underset{|}{C}}}}-CH_3$$

methyl *tert*-butyl ether
(MTBE)

FOLLOW-UP PROBLEMS

1. Give the trivial name and the systematic name for the following ether: $CH_3-CH_2-O-CH_2-CH_2-CH_3$.

2. Draw a structure for an alcohol that is an isomer of the ether, methoxyethane (ethyl methyl ether, $CH_3OC_2H_5$).

Answers:

1. Ethyl propyl ether and ethoxypropane.

2. Two alcohol isomers of the ether are possible:

$$\begin{array}{cccc} & H & H & H \\ & | & | & | \\ H- & C- & C- & C-OH \\ & | & | & | \\ & H & H & H \end{array}$$
1-propanol

$$\begin{array}{cccc} & H & H & H \\ & | & | & | \\ H- & C- & C- & C-H \\ & | & | & | \\ & H & OH & H \end{array}$$
2-propanol

The next two families of organic compounds that we will discuss are the aldehydes and ketones, whose chemistry, like that of the ethers, is largely determined by their carbon-to-oxygen bonds.

ALDEHYDES AND KETONES

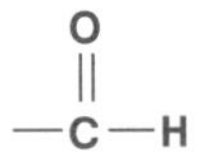

$$
\begin{array}{c} O \\ \| \\ -C-H \end{array}
$$
aldehyde

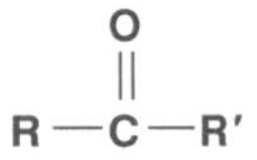

$$
\begin{array}{c} O \\ \| \\ R-C-R' \end{array}
$$
ketone

Aldehydes and ketones are structurally related in that they both contain the *carbonyl group*, $\begin{array}{c} O \\ \| \\ -C- \end{array}$. The simplest aldehyde is methanal, commonly called formaldehyde, which is used as an embalming fluid for preserving biological specimens. Its formula is often written as HCHO, according to its structure:

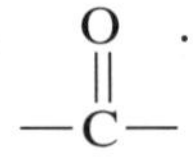

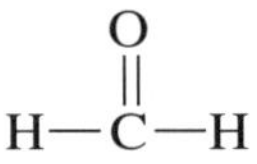

$$
\begin{array}{c} O \\ \| \\ H-C-H \end{array}
$$
methanal
(formaldehyde)

Aldehydes have at least one hydrogen attached to the carbon of the carbonyl group, while ketones have two alkyl groups attached to the carbonyl carbon. The simplest ketone is propanone (acetone, CH_3COCH_3):

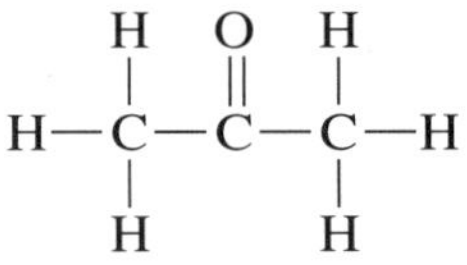

$$
\begin{array}{c} H \quad O \quad H \\ | \quad\ \| \quad\ | \\ H-C-C-C-H \\ | \qquad\quad | \\ H \qquad\quad H \end{array}
$$
propanone
(acetone)

Vanillin is the aldehyde responsible for the flavour of vanilla. The world's largest producer of vanilla is Ontario. The structure of vanillin incorporates an ether, a hydroxyl and a carbonyl group, as shown below:

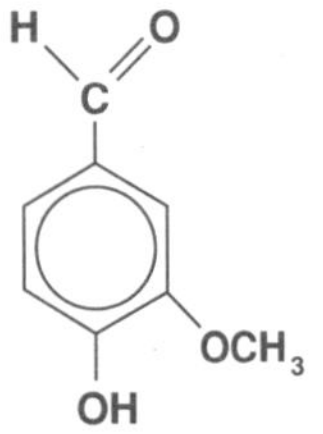

vanillin

Acetone is a common solvent, able to dissolve nail varnish or pigments in paints and is also used in plastic cements and in resin solvents.

5-27
Naming Aldehydes

An aldehyde derives its name from the fact that it is prepared from a primary *al*cohol by means of *dehyd*rogenation (the removal of hydrogen). Simpler aldehydes have trivial and systematic names, as indicated in Table 5-13. The systematic names are formed by replacing the *-e* ending of the corresponding alkane name with *-al*. Because the functional group of an aldehyde is always at the carbon number one position, there is no need to indicate its position when naming it.

TABLE 5-13
REPRESENTATIVE ALDEHYDES

Systematic Name	Common Name	Condensed Formula	Structural Formula	Melting Point (°C)	Boiling Point (°C)
Methanal	formaldehyde	CH_2O		−92	−21
Ethanal	acetaldehyde	CH_3CHO		−121	20.8
Propanal	propionaldehyde	CH_3CH_2CHO		−81	48.8
−	benzaldehyde	C_6H_5CHO		−26	178

TABLE 5-14
REPRESENTATIVE KETONES

Systematic Name	Common Name	Condensed Formula	Structural Formula	Melting Point (°C)	Boiling Point (°C)
Propanone	acetone	CH_3COCH_3		−95.4	56.2
2-Butanone	ethyl methyl ketone	$CH_3CH_2COCH_3$		−86.3	79.6
3-Pentanone	diethyl ketone	$CH_3CH_2COCH_2CH_3$		−39.8	101.7

5-28

Naming Ketones

Ketones have the general formula RCOR′, where R and R′ represent alkyl groups, which may be the same or different. Ketones are named by replacing the -*e* ending of the corresponding alkane name with -*one*. For example, butane (C_4H_{10}) is the root for the name butanone:

$$CH_3-\overset{\displaystyle O}{\overset{\|}{C}}-CH_2CH_3$$

butanone

The location of the carbonyl group must be indicated for any ketone that has five or more carbons in the continuous chain containing the carbonyl group. According to the usual IUPAC naming practice, the location of the carbonyl group is given the lowest possible number. Some structures and names of ketones are shown in Table 5-14 on the previous page.

5-29
Physical and Chemical Properties of Aldehydes and Ketones

The structural similarity of aldehydes and ketones gives them similar physical and chemical properties. Many of their reactions involve additions to the carbonyl group.

Ethanal (CH_3CHO) boils at 21°C, while ethanol (C_2H_5OH) boils at 78.5°C. Similarly, propanone (acetone CH_3COCH_3) boils at 56°C, while 2-propanol ($CH_3CH(OH)CH_3$), with the same length of carbon chain and the oxygen bonded to the same carbon, boils at 82.5°C.

In aldehydes and ketones, the carbonyl group, $-\overset{\displaystyle O}{\overset{\|}{C}}-$, is polar because of the high electronegativity of the oxygen atom. Therefore, simpler aldehydes and ketones are soluble in water. Because aldehydes and ketones cannot form hydrogen bonds between aldehyde and ketone molecules, they have lower boiling points than alcohols of comparable chain length. All ketones have higher boiling points than their respective alkanes because of the interaction between the dipoles of the carbonyl groups. The carbonyl group of aldehydes and ketones is an important functional group, since many of the reactions they undergo involve additions to the group. Aldehydes are easily oxidized to carboxylic acids, while ketones do so under severe conditions.

CARBOXYLIC ACIDS

Carboxylic acids have a hydroxyl group (—OH) bonded to the carbon atom of a carbonyl group ($-\overset{\displaystyle O}{\overset{\|}{C}}-$). The functional group of carboxylic acids is called the *carboxyl group*, COOH. In general, a carboxylic acid is represented by the formula R_1COOH, or $C_nH_{2n+1}COOH$.

One of the most common carboxylic acids is ethanoic acid, commonly called acetic acid, which is found in vinegar. The simplest carboxylic acid, methanoic acid (formic acid), is the irritant in the venom of red ant and bee stings. The carboxylic acids that contain four to twenty-four carbon atoms are called *fatty acids* because they are found in edible oils and fats. We will discuss fatty acids in Chapter 6.

5-30
Naming Carboxylic Acids

The systematic name of a carboxylic acid has the ending *-oic acid* replacing the *-e* ending of the name of the corresponding alkane.

A carboxylic acid has the general formula R_1COOH, where R_1 represents a hydrogen atom—as in methanoic acid—or an alkyl group. However, this formula can be misleading when it comes to naming the acids. The systematic name of a carboxylic acid is based on the name of the corresponding alkane, which is determined by the longest, continuous carbon chain containing the carboxyl group. Note that the carbon atom in the carboxyl group must be included in the determination of the alkane name that should be used.

Carboxylic acids are systematically named by replacing the *-e* ending of the corresponding alkane name of an acid with *-oic acid*. For example, C_3H_7COOH is named butanoic acid because it shows a total of four carbon atoms, although it appears to have a propyl group attached to the carboxyl group. Similarly, the unbranched alkane, pentane ($CH_3CH_2CH_2CH_2CH_3$), corresponds to the carboxylic acid, pentanoic acid:

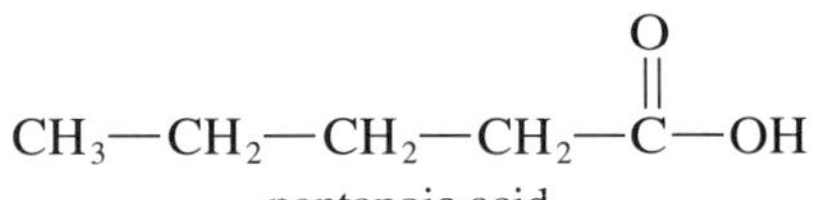

$$CH_3-CH_2-CH_2-CH_2-\overset{\overset{\textstyle O}{\|}}{C}-OH$$
pentanoic acid

The trivial names for carboxylic acids originate from Latin. For example, formic acid is produced by ants and derives its name from *formica*, the Latin word for ant. The trivial name for butyric acid is derived from *butyrum*, the Latin word for butter.

Methanoic acid and ethanoic acid are examples of monocarboxylic acids; however, some carboxylic acids have two or more carboxyl groups. For example, the compound ethanedioic acid (oxalic acid) has two carboxyl groups, as indicated by the suffix *-dioic*:

Between November and December 1987, over 150 people suffered from acute food poisoning after eating blue mussels harvested from eastern Prince Edward Island. The toxic agent was identified as domoic acid I, produced by the organism *Nitzschia pungens*.

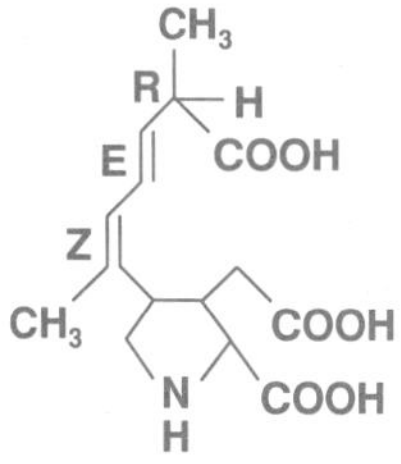

domoic acid I

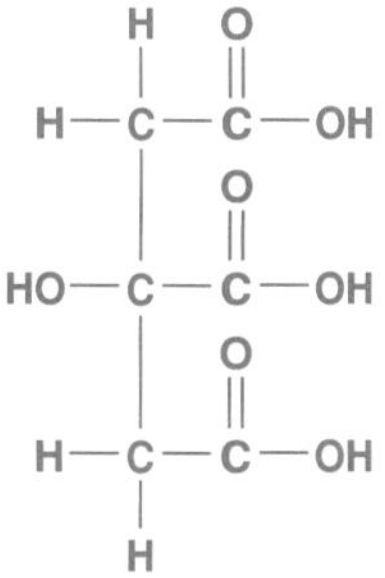

Citric acid is a tricarboxylic acid that contains one hydroxyl group. It is found in citrus fruits.

Oxalic acid is used to remove rust stains from clothing.

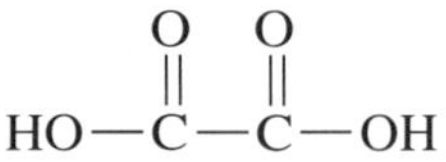

$$
\begin{matrix}
& O & O \\
& \| & \| \\
HO-&C-&C-OH
\end{matrix}
$$

ethanedioic acid
(oxalic acid)

This acid occurs in the leaves of rhubarb and other related plants. Table 5-15 gives the names and structures of the first four carboxylic acids, as well as some of their physical properties.

TABLE 5-15
REPRESENTATIVE CARBOXYLIC ACIDS

Systematic Name	Common Name	Condensed Formula	Structural Formula	Melting Point (°C)	Boiling Point (°C)
Methanoic acid	formic acid	HCOOH	$\begin{matrix} O \\ \| \\ HC-OH \end{matrix}$	8.4	100.7
Ethanoic acid	acetic acid	CH₃COOH	$\begin{matrix} H & O \\ \| & \| \\ H-C-&C-OH \\ \| \\ H \end{matrix}$	16.6	117.9
Propanoic acid	propionic acid	CH₃CH₂COOH	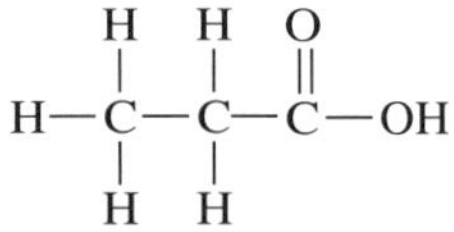 $\begin{matrix} H & H & O \\ \| & \| & \| \\ H-C-&C-&C-OH \\ \| & \| \\ H & H \end{matrix}$	−20.8	141
Butanoic acid	butyric acid	CH₃CH₂CH₂COOH	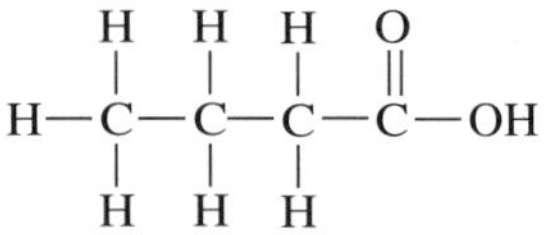 $\begin{matrix} H & H & H & O \\ \| & \| & \| & \| \\ H-C-&C-&C-&C-OH \\ \| & \| & \| \\ H & H & H \end{matrix}$	−4.5	165.5

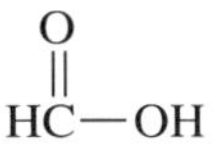

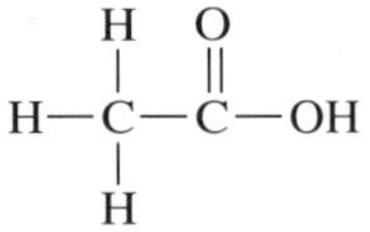

5-31

Physical and Chemical Properties of Carboxylic Acids

The physical properties of short-chain carboxylic acids are determined by the carboxyl group, while the properties of long-chain members resemble those of the corresponding alkanes.

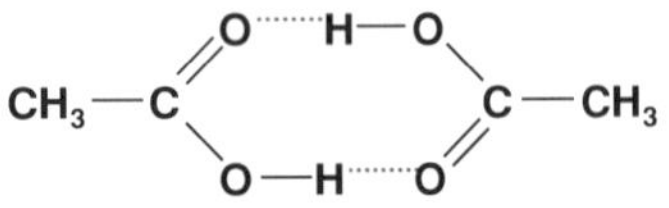

Carboxylic acids have relatively high boiling points (Table 5-15) compared with other organic compounds. For example, although ethanol and methanoic acid have similar molecular masses, ethanol has a boiling point (78°C) lower than that of methanoic acid (100.7°C).

The high boiling points of carboxylic acids are related to the degree of hydrogen bonding between the hydroxyl groups and the carbonyl groups of different molecules. The carbon atom of the

dimer of ethanoic acid
(acetic acid)

carboxyl group bonds in such a way that the functional group of the acid is a planar structure. This structure allows each molecule to form two hydrogen bonds with other molecules. There is experimental evidence that ethanoic acid (acetic acid) exists as a *dimer*, a structure that is made from two identical molecules of the compound.

The simpler carboxylic acids are soluble in water because of the hydrogen-bonding properties of the carboxyl group, and ionize as weak acids:

$$H-\overset{\overset{\displaystyle O}{\|}}{C}-OH + H_2O(l) \rightleftharpoons H_3O^+(aq) + H-\overset{\overset{\displaystyle O}{\|}}{C}-O^-(aq)$$

methanoic acid   methanoate ion
(formic acid)   (formate ion)

$$CH_3-\overset{\overset{\displaystyle O}{\|}}{C}-OH + H_2O(l) \rightleftharpoons H_3O^+(aq) + CH_3-\overset{\overset{\displaystyle O}{\|}}{C}-O^-(aq)$$

ethanoic acid   ethanoate ion
(acetic acid)   (acetate ion)

As the carbon chain increases, the characteristics of the carboxyl group become overshadowed by the properties associated with long hydrocarbon chains. Although the longer molecules are, chemically, carboxylic acids, physically, they tend to resemble a solid alkane.

It should be noted that carboxylic acids have another physical property that should be discussed—they are odoriferous compounds. However, the longer-chain acids are less volatile and therefore have less of an odour than the short-chain acids. For example, lactic acid is found in sour milk, and butanoic acid (butyric acid) is associated with the smell of rancid butter and is also responsible for "locker-room odour."

The chemical behaviour of carboxylic acids is largely determined by the carboxyl group—a combination of a hydroxyl group and a carbonyl group. However, in most reactions the hydroxyl group is replaced by an alkyl group. For example, the reaction of a carboxylic acid with an alcohol produces an ester. Known for their sweet fragrance and flavour, esters are discussed in the next section.

ESTERS.

Esters are derived from carboxylic acids in a process by which the hydroxyl group of the carboxyl group is replaced with an alkoxy group. The general formula of an ester is R_1COOR, where R

Sodium benzoate, a salt of benzoic acid, is added to pickles and soft drinks to prevent fungal growth.

trans-butenedioic acid
(fumaric acid)

cis-butenedioic acid
(maleic acid)

These isomers are used to make antihistamines.

represents an alkyl group, and R_1 represents an alkyl group or a hydrogen atom.

Unlike carboxylic acids, most esters have pleasant odours and are responsible for the flavours of foods. For example,

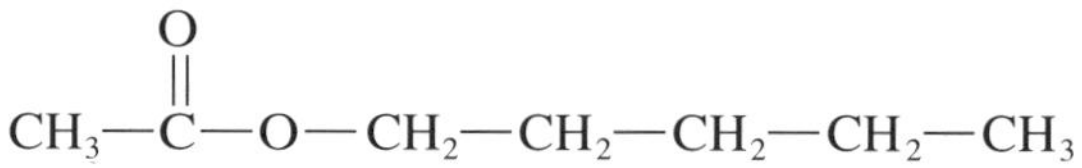

$$CH_3-\overset{\displaystyle O}{\overset{\|}{C}}-O-CH_2-CH_2-CH_2-CH_2-CH_3$$

pentyl ethanoate
(amyl acetate)

has the odour of bananas. Vegetable and animal fats and oils are *triesters*—compounds with three ester groups. Large molecules containing several linked ester groups are known as *polyesters*.

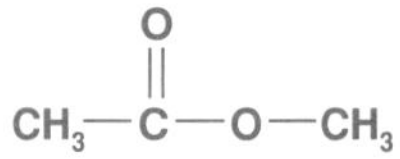

5-32
Naming Esters

The IUPAC and trivial names for esters are derived from the name of the R group in R_1COOR and the name of the carboxylic acid, R_1COOH.

Because esters are produced by a carboxylic acid–alcohol reaction, both the IUPAC and trivial names for exters are based on the names of the reactants. Esters are recognized by names such as methyl ethanoate (methyl acetate) and ethyl propanoate (ethyl propionate). In naming esters, we obtain the first part of the name from the name of the alkyl group attached to the oxygen; the second part is obtained by changing the *-ic acid* ending of the acid to *-ate*. Some examples of ester compounds are shown below and in the margin.

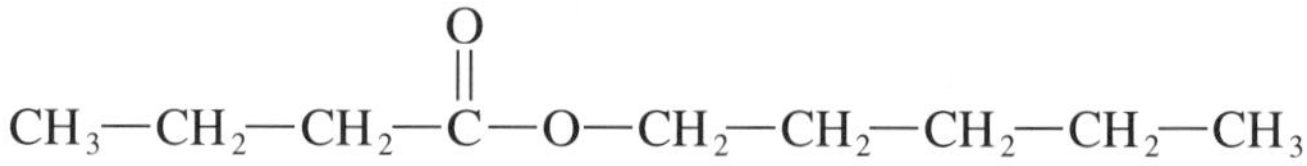

$$CH_3-CH_2-CH_2-\overset{\displaystyle O}{\overset{\|}{C}}-O-CH_2-CH_2-CH_2-CH_2-CH_3$$

pentyl butanoate
(amyl butyrate)

5-33
Physical and Chemical Properties of Esters

The physical properties of esters depend on the length of the molecule.

Esters contain the polar carbonyl group and, thus, should form hydrogen bonds with water. However, like carboxylic acids, only the simpler esters are completely soluble in water. As the length of the alkyl chain or nonpolar portion of the ester increases, the solubility decreases.

The boiling points of esters are relatively low compared with other organic compounds of similar molecular mass. This is because esters cannot form hydrogen bonds with each other. Rela-

$$CH_3-\overset{\displaystyle O}{\overset{\|}{C}}-O-CH_3$$

methyl ethanoate
(methyl acetate)

$$CH_3-\overset{\displaystyle O}{\overset{\|}{C}}-O-CH_2-CH_3$$

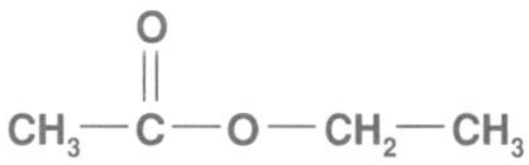

ethyl ethanoate
(ethyl acetate)

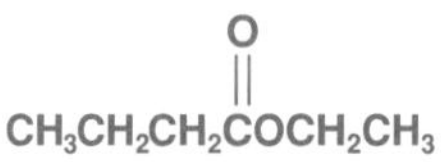

$$CH_3CH_2CH_2\overset{\displaystyle O}{\overset{\|}{C}}OCH_2CH_3$$

ethyl butanoate
(ethyl butyrate)

tively high-boiling esters are used as softening agents in plastics.

Ethyl ethanoate and butyl ethanoate (ethyl acetate and butyl acetate) are volatile solvents. Many esters make excellent solvents for other nonpolar, organic substances such as paints and lacquers. However, overexposure to ester vapours is an industrial hazard; deaths have resulted from the cleaning of large industrial solvent tanks in which there was inadequate ventilation.

Esters are produced when a carboxylic acid and an alcohol are heated together with an acid catalyst in a reaction called *esterification* (Fig. 5-18). During esterification, the hydroxyl group of the alcohol cleaves apart, and the hydrogen atom bonds with the —OH group of the acid to produce water. The O—R group of the

alcohol bonds with the R_1—$\overset{\displaystyle O}{\overset{\displaystyle \|}{C}}$— group of the acid to form an

ester. Esterification reactions are equilibrium reactions and, as such, are reversible; the reverse reaction is called *hydrolysis*. Esters can also chemically react with a strong base in a reaction called *saponification*. Soaps can be produced in the saponification reactions of some fats and oils. We will look at the reactions of esters in detail in Chapter 6.

Figure 5-18
These students are pouring a solution of salicylic acid in methanol into a refluxing apparatus to prepare the ester methyl salicylate.

ESTERS AND ALDEHYDES: THE TASTE OF SUCCESS

We have all heard the story about the prospector who, while spending his life searching for handfuls of gold, failed to notice rich outcroppings of copper and other important metals along the way. Similarly, scientists must always look beyond the focus of their immediate research, lest they fail to make other discoveries that may be just as important.

Dr David Armstrong originally joined Ottawa's National Research Council (NRC) to assist the NRC in its alternative fuels research program. It was 1979, and North America was still shaken by the aftermath of the mid-seventies' energy crisis. The need to find methods of reducing gasoline consumption was particularly urgent.

Much of the focus of the NRC's alternative fuels program centred on the development of low-cost ethanol (ethyl alcohol) recovery techniques. Results in countries such as Brazil indicated that up to 10% ethanol could be blended with gasoline stocks without the need for major adjustments to gasoline-fueled engines.

Ethanol is the major intoxicating component in alcoholic beverages and is produced by the fermentation of sugars, such as glucose, by yeast under anaerobic conditions:

$$C_6H_{12}O_6 \xrightarrow{\text{yeast}} 2C_2H_5OH + 2CO_2$$

glucose   ethanol   carbon dioxide

Ethanol produced in this way was too concentrated and too costly for consideration as a fuel. Potentially cheaper sources, such as crop residue cellulose and hemicellulose, and waste products of the alcoholic-beverage industry, yielded dilute ethanol levels that proved very difficult to recover.

Armstrong thus turned his attention to converting the ethanol into other compounds that could be used as fuel substitutes and that were easily recoverable. He knew that certain yeasts produced ethyl acetate (an ester) and acetaldehyde (an aldehyde) when used with ethanol, both of which could be used as fuel substitutes:

ethyl acetate ($CH_3CO_2CH_2CH_3$)   acetaldehyde (CH_3CHO)

Both ethyl acetate and acetaldehyde can be easily recovered, either by simple solvent methods for ethyl acetate or through low-temperature evaporation (21°C) for acetaldehyde. The trick was to find a yeast that could produce a significant amount of these products in a short time and at minimum expense. Experimentation eventually led Armstrong and his colleagues to *Candida utilis*, a yeast that can produce significant quantities of either ethyl acetate or acetaldehyde, depending on the concentration of ethanol as well as environmental factors. Although the chemical process is not yet fully understood, yeasts are known to break down ethanol through a complex series of catalyzed reactions:

$$\text{ethanol} \xrightleftharpoons{\text{alcohol dehydrogenase}} \text{acetaldehyde}$$

$$\text{acetaldehyde} \xrightleftharpoons{\text{aldehyde dehydrogenase}} \text{acetic acid}$$

$$\text{acetic acid} \xrightleftharpoons{\text{acetyl-CoA synthetase}} \text{acetyl-CoA}$$

It is thought that the acetyl-CoA reacts with ethanol to produce ethyl acetate.

Just as Armstrong was discovering how to manipulate the environment of *C. utilis* cultures to maximize the production of ethyl acetate or acetaldehyde, the urgent need for alternative fuels in North America began to decline as the result of more fuel-efficient vehicles and power plants, and discoveries of domestic fuel deposits. Although the original rationale for his work seemed to disappear, Armstrong continued his research. Realizing that ethyl acetate and acetaldehyde were important chemical feedstocks for the production of ketones, ethers and other compounds, Armstrong also noted that the ethyl acetate and acetaldehyde produced by bioconversion contained no contaminants. It

was apparent that ethyl acetate and acetaldehyde might be used to fill the demand for natural flavours and fragrances in the food industry.

Ethyl acetate and acetaldehyde are naturally present in many of our foods. Esters are responsible for the distinct scents of flowers and the characteristic "fruity" aromas and flavours we associate with apples, oranges, grapes and other fruits. Some common esters and their characteristic odours are listed in the table below. Note that ethyl acetate can be used as a chemical feedstock for many such esters. Many aldehydes are responsible for the aromas and flavours that we associate with freshness in many fruits and vegetables.

ESTERS AND THEIR ASSOCIATED ODOURS

Ester	Formula	Odour
n-Butyl acetate	$CH_3COOC_4H_9$	bananas
n-Octyl acetate	$CH_3COOC_8H_{17}$	oranges
Ethyl butyrate	$C_3H_7COOC_2H_5$	pineapples
n-Amyl butyrate	$C_3H_7COOC_5H_{11}$	apricots
Isoamyl isovalerate	$C_4H_9COOC_5H_{11}$	apples
Methyl anthranilate	$C_6H_4(NH_2)COOCH_3$	Concord grapes

The processed-food industry, Armstrong discovered, strives to preserve the ethyl acetate and acetaldehyde content in products such as condensed fruit juices. During the concentrating process, however, much of this content is boiled off. Cheaper brands of juice are thus deficient in natural flavour, while the more expensive juices are made more flavourful by the addition of expensive natural flavour extracts. However, the reconstituted juice, no matter what the price, still lacks the full taste and aroma of the natural food.

Although ethyl acetate and acetaldehyde can be produced chemically, the resulting products are contaminated with poisons, making them unsafe. Armstrong's biotechnical process has no such disadvantages. It can inexpensively produce abundant, clean supplies of both compounds. The process requires little equipment and, because it is natural, the products appear to meet the huge industrial demand for natural flavours—a demand that has so far outstripped supply. No longer can cost or availability be barriers to full flavour or aroma in many processed foods.

As a result of Armstrong's work, the NRC patented his process and is working to license its use by Canadian companies. Japanese and U.S. firms have also expressed interest.

Armstrong is currently working on the development of other flavours using such biocatalysts as vinegar and various enzymes.

It may be that as a result of this research, the next glass of reconstituted fruit juice that you drink will have the flavour and freshness of the natural fruit. If so, you may wish to raise your glass to toast Armstrong's biotechnical process.

Amines

Amines are considered to be derivatives of ammonia, in which one or more of the hydrogens have been replaced by an alkyl or aryl group. Many amines are characterized by their unpleasant odours; for example, the odour of decaying fish is attributed to simple amines produced by bacterial action. Amines are also found in many biological molecules, including amino acids and vitamins, and are used in the manufacture of pharmaceuticals such as sulfa drugs and anesthetics. The synthetic fibre, nylon, is an amine derivative.

5-34
Naming Amines

Amines, like other families of organic compounds, can be named in several ways. A new system, now gaining acceptance, modifies the alkane name by replacing the suffix *-e* with *-amine*. For example, CH_3NH_2 is called methanamine.

We have learned that alcohols are classified as primary, secondary or tertiary, depending on the number of carbon atoms attached to the carbon bearing the —OH group. Amines can also be labelled as primary, secondary or tertiary; however, they are classified *according to the number of alkyl groups bonded to the nitrogen atom*. Replacement of one hydrogen atom of ammonia with an alkyl group produces a primary amine; replacement of two hydrogens produces a secondary amine; and replacement of all three hydrogens results in a tertiary amine.

H—N—H	R—N—H	R—N—H	R—N—R″
|	|	|	|
H	H	R′	R′
ammonia	primary amine	secondary amine	tertiary amine

According to IUPAC rules, the systematic names of amines are formed by adding the prefix *amino-* to the corresponding alkane name of the amine. Thus, CH_3NH_2 is called aminomethane and

$C_2H_5NH_2$ is aminoethane. These systematic names, however, are being replaced with the new naming system discussed above. Table 5-16 lists the IUPAC and common names of some representative amines.

TABLE 5-16
REPRESENTATIVE AMINES

Systematic Name	Common Name	Condensed Formula	Structural Formula	Melting Point (°C)	Boiling Point (°C)
Aminomethane	methylamine	CH_3NH_2	H | H—C—NH₂ | H	−93.5	−6.3
–	dimethylamine	$(CH_3)_2NH$	H H | | H—C—N—C—H | | | H H H	−93	7.4
–	trimethylamine	$(CH_3)_3N$	CH₃—N—CH₃ | CH₃	−117.1	3.5
Aminobenzene	aniline	$C_6H_5NH_2$	NH₂ (on benzene ring)	−6	184

5-35

Physical and Chemical Properties of Amines

The properties of amines can be derived from their similarities and differences relative to ammonia.

The ammonia (NH_3) molecule has an electronegative nitrogen atom bonded to three hydrogen atoms in a trigonal pyramid shape; the lone-pair electrons on the nitrogen contribute to the polarity of the structure. Ammonia molecules can form hydrogen bonds with other ammonia molecules because the hydrogen of one ammonia molecule is attracted to the lone-pair electrons of a nitrogen of a nearby ammonia molecule, as shown in the margin.

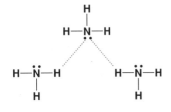

Table 5-17 compares the boiling points of ethane, aminomethane and methanol, which have similar molar masses. We see from the table that nonpolar ethane has the lowest boiling point. Aminomethane has some hydrogen bonding and a higher boiling point. Methanol, with the most hydrogen bonding, has the highest boiling point.

TABLE 5-17
COMPARISON OF ALKANES, ALCOHOLS AND AMINES

Systematic Name	Condensed Formula	Molar Mass (g/mol)	Boiling Point (°C)
Ethane	C_2H_6	30.0	−88.6
Aminomethane	CH_3NH_2	31.0	−6
Methanol	CH_3OH	32.0	65

Primary and secondary amines contain N—H bonds and, thus, show hydrogen bonding and have correspondingly higher boiling points than alkanes of comparable mass. Like all substances that can form hydrogen bonds, primary and secondary amines are soluble in water. Tertiary amines cannot form hydrogen bonds because of the absence of N—H groups and, therefore, have lower boiling points than either primary or secondary amines. Tertiary amines are insoluble in water.

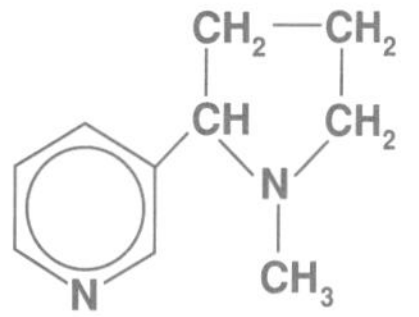

Aliphatic amines are slightly stronger bases than ammonia and can react with acids (for example, hydrochloric acid) to form salts. Aromatic amines, on the other hand, are relatively weaker bases than ammonia. Aromatic hydrocarbons such as benzene (C_6H_6) or naphthalene ($C_{10}H_8$) can have various functional groups such as hydroxyl, carbonyl or carboxyl groups substituted for one or more hydrogen atoms of the aromatic ring. Similarly, there are aromatic amines in which a hydrogen atom of ammonia is replaced by a phenyl group, for example, aminobenzene ($C_6H_5NH_2$). Aminobenzene, commonly called aniline, is the simplest aromatic amine and is used to make synthetic dyes and other aromatic substances.

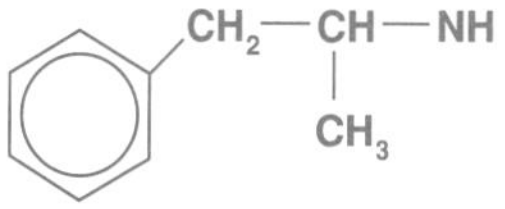

Nicotine is an example of a tertiary amine.

Amphetamine (benzedrine) is a synthetic amine that stimulates the central nervous system. These aromatic amines cause an increase in the blood-glucose level, reducing fatigue and hunger.

FOLLOW-UP PROBLEMS

1. Which of the following structures represent a secondary amine?

(a)

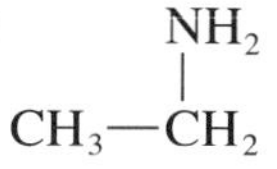

$$CH_3—CH_2—NH_2$$

(b)

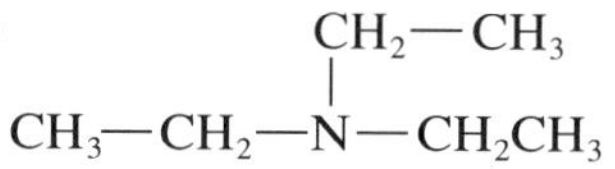

$$CH_3—CH_2—N(CH_2CH_3)—CH_2—CH_3$$

(c)

$$CH_3—CH_2—NH—CH_3$$

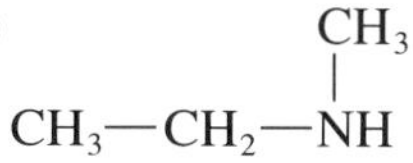

2. Write a formula for a tertiary amine containing a propyl group.

3. Write a condensed formula and a structural formula for the simplest aromatic amine derived from benzene.

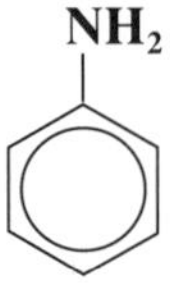

The reactions of both aliphatic and aromatic amines with carboxylic acids produce another family of organic compounds known as *amides*.

AMIDES

The functional group of the simplest type of amides—primary amides—can be regarded as a carboxyl group with the hydroxyl group replaced by an amine group (—NH$_2$). An example of a simple primary amide is:

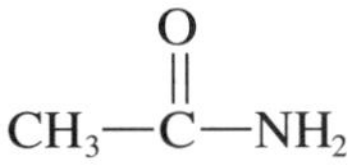

$$CH_3-\overset{\overset{\textstyle O}{\|}}{C}-NH_2$$

ethanamide
(acetamide)

The general formula for an amide is

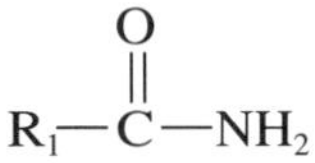

$$R_1-\overset{\overset{\textstyle O}{\|}}{C}-NH_2$$

where R$_1$ represents an alkyl group. Note that R$_1$ represents a hydrogen atom in the simplest amide, methanamide (formamide, HCONH$_2$).

Amides are derived from carboxylic acids and ammonia, or from a primary or secondary amine.

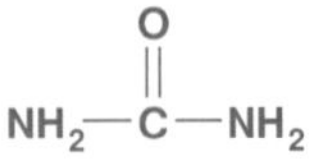

A major industrial chemical, urea (CO(NH$_2$)$_2$), is a diamide derived from carbonic acid (H$_2$CO$_3$). Amides of straight-chain fatty acids having 12, 14, 16 or 18 carbon atoms are used as waterproofing agents, lubricant additives, detergents, emulsifiers and wetting agents.

urea

5-36

Naming Amides

Amides are systematically named by replacing the *-oic acid* ending of the corresponding carboxylic acid with *-amide*. Thus, the amide $C_2H_5CONH_2$, which is derived from propanoic acid (C_2H_5COOH), is called propanamide.

Substituted alkyl groups on the amide nitrogen are named as prefixes preceded by *N*-, or *N,N*- as in the following amides:

$$CH_3—\overset{\overset{\displaystyle O}{\|}}{C}—NH—CH_3 \qquad CH_3—\overset{\overset{\displaystyle O}{\|}}{C}—\overset{\overset{\displaystyle CH_3}{|}}{N}—CH_3$$

N-methyl ethanamide   *N,N*-dimethyl ethanamide
(*N*-methylacetamide)   (*N,N*-dimethylacetamide)

Note that *N* in the systematic names of primary amides indicates that an alkyl group has been substituted for one hydrogen atom bonded to the nitrogen. A secondary amide is indicated by *N,N* because two hydrogen atoms have been substituted by alkyl groups.

5-37
Physical and Chemical Properties of Amides

Amides have relatively high boiling points, since they contain both a polar carbonyl group and a polar —NH group and can thus form hydrogen bonds both in the solid and liquid states. Amides are useful chemical intermediates because they can be hydrolyzed to acids, converted to amines and dehydrated to nitriles. We will look at nitriles in the next section.

NITRILES

Nitriles are a group of organic compounds derived from hydrogen cyanide (HCN), where the hydrogen atom is substituted by an alkyl or aryl group. The general formula for nitriles is $RC{\equiv}N$. Nitriles are very stable compounds but can be hydrolyzed to carboxylic acids. The simplest nitrile, ethanonitrile (acetonitrile), is used as a solvent for inorganic salts and most organic compounds. When nitriles are formed from another compound, such as C_2H_5CN from C_2H_5Br, the carbon chain of the starting substance, in this case C_2H_5Br, is increased by one carbon atom.

5-38
Naming Nitriles

The IUPAC name for nitriles is obtained by replacing the -*e* of the alkane name corresponding to the longest carbon chain in the molecule by *-onitrile*. Note that the carbon of the C≡N group is included in the determination of the alkane name. For example, CH₃CN is called ethanonitrile and has the following structure:

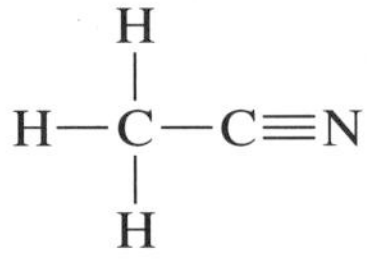

$$H-\underset{\displaystyle \underset{H}{|}}{\overset{\displaystyle \overset{H}{|}}{C}}-C\equiv N$$

ethanonitrile

Similarly, the trivial names for nitriles end in *-onitrile*. Therefore, ethanonitrile is commonly called acetonitrile.

5-39
Physical and Chemical Properties of Nitriles

The C≡N group of the nitrile is polar, due to the presence of the electronegative nitrogen atom bonded to the carbon atom. The boiling points of nitriles are higher than those of nonpolar hydrocarbons of similar mass. Nitriles can be hydrolyzed to amides and thus have a chemical reactivity similar to the corresponding amides. Despite their relationship to hydrogen cyanide, nitriles are generally nontoxic.

HALOGENATED HYDROCARBONS

In this class of compounds, the hydrogen atoms of hydrocarbons have been replaced by halogens. Many of these halogenated hydrocarbons make excellent solvents for nonpolar oils and greases and consequently are used for degreasing industrial metal surfaces and for drycleaning. Some organic halogen compounds are used as fire extinguishers, since they form dense vapours that exclude oxygen from fires. A group of halogenated organic compounds, called *freons*, or CFCs (chlorinated fluorocarbons), are used in air conditioners and in the production of polystyrene polymers. There is much concern about the use of CFCs and their effect on the environment because some have been shown to deplete the earth's protective ozone layer.

5-40
Naming Halogenated Hydrocarbons

Halogenated compounds are named by retaining the hydrocarbon name and adding the individual halogen prefix *fluoro-*, *chloro-*, *bromo-* or *iodo-*. The locations of the halogens are indicated by numbers that go before the prefix. Table 5-18 gives the systematic and common names of some representative halogenated hydrocarbons. Note that when a molecule contains more than one type of halogen, the prefixes appear in alphabetical order.

TABLE 5-18
REPRESENTATIVE HALOGENATED HYDROCARBONS

Systematic Name	Common Name	Structural Formula	Application
Trichloromethane	chloroform	$\begin{array}{c} Cl \\ | \\ H-C-Cl \\ | \\ Cl \end{array}$	solvent, previously used as an anesthetic
Tetrachloromethane	carbon tetrachloride	$\begin{array}{c} Cl \\ | \\ Cl-C-Cl \\ | \\ Cl \end{array}$	solvent, previously used in drycleaning
1,2-Dichloro-1,1,2,2-tetrafluoroethane	freon 114	$\begin{array}{c} F \quad F \\ | \quad | \\ Cl-C-C-Cl \\ | \quad | \\ F \quad F \end{array}$	water repellent, refrigerant
Octafluorocyclobutane	freon C138	$\begin{array}{c} F \quad F \\ | \quad | \\ F-C-C-F \\ | \quad | \\ F-C-C-F \\ | \quad | \\ F \quad F \end{array}$	heat transfer medium
Monochloroethene	vinyl chloride	$\begin{array}{c} H \qquad\quad H \\ \diagdown \quad \diagup \\ C=C \\ \diagup \quad \diagdown \\ H \qquad\quad Cl \end{array}$	monomer for making PVC plastics
1,1,2,2-Tetrachloroethene	perchloroethylene	$\begin{array}{c} Cl \qquad\quad Cl \\ \diagdown \quad \diagup \\ C=C \\ \diagup \quad \diagdown \\ Cl \qquad\quad Cl \end{array}$	drycleaning solvent

The simplest halogenated hydrocarbons are formed by replacing one hydrogen of methane with a halogen atom such as chlorine. The immediate product is chloromethane, commonly called methyl chloride:

$$\begin{array}{c} H \\ | \\ H-C-H \\ | \\ H \end{array} + Cl_2 \longrightarrow \begin{array}{c} H \\ | \\ Cl-C-H \\ | \\ H \end{array} + HCl$$

chloromethane
(methyl chloride)

The substitution of the hydrogen atoms in a methane molecule does not stop at the formation of chloromethane, but goes on to form dichloromethane (methylene chloride), a compound used as a paint stripper. Further substitution results in trichloromethane (chloroform) and tetrachloromethane (carbon tetrachloride). Chloroform was one of the earliest anesthetics used but was found to cause liver and kidney damage. The halogenated hydrocarbons are useful intermediates for making other organic compounds.

In this chapter, we have looked at the classification and nomenclature of organic compounds as well as the different functional groups of each family. We have also briefly examined the physical and chemical properties of each family of compounds.

In the next chapter, we will examine in detail the different types of reactions that are common to each family. We will also discuss petroleum and natural gas as sources of hydrocarbons and the potential of some alternative sources.

MALARIA AND ORGANIC CHEMISTRY

The world has reaped great rewards from the pioneering efforts in organic chemistry, particularly in the twentieth century. Some of these advances have occurred with costs, such as the toxic dangers posed by such compounds as benzene, carbon tetrachloride, phenol and dioxin. Attempts to inform the public about these costs seem to overshadow the valuable benefits we have received from organic compounds. Nowhere are these benefits more apparent than in the development of drugs to fight disease. Chief among such drugs are those that have been developed to combat malaria.

Malaria is an ancient and enduring disease. Accounts of its victims' suffering can be found in many early writings. Characterized by abrupt, recurring bouts of sudden chills followed by debilitating fevers, and frequently culminating in death among the young and weak, malaria has caused incalculable harm to the economy, advancement and well-being of the inhabitants of Earth's warmer latitudes. Indeed, nearly half the world's population lives in malaria-endemic areas, with the World Health Organization reporting a very conservative 6.5 million cases in 1982 alone. The chronic death toll from this one disease gives it the grisly distinction of being our most serious global health problem.

The cause of malaria was variously attributed to breathing bad air, living near swamps and drinking stagnant water. In 1880, a French army surgeon named Charles Louis Alphonse Laveran (1845–1922) identified protozoans from the genus *Plasmodium* in the red blood cells of an infected patient. This discovery spurred

other researchers to find the source of the infection, and in 1898, Italian physicians pinpointed mosquitoes of the *Anophelus* genus as the vectors of transmission in humans.

Countless millions had already suffered or died from malaria by the time of this discovery. The only known treatment was a derivative of the bark of the cinchona tree, a material whose beneficial properties had been discovered by the native people of Peru at least 300 years before. This derivative, quinine, is a heterocyclic compound based on the structure quinoline:

quinoline

Quinine interferes with the ability of the *Plasmodium* parasites to grow and reproduce in red blood cells, probably by preventing them from oxidizing glucose. Its use has benefited more people than any other drug used to fight infectious diseases thus far, and its full synthesis in 1944 marked a great step forward in synthetic organic chemistry.

Quinine, however, is not a cure for malaria. Once a person is bitten by a carrier mosquito, the liver is quickly invaded by the *Plasmodium* species responsible. Quinine eliminates the parasites from the victim's red blood cells, but not from the liver. If quinine treatment is interrupted, the parasites soon re-establish themselves in the bloodstream and the symptoms reoccur.

Shortly before the outbreak of World War II, a new, halogenated, heterocyclic compound known as mepacrine (quinacrine) became available.

$$H-N-CH-(CH_2)_3N(C_2H_5)_2 \cdot 2HCl \cdot 2H_2O$$

mepacrine

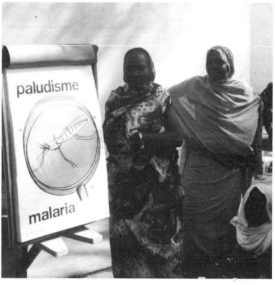

More effective than quinine, mepacrine was used extensively during the war. Unfortunately, it caused side effects such as nausea, dizziness and skin discoloration. More important, it only suppressed the disease; it did not cure it.

This pressed researchers into developing several new compounds, notably chloroquine, primaquine and pyrimethamine. Primaquine, which can destroy parasites hidden in the liver, is administered in an inactive form that is converted to active status once inside the body.

The aim was both to destroy the *Plasmodium* infection and to decimate *Anophelus* populations. By the mid-1970s, malaria had been successfully eliminated from temperate regions such as Mediterranean Europe and the southern United States. Results were not so encouraging, however, in tropical areas such as central Africa and Brazil. Complicating matters was the fact that the pesticide DDT, which had proved so successful in eliminating mosquitoes, was found to be an environmental poison that could seriously harm fish, insect, bird and eventually human popula-

primaquine

Armed with these new drugs and potent insecticides such as DDT, shown below, the World Health Organization initiated a global program in the mid-1950s to eradicate malaria.

1,1,1-trichloro-2,2-bis (*p*-chlorophenyl) ethane
DDT

tions. As a result, its use was severely curtailed or banned in most developed countries.

A further complication was that several mosquito populations were becoming resistant to pesticides such as DDT, and that some *Plasmodium* species had become resistant to the new drugs, particularly chloroquine. Today, scientists and health officials admit that the fight against malaria is far from over.

Along with the continuing development of more effective drugs and safer insecticides, scientists have turned their attention to the development of malarial vaccines. Because of the complex life cycle of the *Plasmodium* species, it is probable that more than one vaccine will be needed, and that all vaccines will have to be administered by injection. Mass immunization by injection has, however, proved difficult in tropical countries.

Perhaps more promising is the concept of biological pesticides to control *Anophelus* populations. One such pesticide, called Skeetal, was recently developed by a British biotechnology firm. Skeetal is made by growing a bacterium, *Bacillus thuringiensis*,

and harvesting the toxins and spores it produces. These natural pesticides can then be sprayed from the air or on land where they will kill a variety of mosquito larvae within 24 hours. In spite of its "quick-kill" factor, Skeetal is very specific toward its hosts and degrades into harmless by-products within a short time.

Regardless of how malaria is eventually defeated, organic chemistry is certain to play a major role.

QUESTIONS

1. Define organic chemistry.

2. Explain how carbon can be tetravalent if the carbon atom in the ground state has a $1s^2$, $2s^2$, $2p^2$ electron configuration.

3. Explain why the rate of reaction of organic compounds is slower than that of inorganic compounds.

4. Use Table 5-4 to show that the melting points of similar organic compounds are proportional to their molecular masses.

5. Using ball-and-stick models for propane, butane, pentane and other hydrocarbons, criticize the term "straight-chain" hydrocarbon.

6. a) Name four classes of hydrocarbons.
   b) Give a general description of each class.

7. What is a structural isomer? Which of the following pairs are structural isomers?

a)

$$Cl-\overset{\displaystyle H}{\underset{\displaystyle H}{C}}-\overset{\displaystyle H}{\underset{\displaystyle H}{C}}-Cl \text{ and } H-\overset{\displaystyle Cl}{\underset{\displaystyle H}{C}}-\overset{\displaystyle H}{\underset{\displaystyle Cl}{C}}-H$$

b)

$$H-\overset{\displaystyle Br}{C}=C-H \text{ and } H-\overset{\displaystyle Br}{C}=\overset{\displaystyle Br}{C}-H$$

c)

$$H-\overset{\displaystyle H}{\underset{\displaystyle H}{C}}-\overset{\displaystyle Cl}{\underset{\displaystyle H}{C}}-Cl \text{ and } H-\overset{\displaystyle Cl}{\underset{\displaystyle H}{C}}-\overset{\displaystyle Cl}{\underset{\displaystyle H}{C}}-H$$

d)

$$H-\overset{\displaystyle H}{\underset{\displaystyle H}{C}}-\overset{\displaystyle CH_3}{\underset{\displaystyle H}{C}}-\overset{\displaystyle H}{\underset{\displaystyle H}{C}}-H \text{ and}$$

$$H-\overset{\displaystyle H}{\underset{\displaystyle H_3C}{C}}-\overset{\displaystyle CH_3}{\underset{\displaystyle H}{C}}-H$$

e)

$$H-\overset{\displaystyle H}{\underset{\displaystyle H}{C}}-\overset{\displaystyle OH}{\underset{\displaystyle H}{C}}-\overset{\displaystyle H}{\underset{\displaystyle H}{C}}-H \text{ and}$$

$$H-\overset{\displaystyle H}{\underset{\displaystyle H}{C}}-\overset{\displaystyle H}{\underset{\displaystyle H}{C}}-\overset{\displaystyle H}{\underset{\displaystyle H}{C}}-OH$$

Answers: c, d, e. Note that (a) and (b) show geometric isomers.

8. (a) Write the general formulas for the alkane series, the alkene series and the alkyne series. (b) Write the name and structural formula for the first member of each group. **Answers: (a) alkanes, C_nH_{2n+2}; alkenes, C_nH_{2n}; alkynes, C_nH_{2n-2}**

9. Write the structural formulas and names of the first five unbranched members of the alkane series.

10. (a) What is a functional group? (b) Name three functional groups.
    Answer: (b) hydroxyl, carbonyl, amino

11. (a) How many isomers can there be for hexane? (b) Write the structural formula for each. (c) Give the systematic name of each.
    Answers:
    (a) 5; (c) hexane, 2-methylpentane, 3-methylpentane, 2,2-dimethylbutane, 2,3-dimethylbutane

12. What is a saturated hydrocarbon?

13. Draw the structural formulas of (a) 2-butene, (b) 1,3-pentadiene, (c) 3,4-dimenthyl-1-hexene, (d) 1,5-hexadiene, (e) 2-chloro-3-methyl-1-butene
    Answers:
    b) $CH_2\!=\!CH\!-\!CH\!=\!CH\!-\!CH_3$
    c) $CH_2\!=\!CH\!-\!CH\!-\!CH\!-\!CH_2\!-\!CH_3$
    ** $\quad\quad\quad\quad CH_3\;\; CH_3$**

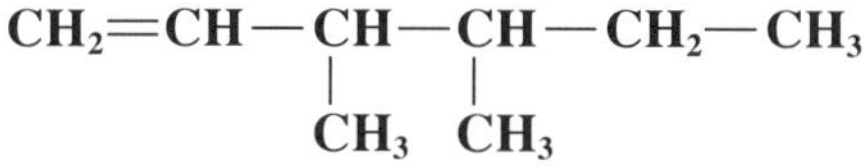

14. How does the structure of aromatic compounds differ from the structures of the members of the alkane and alkene series?

15. Draw the structural formulas for (a) ethanol, (b) ethanal, (c) 2-propanone, (d) 1,3,5-trimethylbenzene.
    Answers:

    (b)

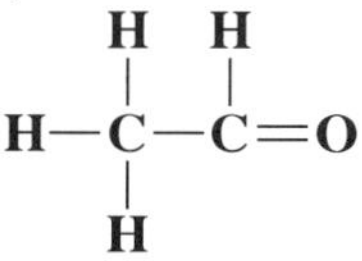

    $H\!-\!\overset{\displaystyle H}{\underset{\displaystyle H}{C}}\!-\!\overset{\displaystyle H}{C}\!=\!O$

    (d) CH_3

    (benzene ring with CH_3, CH_3, CH_3)

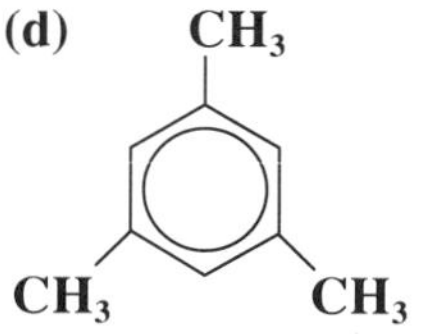

16. Identify the following compounds. Give their systematic names and trivial names, if they exist.

    (a) Cl

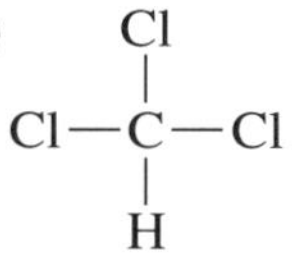

    $Cl\!-\!\overset{\displaystyle Cl}{\underset{\displaystyle H}{C}}\!-\!Cl$

    (b) $H\quad OH\;\; H$

    $H\!-\!\overset{\displaystyle H}{\underset{\displaystyle H}{C}}\!-\!\overset{\displaystyle OH}{\underset{\displaystyle H}{C}}\!-\!\overset{\displaystyle H}{\underset{\displaystyle H}{C}}\!-\!H$

(c) Cl

$Cl\!-\!\overset{\displaystyle Cl}{\underset{\displaystyle Cl}{C}}\!-\!Cl$

(d) $OH\;\; OH\;\; OH$

$H\!-\!\overset{\displaystyle OH}{\underset{\displaystyle H}{C}}\!-\!\overset{\displaystyle OH}{\underset{\displaystyle H}{C}}\!-\!\overset{\displaystyle OH}{\underset{\displaystyle H}{C}}\!-\!H$

(e) $H\!-\!\overset{\displaystyle}{\underset{\displaystyle H}{C}}\!=\!O$

(f) $H\quad H\quad\quad\quad H\quad H$

$H\!-\!C\!-\!C\!-\!O\!-\!C\!-\!C\!-\!H$
(with H substituents above and below)

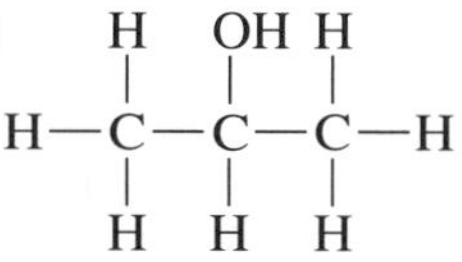

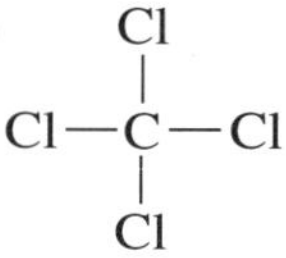

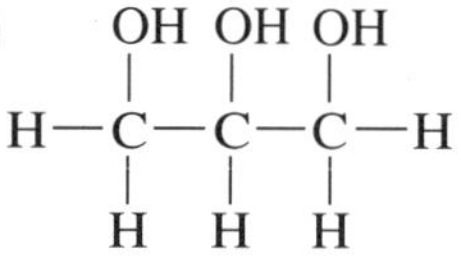

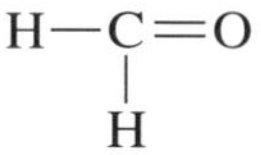

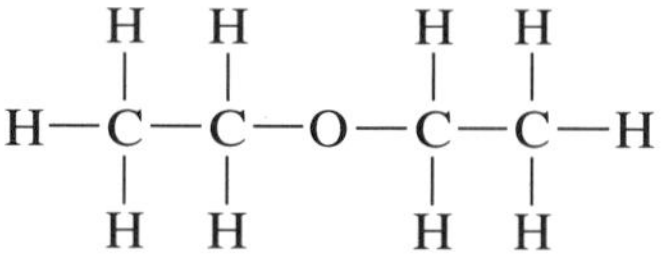

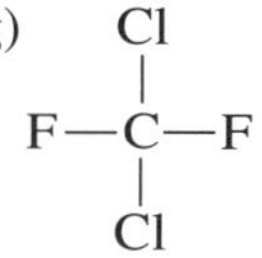

(g) Cl

$F\!-\!\overset{\displaystyle Cl}{\underset{\displaystyle Cl}{C}}\!-\!F$

(h) OH

(benzene ring)

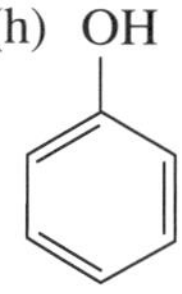

(i) $H\quad H$

$H\!-\!\overset{\displaystyle H}{\underset{\displaystyle H}{C}}\!-\!\overset{\displaystyle H}{\underset{\displaystyle H}{C}}\!-\!OH$

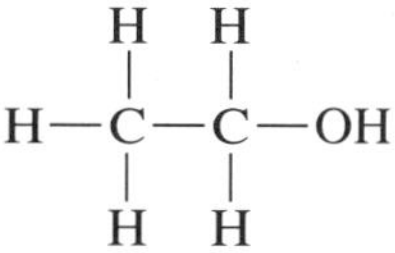

(j) H

$H\!-\!\overset{\displaystyle}{\underset{\displaystyle H}{C}}\!-\!OH$

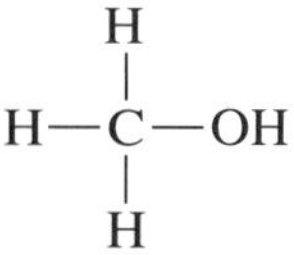

Answers:
a) tricholoromethane (chloroform)
d) 1,2,3-propanetriol (glycerol)
g) dichlorodifluoromethane
h) hydroxybenzene (phenol)

17. (a) Draw a structural formula for aminomethane. (b) Draw the electron-dot structure of aminomethane. (c) Explain why aminomethane is soluble in water, while methane is slightly soluble.
    Answer:

    (b)

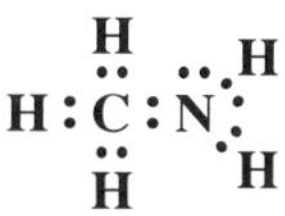

    $H\!:\!\overset{\displaystyle H}{\underset{\displaystyle H}{C}}\!:\!\overset{\cdot\cdot}{\underset{\cdot\cdot}{N}}\!:\!\overset{\displaystyle H}{\underset{\displaystyle H}{}}$

18. Identify the organic family represented by the following general formulas:

    (a) $R_1\!-\!C\!\equiv\!C\!-\!R_2$ (b) $C_n H_{2n+1}OH$
    (c) ArH   (d) $R\!-\!NH_2$

The Canadian Forces aerobatic team, the Snowbirds, fly over the Olympic flame during the opening ceremonies of the XV Olympic Winter Games in Calgary in February 1988. A mixture of natural gases was used to fuel the flame.

Sources and Reactions of Organic Compounds

"The chemists are a strange class of mortals, impelled by an almost insane impulse to seek their pleasure among smoke and vapour, soot and flame, poison and poverty, yet among all these evils I seem to live so sweetly, that may I die if I would change places with the Persian King."
Attributed to Johann Joachim Becher (1635–1682)

Our discussion of organic compounds has so far dealt with the classification of organic structures into families based on their functional groups. Although the diversity of organic substances can appear overwhelming, we have seen that they all have one feature in common—they all contain carbon atoms. The fact that carbon forms the backbone of more compounds than all of the other elements put together suggests that carbon has some very unusual characteristics. We saw in Chapter 3 that carbon atoms are able to readily form covalent bonds with other carbon atoms. The strength of the carbon-to-carbon bond is so great that during many chemical reactions, the carbon skeleton of the molecule remains intact. This ability results in the formation of chainlike molecules that can contain thousands of carbon atoms. In theory, there is no limit to the number of carbon compounds that can be formed.

How can we deal with the chemical properties of so many compounds? Fortunately, studies in organic chemistry show that organic compounds with different functional groups undergo similar types of reactions. In this chapter, we will investigate the principal reactions involving the more common organic compounds. Although there are many different organic reactions used to make more complex organic compounds, it is beyond the scope of this book to go into many of these syntheses in detail. Instead, we will focus on the more important types of reactions, such as oxidation-reduction, hydration and halogenation reactions. Before investigating the classification of these types of reactions, we will first examine the sources of organic compounds.

SOURCES OF ORGANIC MATERIALS

Organic chemistry originally applied only to the chemistry of compounds found in living organisms. All organisms produce organic compounds during biosynthesis, for example, acetic acid, cholesterol and ethyl alcohol. However, the major sources of organic compounds are the fossil fuels: petroleum and natural gas.

Petroleum, from the Latin *petra*, meaning rock, and *oleum*, meaning oil, is a general term for the mixture of natural hydrocarbons found in the earth's crust. Although hydrocarbons can occur in solid, liquid or gaseous forms, the term petroleum is restricted only to the liquid forms. Natural gas refers to the hydrocarbons that are found above the oil layer in a gaseous state. In Canada, our primary sources of organic substances are crude petroleum and natural gas. Coal is not a major source of hydrocarbons because it is so expensive to recover.

Although the refining processes of crude oil from underground wells had begun as early as 1858, it was not until the 1920s that the extraction and processing of petroleum and natural gas from oil fields began to be exploited. By the middle of this century, petroleum and natural gas were the most easily accessible sources of hydrocarbons and primary petrochemicals.

Figure 6-1
A Canadian offshore oil rig.

6-1

Crude Petroleum (Crude Oil)

Petroleum is a mixture of alkanes, cycloalkanes, aromatics and various compounds containing oxygen, sulfur and nitrogen. It can be separated into component fractions according to boiling points.

Crude petroleum, commonly called crude oil, is made up of liquid hydrocarbons, dissolved gases and solids. Most of the components of crude petroleum are hydrocarbons, with smaller amounts of substances containing oxygen, sulfur or nitrogen. Some crude oils, called paraffin crude oils, contain more than 50% saturated hydrocarbons with either unbranched or branched chains. Other crude oils contain large amounts of alicyclic hydrocarbons derived from cyclopentane, cyclohexane and aromatic compounds. The compo-

TABLE 6-1
COMPOSITION OF PETROLEUM

Component	Percentage
Hydrocarbons	50–95
Compounds containing oxygen, sulfur or nitrogen	0.5–8
Resins and asphalts	5–25

sition of a typical petroleum sample is shown in Table 6-1.

The composition of crude oil can vary depending on the source. Thus, crude oils from Alberta do not have the same composition as crude oils from Texas. Analysis of petroleum samples from different areas can yield hundreds of different organic compounds.

Crude oil must be refined before it can be used. *Fractional distillation* is used to separate the petroleum into fractions according to their boiling-temperature ranges. Each fraction is a mixture of a few organic compounds that can then be processed to form commercial products. The separation of crude petroleum into fractions (shown in Table 6-2) is done in a distillation tower (Fig. 6-2).

Figure 6-2
Distillation tower at an oil refinery.

TABLE 6-2
DISTILLATION FRACTIONS FROM CRUDE OIL

Fraction	Boiling Range (°C)	Number of Carbon Atoms	Major Uses
Natural gas	below 20	C_1–C_4	fuel
Petroleum ether	20–60	C_5–C_6	solvents
Ligroin (light naphtha)	60–100	C_6–C_7	primary petrochemicals
Gasoline	40–200	C_5–C_{12}	fuel for combustion engines
Kerosene	175–300	C_{12}–C_{16}	fuel for jet engines, lighting
Heating oil	200–300	C_{15}–C_{18}	furnace oil
Lubricating oil	above 300	C_{17}–C_{40}	lubricant for compressors, automobiles and turbines
Asphalt or petroleum coke	non-volatile solids	C_{20} and above	road resurfacing

Note that petroleum ether does not contain the functional group of ether but is a mixture of alkanes with boiling points comparable to that of diethyl ether.

Although most of the petroleum components are consumed as fuels, a small portion (10%) are called petrochemicals and are used in the synthesis of industrial organic compounds, including plastics, synthetic fibres and insecticides.

Fossils in Your Tank
The organic carbon in petroleum was once part of plants and green algae that lived millions of years ago. It was incorporated into these organisms by means of photosynthesis from CO_2 in the atmosphere:

$$nCO_2 + nH_2O \longrightarrow (CH_2O)_n + nO_2$$

Some of these dead plants and algae sank into the sediments of seas and oceans, where they could not decay completely because of the lack of free oxygen. Over the years, pressure and anaerobic bacteria removed the oxygen and converted the organic material into hydrocarbons: petroleum, natural gas and coal.

TABLE 6-3
COMPOSITION OF NATURAL GAS

Component	Percentage
Methane	60–90
Ethane	5–9
Propane	3–18
Butane	2–14
CO_2	<1
N_2	<1
H_2S	<1
Noble gases	<1

Thiols are sulfur-containing analogs of alcohols and are reputed to be the world's worst smelling compounds. Because natural gas has no odour, methanethiol (CH_3SH) and ethanethiol (CH_3CH_2SH) are added to natural gas so that gas leaks can be easily detected.

6-2
Natural Gas

Natural gas is a mixture of methane, ethane, propane and butane recovered from oil wells and natural-gas fields.

Natural gas is an odourless, colourless mixture of methane, ethane, propane and butane with nitrogen, carbon dioxide and noble gases (Table 6-3). Natural gas may also contain a significant amount of hydrogen sulfide (H_2S), in which case it is called *sour gas*. Sour gas is a poisonous, foul-smelling, corrosive gas that must be handled with extreme caution when it is being drilled. For the sour gas to be suitable for domestic and industrial use, the H_2S must first be removed. This extraction produces elemental sulfur as a by-product.

Natural gas is often found associated with crude-oil deposits as well as in natural-gas fields. However, the natural gas that is transported by pipelines to industrial centres for use as fuel does not have the same composition as the gas recovered from the ground; it is economically more valuable to extract ethane, propane and butane from the natural gas to use for the production of synthetic organic substances. Thus, the component most often used as a fuel is methane, with small amounts of methanethiol or ethanethiol added for safety reasons.

THE ORIGINS OF CANADA'S PETROLEUM INDUSTRY

"Look beneath the surface; let not the several quality of a thing nor its worth escape thee."

Marcus Aurelius Antoninus (121–180 AD)

When brothers Charles and Henry Tripp bought a piece of land in southwest Ontario in 1852, little did they know they were standing over what was to become Canada's first oil well.

The Tripps were interested only in the black, gooey tars lying on the surface of their land, and planned to use it to produce asphalt. After four years, however, their operation was clearly not doing well, and in 1856, the Tripps sold their land to James Miller Williams.

Williams, a carriage maker from Hamilton, Ontario, was determined to find out what lay beneath the tar deposits. In 1857, he drilled beneath the asphalt beds to a depth of 15 m and found crude petroleum oil. The well, located in Enniskillen Township near Oil Springs, was known as Williams No. 1, named after the man who

today is considered the father of Canada's oil industry.

Williams was the first person in North America to drill for oil. His discovery soon launched an exploration boom that made southwest Ontario an important oil-production area during the late nineteenth century. Williams's operation was North America's first integrated oil company, since it was involved in the exploration, production, refining and marketing of oil. About 18 small refineries converted the oil into wheel grease and kerosene, which were the major uses of oil at that time. In the 1860s, the first oil pipeline in North America was built to transport the oil between Petrolia and Sarnia. The jerker-rod system was also developed at this time, enabling oil from many wells to be pumped from one engine.

By 1860, nearly one hundred wells had been dug in the Oil Springs area and were producing an average of 20 barrels a day. In 1862, Canada's first oil gusher occurred in Petrolia and was reported to have yielded 2000 barrels a day for one week.

During this period, Ontario was producing about 10 000 barrels of oil per year, compared with the United States' yearly output of between 250 000 and 500 000 barrels. Ontario's distinction of being the oil-producing capital of North America was soon to fade, however. American businessman Edwin Drake stole the glory from Williams with his discovery of oil in Pennsylvania in 1859, starting an oil boom in the United States and a temporary decline in Canadian production. What made matters worse was that Canada's oil contained greater amounts of sulfur, making it smellier and less desirable than oil from the United States.

With the introduction of the automobile at the start of the twentieth century, the boom was on again and, in a few years, demand for oil outstripped the limited capacity of Ontario's resources. While some gas had been found in the west—the first producing oil well was drilled south of Calgary in 1902—it was not until the Turner Valley discoveries in 1914 that oil riches were again forecast. This boom was brief, however, and all was quiet until oil was found at Le Duc, near Edmonton, in 1946. By this

time geologists were fast becoming promoters of electronic technology, and from then on the wells became deeper, surer and more productive.

James Miller Williams could not have foreseen the impact that his fledgling oil explorations would have in the twentieth century. Williams's curiosity and persistence are testimony to the role that Canada has played in the past, and will continue to play in the discovery and marketing of future energy resources.

6-3

Uses of Petroleum and Natural Gas

Although petroleum and natural gas are used primarily as fuels, they are also used as feedstocks for petrochemicals.

Canada's per-capita rate of consumption of oil and natural gas is one of the highest in the world. The demand for oil has been declining, however, and the Canadian government projects that by the year 2000, oil will be used mostly for transportation (63%), lubricants and asphalt (11%) and petrochemical feedstocks (9%).

Canada's petrochemical industry began during World War II with the production of synthetic rubber. In general, only about 10% of the separated fractions from petroleum and natural gas are used as petrochemicals. The most useful petrochemical feedstocks are methane, ethane, propene, butene and benzene. For example, when ethane, which is a minor component of natural gas, is processed into ethene, it becomes a major constituent of the petrochemical industry (Fig. 6-4).

The products and by-products that are manufactured from petrochemicals are virtually unlimited. Gasoline, diesel fuel, paints, plastics, rubber, synthetic fibres, drugs and insecticides are just some of the products that are available from the processing of petroleum and natural gas. Even crop fertilizers are made from sulfur, a by-product of the processing of sour natural gas.

Figure 6-3
Asphalt is a product of crude oil and is used to pave roads and highways. The Road Manager, a new road-resurfacing machine developed in Ontario, could revolutionize the asphalt recycling industry. The Manager keeps down the cost of road resurfacing, reduces pollution and minimizes traffic disruption. In this new process, old asphalt is cleaned and enhanced and then reapplied to the road. This saves the expense of hauling the old asphalt away and applying a new surface.

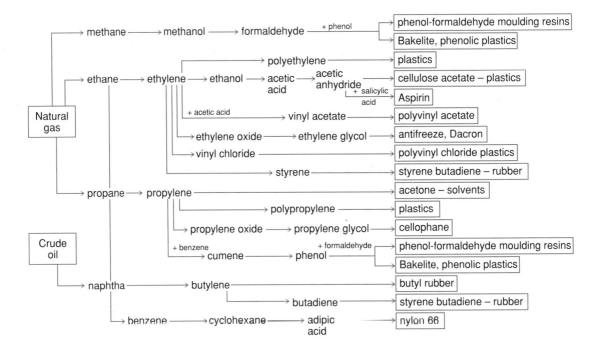

Figure 6-4
Conversion of some primary petro-chemicals to their derivatives.

Hydrocarbons as an Energy Source

In Canada, 75% of our energy is derived from the combustion of fossil hydrocarbons.

Most of our energy comes from petroleum, natural gas and coal. The supply of petroleum and natural gas depends on two sources: proven reserves and speculative reserves. Proven reserves are the quantities that can be recovered from known reserves; speculative reserves are estimated quantities of ultimately recoverable resources. Proven reserves generally provide a 30-year supply. Thus, although some scientists contend that our current supply of oil is running out, most scientists agree that changes in technology will allow for the development of new reserves as needed.

Non-fossil organic sources of biomass energy, which include wood, plant material and animal manure, have been a primary source of energy throughout history. Biomass also represents a potential source of hydrocarbons. Alternative sources of organic compounds are discussed further at the end of this chapter.

In order to understand how hydrocarbons are used to produce energy, we must investigate the reactions involved. The combustion of hydrocarbons is the main reaction responsible for producing energy. However, the initial reaction involves the cracking of long hydrocarbon chains to improve the yield of combustible hydrocarbons from crude petroleum.

6-5

Cracking

Cracking is an industrial process in which long hydrocarbon chains are broken into smaller fragments.

The long-chain saturated hydrocarbons found in crude oil are not particularly useful compounds because they do not contain a functional group that allows them to be converted into other organic compounds. However, they can be cracked to produce smaller unsaturated hydrocarbons that can be used in the synthesis of other compounds.

During cracking, one or more hydrogen molecules are lost. This removal of hydrogen, called *dehydrogenation*, creates reactive, unsaturated sites such as carbon-to-carbon double bonds. For example, ethane (C_2H_6) can be cracked to produce ethene:

$$CH_3CH_3 \xrightarrow{\text{heat}} CH_2{=}CH_2 + H_2$$
$$\text{ethane} \qquad\qquad \text{ethene}$$

The products of the cracking process depend on the hydrocarbon used and the external conditions. At temperatures just above 400°C, butane (C_4H_{10}) yields mainly ethene, as well as methane, ethane, propene, butene and hydrogen. At temperatures above 1000°C, the main products are ethene, propene and butene. Under more extreme conditions, ethyne (acetylene) can be produced.

Thermal cracking occurs at high temperatures. When cracking takes place in the presence of a catalyst, the process is called *catalytic cracking*. Catalytic cracking is carried out in most oil refineries in catalytic-cracking towers, where the high boiling fractions are broken down into smaller molecules that lie within the gasoline range. For example, the catalytic cracking of hexane produces a mixture of hydrogen, methane, ethene, propene and butene.

Cracking is more often used in the production of better fuels than it is in the production of organic compounds. The use of hydrocarbons as fuels involves a process called *combustion*. Easily combustible materials, such as the components of natural gas and the lighter crude-oil fractions, are thus important energy sources.

The cracking of methane produces carbon and hydrogen:

$$CH_4 \xrightarrow{\text{heat}} C + 2H_2$$

Lead vs. Cracking
Until recently, the usual method of improving the quality of gasoline was to add tetraethyl lead ((C_2H_5)$_4$Pb) to make leaded gasoline. Leaded gasoline, however, is being phased out because it can cause environmental damage in high enough doses. Lead also "poisons" catalytic converters, which reduce CO and NO$_x$ emissions. Unleaded gasoline burns more cleanly than leaded gasoline because it contains branched hydrocarbons produced by cracking longer-chain molecules.

6-6

Combustion of Hydrocarbons

The products of complete combustion are carbon dioxide and water; carbon monoxide and carbon are produced during incomplete combustion.

Saturated and unsaturated hydrocarbons, alcohols, ethers, esters

Figure 6-5
A truck fueled with propane.

Octane Ratings
The octane rating of a gasoline is based on its ability to burn without causing engine knock. The perform- ance of gasoline in internal combus- tion engines depends on the degree of branching in the carbon chains. Highly branched 2,2,4-trimethylpen- tane (isooctane) burns very well and is assigned an "octane rating" of 100. Straight-chain *n*-heptane burns poorly because it ignites prematurely, causing knock and reducing power; it is assigned an octane rating of 0. The octane rating of a gasoline sample is the percentage of isooctane in a mix- ture of isooctane and *n*-heptane that has the same knock and power prop- erties as the gasoline sample. Some representative octane ratings of some hydrocarbons and gasoline additives are shown in the table below.

OCTANE RATINGS

Name	Octane Rating
n-heptane	0
n-pentane	62
tert-butyl alcohol	98
isooctane	100
benzene	106
ethanol	112
methanol	116
toluene	118

and many other organic compounds are combustible; that is, they burn in air or oxygen to produce energy in the form of heat and light. The major exceptions are halogenated hydrocarbons, some of which are used as fire-extinguishing chemicals.

The most important combustible compounds are the alkanes. For example, the burner gas used in science labs is methane, and some homes use natural gas for heating or cooking. Automobiles can be fueled by natural gas or propane instead of gasoline to reduce the wear on engines (Fig. 6-5). Combustion of alkanes is an *exothermic* (energy-releasing) process. We will consider the heats of combustion of different compounds in Chapter 8.

Combustion reactions fall into two categories: complete and incomplete. Given a sufficient supply of oxygen or air, a hydrocar- bon undergoes *complete combustion* when it is ignited to produce carbon-dioxide gas and water. There is also a maximum release of energy during a complete combustion.

A major industrial example of a complete combustion reaction occurs in the oxyacetylene torch used in welding or for cutting metals. The heat (enthalpy) of combustion of ethyne (acetylene, C_2H_2) is 1250 kJ/mol, as shown in Equation 6-1:

$$C_2H_2 + \tfrac{5}{2}O_2 \longrightarrow 2CO_2 + H_2O + 1250 \text{ kJ} \qquad [6\text{-}1]$$
ethyne

This highly exothermic reaction is responsible for the extremely high temperature of the oxyacetylene flame (2700°C). Equation 6-1 shows that each mole of ethyne requires 2.5 mol of oxygen for complete combustion. If fewer than 2.5 mol of oxygen are availa- ble, the hydrocarbon is not fully oxidized to carbon dioxide (CO_2) gas and an *incomplete combustion* results.

The products of incomplete combustion are carbon dioxide, carbon monoxide, carbon and water. There are a number of possible balanced equations that can be written for incomplete combustion, provided there is insufficient oxygen to fully convert the hydrocarbon to carbon dioxide and water. Equation 6-2 is one example of a possible incomplete combustion of propane:

$$4C_3H_8(g) + 13O_2(g) \longrightarrow$$
$$4CO_2(g) + 2CO(g) + 6C(s) + 16H_2O(g) \qquad [6\text{-}2]$$

Incomplete combustions waste energy and are hazardous because of the toxicity of carbon monoxide. In North America, hundreds of deaths by carbon-monoxide poisoning are reported each year. Faulty car mufflers and the incomplete combustion of propane in refrigerators have been noted as two sources of toxic carbon-monoxide emissions.

Because the combustion of fuels requires oxygen, it can there- fore be classified as an *oxidation reaction*. We will see in Chapter

13 that any oxidation reaction is accompanied by a corresponding *reduction reaction*; hence, the term *oxidation-reduction*, or *redox*, is used for such chemical reactions. Oxidation-reduction reactions are a major type of organic reaction since almost all organic compounds burn in oxygen.

The *enthalpy of combustion* is the amount of heat or energy evolved during a combustion reaction.

FOLLOW-UP PROBLEMS
1. Write balanced equations for the complete combustion of (a) butane, (b) benzene and (c) 2-butyne.
2. If ten moles of oxygen are available for the combustion of one mole of octane, will a complete or incomplete combustion occur?
3. Explain the presence of water in the exhaust pipe of an automobile that has just been started.

Answers:
1. (c) $CH_3C \equiv CCH_3 + \frac{11}{2}O_2 \longrightarrow 4CO_2 + 3H_2O$
2. **incomplete combustion**

OXIDATION-REDUCTION REACTIONS

Virtually all organic compounds burn in oxygen and, thus, are involved in an oxidation reaction. Oxidation reactions were originally defined as reactions in which oxygen was added to an element or compound; today there are four different, interconnected definitions for oxidation reactions. For our purposes, we will examine the oxidation-reduction reactions involved in organic reactions.

6-7

General Oxidation-Reduction Reactions

An oxidation reaction is the addition of oxygen to a substance, the removal of hydrogen from a compound or an increase in the oxidation state; reduction is the opposite reaction.

We will see in Chapter 13 that oxidation is usually defined as a loss of electrons by an atom and reduction as a gain of electrons. In organic reactions, however, it is easier to classify some reactions as oxidation-reduction reactions using three other definitions. The most common definition for oxidation is the addition of oxygen to a substance:

$$2CO(g) + O_2(g) \longrightarrow 2CO_2(g)$$

Correspondingly, reduction is the removal of an oxygen:

$$H_2O(g) + C(s) \longrightarrow CO(g) + H_2(g) \qquad [6\text{-}3]$$

Note that in Equation 6-3, water is being reduced and carbon is being oxidized.

Since hydrogen is often used to remove oxygen from a compound, the term reduction has been expanded to include any organic reaction in which hydrogen is added to a substance:

$$C_2H_4(g) + H_2(g) \longrightarrow C_2H_6(g) \qquad [6\text{-}4]$$

ethene   ethane

Because oxidation is the opposite reaction, we can also expand the definition of oxidation in an organic reaction to include the removal of hydrogen:

$$CH_3CH_2OH(g) \longrightarrow CH_3CHO(g) + H_2 \qquad [6\text{-}5]$$

ethanol   ethanal

Note that Equation 6-4 can also be called a *hydrogenation reaction* and Equation 6-5 a *dehydrogenation reaction*.

A third type of oxidation reaction occurs when an element increases its oxidation state. Chapter 13 discusses in detail the concepts of oxidation number and oxidation state.

We will now examine the oxidation-reduction reactions that involve particular organic families.

FOLLOW-UP PROBLEMS

1. Propene ($CH_3CH{=}CH_2$) is treated with hydrogen gas and a catalyst. What compound is produced? What type of reaction occurs?

2. Show that the following sequence of compounds represents an oxidation process:

$$C_2H_6 \longrightarrow C_2H_5OH \longrightarrow CH_3CHO \longrightarrow$$
$$CH_3COOH \longrightarrow CH_3OH \longrightarrow CO_2$$

Answer:
1. propane; reduction, or hydrogenation

6-8

Oxidation of Alkenes and Alkynes

Alkenes and alkynes can be oxidized to alcohols or carboxylic acids by the action of an oxidizing agent.

Alkenes can be oxidized to alcohols or carboxylic acids, depending on the type of oxidizing agent. The oxidation of the double bond involves either the oxidation of the pi bond without cleavage of the sigma bond to produce alcohols or the oxidation of the pi bond with cleavage of the sigma bond to produce carboxylic acids. The oxidation of an alkene without cleavage requires a cold, alkaline, aqueous solution of potassium permanganate ($KMnO_4$) and produces an alcohol with two hydroxyl groups and is called a *diol*. Ethylene glycol ($CH_2(OH)CH_2(OH)$) is an example of a 1,2-diol.

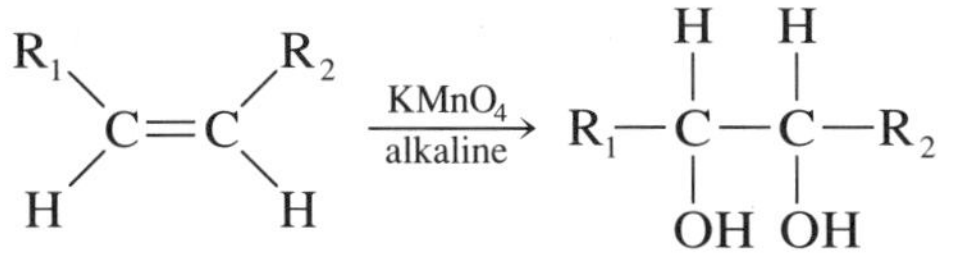

alkene   alcohol

This reaction is also called a *hydroxylation reaction* because two hydroxyl groups are added to the alkene. Although hydrogen and oxygen atoms are added, this reaction is still classified as an oxidation reaction because the carbon atoms in the product are in a higher oxidation state than the carbon atoms in the reactant.

The reaction of alkenes with a cold permanganate solution is usually used to test for unsaturation in compounds of unknown structure. During the reaction, the purple colour of the $KMnO_4$ solution disappears and a brown precipitate of MnO_2 is formed. This test for double bonds is called the **Baeyer test**.

Under more vigorous oxidation by a hot solution of $KMnO_4$ or a stronger oxidizing agent such as potassium dichromate ($K_2Cr_2O_7$), carboxylic acids are formed:

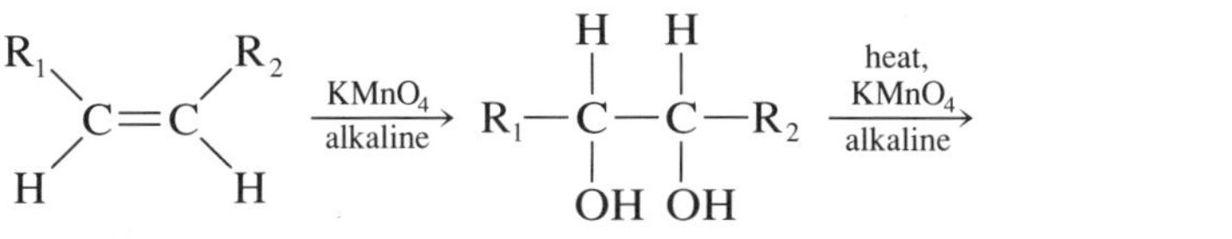

alkene   alcohol

carboxylic acids

Oxidation of the triple bond in alkynes also leads to the formation of carboxylic acids. The net change is the addition of oxygen to a region of high electron density—the pi bond of the alkyne.

FOLLOW-UP PROBLEM

Name the products formed during the oxidation of propene in a hot solution of $KMnO_4$.

Answer: methanoic acid and ethanoic acid

6-9

Oxidation of Alcohols: Dehydrogenation

Alcohols can be oxidized to form aldehydes, ketones or carboxylic acids.

An unspecified oxidizing agent can be represented by [O].

The oxidation of alcohols to produce aldehydes, ketones or carboxylic acids is used in industrial and biological systems. The oxidation of an alcohol occurs in two stages. In the first stage, for example, methanol (CH_3OH), a primary alcohol, is oxidized to form an aldehyde, methanal (CH_2O). Essentially, the primary alcohol loses two hydrogen atoms:

$$H-\underset{\underset{\text{methanol}}{|}}{\overset{\overset{OH}{|}}{C}}-H \xrightarrow[\text{alkaline}]{KMnO_4} H-\underset{\text{methanal}}{\overset{\overset{O}{\|}}{C}}-H + H_2(g)$$

A specialized oxidizing agent, pyridine chlorochromate (PCC), has been developed that will oxidize primary alcohols to the aldehyde stage and then stop.

Note that the oxidation of a primary alcohol to an aldehyde requires an oxidizing agent such as potassium permanganate ($KMnO_4$) or chromic acid (H_2CrO_4).

Because aldehydes are more easily oxidized than alcohols, the oxidation reaction continues to a second stage, where a carboxylic acid is produced:

$$\underset{\underset{\text{(formaldehyde)}}{\text{methanal}}}{\overset{\overset{O}{\|}}{HCH}} \xrightarrow[H_2SO_4]{H_2CrO_4} \underset{\underset{\text{(formic acid)}}{\text{methanoic acid}}}{\overset{\overset{O}{\|}}{HCOH}}$$

The oxidation of a secondary alcohol by oxidizing agents produces a ketone. For example, the oxidation of 2-propanol by potassium dichromate acid solution produces propanone. Acidic conditions are used because ketones can be further oxidized in alkaline solutions:

$$\underset{\underset{\text{(isopropyl alcohol)}}{\text{2-propanol}}}{CH_3\underset{\overset{|}{\overset{OH}{|}}}{C}HCH_3} \xrightarrow[H_2SO_4]{K_2Cr_2O_7} \underset{\underset{\text{(acetone)}}{\text{propanone}}}{CH_3\overset{\overset{O}{\|}}{C}CH_3}$$

Tertiary alcohols cannot be oxidized in alkaline conditions because no hydrogen atom is available on the hydroxylated carbon atom. Under acidic conditions, tertiary alcohols are oxidized to alkenes, which can then be oxidized to ketones or carboxylic acids of shorter carbon chains.

FOLLOW-UP PROBLEM

For the following reactions, draw the structural formula and give the name of the first and second products:

a) $CH_3CH_2OH \xrightarrow[H_2SO_4]{K_2Cr_2O_7}$

            CH_3
            |
b) $CH_3CHCH_2OH \xrightarrow[H_2SO_4]{K_2Cr_2O_7}$

Answer:

        CH_3
        |
b) CH_3CHCHO **2-methylpropanal and**
        CH_3
        |
  $CH_3CHCOOH$ **2-methylpropanoic acid**

6-10
Oxidation of Aldehydes and Ketones

Aldehydes are very easily oxidized to carboxylic acids. Ketones are not easily oxidized.

The carbonyl functional group of an aldehyde is always located at the end of the carbon chain. When an aldehyde is oxidized by mild oxidizing agents such as Ag^+ or Cu^+, it gains an oxygen to form a carboxylic acid. These metal ions are reduced to silver and copper, respectively, if the salts of these metals are used to oxidize aldehydes. *Tollen's reagent* is a solution of silver nitrate in ammonia that, when added to an aldehyde solution in a test tube, forms a deposit of metallic silver on the glass:

Air oxidizes benzaldehyde to benzoic acid:

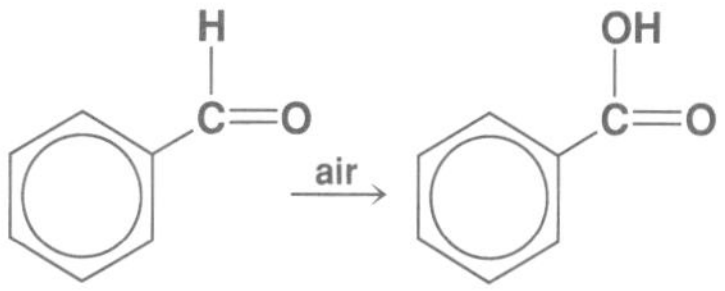

benzaldehyde   benzoic acid

       O
       ‖
CH_3CH_2CH + $Ag(NH_3)_2^+$ + $3OH^-$ $\longrightarrow$
 propanal   Tollen's reagent

                    O
                    ‖
            $CH_3CH_2CO^-$ + Ag + $2NH_3$ + $2H_2O$
             propanoate ion   silver

In this reaction, the aldehyde is oxidized to a carboxylic acid and the silver ion in the reagent is reduced to silver metal. This test is called the *silver-mirror reaction*.

For centuries, mirrors have been made by depositing silver on glass using the oxidation reaction of aldehydes.

Similarly, an alkaline solution of copper(II) ions, called *Fehling's*, or *Benedict's*, *solution*, is used to test for the presence of sugars (aldehydes). The blue Cu^{2+} ion is reduced to red Cu_2O:

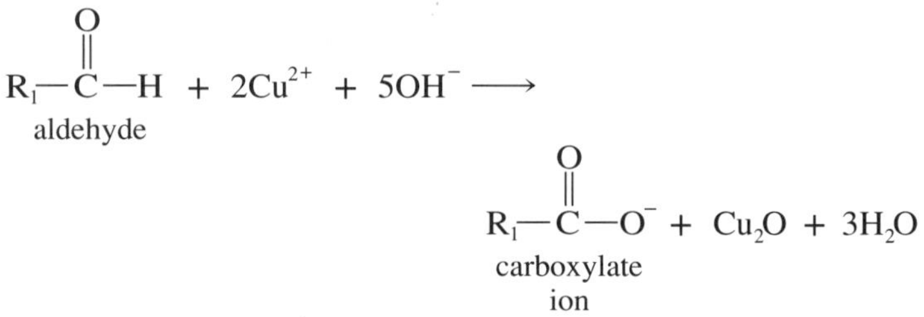

$$R_1-\overset{\overset{\textstyle O}{\|}}{C}-H \ + \ 2Cu^{2+} \ + \ 5OH^- \longrightarrow$$

aldehyde

$$R_1-\overset{\overset{\textstyle O}{\|}}{C}-O^- \ + \ Cu_2O \ + \ 3H_2O$$

carboxylate
ion

The formation of a red precipitate and the disappearance of the blue colour indicate a positive test.

Ketones cannot be easily oxidized to form other compounds. Like the oxidation of tertiary alcohols, the oxidation of a ketone involves breaking the carbon skeleton.

FOLLOW-UP PROBLEM

Draw the structural formulas for and give the names of the products formed in the following reactions:

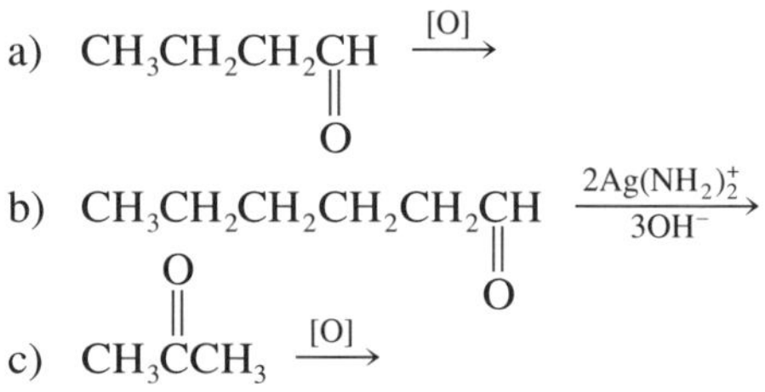

a) $CH_3CH_2CH_2\overset{\overset{\textstyle O}{\|}}{CH} \xrightarrow{[O]}$

b) $CH_3CH_2CH_2CH_2CH_2\overset{\overset{\textstyle O}{\|}}{CH} \xrightarrow[3OH^-]{2Ag(NH_2)_2^+}$

c) $CH_3\overset{\overset{\textstyle O}{\|}}{C}CH_3 \xrightarrow{[O]}$

Answer:
b) $CH_3CH_2CH_2CH_2CH_2COO^-$ **hexanoate ion**

We previously defined a reduction reaction as the loss of oxygen or the gain of hydrogen. Reactions that involve the gain of hydrogen can also be called *hydrogenation reactions*.

6-11

Reduction of Alkenes and Alkynes: Hydrogenation

The reduction (hydrogenation) of alkenes or alkynes occurs during the catalytic addition of hydrogen gas to the C=C and C≡C bonds.

Alkenes and alkynes are unsaturated compounds. The addition of a hydrogen atom to a carbon-to-carbon double bond to produce a fully saturated hydrocarbon was shown in Equation 6-4 as a reduction reaction. This reaction occurs readily if a catalyst such as platinum or fine nickel powder is present:

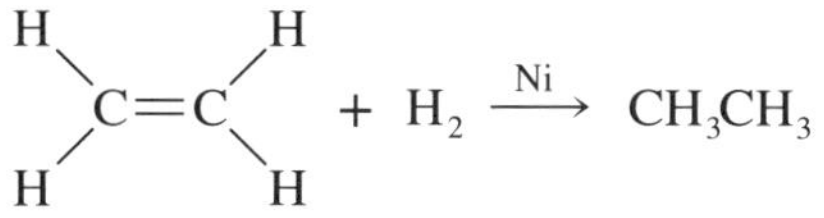

$$\underset{\text{ethene}}{\underset{H}{\overset{H}{\diagdown}}C=C\underset{H}{\overset{H}{\diagup}}} + H_2 \xrightarrow{\text{Ni}} \underset{\text{ethane}}{CH_3CH_3}$$

Similarly, the addition of hydrogen to an alkyne such as propyne makes it less unsaturated by forming propene, or fully saturated by forming propane:

$$\underset{\text{propyne}}{CH_3C\equiv CH} + H_2 \xrightarrow{\text{Pt}} \underset{\text{propene}}{CH_3CH=CH_2} + H_2 \xrightarrow{\text{Pt}} \underset{\text{propane}}{CH_3CH_2CH_3}$$

With appropriate catalysts, the hydrogenation of an alkyne can be controlled (that is, an alkene is formed instead of an alkane).

What happens during hydrogenation? It is believed that the hydrogen gas is attracted (adsorbed) at the surface of the metal catalyst. The H—H bond is weakened so that the $1s$ orbital of each hydrogen atom interacts with the pi electrons of the alkene, resulting in the addition of hydrogen atoms to the formerly unsaturated carbon atoms.

FOLLOW-UP PROBLEMS

1. What is produced when methylpropene is hydrogenated?

2. What product is formed after 1 mol of hydrogen and 2 mol of hydrogen, respectively, are added to 2-butyne?

Answer:
2. 2-butene and butane

6-12
Reduction of Aldehydes and Ketones: Hydrogenation

An aldehyde can be reduced to a primary alcohol and a ketone to a secondary alcohol by catalytic hydrogenation.
Catalytic hydrogenation of an aldehyde produces a good yield of a primary alcohol. As in the hydrogenation of alkenes, platinum or powdered nickel can be used as the catalyst:

Over a billion kilograms of methanol are synthesized each year. Most of this is produced by the catalytic hydrogenation of carbon monoxide.

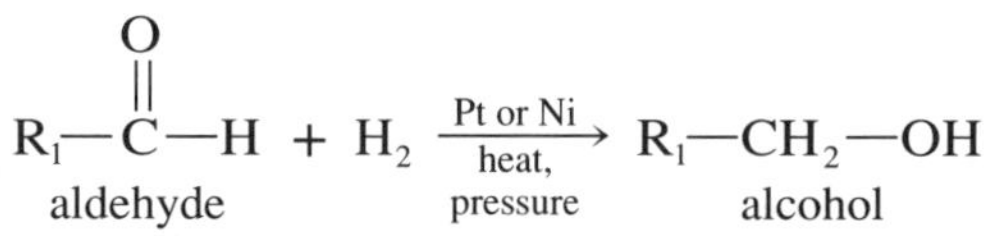

$$R_1-\overset{\overset{\displaystyle O}{\|}}{C}-H + H_2 \xrightarrow[\substack{\text{heat,} \\ \text{pressure}}]{\text{Pt or Ni}} R_1-CH_2-OH$$

aldehyde   alcohol

Note that heat and pressure are also required for the hydrogenation of an aldehyde.

A ketone is reduced to a secondary alcohol by the same method of catalytic hydrogenation:

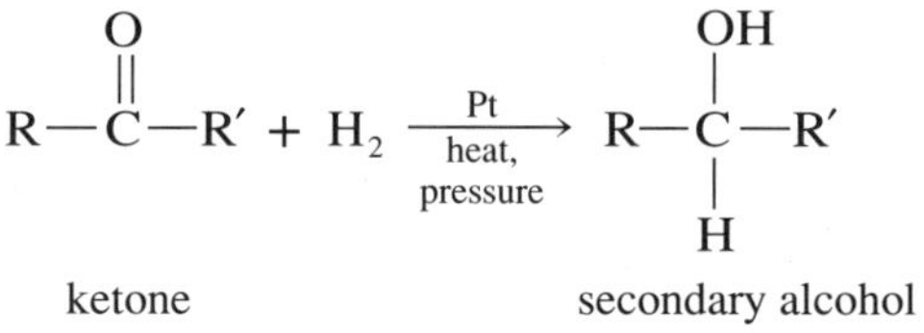

$$R-\overset{\overset{\displaystyle O}{\|}}{C}-R' + H_2 \xrightarrow[\substack{\text{heat,} \\ \text{pressure}}]{\text{Pt}} R-\overset{\overset{\displaystyle OH}{|}}{\underset{\underset{\displaystyle H}{|}}{C}}-R'$$

ketone   secondary alcohol

Common reducing agents for both aldehydes and ketones are sodium borohydride ($NaBH_4$) or lithium aluminum hydride ($LiAlH_4$).

During hydrogenation, the pi bond of the carbonyl group of the aldehyde or ketone is the major point of attack. A more vigorous reduction of the carbonyl compound to form an alkane takes place if an amalgam of zinc in mercury is used with concentrated hydrochloric acid:

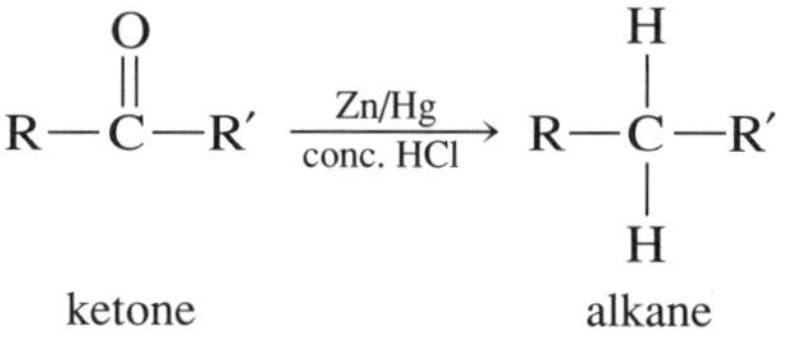

$$R-\overset{\overset{\displaystyle O}{\|}}{C}-R' \xrightarrow[\text{conc. HCl}]{\text{Zn/Hg}} R-\overset{\overset{\displaystyle H}{|}}{\underset{\underset{\displaystyle H}{|}}{C}}-R'$$

ketone   alkane

FOLLOW-UP PROBLEMS

1. What product is formed during the hydrogenation of butanal?

2. What product is formed during the following reaction?

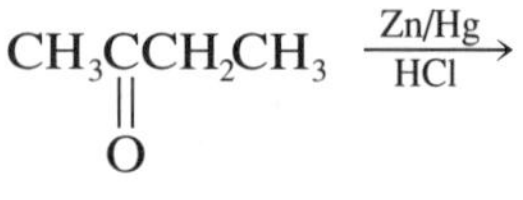

$$CH_3\overset{}{\underset{\underset{\displaystyle O}{\|}}{C}}CH_2CH_3 \xrightarrow[\text{HCl}]{\text{Zn/Hg}}$$

Answer:
1. 1-butanol

HYDRATION AND DEHYDRATION

The addition of water to an organic compound is called a *hydration reaction*. Hydration reactions involving alkenes and alkynes occur when the components of water (H^+ and OH^-) are added to the unsaturated carbon-to-carbon bonds to produce an alcohol. The opposite reaction—the removal of a water molecule from an organic compound—is known as a *dehydration reaction*.

6-13

Hydration of Alkenes

When an alkene is treated with water in the presence of an acid, an alcohol is produced.

Alkenes are often used as intermediates in the production of other chemicals. Many alcohols are produced commercially through the hydration of alkenes. The addition of water to ethene, for example, in the presence of a concentrated solution of sulfuric acid yields ethanol:

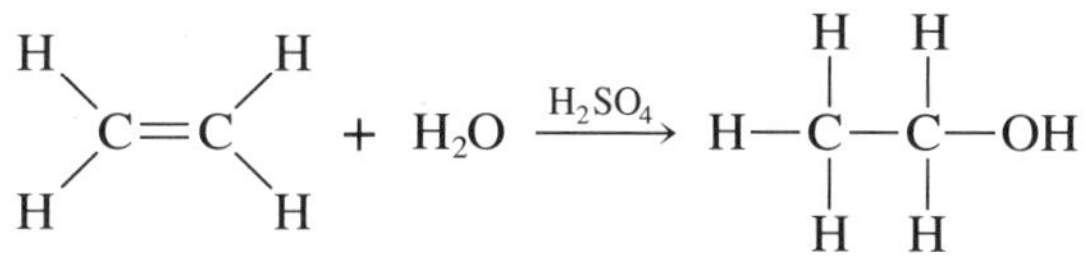

ethene	ethanol (ethyl alcohol)

In the net reaction, one hydrogen atom from water adds to one carbon of the C=C bond, and the —OH group adds to the other carbon. The sulfuric acid provides the hydrogen ion (H^+) that catalyzes the reaction.

What actually happens between the reactant species in this reaction? The search for an understanding of chemical reactivity has led to the proposal of *reaction mechanisms*. Reaction mechanisms are further discussed in Chapter 9. However, because organic reactions are easier to explain with reaction mechanisms, we will investigate the proposed mechanism for the hydration of an alkene to an alcohol.

Hydration of an alkene to an alcohol in the presence of sulfuric acid is believed to occur in two steps. First, a hydrogen ion from the sulfuric acid disturbs the pi electron cloud of the C=C bond and causes it to become polarized. This makes one carbon atom relatively negative so that it attracts the H^+ ion. The other carbon atom thus carries a positive charge and forms a carbonium ion:

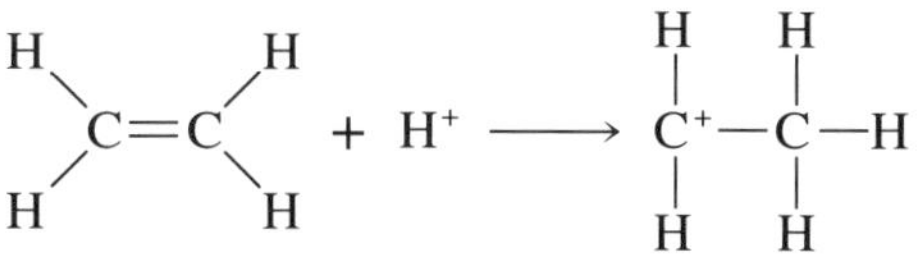

A carbonium ion is an unstable intermediate species that contains a positively charged carbon atom. For example, when tertiary butyl chloride ((CH_3)$_3$CCl) hydrolyzes, the first step in the mechanism is believed to be the formation of a carbonium ion:

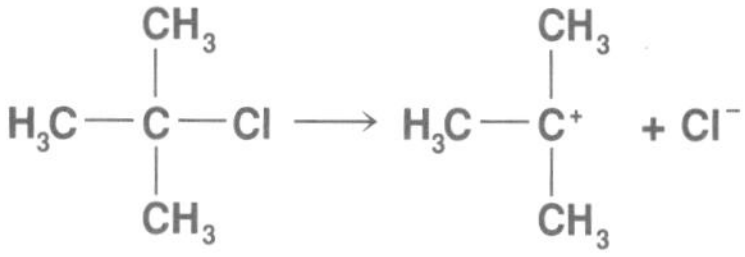

carbonium ion

Because water is a polar molecule with a partially negative charge

The Apple Scare of 1989
In February 1989, the U.S. Natural Resources Defense Council reported that apples and apple products contained a chemical found to be carcinogenic in animal tests.

The possible carcinogen is unsymmetrical dimethylhydrazine (UDMH), which is produced during the alkaline hydrolysis of Alar. Alar (daminozide) is a growth regulator that prevents pre-harvest fruit drop and delays fruit maturity. It is possible that the heat used in apple processing can convert 1% of daminozide to UDMH. Physiological conditions in the body may also convert 1 to 5% of Alar to UDMH.

The U.S. Environmental Protection Agency considers Alar to be safe because studies indicate that risk may occur only from long-term, high-dosage exposure. For example, a person would have to eat more than 1170 kg of apples every day for 70 years in order to attain the exposure levels used in the lab.

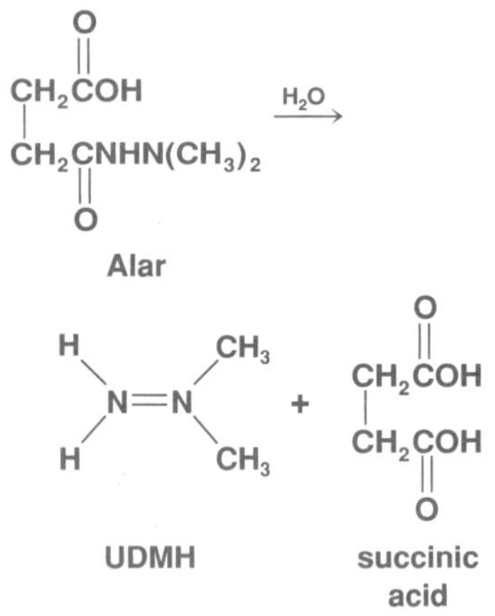

on the oxygen end of the molecule, it is then attracted to the positively charged carbon atom:

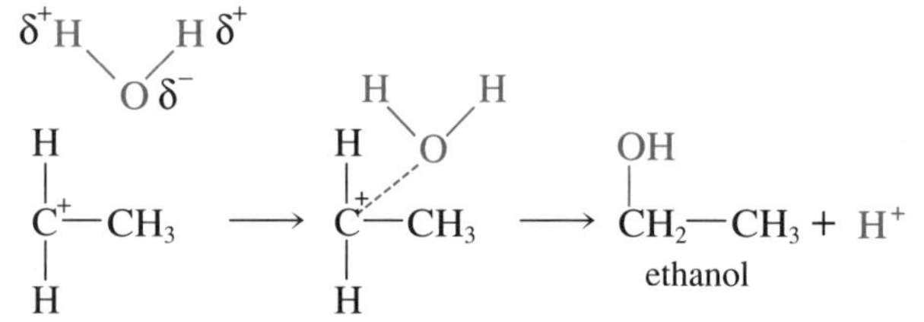

Subsequent shifts in electron density cause one of the hydrogen atoms of the water molecule to cleave as a hydrogen ion and to leave its electron with the oxygen. This overall reaction produces an alcohol.

FOLLOW-UP PROBLEMS

1. What structure is formed during the hydration of propene?

2. Write the structural formula and the name of the product formed during the following reaction:

$$CH_3CH_2CH_2C = CH_2 + H_2O \xrightarrow{H_2SO_4}$$

Alar

UDMH   succinic acid

6-14

Hydration of Alkynes

The hydration of alkynes produces an aldehyde or a ketone. The hydration of alkynes occurs in two stages. The first stage is similar to the first stage in an alkene hydration in which an alcohol is produced. However, in alkyne hydration, an unsaturated structure is formed, called an *enol*. In the second stage, the enol undergoes a structural rearrangement, called *tautomerization*, to produce an aldehyde or ketone. Note that a mercuric salt ($HgSO_4$) and an acid catalyst (H_2SO_4) are needed for this reaction:

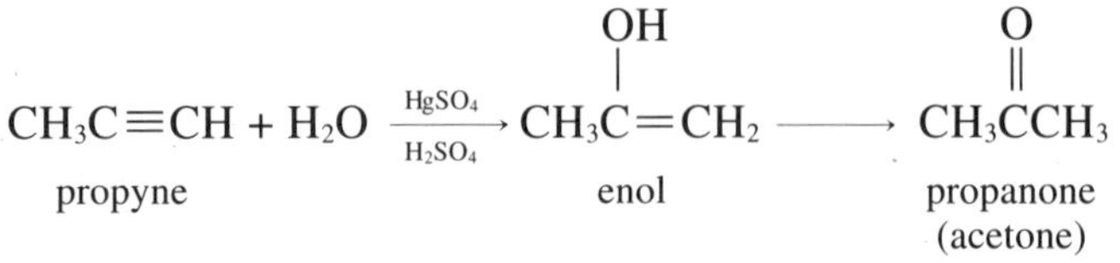

$$CH_3C \equiv CH + H_2O \xrightarrow[H_2SO_4]{HgSO_4} CH_3C = CH_2 \longrightarrow CH_3CCH_3$$

propyne   enol   propanone (acetone)

The opposite reaction to hydration is called *dehydration* and involves the elimination of water from an alcohol.

FOLLOW-UP PROBLEM

What compounds are produced during the hydration of
(a) 2-butyne and (b) 3-methyl-1-butyne?

Answer: (a) butanone

6-15
Dehydration of Alcohols

The dehydration of alcohols produces an alkene or an ether.
The dehydration of alcohols is an important reaction in the synthesis of other organic compounds, particularly alkenes. A dehydration reaction is characterized by the loss of water and the production of an unsaturated bond such as a $C{=}C$ bond. A dehydration reaction is also classified as an *elimination reaction* because a group is lost from the original compound. An example is the dehydration of ethanol to ethene using concentrated sulfuric acid and heat:

$$CH_3CH_2OH \xrightarrow[180°C]{H_2SO_4} CH_2{=}CH_2 + H_2O$$
$$\text{ethanol} \qquad\qquad \text{ethene}$$

Note that the dehydration of alcohols is the reverse reaction of the acid-catalyzed hydration of alkenes. The reaction mechanism is also similar to that of the hydration of alkenes in that an intermediate carbonium ion is formed. Secondary and tertiary alcohols are more readily dehydrated than primary alcohols because the intermediate carbonium ion is more easily formed.

When the conditions of the dehydration reaction (lower H_2SO_4 concentration, higher alcohol concentration) are changed, an ether, in this case ethoxyethane (diethyl ether), is produced:

$$\begin{array}{l} CH_3CH_2OH \\ + \\ CH_3CH_2OH \end{array} \xrightarrow[130°C]{H_2SO_4} CH_3CH_2OCH_2CH_3 + H_2O \quad [6\text{-}6]$$
$$\text{ethanol} \qquad\qquad\qquad \text{ethoxyethane}$$

Equation 6-6 shows that during the formation of ethoxyethane from ethanol, there is a loss of one mole of water from two moles of alcohol. The water comes from the two hydroxyl groups of the alcohols.

Dehydration is also possible between two different organic compounds, as in the reaction of an alcohol with a carboxylic acid to form an ester. This type of reaction is more commonly called an *esterification reaction*.

FOLLOW-UP PROBLEM

What ether is produced by the dehydration of (a) 1-propanol and (b) methanol?

Answer:

a) $CH_3CH_2CH_2OCH_2CH_2CH_3$ propoxypropane (dipropyl ether)

6-16
Esterification

An esterification reaction involves the dehydration of an alcohol and a carboxylic acid to produce an ester.

Esters can be formed by the esterification of an alcohol and a carboxylic acid. Because water is removed in forming the ester, this reaction is also classified as a dehydration reaction. As in the dehydration of alcohols, concentrated sulfuric acid is used to catalyze the esterification reaction. The reaction below shows the formation of an ester from the dehydration of ethanoic acid and ethanol:

Methyl salicylate (oil of wintergreen) is an ester of salicylic acid. It is used to flavour candies and as an additive in skin lotions.

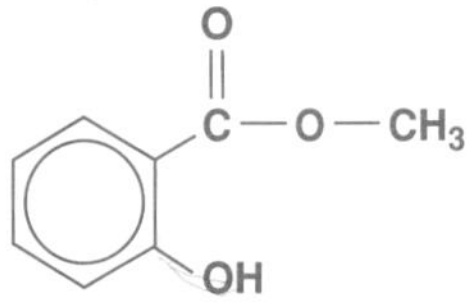

$$CH_3COOH + CH_3CH_2OH \xrightarrow{H_2SO_4} CH_3COOCH_2CH_3 + H_2O$$

ethanoic acid   ethanol   ethyl ethanoate
(ethyl acetate)

Although both the carboxylic acid and the alcohol contain hydroxyl groups, experiments show that in most esterification reactions, it is the carboxylic acid that provides the hydroxyl group and the splitting of the alcohol O—H bond that provides the hydrogen (Fig. 6-6).

Note that esterifications are reversible reactions that tend to reach a state in which there has not been full conversion of reactants to products. Instead, as fast as the alcohol and acid react to form the ester and water, the reverse process occurs at the same rate. This is an example of *chemical equilibrium*, as illustrated by the double arrows in the following equation:

Waxes are esters formed from a carboxylic acid and an alcohol with one hydroxyl group. For example, beeswax ($C_{15}H_{31}COOC_{30}H_{61}$) is an ester of myricyl alcohol ($C_{30}H_{61}OH$).

$$CH_3CH_2CH_2\overset{\overset{\displaystyle O}{\|}}{C}OH + CH_3CH_2CH_2OH \xrightleftharpoons{H_2SO_4}$$

butanoic acid   propanol
(butyric acid)   (propyl alcohol)

$$CH_3CH_2CH_2\overset{\overset{\displaystyle O}{\|}}{C}OCH_2CH_2CH_3 + H_2O$$

propyl butanoate
(propyl butyrate)

We can also look at esterification as a type of substitution reaction in which the —OR′ part of the alcohol is substituted for the —OH part of the carboxylic acid:

$$R_I-\overset{\overset{\displaystyle O}{\|}}{C}-OH + H-OR' \underset{\underset{\text{hydrolysis}}{\text{ester}}}{\overset{\text{esterification}}{\rightleftharpoons}} R_I-\overset{\overset{\displaystyle O}{\|}}{C}-OR' + H_2O$$

The reverse of an esterification reaction is called *ester hydrolysis* and is important in the conversion of natural esters, such as oils and fats, into soaps and detergents.

$$\underset{\substack{\text{ethanoic acid}\\\text{(acetic acid)}}}{CH_3\overset{\overset{\displaystyle O}{\|}}{C}OH} + \underset{\substack{\text{ethanol}\\\text{(ethyl alcohol)}}}{CH_3CH_2OH} \xrightarrow{H_2SO_4} \underset{\substack{\text{ethyl ethanoate}\\\text{(ethyl acetate)}}}{CH_3\overset{\overset{\displaystyle O}{\|}}{C}OCH_2CH_3} + H_2O$$

Figure 6-6
During the esterification reaction of a carboxylic acid and an ester, the hydroxyl group cleaves from the acid and the hydrogen splits from the hydroxyl group of the alcohol to form water.

FOLLOW-UP PROBLEMS

1. Name the ester produced in the following esterification reaction:

$$CH_3CH_2\overset{\overset{\displaystyle O}{\|}}{C}OH + CH_3CH_2OH \longrightarrow$$
$$CH_3CH_2\overset{\overset{\displaystyle O}{\|}}{C}OCH_2CH_3 + H_2O$$

2. The ester $HCOOCH_3$ is made from methanoic acid (formic acid) and methanol. Give the systematic and common names for this ester.

3. Draw the structural formulas and give the systematic and common names for the esters formed in the following esterification reactions:
   a) 1-propanol (propyl alcohol) and ethanoic acid (acetic acid)
   b) 2-propanol (isopropyl alcohol) and propanoic acid (propionic acid)

Answers:
1. **ethyl propanoate (ethyl propionate)**
2. **methyl methanoate (methyl formate)**
3. **(a) propyl ethanoate (propyl acetate)**
(b) isopropyl propanoate (isopropyl propionate)

ASA: ANATOMY OF A PAINKILLER

F or years, the world's most widely used painkiller, acetylsalicylic acid (ASA), has offered relief from aches and pains. Commonly known as Aspirin, acetylsalicylic acid is an effective pain reliever (analgesic), anti-inflammatory agent and fever reducer (antipyretic). North Americans consume ASA at the rate of 20 000 tonnes per year.

For thousands of years before ASA was developed, people consumed an extract of the inner bark of the white willow tree to reduce fever and relieve pain. In 1763, Edward Stone presented a paper to the Royal Society of London describing the value of willow bark in treating malaria. However, Stone did not realize that the willow bark extract was only relieving the symptoms of malaria and not curing the disease itself. The active ingredient in the tree bark, called salicin, was isolated in 1829:

salicin

Two ingredients related to salicin in other pain-relieving plant extracts are salicylaldehyde and methyl salicylate. In 1831, Johann Pagenstecher distilled salicylaldehyde from meadowsweet flowers:

salicylaldehyde

Methyl salicylate was first extracted from oil of wintergreen in 1842 by William Proctor and Auguste Carhours:

methyl salicylate

Salicylic acid can be produced from any of these compounds or synthesized in the laboratory, as was done by H. Gerland in 1852 and by Hermann Kolbe in 1860.

In 1874, a Scottish doctor, T. MacLagen, used himself as a guinea pig by ingesting 2000 mg of salicin. Experiencing no adverse effects, he gave 800 mg to a patient suffering from rheumatism, with positive results. MacLagen's success made salicin and salicylic acid the wonder drugs of the nineteenth century.

Unfortunately, salicin and salicylic acid have a bad taste and cause serious mouth and stomach irritation. This irritation is caused by the release of a hydrogen ion by the carbonyl group on contact with the wall of the stomach. The search for a more palatable painkiller continued.

In 1853, Charles Gerhardt first synthesized acetylsalicylic acid by acetylation of salicylic acid. His process involved replacing the hydrogen atom of the carboxyl group with an acetyl group ($COCH_3$). ASA passes through the stomach more rapidly and is less acidic and, therefore, less irritating. Gerhardt, however, was unable to perfect his process and eventually abandoned it. Forty years later, Felix Hoffman, a chemist at the Bayer Company in Germany, was searching for a drug to relieve his father's rheumatoid arthritis. He simplified Gerhardt's process and successfully produced acetylsalicylic acid.

The Bayer Company decided to mass-produce ASA from the meadowsweet plant, *Spiraea ulmaria*, and in 1899 gave it the trade name Aspirin, derived from the "a" in acetyl, the "spir" in *Spiraea* and the suffix "-in." Bayer lost the exclusive rights to the name after Germany lost World War I. The name was surrendered to England, France, the United States and the Soviet Union as part of the war reparations included in the Treaty of Versailles in 1919. A U.S. court decision of 1921 declared the name to be public property; in Canada, however, Aspirin is still a protected trademark.

Today, Aspirin is produced from synthetic salicylic acid, in which phenol reacts with carbon dioxide to produce salicylic acid:

phenol   salicylic acid
(2-hydroxybenzoic acid)

Salicylic acid is both a carboxylic acid and a phenol, and reacts with acetic anhydride to form the carboxylic ester, acetylsalicylic acid:

salicylic acid   acetic anhydride

OCOCH$_3$

COOH + CH$_3$COOH

acetylsalicylic acid   acetic acid

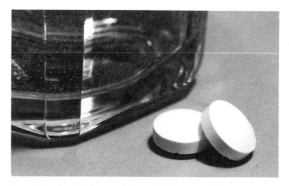

ASA is rapidly absorbed from the gastrointestinal tract and hydrolyzed to salicylate in the bloodstream. Its main effect is to moderate the effects of the body's defence mechanisms. ASA and the various salicylates reduce pain by inhibiting the synthesis of prostaglandins. Prostaglandins are lipid-soluble, hormone-like, regulatory molecules derived from fatty acids. They are produced in inflamed tissues and, in excess, cause pain, fever and inflammation. ASA is especially valuable in the relief of chronic pain caused by rheumatism and arthritis. Because ASA thins blood and reduces clotting by blocking a specific prostaglandin, it may also be useful in preventing heart attacks and strokes.

ASA has its drawbacks, however. When taken in large doses, especially in combination with alcohol, or when ingested over long periods of time, ASA's acidity can cause stomach irritation. ASA tablets containing buffers or starch are less likely to irritate mucous linings. Children who take ASA when they have influenza or chicken pox may develop Reye's syndrome, a rare but some-

times fatal brain disease. Although this connection has not yet been proved, one should avoid giving ASA to children.

An alternative to ASA is acetaminophen:

OH—⬡—NHCOCH$_3$

acetaminophen

one brand of which is Tylenol. Acetaminophen is safer than ASA and less of an irritant because it is not an acid. However, it is not an anti-inflammatory agent and is generally more expensive than ASA.

ESTER HYDROLYSIS

The esterification of a carboxylic acid and an alcohol is a reversible reaction. To cause the acid-catalyzed hydrolysis of an ester in water to a carboxylic acid and an alcohol, an excess amount of water is required. This excess water shifts the equilibrium to the carboxylic acid and alcohol side of the reaction.

If ester hydrolysis is done in an alkaline or base solution, a carboxylic acid salt and an alcohol are produced. This base-catalyzed hydrolysis of an ester is known as a *saponification reaction*. In this process, triesters of glycerol, commonly known as fats and oils, are made into soaps and detergents. We will consider the chemistry of fats and oils before we discuss saponification.

6-17

Oils and Fats

Fats and oils are triesters of glycerol (a trihydroxy alcohol) and long-chain carboxylic acids (fatty acids).

Fats and oils are important sources of energy. Made from 1,2,3-

Carboxylic Acid Salts
Carboxylic acids are weak acids and, thus, can easily react with strong bases to form carboxylic acid salts. To name a carboxylic acid salt, place the name of the cation before the name of the acid, and replace *-ic acid* with *-ate*. Therefore,

$$\overset{O}{\overset{\|}{H-C-OH}} + NaOH \longrightarrow$$

methanoic acid
(formic acid)

$$\overset{O}{\overset{\|}{H-C-O^-Na^+}}$$

sodium methanoate
(sodium formate)

Note that carboxylic acid salts do not react with alcohols. Therefore, reactions involving the base-catalyzed hydrolysis of an ester are not reversible.

The carboxylic acid portions of fats always contain an even number of carbon atoms because the body synthesizes fatty acids from ethanoic acid (acetic acid). Therefore, fatty acids are built up two carbon atoms at a time.

propanetriol (glycerol) and carboxylic acids, fats and oils are triesters of glycerol, or ***triglycerides***. The difference between fats and oils is in their physical state at room temperature: fats are solids and oils are liquids. Since most triglycerides in animals are fats and most triglycerides in plants are oils, we use the terms *animal fats* and *vegetable oils*. The difference in properties is related to the structure of the acid within the triglyceride.

Because fats and oils are esters, they are made of an alcohol (glycerol) and carboxylic acids. The acid component of a triglyceride is called a ***fatty acid***. The fatty acid has a long, unbranched hydrocarbon chain containing four to twenty-four carbon atoms. Some fatty acids are listed in Table 6-4.

TABLE 6-4
SOME COMMON FATTY ACIDS

Common Name	Structural Formula	Number of Carbon Atoms	Number of Double Bonds	Melting Point (°C)
Palmitic acid	$CH_3(CH_2)_{14}COOH$	16	0	63
Stearic acid	$CH_3(CH_2)_{16}COOH$	18	0	72
Oleic acid	$CH_3(CH_2)_7CH{=}CH(CH_2)_7COOH$	18	1	13
Linoleic acid	$CH_3(CH_2)_4CH{=}CHCH_2CH{=}CH(CH_2)_7COOH$	18	2	−5
Linolenic acid	$CH_3CH_2CH{=}CHCH_2CH{=}CHCH_2CH{=}CH(CH_2)_7COOH$	18	3	−11

Triglycerides are formed in a substitution reaction, whereby the O—R part of glycerol is substituted for the hydroxyl groups of three identical or different fatty acids.

glycerol   fatty acids   triglyceride

TABLE 6-5
PERCENTAGE OF SATURATED FATTY ACIDS IN SOME FATS AND OILS

Sunflower oil	11
Corn oil	13
Peanut oil	13
Olive oil	13
Margarine	18
Lard	41
Palm oil	51
Butter	54
Coconut oil	77

The physical properties of fats and oils are related to the degree of saturation of the fatty acid. Saturated fatty acids have only single carbon-to-carbon bonds and, thus, are solids at room temperature. Animal fats contain large amounts of saturated acids, while vegetable oils contain mainly unsaturated acids (Table 6-5). Unsaturated fatty acids have at least one double bond (C=C) in their structure and, thus, are liquids at room temperature. Unsaturated fatty acids are cis isomers. Table 6-6 lists the

TABLE 6-6

AVERAGE PERCENTAGE OF FATTY ACIDS IN SOME COMMON FATS AND OILS

	Lauric Acid	Myristic Acid	Palmitic Acid	Stearic Acid	Oleic Acid	Linoleic Acid	Linolenic Acid
Animal fats							
Beef tallow	–	6.3	27.4	14.1	49.6	2.5	–
Butter	2.5	11.1	29.0	9.2	26.7	3.6	–
Lard	–	1.3	28.3	11.9	47.5	6.0	–
Vegetable oils							
Coconut	45.4	18.0	10.5	2.3	7.5	trace	–
Corn	–	1.4	10.2	3.0	49.6	34.3	–
Cottonseed	–	1.4	23.4	1.1	22.9	47.8	–
Linseed	–	–	6.3	2.5	19.0	24.1	47.4
Olive	–	trace	6.9	2.3	84.4	4.6	–
Peanut	–	–	8.3	3.1	56.0	26.0	–

Until the 1840s, the only source of lamp oils was from animal fats and vegetable oils. In 1846, Abraham Gesner of Halifax produced a new oil, which he called kerosene.

composition of selected fats and oils.

Fats and oils are commonly named as derivatives of the fatty acid. For example, if the fatty acid is stearic acid or palmitic acid, the triglycerides are called tristearin or tripalmitin. Fats and oils can also be named as an ester, as in glyceryl tristearate and glyceryl tripalmitate:

The Canadian Heart Association recommends that people eat less animal fat because saturated fatty acids are a prime factor in heart disease.

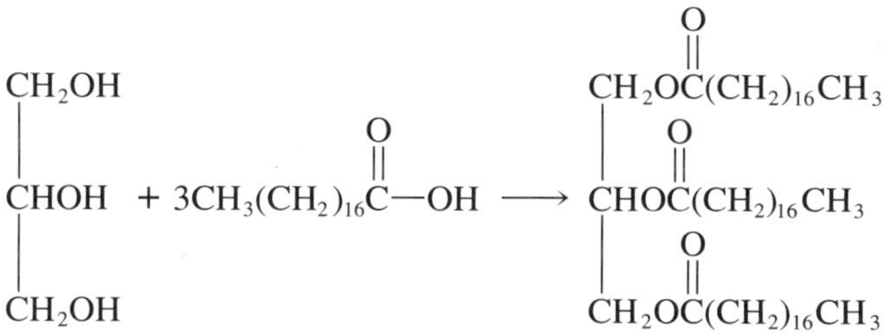

$$CH_2OH \qquad\qquad CH_2O\overset{\displaystyle O}{\overset{\displaystyle \|}{C}}(CH_2)_{16}CH_3$$
$$|$$
$$CHOH \ + 3CH_3(CH_2)_{16}\overset{\displaystyle O}{\overset{\displaystyle \|}{C}}-OH \longrightarrow CHO\overset{\displaystyle O}{\overset{\displaystyle \|}{C}}(CH_2)_{16}CH_3$$
$$|$$
$$CH_2OH \qquad\qquad CH_2O\overset{\displaystyle O}{\overset{\displaystyle \|}{C}}(CH_2)_{16}CH_3$$

glycerol   stearic acid   glyceryl tristearate
                                        (tristearin)

Two important unsaturated fatty acids are oleic acid ($CH_3(CH_2)_7CH\!=\!CH(CH_2)_7COOH$) and linoleic acid ($CH_3(CH_2)_4(CH\!=\!CHCH_2)_2(CH_2)_6COOH$). Linoleic acid has two $C\!=\!C$ bonds, as indicated in the condensed formula. It is considered to be one of the most healthy components of triglycerol esters in our diet.

Vegetable oils contain unsaturated fatty acids that can be converted to solid fats by catalytic hydrogenation. The reaction involves the addition of hydrogen to the double bond, which increases the degree of saturation. For example, triolein, an unsaturated liquid oil (m.p. 16°C), can be converted by catalytic hydrogenation into tristearin (m.p. 70°C), a solid fat. Cottonseed and

Polyunsaturated liquid oils can be converted to such semisolid fats as shortening and margarine by partial hydrogenation (addition of hydrogen). However, if all the double bonds are hydrogenated, the resulting fat will be too brittle and have too high a melting temperature to be used in cooking.

Some fish oils, considered to be a beneficial addition to the diet, have five C=C bonds in their structure.

Butylated hydroxytoluene (BHT) is added to some oils such as corn oil as an antioxidant.

other oils are commercially hydrogenated to produce solid cooking fats or shortening. An alternative method of reducing unsaturation in natural vegetable oils is to genetically breed plants to reduce the amount of unsaturated acids such as linolenic acid, which has three C=C bonds, and to increase the amount of linoleic acid. This has been an area of research in Canada.

Oils that contain a large amount of unsaturated acids are susceptible to oxidation, which gives edible oils a rancid taste. Processed food oils may contain inhibitors that slow the oxidation processes.

Fats and oils can be hydrolyzed by a strong base to produce glycerol and fatty-acid salts. Such a hydrolysis is called *saponification* because soaps are manufactured from these fatty-acid salts.

6-18
Soaps and Synthetic Detergents

Soaps are the salts of fatty acids produced during the saponification of fats and oils. Detergents are produced from the saponification of sulfonic esters.

Soaps are manufactured by a process called saponification, which is the alkaline hydrolysis of esters. During saponification, the ester reacts with the hydroxyl group of a base, such as sodium hydroxide (NaOH) or potassium hydroxide (KOH), to form glycerol and a salt of the carboxylic acid constituent of the ester. As an example, glyceryl tripalmitate reacts with sodium hydroxide to form glycerol and sodium palmitate:

$$C_3H_5(O-\overset{\overset{\displaystyle O}{\|}}{C}-C_{15}H_{31})_3 \ + \ 3NaOH \ \longrightarrow$$

glyceryl tripalmitate
(tripalmitin)

$$C_3H_5(OH)_3 \ + \ 3C_{15}H_{31}COONa$$

glycerol   sodium palmitate

In the initial process, the fat and alkali are mixed and heated. Sodium ions from saturated brine are then added to lower the solubility of the soap in the aqueous alkali solution and to make the soap float to the top where it is drawn off.

Soaps can also be produced when fats are hydrolyzed by steam to produce glycerol and fatty acids:

$$C_3H_5(O-\overset{\overset{\displaystyle O}{\|}}{C}-C_{17}H_{35})_3 \ + \ 3H_2O \ \longrightarrow$$

glyceryl tristearate
(tristearin)

$$C_3H_5(OH)_3 \ + \ 3C_{17}H_{35}COOH$$

glycerol   stearic acid

The two products are then separated and the fatty acids are reacted with sodium hydroxide to form soaps:

$$\underset{\text{stearic acid}}{C_{17}H_{35}COOH} + NaOH \longrightarrow \underset{\text{sodium stearate}}{C_{17}H_{35}COONa}$$

When used in hard water, ordinary soaps produce an insoluble scum. The hardness of water is caused by calcium ions (Ca^{2+}) or magnesium ions (Mg^{2+}). Formation of the soap scum involves a reaction between the carboxylate anions of the soap and the calcium or magnesium ions in the hard water:

$$\underset{\text{stearate ion}}{2C_{17}H_{35}COO^{-}(aq)} + Ca^{2+} \longrightarrow \underset{\text{calcium stearate}}{Ca(C_{17}H_{35}COO)_2(s)}$$

The cleansing ability of the soap is destroyed by this reaction.

Synthetic detergents, on the other hand, do not form insoluble solids in hard water. Synthetic detergents are sulfonic esters of long-chain alcohols; for example, the 12-carbon alcohol, 1-dodecanol, commonly called lauryl alcohol, reacts with concentrated sulfuric acid to produce lauryl hydrogen sulfate:

$$\underset{\text{lauryl alcohol}}{C_{12}H_{22}OH} + \underset{\text{sulfuric acid}}{OH{-}\overset{\overset{\displaystyle OH}{|}}{\underset{\underset{\displaystyle O}{\|}}{S}}{=}O} \longrightarrow \underset{\text{lauryl hydrogen sulfate}}{C_{12}H_{22}O{-}\overset{\overset{\displaystyle OH}{|}}{\underset{\underset{\displaystyle O}{\|}}{S}}{=}O} + H_2O$$

Lauryl hydrogen sulfate is then neutralized with sodium hydroxide to form the sodium salt, sodium lauryl sulfate, a detergent.

The cleansing action of soaps and detergents is related to the structure of their component particles. The anions of both substances consist of a polar group attached to a long, nonpolar hydrocarbon chain. The polar group forms the hydrogen bonds with water and is, therefore, *hydrophilic* (literally, water-loving); the nonpolar chain is *hydrophobic* (water-fearing). The hydrophilic end of the soap molecule dissolves in water, while the hydrophobic end dissolves in dirt. Thus, the soap molecules surround dirt particles as the hydrophobic end interacts with the hydrophobic dirt particle, and the hydrophilic group attracts water molecules. The dirt particle is then washed away in water.

As an example, consider the interaction between a detergent, oil and water. The cleansing action of the detergent takes place at the interface, that is, the surface between the oil and water. The detergent anions arrange themselves at this interface so that the nonpolar ends are directed toward the surface, while the polar ends are attached to the water molecules. Thus, the oil becomes emulsi-

Keeping Skin Soft

Dry skin is related to the structure of the top skin layer and its water content. This region contains two kinds of organic substances—lipids and keratin, which is a protein. Water usually escapes outward through the skin. If the water loss is excessive, the lipids form solid crystals, allowing even more water loss and causing the skin to become drier.

If water is applied externally to minimize dryness, it readily evaporates, leaving the skin dryer than before. Another solution is to apply a humectant such as glycerol to replace the water inside the skin structure and to absorb moisture from the air. However, glycerol is a polyhydroxy alcohol, miscible with water, and is easily removed from the skin during washing.

One possible treatment for dry skin is the development of synthetic triglycerides that will help keep the lipids of the skin in a smooth, liquid, crystal form and thus help skin retain a soft, glossy appearance.

Scientists have experimented with triglyceride compounds that can make the skin smoother. These compounds may soon become important components of commercial cosmetic products.

Figure 6-7
The removal of oil from a solid surface by a detergent solution is favoured because the energy state of the system is lowered. In the presence of a detergent, the surface energy between oil and a solid surface is greater than that between the oil and water phase plus that of the water and solid phase. Once the grease globules have been removed from the solid surface, the polar "heads" of the detergent molecules repel so that the grease droplets cannot coalesce. Once solubilized, the grease can be washed away.

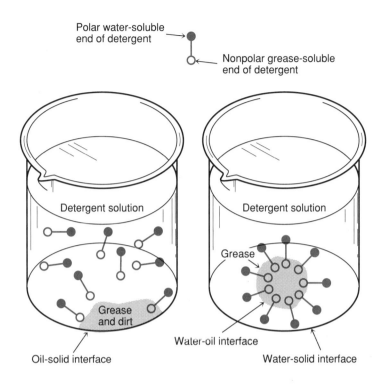

fied in water and can be subsequently washed away (Fig. 6-7).

The first synthetic detergents were alkylbenzene sulfonates with many branches on the alkyl side chain (Fig. 6-8(a)). However, these detergents were found to be harmful to the environment because micro-organisms in sewage treatment plants could not break down the branched alkyl side chains. The detergents then collected on the surfaces of rivers and lakes, causing sudsing of the waters (Fig. 6-8(c)) and contamination of drinking water. Today, common laundry detergents contain linear alkylbenzene sulfonates, which are biodegradable (Fig. 6-8(b)). Detergents may also contain other cleansers such as sodium carbonate, sodium silicate, sodium sulfate and optical brighteners.

Figure 6-8
Branched alkylbenzene sulfonates (a) were not biodegradable and caused the pollution of waters, as shown in the photo (c). Most of today's detergents are linear alkylbenzene sulfonates (b), which are biodegradable.

branched alkyl-
benzene sulfonate
(a)

linear alkyl-
benzene sulfonate
(b)

(c)

HALOGENATION

Many halogenated organic compounds are formed by the reaction of hydrocarbons and halogens. In a halogenation reaction, a halogen atom either is added to an unsaturated bond or replaces a hydrogen atom in an addition or substitution reaction.

6-19
Halogenation of Alkanes: Substitution

One or more halogen atoms can be substituted for the hydrogen atoms of an alkane in a halogenation reaction.

Alkanes undergo direct halogenation reactions through a free-radical mechanism. A *free radical* is any atom or group of atoms that has one or more unpaired electrons. Free radicals are high-energy, highly reactive, short-lived intermediate species and are symbolized by a dot, representing the unpaired electron. For example, when sufficient energy is supplied to a chlorine molecule, the molecule reaches an excited state and splits to form two chlorine free radicals (Cl•).

The halogenation of methane is an example of a free-radical reaction. This reaction generally involves three steps. During the first step, the free radical is formed:

$$Cl_2 \xrightarrow{\text{light or heat}} Cl\bullet + Cl\bullet$$

In the second step, a hydrogen atom is removed from methane to form a methyl free radical and HCl:

$$Cl\bullet + H{-}CH_3 \longrightarrow HCl + CH_3^\bullet$$

The methyl free radical then reacts with a chlorine atom from Cl_2:

$$Cl_2 + CH_3^\bullet \longrightarrow CH_3Cl + Cl\bullet$$

Because a new chlorine free radical is formed, this species can now remove a hydrogen atom from another methane molecule to repeat the whole process. This chain reaction, however, stops when free radicals are not produced or when the free radicals combine with other free radicals to form stable, non-reactive compounds.

Subsequent reactions of a chlorine free radical with chloromethane form dichloromethane (methylene chloride), trichloromethane (chloroform) and, finally, tetrachloromethane (carbon tetrachloride):

$$\underset{\text{chloromethane}}{CH_3Cl} + Cl\bullet \longrightarrow \underset{\substack{\text{dichloro-}\\\text{methane}}}{CH_2Cl_2} \xrightarrow{Cl\bullet} \underset{\substack{\text{trichloro-}\\\text{methane}}}{CHCl_3} \xrightarrow{Cl\bullet} \underset{\substack{\text{tetrachloro-}\\\text{methane}}}{CCl_4}$$

GERHARD HERZBERG
1904–
Gerhard Herzberg was born in Hamburg, Germany. He studied engineering physics at Darmstadt Technical University and earned his PhD in molecular spectroscopy in 1928. Finding it increasingly difficult to live in Nazi Germany, he fled to Canada in 1935. Herzberg held a position at the University of Saskatchewan from 1935 to 1945 and continued his work in spectroscopic research. After joining the Yerkes Observatory in Chicago for three years, he returned to Canada in 1948 and became the Director of Physics for the National Research Council (NRC).

Although Herzberg is a physicist, he has made valuable contributions to the field of chemistry. He used spectroscopy to identify molecules in the atmosphere of planets and interstellar space. In 1931, he discovered bands of oxygen, called *Herzberg bands*, in the upper atmosphere, which account for the production of ozone in the atmosphere. Herzberg was awarded the Nobel Prize in chemistry in 1971 for his determination of the structure of free radicals.

Herzberg has received many honours, including the Order of Canada. In 1975, the NRC's astronomy and spectroscopy units were reorganized as the Herzberg Institute of Astrophysics.

At the age of 80, this remarkable scientist was still doing research in his lab five days a week.

FOLLOW-UP PROBLEM

Draw a structural formula for one product formed during the halogenation reaction of propane with Br_2.

6-20
Halogenation of Alkenes and Alkynes: Addition

Halogen atoms can be added to alkenes and alkynes to form haloalkanes and haloalkenes.

In a halogenation reaction of alkenes and alkynes, halogen atoms such as bromine and chlorine are added to the carbon atoms of the carbon-to-carbon double bond or triple bond to produce haloalkanes. For example, bromine reacts with ethene to form 1,2-dibromoethane, and chlorine reacts with ethyne to form 1,1,2,2-tetrachloroethane:

Markovnikov's Rule
When an alkene reacts with a hydrogen halide (HX), the formation of two different products is possible because a different group (H or X) adds to each of the carbons of the double bond.

$$CH_3CH=CH_2 + HCl \longrightarrow$$

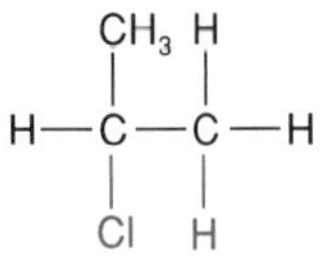

2–chloropropane

or

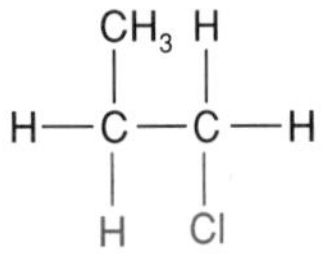

1–chloropropane

After studying alkene addition reactions, Russian chemist Vladimir Markovnikov (1838–1904) determined a rule for predicting which product will predominantly be formed. *Markovnikov's rule* states that during the addition of HX, the hydrogen is added to the carbon with the greater number of hydrogen atoms bonded to it, and the X goes to the carbon atom with the fewer hydrogens. The saying, "the rich get richer," may help you remember this rule. In the reaction above, 2-chloropropane is predominantly produced.

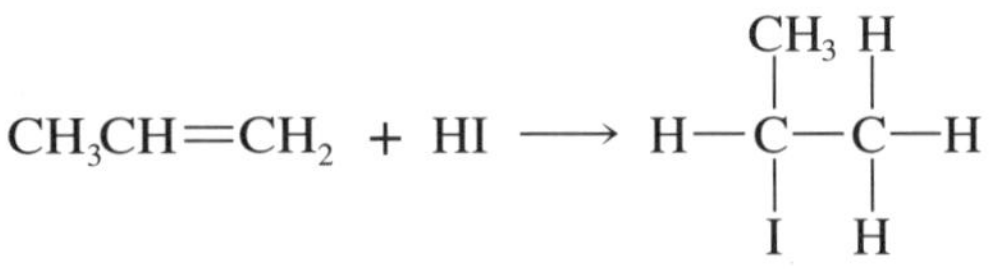

Markovnikov's rule also applies to alkyne reactions with hydrogen halides as well as to alkene hydration reactions.

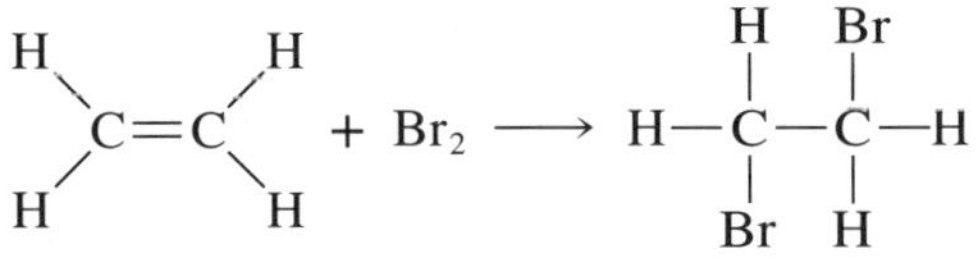

ethene   1, 2-dibromoethane

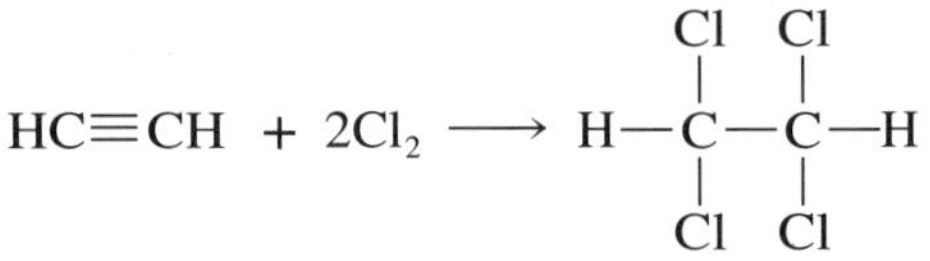

$$HC \equiv CH + 2Cl_2 \longrightarrow$$

ethyne   1,1,2,2-tetrachloroethane

During the reaction of ethene with bromine, the red colour of the bromine disappears. This reaction is used to distinguish between saturated and unsaturated compounds. Because alkanes do not readily react with bromine, the destruction of the red colour during a reaction with a hydrocarbon indicates the presence of carbon-to-carbon double or triple bonds within the hydrocarbon.

Note that for alkynes, two moles of halogen are needed to convert a triple bond to a single bond.

Hydrogen halides such as HCl, HBr and HI can also react with alkenes and alkynes to produce haloalkanes:

$$CH_3CH=CH_2 + HI \longrightarrow$$

2-iodopropane

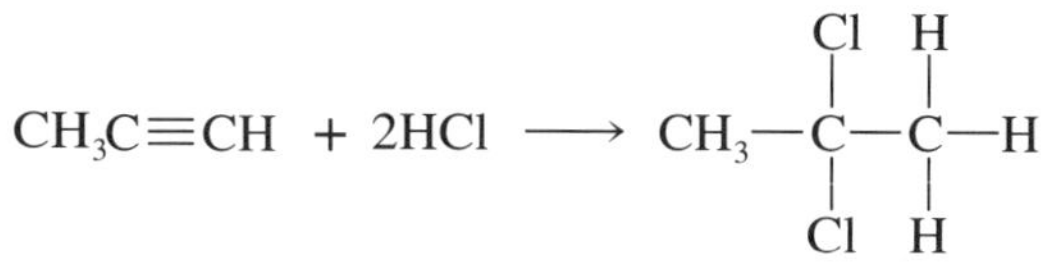

$$CH_3C{\equiv}CH \ + \ 2HCl \ \longrightarrow \ CH_3{-}\underset{\underset{\displaystyle Cl}{|}}{\overset{\overset{\displaystyle Cl}{|}}{C}}{-}\underset{\underset{\displaystyle H}{|}}{\overset{\overset{\displaystyle H}{|}}{C}}{-}H$$

2,2-dichloropropane

During the halogenation of alkynes, the pi electrons of the triple bond are readily attacked by halogens and hydrogen halides. Addition reactions involving these substances result in the destruction of weak pi bonds and the formation of strong sigma bonds. For example, in the halogenation of ethyne with chlorine, four strong sigma bonds are formed, while two weak pi bonds in the triple bond and two Cl—Cl bonds are destroyed.

We might expect aldehydes and ketones to undergo halogenation reactions similar to those of the alkenes, since the double bond in the carbonyl group is similar to that in the alkenes. It turns out that there are more differences than similarities in the reactions of the two groups. Although hydrogen can be added to both the carbon-to-carbon double bond and the carbonyl bond, the carbonyl group does not undergo addition reactions with halogen atoms or hydrogen halides. This is caused by the greater stability of the carbon-to-oxygen double bond.

FOLLOW-UP PROBLEMS

1. Complete the following reactions:
    a) $CH_3CH_2CH_2CH{=}CH_2 + Br_2 \longrightarrow$
    b) $CH_3CH_2CH{=}CH_2 + HBr \longrightarrow$
    c) $CH_3C{\equiv}CH + HI \longrightarrow$
    d) $CH_3CH_2C{\equiv}CH + 2Cl_2 \longrightarrow$

2. How would you prepare 1,2-dibromobutane?

Answers:
1. a) $CH_3CH_2CH_2CHBrCH_2Br$
    d) $CH_3CH_2CCl_2CHCl_2$

Halogenation of Aromatic Compounds: Substitution

During halogenation of an aromatic compound, a halogen atom is substituted for a hydrogen atom on the aromatic ring. Aromatic molecules such as benzene also react with halogen atoms by the substitution of a halogen atom, such as bromine, for a hydrogen atom of the benzene ring. A catalyst such as iron(III) bromide speeds up the reaction:

$$benzene + Br_2 \xrightarrow{FeBr_3} bromobenzene + HBr$$

benzene   bromobenzene

In aromatic substitutions with a halogen, the reaction does not involve a free radical. Instead, a halogen ion, such as a bromide ion, reacts with the pi electrons of the benzene ring.

FOLLOW-UP PROBLEM
How would you prepare chlorobenzene?

We have previously noted that some reactions can be classified as addition, substitution or elimination reactions. We will now look at these terms and investigate the specific reactions that are defined by them.

TYPES OF REACTIONS

In the previous sections, we looked at the specific reactions that are characteristic of particular organic compounds. However, most of these reactions can be divided into three types: addition, elimination and substitution reactions.

6-22
Addition Reactions

Computers in Chemistry
The diversity of organic compounds is matched only by the diversity of organic chemical reactions. The advent of the computer has simplified the area of organic reactions with the availability of the database ORAC (Organic Reactions Accessed by Computer), which was developed at the University of Leeds in 1984. The ORAC database contains over 30 000 chemical reactions and is organized so that a chemical compound can be found by formula or structure.

In addition to providing specific information on organic compounds, such as whether the compound is active or not, the database provides any information that has been found on that compound. Computer graphics also provide additional information on compounds and are useful for studying molecular architecture.

In an addition reaction, atoms are added to a double or triple bond.
One of the main types of organic reactions characteristic of alkenes, alkynes, aldehydes and ketones is the addition reaction. In addition reactions, two or more atoms are added to an unsaturated compound. Recall that an unsaturated hydrocarbon does not contain the maximum possible number of hydrogen atoms and thus contains carbon-to-carbon double or triple bonds. The following is a summary of some important addition reactions:

Hydroxylation of alkenes and alkynes (Section 6-8). Hydroxylation occurs when a hydroxyl group is added to form alcohols or carboxylic acids:

$$\underset{alkene}{\underset{H}{\overset{R_1}{\diagup}}C=C\underset{H}{\overset{R_2}{\diagdown}}} \xrightarrow[alkaline]{KMnO_4} \underset{alcohol}{R_1-\overset{\overset{H}{|}}{\underset{\underset{OH}{|}}{C}}-\overset{\overset{H}{|}}{\underset{\underset{OH}{|}}{C}}-R_2} \xrightarrow[alkaline]{heat, \; KMnO_4}$$

alkene   alcohol

$$R_1-\overset{\overset{\displaystyle O}{\|}}{C}-OH \;+\; R_2-\overset{\overset{\displaystyle O}{\|}}{C}-OH$$
carboxylic acids

Reduction, or hydrogenation, of alkenes and alkynes (Section 6-11). The simplest addition reaction is the catalytic addition of hydrogen to the carbon-to-carbon double or triple bond to form an alkane. Two moles of hydrogen are added to convert the triple bond to a single carbon-to-carbon bond. With the proper catalyst, a number of unsaturated compounds can be hydrogenated at room temperature and at pressures of 100 to 500 kPa.

$$CH_3CH \!\equiv\! CH + 2H_2(g) \xrightarrow{\;Pt\;} CH_3CH_2CH_3$$
propyne   propane

Hydration of alkenes and alkynes (Sections 6-13 and 6-14). The addition of water during hydration of an alkene in the presence of H_2SO_4 yields an alcohol:

$$CH_2 \!=\! CH_2 + H_2O \xrightarrow{\;H_2SO_4\;} CH_3CH_2OH$$
ethene   ethanol
(ethyl alcohol)

The addition of water to an alkyne produces an aldehyde or a ketone:

$$CH_3C \!\equiv\! CH + H_2O \xrightarrow[HgSO_4]{H_2SO_4} CH_3\overset{\overset{\displaystyle O}{\|}}{C}CH_3$$
propyne   propanone
(acetone)

Halogenation of alkenes and alkynes (Section 6-20). The addition of halogen atoms or hydrogen halides produces haloalkanes:

$$CH \!\equiv\! CH + 2Br_2 \longrightarrow H-\overset{\overset{\displaystyle Br}{|}}{\underset{\underset{\displaystyle Br}{|}}{C}}-\overset{\overset{\displaystyle Br}{|}}{\underset{\underset{\displaystyle Br}{|}}{C}}-H$$

Oxidation of aldehydes (Section 6-10). Aldehydes are easily oxidized to carboxylic acids when an oxygen atom is added to the compound. For example, air can oxidize benzaldehyde to benzoic acid. Recall that ketones cannot be oxidized without breaking C—C bonds and destroying the carbon skeleton.

benzaldehyde   benzoic acid

Hydrogenation of aldehydes and ketones (Section 6-12). A carbonyl group in either aldehydes or ketones can be converted to a hydroxyl group by the catalytic addition of hydrogen (hydrogenation). For example, 2-propanol (isopropyl alcohol) can be prepared by the hydrogenation of propanone (acetone):

$$CH_3\overset{\overset{\displaystyle O}{\|}}{C}CH_3 + H_2(g) \xrightarrow{\text{catalyst}} CH_3 - \overset{\overset{\displaystyle OH}{|}}{\underset{\underset{\displaystyle H}{|}}{C}} - CH_3$$

Now that we have looked at addition reactions in which two or more atoms or groups are added to an unsaturated compound, we can investigate their opposite reaction, elimination reactions.

6-23

Elimination Reactions

An elimination reaction takes place when atoms are removed from a compound to form a double bond.

An elimination reaction is the reverse of the addition reaction. Elimination reactions involve the removal of two groups of atoms from adjacent carbon atoms to form a double bond. This converts a saturated molecule into an unsaturated molecule. The following are some important elimination reactions:

Dehydration of alcohols (Section 6-15). The dehydration of alcohols involves the elimination of water in the presence of an acid catalyst to produce an alkene. Secondary and tertiary alcohols are more easily dehydrated than primary alcohols. Under certain conditions, an ether can be produced.

$$\underset{\text{ethanol}}{CH_3CH_2OH} \xrightarrow{H_2SO_4} \underset{\text{ethene}}{CH_2{=}CH_2} + H_2O$$

Oxidation, or dehydrogenation, of alcohols (Section 6-9). Primary and secondary alcohols can be oxidized to aldehydes and carboxylic acids. The oxidation of a secondary alcohol can also produce a ketone.

$$\underset{\text{alcohol}}{R_1 - CH_2 - OH} \xrightarrow[\text{alkaline}]{KMnO_4} \underset{\text{aldehyde}}{R_1 - \overset{\overset{\displaystyle O}{\|}}{C} - H} \xrightarrow[\text{H}_2\text{SO}_4]{H_2CrO_4} \underset{\text{carboxylic acid}}{R_1 - \overset{\overset{\displaystyle O}{\|}}{C} - OH}$$

Esterification of a carboxylic acid with an alcohol (Section 6-16). Carboxylic acids react with alcohols in the presence of an acid catalyst to form esters and water. The overall net reaction involves the elimination of the components of water from the reactant molecules.

$$R_1-\overset{\overset{\displaystyle O}{\|}}{C}-OH + R'OH \overset{H^+}{\rightleftharpoons} R_1-\overset{\overset{\displaystyle O}{\|}}{C}-OR' + H_2O$$

carboxylic   alcohol   ester
acid

Dehydrohalogenation of haloalkanes. Haloalkanes react in elimination reactions in which a hydrogen halide is lost. In this reaction, a hydrogen atom and a halogen atom are removed from adjacent carbons in the presence of a strong base, and an alkene is produced:

$$CH_3CH_2Cl \xrightarrow{KOH} CH_2{=}CH_2 + HCl$$

chloroethane   ethene

Finally, let us look at the third type of organic reaction, the substitution reaction.

6-24

Substitution Reactions

In a substitution reaction, atoms or groups of atoms in an organic compound are replaced by another atom or group. Substitution reactions are very common in organic reactions involving halogenated compounds. In substitution reactions, the reagent does not attack the double bond but, rather, displaces one of the atoms or groups in the organic compound. The following is a summary of important substitution reactions:

Halogenation of alkanes (Section 6-19). Alkanes undergo halogenation, in which a halogen is substituted for a hydrogen atom:

$$CH_4 + Cl_2 \longrightarrow$$
methane

$$CH_3Cl + CH_2Cl_2 + CHCl_2 + CCl_4 + HCl$$

chloro-   dichloro-   trichloro-   tetrachloromethane   methane   methane   methane

Halogenation of aromatic compounds (Section 6-21). When a reagent such as Br_2 reacts with aromatic hydrocarbons, it displaces one of the hydrogen atoms from the benzene ring. The net equation for the $FeBr_3$-catalyzed reaction between benzene and bromine is

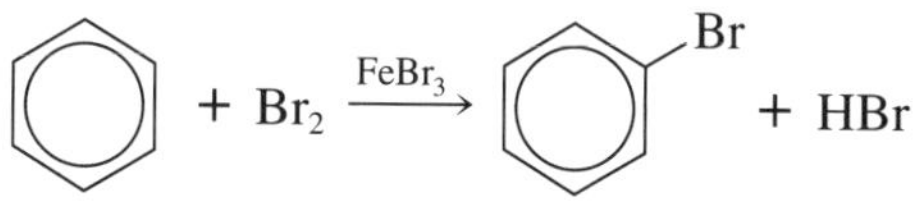

benzene   bromobenzene

Nitration. Benzene can be nitrated by reacting it with a mixture of concentrated nitric acid and concentrated sulfuric acid. The equation for the net reaction is

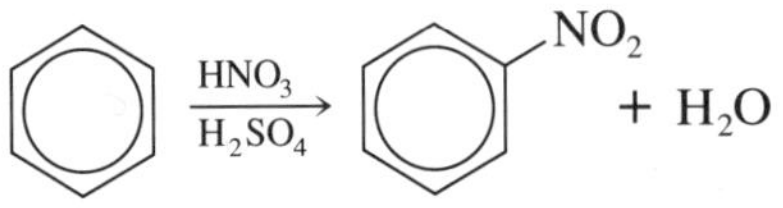

nitrobenzene

The reaction mechanism involves *electrophilic* (literally, electron-loving) nitronium ions (NO_2^+) attacking the delocalized pi electrons of the benzene ring and the subsequent loss of an H^+ ion to an HSO_4^- ion. Thus, H_2SO_4 is regenerated and not consumed by the reaction.

Halogenation of alcohols. Alcohols also undergo substitution reactions in which the hydroxyl group in primary, secondary and tertiary alcohols is replaced by various reagents. For example, alkyl halides are prepared by substituting a halogen atom for the hydroxyl group:

$$CH_3CH_2OH + HBr \longrightarrow CH_3CH_2Br + H_2O$$

ethanol   bromoethane

Esterification of alcohols and carboxylic acids (Section 6-16). We can think of the esterification reaction between an alcohol and a carboxylic acid as a substitution reaction in which the O—R′ part of the alcohol is substituted for the —OH part of the acid:

Substitution of haloalkanes. In the presence of NaOH, for example, the hydroxyl group of the base can be substituted for the halogen atom of a haloalkane to produce an alcohol. Ethers can also be produced in haloalkane substitution reactions.

$$CH_3Cl \xrightarrow{\text{NaOH}} CH_3OH + NaCl$$

chloromethane   methanol

Alkylation of ammonia. Primary amines can be prepared by the alkylation of ammonia, which involves the substitution of an alkyl or substituted alkyl group for one hydrogen atom in ammonia. The most common alkylating agents are the alkyl halides. The reaction of ammonia with an alkyl halide yields an ammonium salt, which can be converted to an amine by reaction with OH^- ions. The synthesis of ethylamine from chloroethane (ethyl chloride) is

$$CH_3CH_2Cl + NH_3 \longrightarrow CH_3CH_2NH_2 + Na^+ + Cl^- + H_2O$$

chloroethane   ethylamine

Now that we have examined both the specific and general types of organic reactions, it may be helpful to summarize all of these reactions.

6-25
Summary of Organic Reactions

There are millions of known organic compounds, the majority of which are synthetically produced. The area of organic chemistry involves millions of organic reactions. We have looked at some of the principal organic reactions involving the more common organic compounds. A summary of these reactions, their reactants and products is given in Table 6-7.

TABLE 6-7
PRINCIPAL REACTIONS AND PRODUCTS OF
ORGANIC COMPOUNDS

Organic Family	Chemical Reaction	Type	Product
Alkanes	combustion	–	$CO_2 + H_2O$
	halogenation	substitution	haloalkanes
Alkenes	hydrogenation	addition	alkanes
	hydroxylation	addition	alcohols or carboxylic acids
	hydration	addition	alcohols
	halogenation	addition	haloalkanes
Alkynes	hydrogenation	addition	alkenes or alkanes
	hydroxylation	addition	carboxylic acids
	hydration	addition	aldehydes or ketones
	halogenation	addition	haloalkenes or haloalkanes
Aromatic compounds	halogenation	substitution	halogenated aromatic compounds
Alcohols	dehydrogenation	elimination	aldehydes, ketones or carboxylic acids

TABLE 6-7 (continued)
**PRINCIPAL REACTIONS AND PRODUCTS OF
ORGANIC COMPOUNDS**

Organic Family	Chemical Reaction	Type	Product
	dehydration	elimination	alkenes or ethers
Alcohols and carboxylic acids	esterification	elimination or substitution	esters
Aldehydes	oxidation	addition	carboxylic acids
	hydrogenation	addition	alcohols
Ketones	hydrogenation	addition	alcohols
Esters	hydrolysis	–	soap

NATURE'S DEFENCE AGAINST OIL SPILLS

On March 27, 1989, the oil tanker, *Exxon Valdez*, struck a reef off Alaska, flooding Prince William Sound with millions of litres of oil. Horrible pictures of oil-soaked birds and mammals flooded our newspapers and television screens. The oil spill seriously damaged a fragile ecosystem that may take years to recover.

It is estimated that about six million tonnes of petroleum seep into the world's oceans every year, adding to the 400 million tonnes of dissolved petroleum already there. Half of this total comes from automobile exhaust, discarded oil and street runoff. The remainder comes mainly from oil lost by small tankers. Some oil naturally enters the ocean from underwater crevices in the earth's crust. Thus, major oil spills such as the *Exxon Valdez* accident are only the tip of the "marine-oil" iceberg.

When crude oil is spilled into a body of water, it forms a slick several centimetres thick. The marine ecosystem acts as a buffer to the oil through various natural agents such as wind, sunlight and bacteria. Aided by the wind, the lighter fractions of oil evaporate into the atmosphere, while heavier fractions may sink. Sunlight acts to break down the oil through photochemical changes. Wave action causes the oil to dissolve and mix with the water. These natural actions gradually reduce the slick's density and concentration. Bacteria, assisted by sunlight and wave action, eventually biodegrade the oil. In cold regions or in sheltered coves, biodegra-

dation may take up to a decade.

Until biodegradation occurs, however, the oil can disable or kill marine wildlife and plants in the following ways:

- Light oils allow water to enter the down layer of seabirds, reducing its buoyancy and insulation. Heavy oils weigh birds down, making it hard for them to fly and swim.
- Marine mammals, such as the endangered sea otter, depend on their dense fur to protect them from frigid water; light oils destroy the insulating properties of their fur.
- Fish suffocate when their gills become coated with oil.

- Shellfish living in coastal waters are vulnerable to smothering by massive oil spills or contamination through the ingestion of oil.
- Studies have shown that lobsters exhibit behaviour modifications when exposed to small amounts of hydrocarbons.
- The filtering organisms of molluscs and baleen whales can be affected through the ingestion of oil.
- Marine plants can be destroyed when oil soaks into sediments or encrusts the plant. However, plants seem to recover more rapidly than animals, unless the water is chronically polluted.

Damage to marine organisms and plants upsets the balance of the marine ecosystem. This damage can affect humans indirectly by reducing tourism and fishing. Contamination of shellfish and fish can lead to bans on commercial harvesting that may last for years.

However, there is reason to believe that marine ecosystems can survive oil spills because they are capable of absorbing and ultimately recovering from large deposits of oil. After the *Amoco Cádiz* disaster off the coast of France in 1978, it was predicted that the area would be lifeless for decades. Five years later, commercial fishing had resumed and it was hard to find obvious traces of oil, although the soft sediments still contained oil.

The natural buffering system of marine ecosystems may lessen the anxiety about the impact of oil spills, but the reality is that oceans cannot absorb unlimited amounts of oil. Humans must search for ways to minimize the damage oil can do to the environment.

ALTERNATIVE SOURCES OF ORGANIC COMPOUNDS

Petroleum and natural gas are convenient fuels, and the exploitation of these resources has been increasing. Forecasts project that by the year 2000, the consumption of fossil fuels will exceed 28×10^{18} J/year.

Petroleum and natural gases are not only fuels; petrochemicals supply 90% of the organic chemicals needed to produce synthetic organic compounds. If the cost of extracting fossil fuels rises and the risks to the environment associated with the burning of them cannot be lessened, alternative sources of both fuels and hydrocarbons will have to be found.

Following the oil embargo imposed by the Arab members of the Organization of Petroleum Exporting Countries (OPEC) in 1973, the National Research Council of Canada initiated research into the development of alternative sources of energy such as solar, wind and nuclear energy. As well, research into alternative sources of organic compounds was also undertaken. Although such potential sources as tar sands and oil shale are important, we will investigate the two major alternative sources of hydrocarbons: coal and biomass.

6-26

Coal

The conversion of coal into liquid oil produces organic compounds.

Coal was formed under different geological conditions than those that produced petroleum and natural gas. Coal is more widely

Coal is widely used for steam turbine generation of electricity in North America.

deposited than petroleum (coal represents 75% of fossil fuels) and contains approximately 25 times more carbon. However, it is not as convenient a fuel as petroleum and natural gas because it is not a liquid and does not burn cleanly. Coal contains 2–6% sulfur, which is released as sulfur dioxide (SO_2) during combustion and is directly linked to atmospheric pollution and acid rain.

The four types of coal are classified according to carbon content—anthracite (hard coal) contains the most carbon, followed by bituminous coal, lignite and peat. On heating and distillation in the absence of oxygen, coal produces coal gas (CH_4 and H_2), coal tar and coke (residue). Coal gas is a useful fuel. Coal tar can be distilled to produce a variety of aromatic compounds (Fig. 6-9). Coke is used in the reduction of iron oxide during the manufacture of steel.

The use of coal as an alternative source of hydrocarbons has its limitations. Recovering and refining coal is a much more expensive process than that for petroleum. The coal-refining process releases SO_2, which is harmful to the environment. Because it is not a liquid, coal cannot be used as a fuel for automobiles. One solution to these drawbacks is to convert the coal to oil and gas. One method of conversion, called *coal gasification*, involves treating the coal with steam to produce *synthesis gas*, a mixture of CO and H_2. Synthesis gas is used as a fuel or as a starting material for the production of CH_4. In this process, the synthesis gas is treated with hydrogen and a nickel catalyst to produce methane (CH_4) and water:

$$\underset{\text{coal}}{C} + \underset{\text{steam}}{H_2O} \xrightarrow{\text{heat}} \underset{\text{synthesis gas}}{\underbrace{CO + H_2}} \xrightarrow[\text{Ni catalyst}]{2H_2} \underset{\text{methane}}{CH_4} + H_2O$$

Synthesis gas can also be used to produce methanol, acetic anhydride and cellulose acetate.

A similar reaction, called the *Fischer-Tropsch synthesis*, results

Figure 6-9
Conversion of primary petrochemicals to their derivatives from the processing of coal.

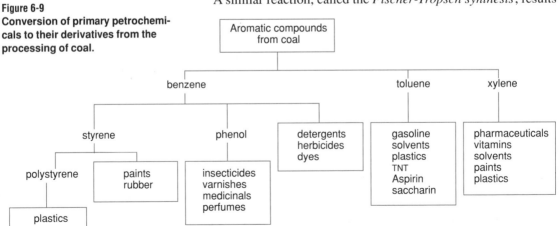

in coal liquefaction and produces a low-grade gasoline:

$$C + H_2O \xrightarrow{\text{heat}} CO + H_2 \xrightarrow[\substack{\text{heat,} \\ \text{pressure}}]{\substack{H_2 \\ \text{Fe catalyst}}} \text{alkanes} + H_2O$$

coal   steam

One promising alternative source of hydrocarbons is biomass, from which hydrocarbon fuels and organic compounds can be obtained directly.

Coal liquefaction was developed in Germany in 1923 by Franz Fischer and Hans Tropsch to produce automotive fuel from Germany's abundant supply of coal. The Germans used this process extensively during World War II when their supply of oil was cut off.

6-27
Biomass

Various sources of biological materials, including wood, plant materials and animal wastes, can be used to produce organic compounds.

Biomass materials are non-fossil, organic substances. Humans have been using wood, plants and animal wastes as energy sources for thousands of years. Different methods can be used to convert various biological materials to fuels and organic compounds. In the following section we will look at four of the major sources of biomass and the processes used to produce organic compounds.

Wood biomass. Wood waste, or wood biomass, is readily available from forest-harvesting operations (Fig. 6-10). There are many ways to use wood as a source of energy. For example, woodburning stoves have become increasingly popular in recent years. Wood pellets produced from wood wastes can be used to fire boilers. An Abitibi-Price newsprint mill, for example, saved more than $1 million in annual fuel costs by using wood pellets.

Wood wastes can also be used as a source of organic compounds. One method involves converting wood wastes into methanol through combustion and gasification technology. In the gasification process, wood is mixed with air at a temperature of 850°C to form a synthesis gas composed of 25–35% CO, 8–20% H_2, 15–20% of CO_2, 10–20% hydrocarbons and 15–30% H_2O. The raw synthesis gas can be converted to methanol.

Wood and plants can be fractionated into their components: lignin, hemicellulose and cellulose. Acid hydrolysis of these components can eventually convert them into methanol.

Anaerobic digestion of animal, plant and industrial wastes. Bacterial fermentation of these wastes produces a gas with a high (65%) methane content. One kilogram of waste digested anaerobically produces 0.62 m^3 of methane. In addition to methane, animal feed and plant fertilizers are also produced.

Figure 6-10
Much wood biomass is produced as a by-product of logging practices.

Ethanol

Ethanol, or ethyl alcohol (CH_3CH_2OH), is both the intoxicating ingredient in alcoholic beverages and an important industrial chemical. By law, ethanol in beverages must be produced by fermentation:

$$C_6H_{12}O_6 \longrightarrow 2CH_3CH_2OH + 2CO_2$$

This ethanol is chemically identical to industrial ethanol, which is usually produced during catalyzed hydration of ethene:

$$C_2H_4 + H_2O \xrightarrow{H_2SO_4} CH_3CH_2OH$$

Ethanol produced by either method can be used as a fuel additive.

Laboratory ethanol is often denatured by adding a toxic substance such as methanol (CH_3OH), which makes it undrinkable.

Sewage treatment. Sewage sludge is the residue left after raw sewage is treated. The Canadian government recently allocated $200 million to develop a process to make a synthetic oil from sewage sludge. A pilot plant in Hamilton, Ontario, has been processing a tonne of sewage sludge a day to yield 240 L of oil. An alternative method of sewage treatment involves bacterial fermentation to produce methane.

Animal wastes. Scientists have studied the use of animal wastes as possible sources of hydrocarbons. Heating manure with carbon dioxide at a high pressure produces a crude oil. Organic compounds can be fractionally distilled from this oil.

Various federal and provincial research organizations are studying methods for developing and producing biomass energy. For example, the federal government has proposed a program in which forest biomass would supply 5% of Canada's primary energy demands by the year 2000. The major concerns about the use of biomass energy are the high costs involved in the research and development of facilities equipped to efficiently process biomass and the problem of deforestation and pollution. However, biomass could eventually become a relatively important source of energy and hydrocarbons.

In this chapter we have investigated the sources and chemical reactions of organic compounds. We have also seen that there are alternative sources of hydrocarbons such as coal and biomass conversion.

We have discussed the use of petrochemicals to produce synthetic organic compounds such as polyethylene, polystyrene, nylon and synthetic rubbers. These compounds, called polymers, will be discussed in the next chapter, where we will also look at such natural polymers as carbohydrates, proteins and nucleic acids.

CHROMATOGRAPHY

The nineteenth-century physiologist, Claude Bernard (1813–1878), said that progress in science frequently depends on the development of good methods. One of the most useful branches of applied chemistry is the branch that deals with methods of separating mixtures of compounds. Distillation, widely used in oil refining and the alcoholic-beverage industry, relies on the difference in volatility and boiling points between different compounds. A lesser known but equally important method is chromatography, which relies on the differences in polarity and solubility between different compounds.

Chromatography is the process of separating components of a dissolved mixture according to the degree to which they are adsorbed by the material through which they are passed. When an appropriate solvent is poured through a column, the components of a mixture separate into bands as they move down the column. The components of the mixture are like athletes in an 800 m run:

they start together but spread out by the end of the race. Various chromatographic techniques are used to identify unknown components in mixtures, to detect bombs in airports, to find pesticide residues on fruit and for many other valuable purposes.

The first known application of chromatography was D.T. Day's use of a column of powdered limestone (calcium carbonate) to purify natural petroleum in 1897. In 1906, Mikhail Tswett separated the coloured chlorophyll pigments in green leaves by passing an ether solution of these pigments through a tube of calcium carbonate. The new technique was called chromatography, from the Greek words *chroma*, meaning "colour," and *graphos*, meaning "writing." The name has stuck, even though chromatography is now used mainly for colourless products.

How does chromatography work? In *column chromatography*, the earliest type of chromatography developed, the speed at which a substance moves through a column depends on how well it is dissolved in the solvent (the moving phase) and how well it is adsorbed by the material in the column (the stationary phase). These factors, in turn, depend on the polarity of the solutes. Compounds that dissolve well in the solvent but are not easily adsorbed by the stationary phase will be carried through the column much more rapidly than compounds that do not dissolve well in the solvent but are easily adsorbed by the stationary phase. The compounds will form separate bands within the stationary phase and can be sequentially extracted by further addition of the solvent. For the greatest degree of separation, different polar and nonpolar solvents can be used, as well as a variety of solid, stationary-phase materials, including aluminum oxide (Al_2O_3), starch, powdered sugar and charcoal.

Increasing the fineness of the stationary-phase particles improves the separating ability but also makes the process intolerably slow. One solution to this problem is to pump the solvent containing the mixture through the column at pressures as high as 2000 kPa. *High-pressure liquid chromatography*, as this technique is known, is widely used to detect and identify traces of drugs in blood and urine samples and to separate mixtures of similar reaction by-products.

Another chromatographic method, often used in first-year university laboratories, is *paper chromatography*. A sample of the unknown mixture is placed on a spot near the end of a strip of adsorbent paper. The strip of paper is then suspended so that one end is dipped in a solvent such as water or alcohol and the spot is just above the level of the solvent. As the solvent is adsorbed into the paper by capillary action, it dissolves the various components of the sample and carries them up the paper. As in column chromatography, the degree of separation depends on the solubility of the compounds in the moving phase and the degree to which they are adsorbed by the paper. Once the solvent has reached the top, the paper is removed and dried. If necessary, it can be chemically treated to show the presence of colourless compounds.

A series of known compounds can be run with the sample on the same piece of paper for purposes of comparison. Alternatively, the paper can be turned sideways after the first run and a second run performed using a different solvent to further separate similar compounds. The result is called a *two-dimensional paper chromatogram*. This technique is especially useful for analysing amino-acid mixtures produced by the hydrolysis of proteins. You can experiment with paper chromatography yourself: try to separate the components of various water-soluble inks or vegetable dyes, using water as the liquid phase and ordinary newsprint as the stationary phase.

A technique similar to paper chromatography is *thin-layer chromatography*. In this process, a glass plate coated with an adsorbent material such as silica gel is used instead of paper.

Complex mixtures of gases can be separated in a gas chromatograph in a process known as *gas-liquid chromatography* (shown in photo). A sample containing a mixture of gases is injected through a column into a stream of carrier gas, such as helium or nitrogen. The column is packed with a granular, solid material coated with a non-volatile liquid, called a *partitioner*. As the carrier gas propels the sample through the column, the compounds of the mixture arrive at the outlet at different times. This separation is caused by the interaction of the compounds of the partitioner liquid and the compounds of the gas—the soluble, less volatile gases are slowed by the partitioner while more volatile gases are swept ahead. At the outlet, the gases pass through a device called a *thermal conductivity cell*, which signals the change in composition of the gas. Gas-liquid chromatography is used for discovering and measuring minute traces of toxins in air and water as well as for detecting bombs—trace quantities of compounds used in explosives will produce a characteristic signal from the gas chromatograph. Gas-liquid chromatography can also identify pesticide residues on fruits and vegetables.

Mixtures of all types of chemical substances including organic compounds and polymers and inorganic salts can be separated by chromatography. It is one of the most important tools of chemistry because it can analyse small quantities of complex mixtures. More important, chromatography can be used as a key to unlock the identity of various unknown components within mixtures. The potential of this versatile method is almost unlimited in its applications.

QUESTIONS

1. (a) What is the source of most hydrocarbons? (b) How are they separated from each other?

2. State the origin of petroleum and natural-gas deposits in the earth's crust.

3. Why are thiols added to natural gas?

4. (a) What is cracking? (b) Why is it economically important?

5. Distinguish between thermal cracking and catalytic cracking.

6. Indicate the primary petrochemical and the intermediate organic substance formed in the synthesis of ethylene glycol.

7. Write an equation for the incomplete combustion of propane.

8. State two disadvantages of incomplete combustion of hydrocarbon fuels.

9. Write three reactions illustrating the three different types of oxidation reactions.

10. Propylene glycol ($CH_3CH(OH)CH_2OH$) is the product of a hydroxylation reaction. Write a structure of the organic reactant used and name it.

11. Write the structural formulas for and give the names of the substances in the following series of oxidation reactions:

ethene $\xrightarrow{+H_2O}$ primary alcohol $\xrightarrow{-2H}$ aldehyde $\xrightarrow{[O]}$ carboxylic acid

12. When a gasoline sample with a dilute aqueous solution of potassium permanganate is shaken vigorously, the purple colour of the permanganate (MnO_4^-) is discharged. What can we conclude about the gasoline?

13. (a) What is the name of $C_4H_9\overset{\displaystyle O}{\overset{\displaystyle \|}{C}}C_3H_7$? (b) What alcohol could be used as a source for this compound?

14. Describe the silver-mirror test.

15. In chemical terms, how would you distinguish hexane from hexene?

16. What are the essential features of a hydration reaction of a hydrocarbon if an alcohol is produced?

17. What reaction would produce the ether CH_3OCH_3?

18. (a) What is an addition reaction? (b) Use structural formulas to show how pentene can be changed to pentane by reaction with hydrogen. (c) If propene reacts with chlorine, what compound is formed?

19. Give an example of an elimination reaction.

20. Give an example of a substitution reaction.

21. Use appropriate reactants to show that an esterification reaction could also be classified as a dehydration reaction.

22. What is the name of the following ester?

$$CH_3—CH_2—\underset{\underset{O}{\|}}{C}—O—CH_2—CH_2—CH_2—CH_3$$

23. What are the two components of food oils and fats?

24. The hydrolysis of an ester yields glycerol and linoleic acid. Name the ester and give its condensed formula.

25. What is the major change in physical property in a series of glyceryl esters that have an increasing number of C=C bonds?

26. State a major disadvantage of saturated fatty acids.

27. (a) What is a soap? (b) Describe how a soap can be prepared from a fat.

28. Give an example of a saponification reaction.

29. How do soaps differ from synthetic detergents?

30. Explain the cleansing action of detergents.

31. Why are detergents that contain linear alkylbenzene sulfonate ecologically desirable?

32. (a) What is biomass? (b) Why is it necessary to investigate the uses of biomass?

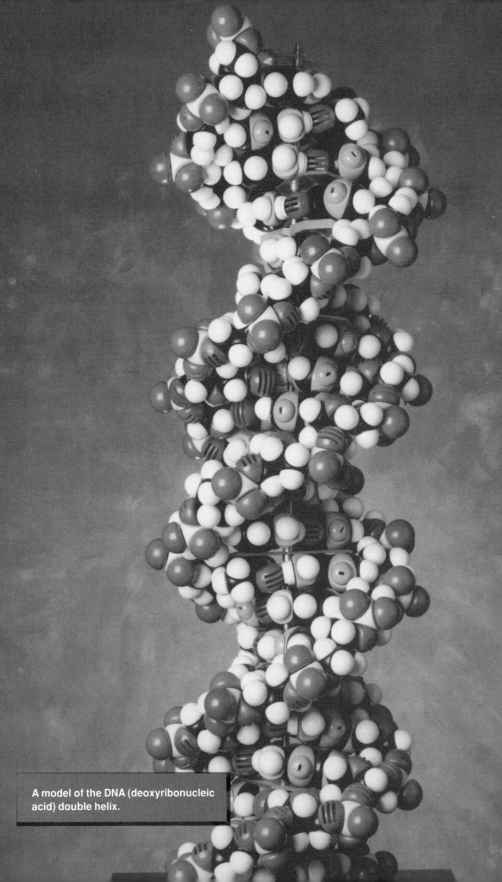

A model of the DNA (deoxyribonucleic acid) double helix.

Polymers:
Synthetic and Natural
Macromolecules

Even though synthetic polymers have only been available since World War II, they have become essential to our daily lives: many of our clothes are made of nylon or polyester; we cook our food in Teflon-coated pans; and our homes contain a variety of plastics and rubbers. Synthetic polymers (plastics, fibres and rubber) are so widely used that they make up approximately 80% of all organic chemicals produced today.

Natural polymers include natural rubber and such fibres as cotton and silk. In addition, all living organisms produce and depend on natural polymers (biopolymers) such as carbohydrates, proteins and nucleic acids.

Polymers are very large molecules, or *macromolecules*, formed from the linking of many small units, called *monomers*. Polymers are formed during one of two types of polymerization reactions: addition or condensation reactions. They are classified on the basis of their physical properties, which depend on the chemical composition and structure of the monomers. Synthetic polymers are also classified as plastics, elastomers or fibres.

In this chapter we will investigate the composition and uses of a variety of synthetic and natural polymers. First, we will look at the different types of polymerization reactions.

POLYMERIZATION REACTIONS

Polymers, from the Greek words *polus*, meaning "many," and *meris*, meaning "part," are giant molecules whose long chains are composed of recurring units called *monomers*. Polymers containing one kind of fundamental repeating unit are called *homopolymers*; those containing different types of repeating units are called *copolymers*.

Polymers are formed by the chemical bonding of thousands of monomers. For example, when thousands of ethene molecules ($CH_2\!\!=\!\!CH_2$) are connected, the polymer polyethene is obtained. The reaction in which monomers are joined together is known as *polymerization*. There are two types of polymerization reactions: addition and condensation.

7-1

Addition Polymerization

Addition polymerization is the successive joining of unsaturated monomer units to form an addition polymer. No by-products are formed.

Addition polymerization involves the combination of unsaturated compounds (monomers) whereby the double bonds break open to form single bonds. The reaction involves three steps: initiation, propagation and termination. Let us examine the addition polymerization of ethene (ethylene) to form polyethene (polyethylene) (Fig. 7-1).

The polymerization of ethylene to polyethylene begins when an initiator such as oxygen or peroxide is converted to a free radical; the initiator is represented as I. The activated initiator, or free radical, which we can represent as I·, reacts with an ethylene molecule to form a longer free radical:

$$I\cdot + CH_2\!\!=\!\!CH_2 \longrightarrow I\!-\!CH_2\!-\!CH_2\cdot$$

The product of this reaction is able to add another ethylene molecule, which can then add another molecule and so on. Propagation of the ethylene polymer continues until the reactive end of the chain bonds to a terminator species (T) such as a controlled additive, an impurity or another free-radical species, which makes the polymer non-reactive:

$$I\!-\!CH_2\!-\!CH_2\!-\!CH_2\!-\!CH_2\cdot + T \longrightarrow$$
$$I\!-\!CH_2\!-\!CH_2\!-\!CH_2\!-\!CH_2\!-\!T$$

No by-products are formed during addition polymerization reactions.

Figure 7-1
Hot-air balloons are made from such synthetic polymers as polyethylene, Dacron and nylon.

TABLE 7-1
ADDITION POLYMERS OF VARIOUS SUBSTITUTED ALKENES

Monomer Name	Monomer Formula	Polymer Name	Polymer Formula	Uses
Ethene (ethylene)		polyethene (polyethylene)		bags, flexible bottles, ice-cube trays
Propene (propylene)		polypropene (polypropylene)		indoor-outdoor carpeting, ropes
Chloroethene (vinyl chloride)		polyvinyl chloride (PVC)		shower curtains, floor tiles, vinyl siding
Vinylbenzene (styrene)		polystyrene		styrofoam insulation, containers
Tetrafluoroethene (tetrafluoro-ethylene)		polytetrafluoro-ethylene (PTFE, Teflon)		non-stick pan coatings
Cyanoethene (acrylonitrile)		polyacrylonitrile (Orlon)		plastic windows, clear plastic jewellery
Methyl-2-propenoate (methyl methacrylate)		polymethyl methacrylate (Lucite, Plexiglas)		acrylic fibres for carpets, crease-resistant fabrics

We can represent the polymer of ethylene as

$$-\!\!\left(CH_2\!-\!CH_2\right)_{\!n}$$

where the group in the brackets is repeated n times. Note that polyethylene is a homopolymer because it is formed by the polymerization of a single type of monomer. Copolymers, formed by the polymerization of two or more different monomer units, can also be formed. A copolymer made by the addition of monomers A and B does not necessarily form a regular alternating sequence of monomer units, as in

$$+(A-B-A-B)_n$$

If the relative ratios of the monomers are varied, copolymers of different sequences and properties are obtained. An example of a common copolymer is Saran, formed by the addition polymerization of chloroethene and 1,1-dichloroethene:

$$\begin{matrix} H \\ \diagdown \\ C=C \\ \diagup \quad \diagdown \\ H \quad\quad H \end{matrix} + \begin{matrix} H \\ \diagdown \\ C=C \\ \diagup \quad \diagdown \\ H \quad\quad Cl \end{matrix} \longrightarrow \left(CH_2-\underset{\underset{H}{|}}{\overset{\overset{Cl}{|}}{C}}-CH_2-\underset{\underset{Cl}{|}}{\overset{\overset{Cl}{|}}{C}} \right)_n$$

A large number of different addition polymers can be prepared by the addition polymerization of various alkenes (Table 7-1).

7-2
Condensation Polymerization

Condensation polymerization is the joining of monomers through the elimination of small molecules such as water from the functional groups of the monomers.

Condensation polymerization involves the combination of two different monomers that have functional groups at both ends of the molecule. Thus, all condensation polymers are copolymers. Usually, a small molecule is eliminated during the combination of the two functional groups. For example, the polyamide nylon-66 is produced by the reaction between a dicarboxylic acid, 1,6-hexanedioic acid (adipic acid), and a diamine, 1,6-diaminohexane (hexamethylenediamine). The reaction can be represented as

$$HO-\overset{\overset{O}{\|}}{C}-(CH_2)_4-\overset{\overset{O}{\|}}{C}-OH + H-NH-(CH_2)_6-NH_2 \longrightarrow$$

1,6-hexanedioic acid   1,6-diaminohexane
(adipic acid)   (hexamethylenediamine)

$$\left(\overset{\overset{O}{\|}}{C}-(CH_2)_4-\overset{\overset{O}{\|}}{C}-NH-(CH_2)_6-NH \right)_n + H_2O$$

polyhexamethylene adipamide
(nylon-66)

The elimination of a water molecule enables the carboxylic acid to link up covalently with the amine. Continuation of the condensation reaction is possible because both the acid and amine molecules have reactive groups at both ends of the chain.

Two other examples of condensation copolymers are those formed by the condensation of methanal (formaldehyde) with hydroxybenzene (phenol) or with urea. Bakelite is a hard, thermosetting plastic made from the reaction of formaldehyde (HCHO) with phenol (C_6H_5OH):

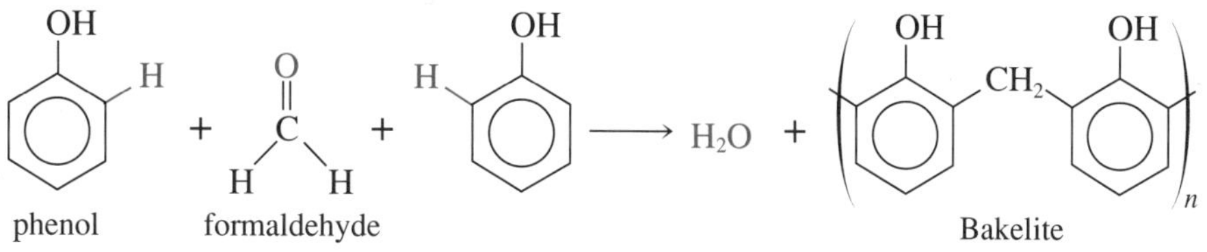

The oxygen of the formaldehyde molecule reacts with two hydrogen atoms to form water, which is eliminated. A CH_2 bridge then forms between the two phenol molecules. The application of more heat and pressure to this reaction establishes more and more cross-linkages in a three-dimensional network to form a hard, brittle solid.

Urea-formaldehyde is another example of a condensation polymer. The oxygen atom of the formaldehyde reacts with the hydrogen from the two adjacent urea molecules, and water is eliminated:

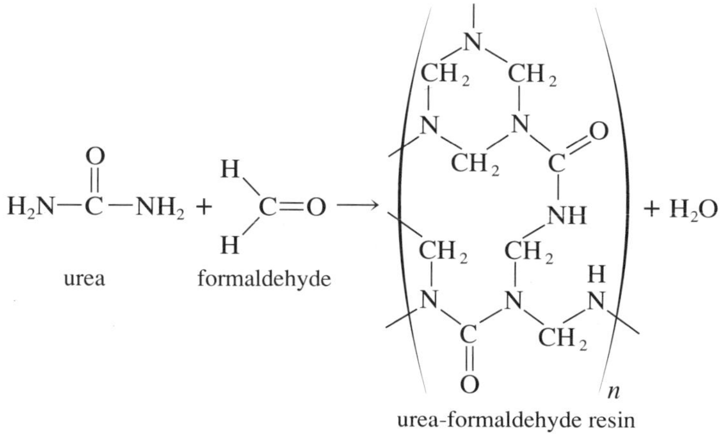

Bakelite was the first completely synthetic plastic manufactured. Produced in 1909 by Leo Baekeland, this phenol-formaldehyde resin spurred the development of the plastics industry. Bakelite has many industrial applications. It is used as an electric insulator and as an adhesive, as well as in paints and enamel coatings. It is also used in manufacturing chemical equipment and machine and electric components.

urea-formaldehyde resin

A wide range of condensation polymers can be obtained from the condensation polymerization of various difunctional compounds (Table 7-2). Note that the eliminated product depends on the two reactants.

TABLE 7-2
CONDENSATION POLYMERS

Reaction	Polymer	By-product

$$\underset{\substack{\text{1,6-hexanedioic acid}\\\text{(adipic acid)}}}{\text{HOC(CH}_2)_4\text{COH}} + \underset{\substack{\text{1,6-diaminohexane}\\\text{(hexamethylene diamine)}}}{\text{H}_2\text{N(CH}_2)_6\text{NH}_2} \longrightarrow \underset{\substack{\text{polyhexamethylene adipimide}\\\text{(nylon-66)}}}{\left(\!\!-\text{C(CH}_2)_4\text{CNH(CH}_2)_6\text{NH}-\!\!\right)_n} + \text{H}_2\text{O}$$

$$\underset{\substack{\text{1,2-ethanediol}\\\text{(ethylene glycol)}}}{\text{HOCH}_2\text{CH}_2\text{OH}} + \underset{\substack{\text{1,4-benzenedicarboxylic acid}\\\text{(terephthalic acid)}}}{\text{HOC}-\!\!\bigcirc\!\!-\text{COH}} \longrightarrow \underset{\substack{\text{polyethylene terephthalate}\\\text{(Dacron)}}}{\left(\!\!-\text{CH}_2\text{CH}_2\text{OC}-\!\!\bigcirc\!\!-\text{CO}-\!\!\right)_n} + 2n\text{CH}_3\text{OH}$$

$$\underset{\substack{\text{1,4-butanediol}}}{\text{HO(CH}_2)_4\text{OH}} + \underset{\substack{\text{1,6-hexanediisocyanate}}}{\text{O}=\text{C}=\text{N(CH}_2)_6\text{N}=\text{C}=\text{O}} \longrightarrow \underset{\substack{\text{polyurethane}}}{\left(\!\!-\text{CH}_2(\text{CH}_2)_3\text{OCNH(CH}_2)_6\text{NHCO}-\!\!\right)_n} + 2n\text{H}_2\text{O}$$

FOLLOW-UP PROBLEMS

1. Draw a structure for the repeating unit in the homopolymer made from 4-methyl-1-pentene.
2. A plastic wrap has the following repeating structural unit:

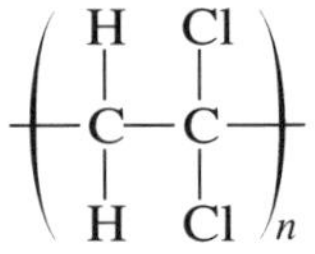

$$\left(\!\!-\overset{\displaystyle\underset{|}{\text{H}}}{\underset{|}{\text{C}}}-\overset{\displaystyle\underset{|}{\text{Cl}}}{\underset{|}{\text{C}}}-\!\!\right)_n$$

Draw a structure for the monomer and name it.

Answers:

1.

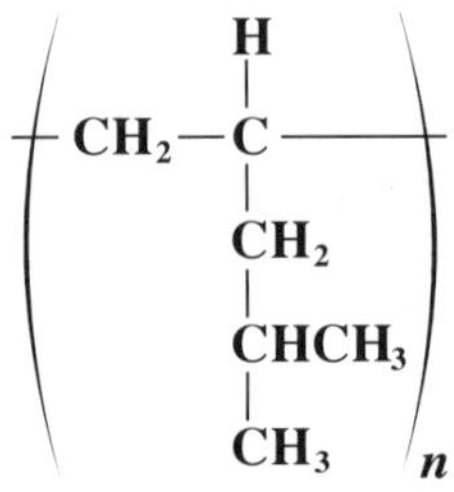

$$\left(\!\!-\text{CH}_2-\overset{\displaystyle\text{H}}{\underset{\displaystyle\underset{\displaystyle\underset{\displaystyle\text{CH}_3}{|}}{\underset{|}{\text{CHCH}_3}}}{\underset{|}{\overset{|}{\text{C}}}}}\!\!\right)_n$$

This is poly-4-methylpentene (PMP), which is used to make laboratory flasks and beakers.

2. $\text{CH}_2{=}\text{CCl}_2$; **1,1-dichloroethene**

Now that we have discussed the two types of polymerization reactions, let us look at the classification, properties and uses of synthetic polymers.

SYNTHETIC POLYMERS

Synthetic polymers include the plastics in such objects as cars, floor coverings, telephones, furnishings, bags and containers, as well as synthetic fibres, such as Dacron used in clothing, and synthetic rubbers (Fig. 7-2).

Figure 7-2
The variety of synthetic polymers has only been available since World War II.

The properties of synthetic polymers vary widely. By adjusting the temperature, pressure and type of monomer, chemists can produce specific polymers with distinctly different properties. Some synthetic polymers, such as Bakelite, are hard and brittle.

Others, such as synthetic rubbers, are elastic. Some can be formed into thin, flexible sheets, such as Saran, which is used in plastic food wrap. Many plastics are biologically inert and can be used as containers for tissue cultures or for storage of distilled water.

Synthetic polymers are classified as plastics, elastomers or fibres, depending on their elasticity. Elastomers are the most easily stretched polymer, while fibres are the least elastic. Plastics can be further classified as thermoplastics or thermosetting plastics on the basis of their response to heating.

7-3

Thermoplastic Polymers

A thermoplastic polymer will soften when heated and harden when cooled. This process can be repeated many times.

Thermoplastic polymers have the ability to soften when heated without being chemically altered during the process. This property is related to their linear shape and the fact that they are made from monomers that can form only two bonds with neighbouring monomers. Thus, monomers in thermoplastic polymers are combined into separate chains with few branches; forces between the chains are relatively weak.

Five common thermoplastics are polyethylene, polypropylene, polystyrene, polyvinylchloride and polyvinyl acetate. The simplest example of a thermoplastic polymer is polyethylene, of which there are two types: low-density and high-density. Low-density polyethylene is produced under high pressure and consists of irregularly placed side branches off the main molecular chain. Low-density polyethylene is mainly used for plastic squeeze bottles and plastic bags because it is soft and flexible. High-density polyethylene is an unbranched, semi-rigid, crystalline polymer used to make plastic toys and bottles.

Deteriorating Lawn Furniture
Have you ever noticed that lawn chairs begin to deteriorate after they have been left outside? This is not the action of acid rain but, rather, the action of sunlight on the plastic webbing of the chairs. Lawn chairs are made of polypropylene webbing. Ultraviolet radiation has sufficient energy to break some of the bonds holding the polymer together and, thus, to degrade the compound.

Some substances, such as 2-hydroxy-benzophenone, absorb ultraviolet radiation and convert it into heat. Unfortunately, plastic materials rarely contain sufficient radiation absorbers to prevent the decay of plastics. Therefore, unless guaranteed for outdoor use, plastic lawn chairs should be kept indoors when not in use.

$$-(CH_2-CH_2)_n-CH \qquad\qquad -(CH_2-CH_2)_n-$$
$$\qquad\qquad\quad | $$
$$\qquad\qquad\quad CH_2$$
$$\qquad\qquad\quad | $$
$$\qquad\qquad\quad CH_3$$

low-density polyethylene   high-density polyethylene

Polypropylene contains methyl groups (CH_3) branching off the main chain at regular intervals. Similarly, polystyrene has a phenyl group (C_6H_5) branching at specific points; these branches influence the softening point and the stiffness of the polymer. Polypropylene is readily melted by heating and can then be shaped by injecting the material into moulds.

THE FUROR OVER UREA-FORMALDEHYDE

M ost people recognize methanal (HCHO), commonly known as formaldehyde, as the compound responsible for the strong, pungent odour associated with biology labs. In recent years, formaldehyde has become better known for its use in plastic resins and for the problems that have been linked with it.

Formaldehyde is a strong irritant that dissolves easily in the water of the eyes and mucous membranes where it stimulates nerve endings. Because of its extreme reactivity, formaldehyde is usually in a solution of 37–50% formaldehyde and 1–15% methanol, and is called *formalin*. Formalin is used as an embalming fluid and disinfectant. The major use of formaldehyde, however, is in the production of thermoplastic resins and adhesives. Urea-formaldehyde and phenol-formaldehyde resins are used in the production of plywood and particle board, foam insulation and in moulded plastics.

Urea-formaldehyde resins are prepared by heating urea and formaldehyde in the presence of a catalyst such as ammonia:

$$\underset{\text{urea}}{\overset{\displaystyle \text{NH}_2}{\underset{\displaystyle \text{NH}_2}{\text{C}=\text{O}}}} + \underset{\text{formaldehyde}}{\text{HCHO}} \xrightarrow[\text{heat}]{\text{catalyst}} \underset{\text{intermediate}}{\overset{\displaystyle \text{HN}-\text{CH}_2\text{OH}}{\underset{\displaystyle \text{NH}_2}{\text{C}=\text{O}}}} \xrightarrow{\text{polymerization}}$$

$$\underset{\text{resin}}{\overset{\displaystyle \text{HN}-\text{CH}_2-\text{N}-\text{CH}_2\text{OH}}{\underset{\displaystyle \text{NH}_2 \qquad \text{NH}_2}{\text{C}=\text{O} \qquad \text{C}=\text{O}}}} + \text{H}_2\text{O}$$

This thermoplastic resin is water soluble and, under the influence of heat and pressure, becomes an insoluble and infusible form of urea-formaldehyde:

$$\underset{\displaystyle \text{NH}_2}{\overset{\displaystyle \text{HN}-\text{CH}_2\text{OH}}{\text{C}=\text{O}}} \xrightarrow[\text{pressure}]{\text{heat}} \left(\overset{\displaystyle \text{N}-\text{CH}_2}{\underset{\displaystyle \text{NH}_2}{\text{C}=\text{O}}}\right)_n + (n-1)\text{H}_2\text{O}$$

Additional formaldehyde may be needed to create more cross-links between the amine groups. However, if too much formalde-

hyde is added, the excess will slowly diffuse into the air. As well, the absorption of water by some types of urea-formaldehyde resins can cause the slow release of formaldehyde. This phenomenon has raised fears that objects containing urea-formaldehyde, such as foam insulation (UFFI), particleboard and plywood, paper products and some textiles, may leak formaldehyde into the air.

In the late 1970s and early 1980s, a major controversy erupted over the safety of UFFI in Canadian homes. In 1977, between 40 000 and 45 000 Canadian homeowners had been given government grants to insulate their homes with UFFI. In total, approximately 80 000 Canadian homes were insulated with UFFI. Because of U.S. reports relating health problems to formaldehyde leaking from UFFI into homes, a temporary ban was instituted in both the United States and Canada in 1980. This ban led to a public outcry against UFFI. Homes insulated with UFFI lost almost all of their value and some were renovated, as shown above, or demolished.

The temporary ban was initially recommended by the Expert Advisory Committee on UFFI until studies could be completed on the amounts of formaldehyde in UFFI-insulated homes. However, these studies tested formaldehyde levels only in homes where health complaints had been reported. In addition, health complaints were not medically verified, and no measurements were made of other possible sources of formaldehyde such as cigarette smoke, which contains 40–60 ppm of formaldehyde.

The UFFI ban resulted in extensive media coverage and public concern. Newspapers carried pictures of houses being torn down and UFFI contractors entering contaminated homes wearing gas masks. UFFI insulation was blamed for a variety of sicknesses, including constipation, lymphoma and deafness. Eventually, the media's focus shifted, and in 1981 the U.S. ban was lifted.

The Canadian ban on UFFI remains, even though recent studies have reported that on purely scientific grounds, there is insufficient evidence to conclude that UFFI is responsible for health problems. These reports, done in 1985 and 1986, concluded that houses with UFFI had similar levels of formaldehyde as houses that did not contain UFFI and that these levels were below the acceptable safety level of 0.1 ppm. As well, it was found that the levels in some UFFI-insulated homes were significantly lower than the concentration of formaldehyde in cigarette smoke or in an embalming room. Undertakers who have been exposed to the on-the-job industrial limit of 1.0 ppm have not shown any long-term health disorders. Other studies reported no significant differences in health problems between residents of UFFI houses and those in non-insulated homes, except in a few isolated cases in which the UFFI was improperly installed or where residents experienced allergic sensitivity.

Many of the concerns about UFFI have not been substantiated by scientific research. Despite this fact, the Canadian ban on UFFI remains. Ultimately, most of the suffering from UFFI has been economic, since people have lost their homes and insulating companies and contractors have lost their businesses.

7-4
Thermosetting Polymers

Thermosetting polymers are rigid and do not melt at high temperatures.

Thermosetting polymers consist of monomers that form more than two bonds with neighbouring units. These polymers can thus be highly branched and/or cross-linked. Examples of thermosetting plastics include Bakelite, urea-formaldehyde resins and melamine.

Bakelite, discovered by Leo Baekeland in 1909, was the first synthetic resin or plastic developed. As we discussed earlier, Bakelite is a copolymer made from the condensation reaction of formaldehyde and phenol. The rigidness and resistance to heat are caused by the three-dimensional, highly cross-linked network architecture of the plastic. Bakelite is resistant to heat unless very high temperatures are used to degrade the structure.

7-5
Elastomers

Elastomers are polymers that do not undergo a permanent change when stretched but return to their original shape and size when the stress is removed.

Although natural rubber is not a synthetic polymer, it is the best example of an elastomer because of its elastic properties. Natural rubber, also called Hevea rubber, is composed of repeating units of 2-methyl-1,3-butadiene (isoprene) arranged in a *cis* structure:

$$
\begin{array}{c}
CH_3 \\
| \\
CH_2{=}C{-}CH{=}CH_2 \longrightarrow \\
\text{isoprene}
\end{array}
$$

$$
\left(
\begin{array}{c}
CH_3\qquad\qquad H\qquad\ CH_3\qquad\qquad H\\
\diagdown\quad\diagup\qquad\qquad\diagdown\quad\diagup\\
C{=}C\qquad\qquad\quad C{=}C\\
\diagup\qquad\diagdown\qquad\qquad\diagup\qquad\diagdown\\
{+}CH_2\qquad CH_2{-}CH_2\qquad CH_2{+}
\end{array}
\right)_n
$$

Hevea rubber

That is, the substituted methyl groups (CH_3) lie on the same side of the carbon-to-carbon double bond. Because the substituted groups are in the *cis* form, natural rubber has been difficult to produce synthetically. Only recently have catalysts been discovered that will polymerize isoprene so that the substituted groups have a *cis* configuration. Evidence indicates that, in nature, rubber is not formed by the direct combination of isoprene units. The *trans* form of rubber, called gutta-percha rubber, does exist in nature, although it is hard and non-elastic.

$$
\left(
\begin{array}{c}
{+}CH_2\qquad\quad H\qquad\quad H\qquad CH_2{+}\\
\diagdown\quad\diagup\qquad\quad\diagdown\quad\diagup\\
C{=}C\qquad\qquad\quad C{=}C\\
\diagup\quad\diagdown\qquad\qquad\diagup\quad\diagdown\\
CH_3\qquad CH_2{-}CH_2\qquad CH_3
\end{array}
\right)_n
$$

gutta-percha rubber

When a piece of rubber is stretched, the molecules uncoil and elongate in the direction of the stretch. In the stretched condition, the molecular chains assume a more ordered, "crystalline-like" arrangement. When the stress is removed, the chains tend to return to their original, randomly coiled arrangement. At low temperatures, the kinetic energy of the molecules is reduced so that attractive forces between chains become more effective. This causes the rubber to assume a more rigid structure. Thus, elasticity depends on temperature.

$$
\left(
\begin{array}{c}
CH_3\qquad\qquad\qquad CH_3\\
|\qquad\qquad\qquad\ \ |\\
{+}CH_2{-}C{=}CH{-}CH_2{-}CH_2{-}C{=}CH{-}CH_2{+}
\end{array}
\right)_n
\ \xrightarrow{\text{heat with sulfur}}
$$

$$
\left(
\begin{array}{c}
{+}CH_2{-}C{=}CH{-}CH_2{-}CH_2{-}C{=}CH{-}CH_2{+}\\
|\qquad\qquad\qquad\ \ |\\
CH_3\qquad\qquad\qquad CH_3
\end{array}
\right)_n
$$

$$
\left(
\begin{array}{c}
CH_3\qquad\qquad\qquad CH_3\\
|\qquad\qquad\qquad\ \ |\\
{+}CH_2{-}C{=}CH{-}CH{-}CH_2{-}C{=}CH{-}CH_2{+}\\
|\\
S\\
|\\
S\\
|\\
{+}CH_2{-}C{=}CH{-}CH{-}CH_2{-}C{=}CH{-}CH_2{+}\\
|\qquad\qquad\qquad\ \ |\\
CH_3\qquad\qquad\qquad CH_3
\end{array}
\right)_n
$$

The rigidity and hardness of natural rubber can be varied by adding different quantities of sulfur to hot rubber. This process, accidentally discovered by American inventor Charles Goodyear

Charles Goodyear and the Invention of Vulcanization
The process of vulcanization, named after Vulcan, the Roman god of fire, was discovered accidentally by Charles Goodyear in 1838. Goodyear had bought the rights to a process for treating rubber with sulfur so that it would not be sticky. While working sulfur-treated rubber, he accidentally dropped some of it on a hot stove. Goodyear noticed that the addition of heat greatly improved the properties of the rubber. Vulcanization gives rubber more tensile strength, resistance to swelling and abrasion, and elasticity over a wider range of temperature.

(1800–1860) in 1838, is called *vulcanization* and is shown in the previous reaction. During the vulcanization of rubber, the sulfur atoms form cross-links between adjacent chains and, thus, strengthen the rubber. When vulcanized rubber is stretched and then released, it returns to its original shape. The sulfur cross-links keep the long-chain molecules from separating and tend to "pull" them back into their original positions. The hardness of the rubber increases as the sulfur content increases. Hard rubber, such as that used to manufacture battery cases, contains up to 35% sulfur.

Several types of synthetic rubber have been developed; for example, styrene-butadiene rubber, a copolymer of 1,3-butadiene and styrene, has properties similar to natural rubber:

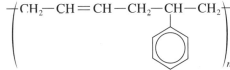

1,3-butadiene   styrene

styrene-butadiene rubber

Neoprene rubber is formed from the polymerization of 2-chloro-1,3-butadiene (chloroprene):

neoprene rubber

Neoprene is a tough oil- and fire-resistant rubber used for gasoline hoses and protective gloves.

Figure 7-3
Julian Hill, a colleague of Wallace Carothers, re-enacts the discovery of the first synthetic fibre as he pulls a molten mass of polymer out of a test tube, stretching it into a thin fibre. The event took place at Du Pont's Experimental Station near Wilmington, Delaware, in the mid-1930s.

7-6

Fibres

Fibres are the least elastic of the polymers. Synthetic fibres have very high tensile strength.

There are two types of synthetic fibres: synthetic and semi-synthetic. Synthetic fibres are made by condensation polymerization. The first synthetic fibre produced was nylon-66, discovered by Wallace Carothers (1896–1937) in the mid-1930s (Fig. 7-3). Nylon-66, so named because each monomer has six carbon atoms, is a linear polyamide produced by the reaction of adipic acid and hexamethylenediamine (Fig. 7-4). There is a relatively strong

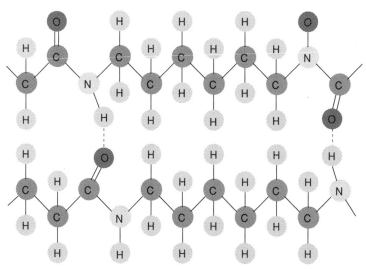

Figure 7-4
In fabrics, adjacent nylon molecules are aligned and linked together by hydrogen bonds.

attraction between the hydrogen of the NH group in one chain and the oxygen in the adjacent chain. The presence of the electronegative oxygen atom and the NH group allows hydrogen bonding between polymer chains. The attractive force allows the close packing of the chains and produces a polymer that, when stretched, has crystalline characteristics, considerable strength and resistance to dissolution and chemical attack.

The characteristics of nylon and other fibres reflect the structure of the individual molecules and the aggregates of molecules that compose the fibre. One possible arrangement of nylon is shown in Fig. 7-4. The diagram implies that molecules are highly ordered in nylon fabrics and cords.

Polyesters are condensation polymers that can also be used as synthetic fibres. Polyethylene terephthalate (Dacron) is the most common polyester formed from 1,2-ethanediol (ethylene glycol) and 1,4-benzenedicarboxylic acid (terephthalic acid):

In addition to nylon-66, other nylons with different properties have also been developed, such as nylon 6-10 and nylon 6-12. In the late 1980s, a new nylon, 6-18, was developed in France.

$$\text{HOCH}_2\text{CH}_2\text{OH}_2 \; + \; \text{HOC}\overset{\text{O}}{\overset{\|}{}}\!\!-\!\!\bigcirc\!\!-\!\!\overset{\text{O}}{\overset{\|}{\text{C}}}\text{OH} \longrightarrow$$

ethylene glycol   terephthalic acid

$$\left(\!\!\text{CH}_2\text{CH}_2\text{OC}\overset{\text{O}}{\overset{\|}{}}\!\!-\!\!\bigcirc\!\!-\!\!\overset{\text{O}}{\overset{\|}{\text{C}}}\text{O}\!\!\right)_{\!n} + \; 2n\text{CH}_3\text{OH}$$

Dacron

Semi-synthetic fibres are made from cellulose, which is a natural polymer of repeating glucose (sugar) molecules. When cellulose is treated with sodium hydroxide, a syrupy liquid, called viscose, is formed. If the viscose is forced through small holes, it

Figure 7-5
The first unveiling of nylon stockings took place at the 1939 New York World's Fair. Unfortunately, the outbreak of World War II halted the commercial production of nylon until 1945.

Wash-and-wear fabrics are made from cellulose acetate, a semi-synthetic fibre made from cellulose and acetic acid.

produces filaments. When these filaments are added to sulfuric acid, modified cellulose fibres are regenerated and can be woven into a fabric known as rayon.

In Section 7-5, we briefly discussed the properties of natural rubber, a natural polymer. Most biologically important compounds responsible for many of the unique properties of living organisms are natural polymers. We will now investigate the three major classes of natural polymers: carbohydrates, proteins and nucleic acids.

DEGRADABLE PLASTICS: A SOLUTION TO A TRASHY PROBLEM

In a world faced with environmental problems such as air pollution and acid rain, one of the most visible and disturbing sights is a beach littered with plastic debris. Each year thousands of sea mammals and birds are drowned or strangled after becoming entangled in plastic garbage that has been thrown into oceans and lakes. Plastics, which were introduced this century, are causing problems that may threaten our environment well into the next century.

Plastics are composed of long chains of polymers that are linked together with strong bonds. The widespread use of plastics is a result of their chemical stability, strength, durability, flexibility and low cost. Unfortunately, these properties mean that the plastic thrown away by the tonne each year may take 200 years to degrade naturally. In response to this problem, scientists are now conducting research into the production of degradable plastics. So far, however, these plastics are too expensive for all but highly specialized applications, although this situation may change as research proceeds.

There are three types of self-degrading plastics: photodegradable, biodegradable and chemically degradable. Most of the currently available degradable plastics are *photodegradable*. Photodegradable plastics were first developed by James Guillet, a University of Toronto chemist who was prompted to develop degradable plastics after being sickened by the sight of plastic litter scattered on roadsides and at campsites. These plastics are based on vinyl ketones and degrade when exposed to light. The carbonyl groups in the polymers absorb ultraviolet rays, which cause the bonds holding the long chains together to break. Thus, short polymers are formed, presenting bacteria with a larger surface area on which to act to degrade the plastic. Although some plastic residue remains, photodegradable plastics represent a viable alternative to conventional plastics and are now being used commercially to reduce environmental litter. Because these plastics require ultraviolet light to degrade, they will only break down if left out in the open and will not degrade indoors or in landfill sites.

For a substance to be truly *biodegradable*, it must be easily and completely broken down by bacteria and other organisms in the environment. Biodegradable plastics contain within their structures compounds that are digestible by micro-organisms. The only biodegradable synthetic polymers are polyesters, which contain esters within their structures; bacteria can easily digest ester groups and, thus, dissolve the polymer.

At the University of Maryland, chemists are trying to induce the formation of esters in conventional plastics such as polyethylene, which is used to make plastic bags. This procedure uses free radicals to break chemical bonds between molecules and causes a chain reaction to occur that breaks the polymer into ester groups. As well, biodegradable plastics made of polystyrene grafted as a side chain onto starch or cellulose are being developed and may soon be available. However, these plastics tend to become mouldy when exposed to food bacteria.

Biodegradable plastics are commonly used in medicine. For example, surgical sutures made of polyglycolate acid will degrade harmlessly inside the body into carbon dioxide and water. Biodegradable plastics are also used instead of metal for plates and screws to hold broken bones together. Biodegradable plastic sheaths were once used to protect newly planted seedlings, but this practice was abandoned because of the high cost of the plastic.

Chemically degradable plastics contain fillers such as cornstarch, which causes the material to crumble when submerged in water or buried in soil. For example, the St Lawrence Starch Company makes a degradable plastic that consists of a plastic polymer coated with cornstarch. Under ideal conditions, 50% of such plastics will degrade into powder within six months. This degradation, like photodegradation, leaves a plastic residue behind. Research is underway to devise a plastic that is made up of 60% corn. The problem with all chemically degradable plastics is that the percentage composition of filler materials affects the durability and strength of the plastic. Thus, chemically degradable plastics may have limited applications.

Unfortunately, the introduction of degradable plastics will not totally solve the garbage problem, since they present a few problems of their own. Conditions at landfill sites are not ideal for degradation to occur. Photodegradable plastics must be exposed to light, and chemically degradable plastics to water or soil. Bacteria that break down biodegradable plastics require oxygen and water, often absent in some refuse sites where even newspapers can take up to ten years to degrade. Also, nothing is known about the environmental effects of plastic residues that are left behind. Environmentalists are concerned that these residues may release toxic gases or leachable by-products. With the growing interest in programs for recycling plastics, care will have to be taken to ensure that degradable plastics are not recycled, since they would contaminate new products. Clearly, much research remains to be done before degradable plastics become reliable and economical enough to be widely used.

NATURAL POLYMERS

Natural polymers, or biopolymers, like synthetic polymers, are large molecules made up of many identical or repeating units. The sequence in which the repeating units are linked is important to the properties and functions of the polymer.

There are three classes of natural polymers produced by all organisms—carbohydrates, proteins and nucleic acids. Table 7-3 compares the amounts of these polymers present in micro-organisms and mammalian cells. Sugars, starches and cellulose are examples of carbohydrates. Proteins are found in all parts of the body and perform a variety of functions. Nucleic acids preserve genetic information and control the synthesis of proteins.

TABLE 7-3
PERCENTAGE OF BIOPOLYMERS IN CELLS

Polymer	Micro-organism	Rat Liver
Carbohydrate	3.0	3.8
Protein	15.0	21.0
Nucleic acids	7.0	1.2

7-7

Carbohydrates

Carbohydrates are sugars or their polymers.

Carbohydrates constitute one of the three basic groups of foodstuffs and represent, in the form of sugar and starch, the major part of the total caloric intake for most organisms. Carbohydrates are composed of carbon, hydrogen and oxygen atoms and are represented by the formula $C_n(H_2O)_n$. The term carbohydrate was initially used because these compounds were believed to be carbon hydrates having a ratio of carbon to hydrogen to oxygen of 1:2:1.

Carbohydrates are synthesized by plants from carbon dioxide and water in the presence of chlorophyll and sunlight. This process, called *photosynthesis*, produces simple sugars with the formula $C_6H_{12}O_6$. The overall equation for the reaction, which does not include the intermediate products, is represented as

$$6CO_2 + 6H_2O \xrightarrow[\text{chlorophyll}]{\text{energy from sunlight}} C_6H_{12}O_6 + 6O_2$$

obtained from   simple   released
air and soil   sugar in   to air
                                 plant
                                 tissue

Through photosynthesis, energy from the sun is stored in carbohydrates on earth.

There are three types of carbohydrates: monosaccharides, disaccharides and polysaccharides. **Monosaccharides** have the general formula $(CH_2O)_n$ and are simple sugars that cannot be broken down chemically to produce simpler carbohydrates; thus, monosaccharides form the building blocks of carbohydrates. Monosaccharides are crystalline solids that are soluble in water and insoluble in nonpolar solvents.

The backbone of monosaccharides is an unbranched carbon chain, which generally contains three to eight atoms, several hydroxyl groups and a carbonyl group. Aldehyde monosaccharides contain the carbonyl group at the end of the chain and are referred to as polyhydroxy aldehydes, or *aldoses*; ketone monosaccharides contain the carbonyl group at any other place along the chain and are called polyhydroxy ketones, or *ketoses*. The most familiar monosaccharides are glucose, fructose, galactose and ribose. From the structural formulas on the next page, we can identify glucose, galactose and ribose as polyhydroxy aldehydes, and fructose as a polyhydroxy ketone. We can also identify glucose, fructose and galactose as hexoses because they contain six carbon atoms. Ribose is a pentose because it has five carbon atoms. Note that glucose, fructose and galactose contain the same number of carbon, hydrogen and oxygen atoms. They

**glyceraldehyde
(an aldose)**

**dihydroxyacetone
(a ketose)**

```
        H                    CH₂OH
        |                     |
        C=O                   C=O
        |                     |
       HC—OH            HO—C—H
        |                     |
    HO—C—H             H—C—OH
        |                     |
     H—C—OH             H—C—OH
        |                     |
     H—C—OH              CH₂OH
        |
      CH₂OH
     D-glucose            D-fructose
```

```
        H                     H
        |                     |
        C=O                   C=O
        |                     |
     H—C—OH             H—C—OH
        |                     |
    HO—C—H              H—C—OH
        |                     |
    HO—C—H              H—C—OH
        |                     |
     H—C—OH              CH₂OH
        |
      CH₂OH
    D-galactose           D-ribose
```

The prefix D-, as in D-glucose and D-fructose, indicates the configuration of the carbon that is most distant from the carbonyl carbon atom. When the hydroxyl group of the carbon projects right, it designates a D-sugar; when it projects left, it refers to an L-sugar. Most L-sugars are relatively uncommon.

glucose

fructose

differ only in the spatial orientation of their atoms and are, therefore, isomers.

The structural formulas above show that these sugar molecules have a straight-chain configuration. However, studies show that these substances have heterocyclic structures. The cyclic structures for glucose and fructose are shown in the margin.

The most common monosaccharide is glucose, which is found in the juices of fruits, in honey and in blood. It exists in relatively large amounts in all plants and is probably the most abundant organic compound. Fructose, the sweetest of all sugars, is found in some fruits as well as in blood. Galactose does not exist as a separate species in living organisms but is a component of other complex carbohydrates such as lactose (milk sugar). Pentoses such as ribose and deoxyribose are components of nucleic acids and of adenosine triphosphate (ATP), the compound that supplies the energy needed for the body's endothermic reactions.

Although glucose can exist as a simple sugar, it is most often found in a combined form as a ***disaccharide***. Disaccharides are formed when two monosaccharide molecules are joined together by glycosidic linkages and lose a molecule of water. A glycosidic bond is formed when a hydroxyl group of one sugar reacts with a carbonyl carbon atom of the second sugar. The simplest disaccha-

Adenosine Triphosphate
Adenosine triphosphate (ATP) is the major carrier of chemical energy in all living cells; ATP provides the energy to drive the energy-requiring processes of cells. All of the energy that is obtained from photosynthesis or from the oxidation of food is stored in the form of ATP.

Each ATP molecule is composed of ribose, adenine (a nitrogenous base) and three phosphate groups. The three phosphate groups are linked together by high-energy covalent bonds. When a phosphate bond is broken, the energy stored in the bond is released and ATP is converted to adenosine diphosphate (ADP). Energy-poor ADP can acquire energy by regaining a phosphate group and becoming energy-rich ATP.

Lactose Intolerance

Lactose is a disaccharide that occurs only in milk. Hydrolysis of this sugar is mediated in the intestines by the enzyme lactase. Although all infants produce this enzyme, only northern Europeans and some Africans retain intestinal lactase activity into adulthood. Adults of other groups have little intestinal lactase and many are unable to digest lactose, or are *lactose intolerant*. Without lactase, lactose remains unabsorbed in the intestinal tract. Lactose ingested in large amounts can cause diarrhea, abnormal intestinal flow and abdominal pain.

ride is maltose, which is formed by the joining of two glucose molecules. The most common disaccharide is sucrose, which makes up common table sugar:

sucrose

Sucrose is formed from a molecule of glucose and a molecule of fructose:

$$C_6H_{12}O_6 + C_6H_{12}O_6 \longrightarrow C_{12}H_{22}O_{11} + H_2O \qquad [7\text{-}1]$$
$$\text{glucose} \quad \text{fructose} \qquad \text{sucrose}$$

Hydrolysis of a disaccharide is the reverse of Equation 7-1. In the laboratory, sucrose can be hydrolyzed by heating it in an acid solution. In the body, the action of the enzyme sucrase breaks down sucrose into its simpler sugars—glucose and fructose:

$$C_{12}H_{22}O_{11} + H_2O \xrightarrow{\text{sucrase}} C_6H_{12}O_6 + C_6H_{12}O_6$$
$$\text{sucrose} \qquad \qquad \text{glucose} \quad \text{fructose}$$

Artificial sweeteners stimulate the tastebuds, but are not converted to energy by the body. A common artificial sweetener is saccharine.

In the human body, disaccharide molecules are too large to diffuse through cell membranes where they can be absorbed into the blood. Thus, all disaccharides are first hydrolyzed in the small intestine by the action of enzymes. The monosaccharides then diffuse first into intestinal cells and, after a series of reactions, into the bloodstream. Some monosaccharides are synthesized into glycogen, a polysaccharide that is stored in the liver and in muscles. Other carbohydrates are carried by the blood to other tissues or oxidized in various cells to carbon dioxide and water, yielding immediate energy.

The Isolation of Insulin

In 1921, Canadian chemists, Frederick Banting and Charles Best, first isolated insulin in the laboratory of J. J. R. MacLeod at the University of Toronto. Insulin is effective in treating *diabetes mellitus*, a disease in which insulin is not produced in adequate quantities. As principal discoverer of insulin, Banting, along with MacLeod, was awarded the 1923 Nobel Prize for physiology or medicine.

Since Banting's and Best's discovery, insulin has been extracted from beef and pork pancreases. Recent developments in genetic engineering have also made biosynthetic human insulin available.

The efficient oxidation of glucose in the cells requires the presence of the hormone insulin. Insulin is secreted by the pancreas in response to the concentration of glucose in the blood. When the blood-glucose level rises, insulin is secreted at an increased rate. Insulin accelerates the rate at which glucose is converted into glycogen. When there is a deficiency of insulin, the level of blood glucose rises. This occurs in people who have the disease *diabetes mellitus*.

Polysaccharides are polymers that contain many thousands of monosaccharides joined by glycosidic linkages. The general formula can be represented as $(C_6H_{10}O_5)_n$ because each monosaccharide bonds to two other monosaccharides, and one water molecule is eliminated for each link formed. Most carbohydrates in nature are polysaccharides. The major functions of polysaccharides are for storage of monosaccharides or as structural components in cell walls and tissues. The three most important polysaccharides are glycogen, starch and cellulose.

The primary storage polysaccharide in animals is glycogen; in plant cells it is starch. In the human body, glucose is converted to glycogen in a series of steps controlled by enzymes; the polysaccharide is then stored in the liver and muscles. Glycogen is a highly branched, compact polysaccharide that contains over 5000 glucose units connected by α-glycosidic linkages.

Starch is a common polysaccharide found in rice, potatoes and wheat. There are two forms of starch: amylose and amylopectin. Amylose is a long, unbranched polymer of between 60 and 300 glucose molecules connected by α-glycosidic linkages. Amylose is soluble in water and constitutes 22–26% of all starches. Amylopectin is a highly branched polysaccharide containing 1000 glucose units bonded together by α-glycosidic linkages.

Amylose can be extracted from potatoes by boiling them in hot water; the evidence is in the milky white water.

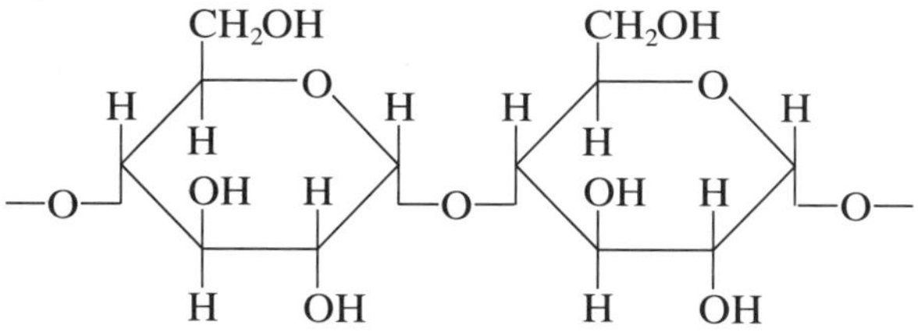

amylose

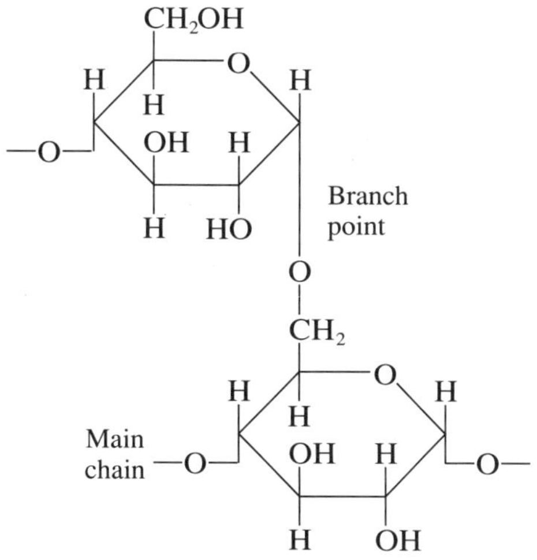

amylopectin

Both glycogen and starch must be hydrolyzed to monosaccharides before they can be absorbed by the body. This hydrolysis involves the enzyme group called α-amylases, which catalyzes the

The only animals able to use cellulose as food are cattle and other ruminants, including goats, sheep and giraffes. Ruminants, however, are not able to digest cellulose; cellulose is digestible only by some micro-organisms and fungi. Ruminants possess four stomachs; the first two stomachs, which constitute the rumen, contain micro-organisms that produce the enzyme cellulase. The cellulase breaks the cellulose into D-glucose, which is further fermented into fatty acids, carbon dioxide and methane. The micro-organisms, along with the fatty acids, are digested in the remaining two stomachs and used as food. The carbon dioxide and methane are released in a process called *eructation*, or belching.

hydrolysis of the α-glycosidic linkages of glycogen and starch to break them down mainly to glucose and maltose. Hydrolysis begins in the mouth and continues in the stomach and small intestine.

Cellulose is a tough, fibrous, water-insoluble polysaccharide found in the stalks, stems and woody parts of all plants. Cellulose contains thousands of glucose units bonded together by β-glycosidic linkages. Because these linkages cannot be hydrolyzed by α-amylases, cellulose cannot be digested by non-ruminant animals.

Since glucose is a ring structure, additional units are added to opposite ends of cellulose to make a rigid, rodlike structure. Large numbers of cellulose molecules cluster together to form cellulose fibres. The large degree of hydrogen bonding between adjacent hydroxyl groups of the close-packed chains is responsible for the rigidity of the cellulose fibres.

cellulose

7-8
Proteins

Proteins are polymers of amino acids and have high molecular weights.

Proteins are the most abundant intracellular macromolecules present in living material. Muscle, cartilage, hair and nails, as well as enzymes, are all composed of protein. Proteins are complex polymers of twenty simple molecules called *amino acids* (Table 7-4). All amino acids contain a carboxyl group (—COOH) and an amino group (—NH$_2$) bonded to the same carbon. However, each amino acid possesses different side chains or functional groups. The structures and names of some common amino acids are given below and in the margin.

Insulin, one of the smallest proteins, has a molecular mass of about 6000.

lysine (Lys)

alanine (Ala)

serine (Ser)

glycine (Gly)

Amino acids can be classified into three groups, depending on the polarity of their side chains. Those that have nonpolar side chains include alanine, valine and leucine. Serine, cysteine, glycine and tyrosine have polar side groups. Other amino acids have positive and negative side groups: glutamic acid and aspartic acid have negatively charged side groups, while lysine and histidine have positively charged side groups.

Amino acids are solids that are reasonably soluble in water and have relatively high melting points. These properties suggest that amino acids have a saltlike structure. Infrared spectra and other experimental data reveal that crystals of amino acids are composed of *dipolar ions*. Thus, glycine can be formulated as an "inner salt," and represented as $H_3\overset{+}{N}CH_2COO^-$. Ions that carry both a positive and negative charge are sometimes referred to as *zwitterions*. In aqueous solution this ion may behave as an acid and donate a proton to water,

$$H_3\overset{+}{N}CH_2COO^- + H_2O \longrightarrow H_3O^+ + H_2NCH_2COO^-$$

or it may behave as a base and accept a proton from water,

$$H_3\overset{+}{N}CH_2COO^- + H_2O \longrightarrow H_3\overset{+}{N}CH_2COOH + OH^-$$

The species that predominates in solution is determined by the pH of the solution. Application of equilibrium principles reveals that in strongly acid solutions, the cationic form predominates ($H_3\overset{+}{N}CH_2COOH$), while in strongly basic solutions the anionic form predominates ($H_2NCH_2COO^-$). At some intermediate pH, most of the amino acid is in the dipolar form ($H_3\overset{+}{N}CH_2COO^-$). The dipolar nature of the amino acids accounts for many of their properties, such as relatively high melting and boiling points.

Amino acids are linked together by *peptide bonds*. A peptide bond occurs between the carboxyl group (—COOH) of one amino acid and the amino group (—NH₂) of another amino acid. During bonding, a water molecule is eliminated between the carboxyl group of one amino acid and the amino group of an adjacent amino acid, as shown below:

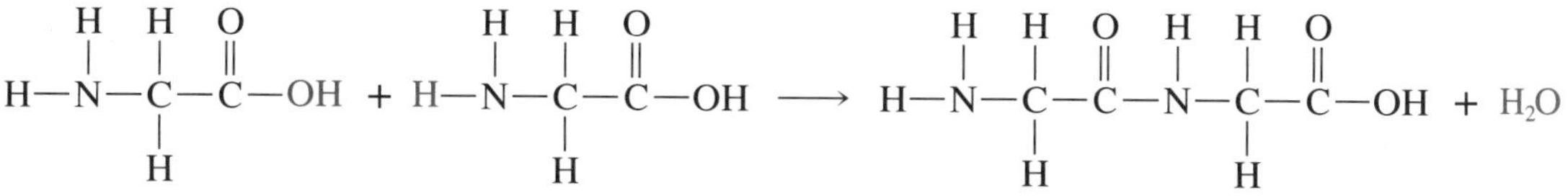

TABLE 7-4	
THE AMINO ACIDS	
Amino Acid	Abbreviation
Alanine	Ala
Arginine	Arg
Asparagine	Asn
Aspartic acid	Asp
Cysteine	Cys
Glutamine	Gln
Glutamic acid	Glu
Glycine	Gly
Histidine	His
Isoleucine	Ile
Leucine	Leu
Lysine	Lys
Methionine	Met
Phenylalanine	Phe
Proline	Pro
Serine	Ser
Threonine	Thr
Tryptophan	Trp
Tyrosine	Tyr
Valine	Val

The carboxyl group of the second amino acid can now bond to a third amino acid. Note that when two amino acids are joined by a peptide bond, they form a *dipeptide*. When three amino acids are joined together, they form a *tripeptide*:

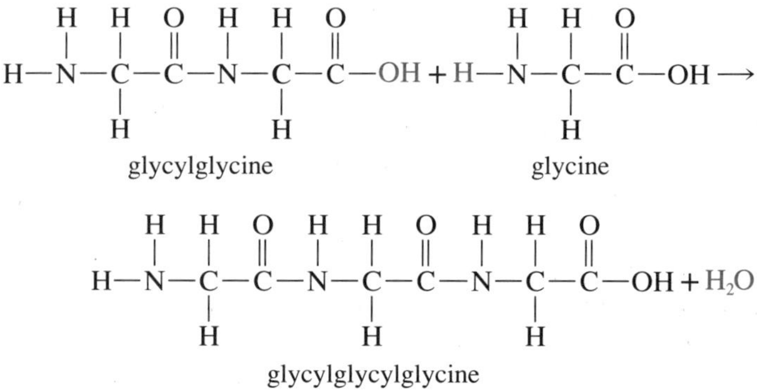

$$H-\underset{\underset{H}{|}}{\overset{\overset{H}{|}}{N}}-\underset{\underset{H}{|}}{\overset{\overset{H}{|}}{C}}-\overset{\overset{O}{\|}}{C}-\underset{}{\overset{\overset{H}{|}}{N}}-\underset{\underset{H}{|}}{\overset{\overset{H}{|}}{C}}-\overset{\overset{O}{\|}}{C}-OH + H-\underset{}{\overset{\overset{H}{|}}{N}}-\underset{\underset{H}{|}}{\overset{\overset{H}{|}}{C}}-\overset{\overset{O}{\|}}{C}-OH \rightarrow$$

glycylglycine　　　　　　　　　　　　　glycine

$$H-\underset{}{\overset{\overset{H}{|}}{N}}-\underset{\underset{H}{|}}{\overset{\overset{H}{|}}{C}}-\overset{\overset{O}{\|}}{C}-\underset{}{\overset{\overset{H}{|}}{N}}-\underset{\underset{H}{|}}{\overset{\overset{H}{|}}{C}}-\overset{\overset{O}{\|}}{C}-\underset{}{\overset{\overset{H}{|}}{N}}-\underset{\underset{H}{|}}{\overset{\overset{H}{|}}{C}}-\overset{\overset{O}{\|}}{C}-OH + H_2O$$

glycylglycylglycine

The *primary structure* of a protein is determined by the sequence of amino acids that make up the protein.

The formation of peptide bonds can continue until a molecule containing hundreds or thousands of amino acids is formed. Such a molecule is called a *polypeptide*, or *protein*, and can be represented as

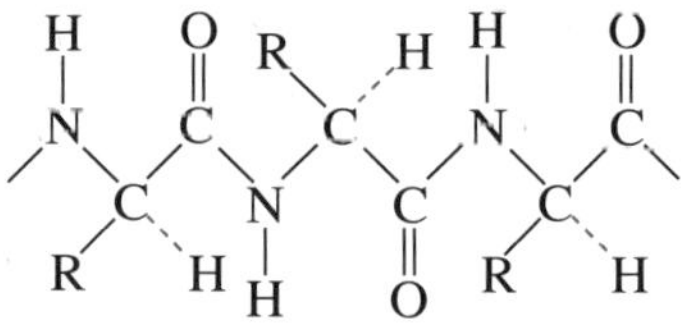

In 1954, English chemist Frederick Sanger (1918–) became the first person to identify the amino-acid sequence of a protein, the hormone insulin. He first completely hydrolyzed bovine insulin to determine the proportions of the various amino acids. Then he partially hydrolyzed the insulin into smaller fragments, which he identified by means of chromatography. Identical sequences indicated where the fragments overlapped, allowing Sanger to deduce the entire amino-acid sequences of the two chains. This historic achievement won Sanger the Nobel Prize for biochemistry in 1958.

The order in which different amino acids are linked together in a polypeptide chain determines the protein that is formed. For example, the sequence of amino acids that results in the formation of the protein insulin is shown in Fig. 7-6. This simplified illustration shows the order of the different amino acids, not the arrangement of atoms in space.

Proteins do not exist as straight chains of amino acids; instead, they coil and fold into complex spatial configurations. Once a polypeptide is formed, additional bonding, such as hydrogen bonding and disulfide linkages, can occur within the chain or between different polypeptide chains, as shown below:

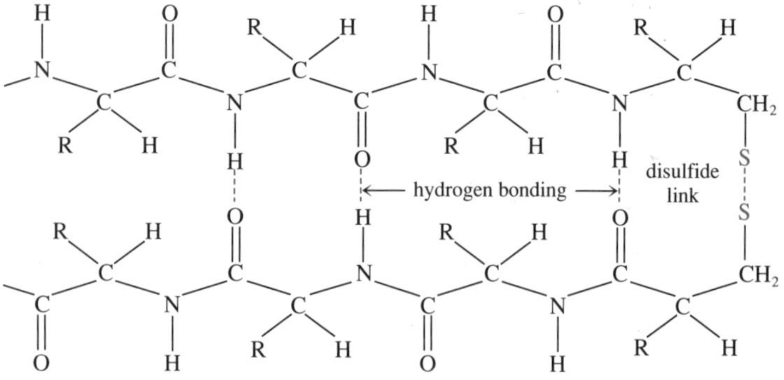

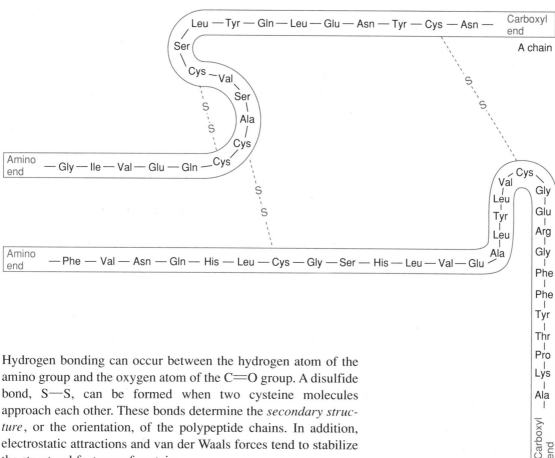

Hydrogen bonding can occur between the hydrogen atom of the amino group and the oxygen atom of the C=O group. A disulfide bond, S—S, can be formed when two cysteine molecules approach each other. These bonds determine the *secondary structure*, or the orientation, of the polypeptide chains. In addition, electrostatic attractions and van der Waals forces tend to stabilize the structural features of proteins.

Assuming that the most stable structure of a protein is one in which there is maximum hydrogen or secondary bonding, Linus Pauling proposed, in 1951, that most protein molecules have either an α-helical shape (Fig. 7-7) or a β-pleated sheet structure (Fig. 7-8). The α-helix is held in place by hydrogen bonds between the hydrogen atom of one amino acid and the oxygen atom of another acid further along the chain. Alpha-helices and β-pleated sheets are common examples of secondary structures. This type of structure adds to the stability of the protein.

There are two general types of proteins: fibrous and globular. The polypeptide chains of fibrous proteins are arranged in long, parallel strands or sheets to form a fibre. The molecular structure of fibrous protein such as that found in hair is shown in the margin. Each strand in the seven-strand cables is a polypeptide chain that has an α-helical structure. In globular proteins, each polypeptide chain is arranged into a folded shape, which makes up the protein's *tertiary structure*. The manner in which the polypeptide chains fit together is called the *quaternary structure*.

Figure 7-6

Insulin was the first protein to have its full amino-acid sequence deciphered and written out.

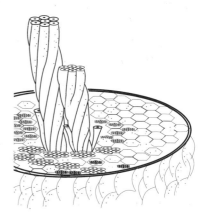

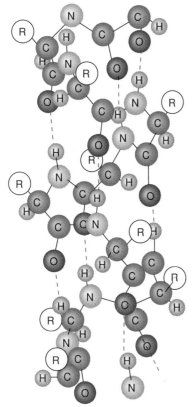

Figure 7-7
Schematic diagram showing the α-helical structure of protein.

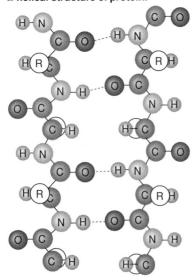

Figure 7-8
Schematic diagram showing the β-pleated sheet structure of protein.

Fibrous proteins play an important role in the anatomy and structure of all animals, forming the main constituent of the outer skin, hair, nails and horns. Fibrous proteins are also the major components of connective tissues, muscles, tendons, cartilage and bone. Globular proteins have a greater variety of biological functions than fibrous proteins. They transport oxygen and nutrients in the blood and serve as antibodies, enzymes and hormones. An example of a globular protein is hemoglobin, which is composed of four polypeptide chains.

During digestion, proteins must undergo enzymatic hydrolysis into their component amino acids since the intestinal cells can only absorb relatively small molecules into the bloodstream. Digestion reverses the synthetic process by which proteins are formed. For example, hydrochloric acid in gastric juices aids the hydrolysis process, which breaks down proteins into smaller peptide chains or amino acids:

$$NH_2{-}CH_2{-}\overset{\overset{\displaystyle O}{\|}}{C}{-}NH{-}CH_2{-}\overset{\overset{\displaystyle O}{\|}}{C}{-}OH \ + \ H_2O \ \xrightarrow{\text{[HCl]}}$$

glycylglycine

$$2\left(NH_2{-}CH_2{-}\overset{\overset{\displaystyle O}{\|}}{C}{-}OH\right)$$

glycine

These smaller molecules can thus diffuse through the intestinal wall and enter the bloodstream where they are carried to various cells and synthesized into specific proteins needed by the body.

When proteins are treated with heat or certain substances such as alcohol or heavy metals, they lose their specific properties in a process called *protein denaturation*. When a protein is denatured, its function is destroyed. For example, when an egg is fried, the protein coagulates irreversibly. Surgical instruments are sterilized at high temperatures so that the proteins of any bacteria that may be present are denatured. The ions of such heavy metals as mercury and lead cause proteins to precipitate out of solution. If such heavy metals are consumed accidentally, it is recommended that egg whites or milk be consumed because both substances contain large amounts of protein; the metals react with the ingested proteins instead of with the body proteins. Denaturing agents are thought to break the hydrogen bonds and disulfide linkages between polypeptide chains, causing the spherical structure of the protein to unfold and effectively destroying the protein. The long, uncoiled chains may become tangled and coagulate, forming an insoluble mass (shown at the top of page 301).

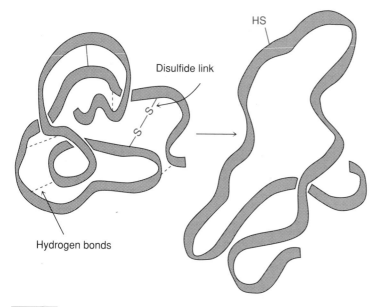

R. Bruce Merrifield
1921–
Robert Bruce Merrifield was born in Fort Worth, Texas. He earned his PhD from UCLA in 1949 for his research on the techniques of microbiological assay of purines and pyrimidines.

Merrifield then moved to New York's Rockefeller Institute for Medical Research where he became involved in the separation and sequencing of protein growth factors. He also synthesized several complex polypeptides containing as many as 40 amino acids. In 1965, he assembled insulin from its component amino acids.

This process was very time-consuming and led Merrifield to develop an automatic protein synthesizer for which he won the Nobel Prize for chemistry in 1984. In this machine, the first amino acid in a chain is anchored to an insoluble solid, and subsequent amino acids are added to the chain one by one. The completed chain can then be detached. The mechanization of protein synthesis benefited research into substances such as hormones and enzymes as well as the commercial manufacture of proteins such as insulin and interferon.

Merrifield continues to work and teach at Rockefeller University.

7-9
Nucleic Acids

Nucleic acids are polymers of repeating units called nucleotides. Each nucleotide has three parts: a five-carbon sugar, an organic, nitrogen-containing base and a phosphate group.

Nucleic acids constitute the third class of organic compounds that are necessary for life. Nucleic acids participate in the storage, transmission and translation of genetic information. Deoxyribonucleic acid (DNA) carries the genes responsible for transmitting hereditary information. Ribonucleic acids (RNA) are responsible for translating the information carried by DNA into protein structure. We will first examine how DNA determines the specific traits of an organism. We will then briefly consider the manufacture of proteins in which both DNA and RNA work closely together.

Nucleic acids are made up of several thousand nucleotides joined together by ester linkages. Each nucleotide consists of a five-carbon sugar—either ribose or deoxyribose—an organic nitrogen-containing base and a phosphate group (Fig. 7-9). The nitrogenous bases are derived from two heterocyclic compounds, pyrimidine and purine:

pyrimidine   purine

Phosphate group

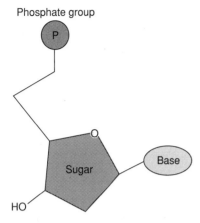

Figure 7-9
Diagram of a nucleotide.

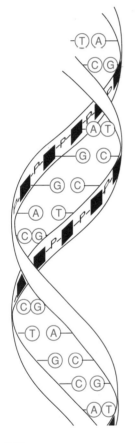

Figure 7-10
Three-dimensional representation of a section of DNA, illustrating the double helix and the pairing of specific organic bases.

Three bases found in nucleic acids are derived from pyrimidine:

cytosine (C)   thymine (T)   uracil (U)

Two other bases are derived from purine:

adenine (A)   guanine (G)

In the sequence of DNA, as shown in Fig. 7-10, an adenine base always bonds with a thymine base, and a guanine base always bonds with a cytosine base. Note that adenine forms two hydrogen bonds with thymine and guanine forms three hydrogen bonds with cytosine (Fig. 7-11). DNA has a backbone of alternating phosphate and deoxyribose groups to which organic bases can be attached.

Deoxyribonucleic acid (DNA) and ribonucleic acid (RNA) differ in four ways:

1. The sugar in DNA is deoxyribose; the sugar in RNA is ribose.

2. The four bases in DNA are adenine, cytosine, guanine and thymine; in RNA, uracil takes the place of thymine.

3. DNA is usually double stranded; RNA is always single stranded.

4. DNA carries genetic information; RNA uses this information to manufacture proteins. The genetic information is encoded in the sequence of the four organic bases in the DNA structure.

The way in which DNA passes its genetic message from generation to generation was discovered by James Watson and Francis Crick in 1953 once they had determined the structure of DNA. Their model (Fig. 7-12) shows that DNA has a double-stranded helical structure in which the two strands, composed of alternating sugar and phosphate groups, are bonded together by hydrogen bonds between adenosine and thymine from opposite strands and

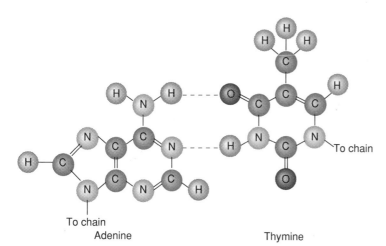

Figure 7-11
Two-dimensional representation of a section of DNA, showing the two hydrogen bonds between adenine and thymine, and the three hydrogen bonds between guanine and cytosine.

Adenine   Thymine

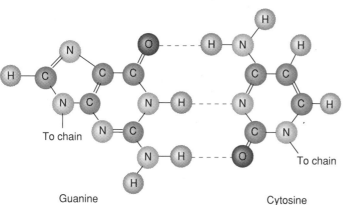

Guanine   Cytosine

Xeroderma Pigmentosum
Ultraviolet light can cause damage to skin cells by causing adjacent pyrimidines—usually thymine—in DNA to bond covalently to each other and form a thymine dimer. If this damage is not repaired, the DNA cannot replicate and skin cells will not grow properly. Normally, the DNA is repaired by enzymes, which remove the portion containing the thymine dimer and replace it with a patch of new nucleotides.

Xeroderma pigmentosum is a rare genetic defect in which one of the key repair enzymes is absent. Thus, the ultraviolet damage is not repaired. The skin becomes very dry and thick, and skin cancer is almost inevitable. There is no treatment for this condition except to keep the skin completely shielded from sunlight.

Figure 7-12
James Watson (left) and Francis Crick in front of their model of DNA.

FRANCIS H.C. CRICK   JAMES D. WATSON
(1916–   )   (1928–   )
Francis Harry Compton Crick was
born in Northampton, England, edu-
cated at University College, London,
and received his PhD from Cambridge
University. He interrupted his educa-
tion during World War II to work on
the development of radar and on mag-
netic mines. After the war, he worked
on X-ray diffraction as a tool for
studying the molecular structure of
large organic molecules.

In 1951, Crick met James Watson at
Cambridge and began the work that
led them to propose that DNA had a
double-helix structure. In 1962, Crick
shared the Nobel Prize in physiology
or medicine with Watson and Maurice
Wilkins.

James Dewey Watson was born in
Chicago, Illinois. A child prodigy, he
enrolled at the University of Chicago
at age 15, graduated in 1947 and
earned his PhD from the University of
Illinois in 1950 at age 22.

Watson is the author of *The Double*
Helix **(1968), a widely read account of**
the discovery of the double helix. This
book has been accused of slighting
Rosalind Franklin (1920–1958), who
had applied X-ray diffraction methods
to the study of DNA. She established
the density of DNA and discovered
that it was a helix.

Rosalind Franklin died of cancer in
1958 at the age of 38, never knowing
that her work had played a crucial
part in Crick's and Watson's discov-
ery of the structure of DNA.

between guanine and cytosine from opposite strands. Watson and Crick deduced that if the two strands of a DNA molecule are broken apart, each strand provides all the information necessary for synthesizing a new partner strand, since the sequence of nucleotides in one strand precisely determines what the sequence of nucleotides must be in the other strand. DNA, therefore, has the unique ability to replicate itself. The process of DNA replication is very complex. Generally, the hydrogen bonds between the two strands are broken and the strands are separated with the help of enzymes; each strand serves as a template for the synthesis of a new strand. Each new polynucleotide strand has a base sequence identical to that of the strand to which its template was bonded in the original DNA molecule. For example, adenine on the template would have been paired originally with thymine and could join another thymine by hydrogen bonding on the new strand. A complementary strand is then made for each of the original strands, and the cell divides, leaving a double strand of DNA in each of the newly formed nuclei, as shown below:

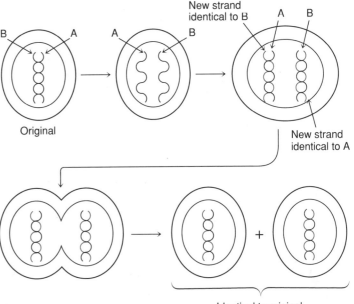

Original

New strand identical to B

New strand identical to A

Identical to original

How does DNA control the specific traits of an organism? The sequence of organic bases in DNA represents a code, which is specific to a particular protein. Each three-base sequence in the DNA represents one specific amino acid and is called a *codon*. The sequence of bases in DNA is translated by RNA for the synthesis of all proteins. Because proteins are an integral part of cell structure and enzymes control all cellular chemical reactions, DNA ultimately determines the characteristics of an organism.

The process begins with *transcription*, in which an RNA strand is transcribed from DNA. This RNA is complementary to the base sequence of the DNA, as shown below:

```
                        RNA
        ┌─
        U---A—T---A
        │   │ │   │
        C---G—C---G
        │   │ │   │
        A---T—A---U
        │   │ │   │
        G---C—G---C
        │   │ │   │
        A---T—A---U
   RNA  └   │  └→
           DNA
```

The RNA formed in the nucleus is referred to as *messenger-RNA* (m-RNA) since it carries the amino-acid sequence of a specific protein from the nucleus to the cytoplasm where the protein is produced.

Protein is synthesized when the message of the m-RNA is translated into a particular sequence of amino acids. The process of translation takes place on the ribosomes, which consist of ribosomal-RNA, enzymes and structural proteins. The substance that translates the code of the m-RNA is called *transfer-RNA* (t-RNA). When a particular amino acid is required, a specific t-RNA attaches to the surface of the m-RNA. Because the factor that determines the order of amino acids in a specific protein is the sequence of the organic bases of the m-RNA, there is a specific t-RNA for each amino acid. Thus, the t-RNA translates the sequence of organic bases in the m-RNA into a sequence of amino acids, which then form peptide bonds to produce proteins.

In summary, the DNA of a gene determines the m-RNA, which, in turn, determines the protein structure. The protein structure controls the chemical reactions, which, in turn, control the characteristics of an organism.

In this chapter, we described the variety of synthetic and natural polymers as well as the different types of polymerization reactions. We also examined the molecules responsible for controlling the chemical reactions and changes that occur in our bodies.

We will now turn our attention to the energy involved in chemical changes. The energy possessed by chemical substances and the energy changes associated with a chemical reaction are often just as important to a chemist as the products of the reaction. In the next chapter we will discuss the energy changes associated with chemical and nuclear reactions. We will also discuss the composition, nature and reactions of atomic nuclei.

Proofing by DNA Polymerases

DNA polymerases I and III are enzymes in bacteria that make the polymer DNA by adding successive nucleotides to the parent DNA strand. They also remove nucleotide residues from the 5′ end of DNA molecules and are capable of removing 3′ residues as well. This latter phenomenon initially puzzled researchers because the polymerase moves in the opposite direction. They discovered, however, that this property enables the polymerase to replace an incorrect nucleotide by backing up and replacing it with the correct one. This process lowers the error rate in the replication of DNA in *Escherichia coli* to about one-ten-thousandth of what it would be without this mechanism. Accuracy is much more important in replication than in transcription or translation, since the latter two processes affect only single cells.

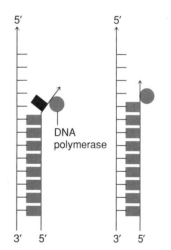

DNA polymerase inserts wrong nucleotide.

DNA polymerase inserts correct base and resumes replication.

VIRUSES AND AIDS

What do the following diseases have in common: polio, the common cold, smallpox, tobacco mosaic, cold sores and AIDS? They are all caused by viruses—tiny particles made up mostly of nucleic acids and proteins. Viruses are so small and simple that it is hard to understand why they can cause so much human suffering and economic damage and be so difficult to combat.

Although viral diseases have been around for centuries, virology, the study of viruses, is less than one hundred years old. In the 1700s, the cowpox virus was used as a vaccine against smallpox. In 1884, Louis Pasteur used a weakened rabies virus therapeutically. However, it was not until 1899 that it was discovered that viruses could cause certain diseases.

Most information about viruses comes from the study of bacteriophages—viruses that infect bacteria (shown below). Viruses range from 15 to 400 nm in size. They contain a single or double strand of DNA or RNA surrounded by a protein coat called a capsid. The capsid protects the genetic material of the virus and assists the virus in invading other cells. Some viruses also contain proteins associated with the DNA or RNA; viruses that infect animals often have an envelope of glycoprotein and lipid surrounding the capsid.

Viruses have proved difficult to classify because little is known

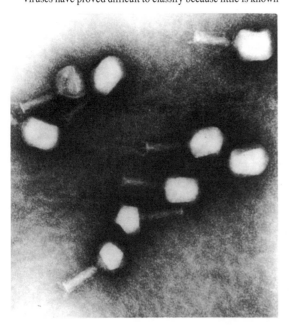

about their evolutionary relationships. Viruses are classified based on the type and number of strands of genetic material, the shape and structure of the capsid, and the presence or absence of a protein envelope. Because they contain genetic material, viruses are able to mutate and recombine, which allows them to evolve and adapt to their surroundings. Viruses, however, do not grow and, because they have no ribosomes, mitochondria or any mechanism of protein synthesis, can only reproduce by invading host cells and taking over their "machinery." It is for this reason that most scientists do not classify viruses as living organisms.

All viruses invade host cells by using envelope or capsid proteins to recognize and bond with receptor molecules on the surface of the host cell. Enzymes in the capsid break down the cell wall and the viral DNA or RNA is injected into the cell. The host's DNA is destroyed and its ribosomes and ATP are used to produce viral proteins and DNA or RNA. Virulent bacteriophages destroy the host cell wall, thus killing the host cell and enabling the release of thousands of new viruses, which in turn infect new host cells. Other viruses break cell walls only under certain conditions and are therefore not considered to be as dangerous as virulent bacteriophages. These include the various herpes viruses, which can be controlled but never eliminated since stress or illness can cause the virus to become virulent.

One virus that has been the subject of intense research is the human immunodeficiency virus (HIV) (shown on the next page), which causes AIDS (acquired immune deficiency syndrome). HIV kills lymphocytes, thereby reducing the immune system's ability to fight off pathogens. The disabling of the immune system leaves people infected with the virus open to infection by other pathogens such as pneumonia or an otherwise rare form of cancer, called Kaposi's sarcoma. The affected individual dies—not, strictly speaking, from AIDS itself, but because AIDS has left the body vulnerable to life-threatening infections.

HIV does not completely destroy the immune system. Some people exposed to the virus do not become infected. Other people infected with HIV may never develop AIDS and are called *asymptomatic carriers* because they exhibit no clinical signs of AIDS.

The first cases of AIDS appeared in North America in 1981. In 1983, the virus was identified; a blood test to detect antibodies to HIV was made available to physicians in 1985. A positive HIV test does not mean that the person will develop AIDS; it does mean that the person has been exposed to and infected with HIV.

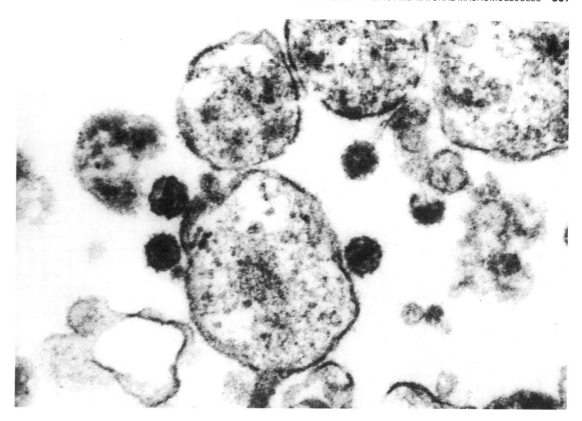

A negative test may mean that the person has been infected with HIV but has not yet produced antibodies. It takes between two and six months after exposure to the virus for the body to produce antibodies.

A cure for AIDS, like cures for most viral diseases, has been very hard to find. Antibiotics, which help fight bacterial infections, have no effect on viruses. The drug azidothymidine (AZT) has prolonged the lives of many AIDS patients by killing replicating viruses; however, AZT has been found to interfere with normal cell division, thus reducing the number of new lymphocytes produced in bone marrow. Several potential anti-AIDS drugs show similar effects.

The most promising AIDS research lies in developing a vaccine that would stimulate the production of antibodies. These antibodies would bind to the protein envelope of the virus, thereby neutralizing it; the antibodies would also destroy cells that had already been infected. The development of a vaccine has been slow because, unlike most viruses, HIV mutates rapidly, creating many strains of the virus. A successful vaccine would have to neutralize all of the variants of the virus. So far, experimental vaccines have only produced short-lived protection against HIV.

HIV has been isolated from blood and seminal fluids and in small amounts from tears, saliva and vaginal fluids. Therefore, unprotected sexual intercourse with an infected person and the sharing of contaminated needles for intravenous drug use are the most common means of transmitting the virus from one person to another. HIV can also be transmitted from an infected mother to her infant in the womb. Blood transfusions no longer present a significant danger because all donated blood is screened for the HIV antibodies and infected blood is destroyed. There is a slight risk in using donated blood because an infected individual may not develop viral antibodies until several months after exposure to the virus.

People can protect themselves from AIDS by understanding how the virus is spread and by taking steps to prevent infection. The proper use of condoms, monogamy between two uninfected people, as well as sexual abstinence will help reduce the risk of exposure to HIV through sexual contact. Avoiding intravenous drug use is another way of preventing the transmission of AIDS. Drug users are encouraged not to share needles, and needle exchange programs have been set up in many cities across North America.

In addition to understanding how HIV is spread, people must be made aware of situations in which it cannot be transmitted, such as through casual contact, kissing, from toilet seats or from mosquito bites. Like all agents that cause sexually-transmitted diseases, HIV requires the human body to survive.

Until researchers find a vaccine or a cure for AIDS, it is clear that, at present, the most effective way of fighting AIDS is through education.

QUESTIONS

1. Define *polymer*.

2. What is necessary for a polymerization reaction to occur?

3. What is the common structural feature of monomers that form addition polymers? Give an example of a common addition polymer.

4. From what monomers are the following polymers formed? (a) Saran, (b) Teflon, (c) PVC, (d) Plexiglas

5. Write formulas to represent the polymers formed from the following monomers:

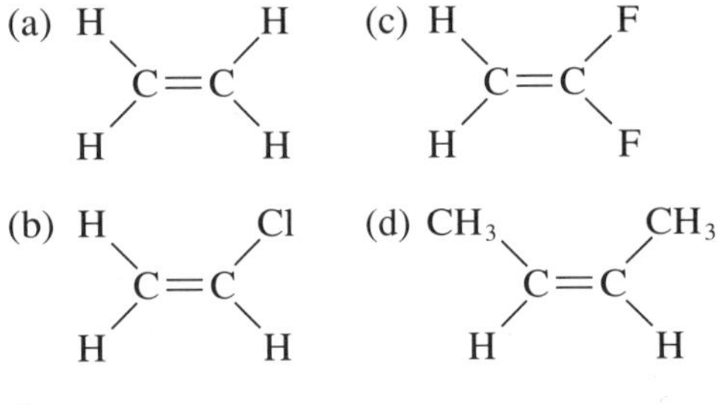

(a)

(b)

(c)

(d)

Answers:

(c)

(d)

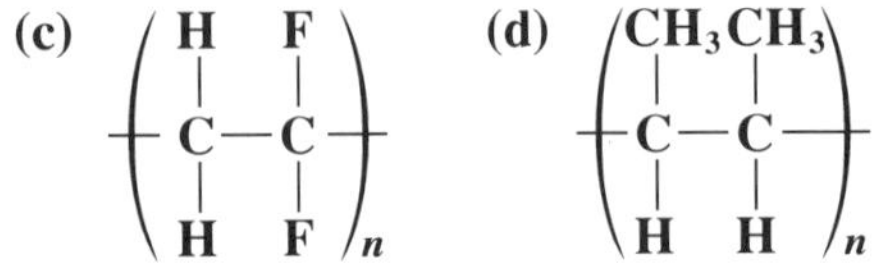

6. Distinguish between an addition polymer and a condensation polymer.

7. Illustrate the condensation reaction of nylon-66.

8. Define and give an example of a copolymer.

9. What type of polymer would form during the reaction of a diol and a dicarboxylic acid?

10. Describe the four types of synthetic polymers and give an example of each.

11. Distinguish between a thermoplastic and a thermosetting polymer.

12. (a) Explain, on the molecular level, the elasticity of rubber. (b) How does vulcanization harden rubber according to the model used in (a)?

13. Why does nylon dissolve rapidly in concentrated hydrochloric or sulfuric acid?

14. 1,6-Diaminohexane ($NH_2(CH_2)_6NH_2$) reacts with 1,10-decanedioic acid (sebacic acid, $COOH(CH_2)_8COOH$) to form a nylon. Write the structural formula and name for this nylon.

15. Define (a) carbohydrate, (b) monosaccharide.

16. How do the following sugars differ? Give an example of each.
a) monosaccharides, dissacharides and polysaccharides
b) pentoses and hexoses

17. Using structural formulas, write an equation to show the formation of sucrose from glucose and fructose.

18. Using structural formulas, show that a sim-

ple sugar can be a polyhydroxy aldehyde or a polyhydroxy ketone.

19. What are the differences between starch and cellulose? Explain why the human body can hydrolyze starch but not cellulose.

20. Explain the rigidity and rodlike structure of cellulose in terms of bonding.

21. How is the hydrolysis of polysaccharides accomplished (a) in the laboratory? (b) in organisms?

22. Explain why disaccharides and polysaccharides must be hydrolyzed before the body can use them.

23. Why can an amino acid not exist in a non-ionized form at any pH?

24. What are the structural features of amino acids that make them soluble in polar solvents such as water?

25. Label the peptide bond in the following dipeptide:

$$H_2N-CH_2-\overset{\overset{\displaystyle O}{\|}}{C}-NH-\underset{\underset{\displaystyle CH_2SH}{|}}{CH}-COOH$$

26. Why is it necessary for humans to eat protein?

27. Define the terms *primary* and *secondary structure* of proteins.

28. Define fibrous and globular proteins and give an example of each.

29. How is the structure of nylon related to that of proteins?

30. (a) What is meant by the *denaturation* of a protein? (b) Name three denaturation agents.

31. Describe the structure of DNA. What role does hydrogen bonding play in the structure of DNA?

32. What are the structural units of nucleic acids?

33. How is genetic information contained in DNA?

The Ontario Hydro Nuclear Generating Site at Pickering, Ontario. The site consists of two stations—each station is powered by four CANDU reactors. Pickering is among the world's largest nuclear generating sites.

ENERGY ASSOCIATED WITH CHEMICAL AND NUCLEAR REACTIONS

O f all the factors responsible for our economic well-being, the way we use energy is one of the most important. Nations that are able to control and convert available energy into useful forms have the highest standard of living and wield the greatest influence in the world today.

Energy is defined as the ability to do work. It has only been during the past two centuries that a large part of our work has been performed by machines instead of muscles. One of the first machines to convert heat energy into motion was the steam engine. Since then, scientists have constantly been seeking new energy sources and developing new ways to change available energy into forms that can be made to do practical work.

The three primary sources of available energy are solar energy, chemical energy and nuclear energy. Solar energy has been used for centuries and can now heat houses and water and generate electricity. In the future, satellites may use giant solar panels to generate electricity in space and beam it down to earth.

Chemical energy in matter is one of our primary sources of energy. There are countless examples of the conversion of chemical potential energy into heat or electric energy: In batteries, the chemical energy of the reactants is converted into useful electric

ALBERT EINSTEIN
1879–1955
To most people, the name Einstein is synonymous with genius. He is probably the most famous scientist of the twentieth century. Born in Ulm, Germany, Einstein was primarily a theoretician, not an experimenter.

Einstein is best known for his *theory of relativity*, which he developed in 1905 while working in a patent office in Berne, Switzerland. This theory related time, space, mass and motion and played a major role in revolutionizing physics. His famous equation, $E = mc^2$, was part of the theory of relativity. This equation suggests that matter is a form of energy. Einstein received the Nobel Prize in 1921 for his photoelectric law.

While on a lecture tour in 1933, Einstein was stripped of his property, position and citizenship in Nazi Germany. He accepted a position as professor of mathematics at The Institute for Advanced Studies at Princeton University the same year.

In addition to science, Einstein enjoyed playing the violin and was interested in world peace. His famous 1939 letter to Franklin Roosevelt warned of the possible preparation of nuclear weapons by Nazi Germany.

Einstein had little interest in money. He once used a pay cheque as a book mark, and then lost the book.

Einstein's last scientific work was a paper on the unified field theory, which was an attempt to relate gravity and magnetism.

energy. Chemical energy stored in foods and released through biochemical processes maintains proper body temperature, promotes growth and enables people to do work. In power plants, the chemical energy of fossil fuels is released by burning.

Nuclear reactions are now being used as sources of heat energy throughout the world and are also able to liberate energy in the form of radioactive rays. The radioisotopes that emit these rays are among the most important tools used by scientists.

In this chapter, we will investigate the energy absorbed and liberated during chemical reactions. We will consider the origin, measurement and calculation of this energy, as well as its theoretical and practical significance. In the final part of the chapter, we will look at the structure and properties of nuclei and the different kinds of nuclear reactions.

WHAT IS ENERGY?

We are familiar with many forms of energy: heat, light, electric energy and nuclear energy, for example. Energy is usually defined as the ability to do work. For example, if you push a box across a floor, you use energy. Work is being done as a force (your muscles) moves the box some distance. Thus, work is performed when a force moves an object over a distance.

The *law of conservation of energy*, or the *first law of thermodynamics*, states that energy cannot be created or destroyed. The law requires that the heat lost by a system be equal to that gained by the surroundings. However, energy can be converted into mass. The *law of conservation of mass-energy* unifies the law of conservation of mass and the law of conservation of energy by stating that *mass and energy can be transformed into each other but that mass-energy can neither be created nor destroyed*.

Albert Einstein visualized mass as concentrated energy, and energy as deconcentrated mass. He related mass and energy in his famous mass-energy equation:

$$E = mc^2$$

where E is the amount of energy in joules, m is the mass in kilograms and c is the speed of light (3.0×10^8 m/s). Since c^2 is 9.0×10^{16} m^2/s^2, this means that a very small mass is equivalent to a large amount of energy.

Einstein's equation applies to both chemical and nuclear reactions. However, for chemical reactions, the decrease in mass is infinitesimal; therefore, the energy produced is negligible compared with the amount of energy evolved during a nuclear reaction. For all chemical reactions, we use the laws of conservation of mass and energy separately. In a nuclear reaction, a small but measurable mass is converted into an enormous amount of energy.

There are two basic forms of energy: kinetic energy and potential energy. ***Kinetic energy*** (E_k) is the energy of motion. Experiments show that the kinetic energy possessed by a moving particle depends on the mass of the particle and its velocity. The quantitative relationship is

$$E_k = \tfrac{1}{2} mv^2$$

Potential energy (E_p) is the stored energy that matter possesses because of its position, condition, composition or electric charge. In an exothermic chemical reaction in which heat is liberated, there is more energy stored in the reactant than in the product. This type of potential energy is known as *chemical energy*.

ORIGIN OF CHEMICAL ENERGY

The chemical energy stored in matter and released during chemical reactions is one of our primary sources of energy. In general, all chemical reactions either liberate or absorb energy. Let us first investigate the source of the energy liberated or absorbed during a chemical reaction.

The origin of chemical energy lies in the position and motion of atoms, molecules and subatomic particles. The total energy possessed by a molecule is the sum of all the forms of potential and kinetic energy associated with it. We will now consider the kinetic and potential energy associated with a molecule of hydrogen chloride (HCl).

8-1

Kinetic Energy of a Molecule

The kinetic energy of a molecule results from the vibrational energy of the atoms in the molecule and from the translational and rotational motion of the molecule itself.

Vibrational, translational and rotational energy all contribute to the kinetic energy of liquid and gaseous substances. In general, the molecular kinetic energy of solids is associated with the vibrational motion of the molecule. For example, the kinetic energy of water molecules in an ice crystal is the result of the vibrational motion about fixed points in the crystal, as well as the vibrations of the hydrogen and oxygen atoms within each water molecule.

Vibrational energy (E_v) is one form of kinetic energy associated with a molecule and is the energy produced by the vibration of the atoms with respect to each other. For example, in an HCl mole-

$1 \text{ J} = 1 \text{ N·m} = 1 \text{ kg·m}^2/\text{s}^2$

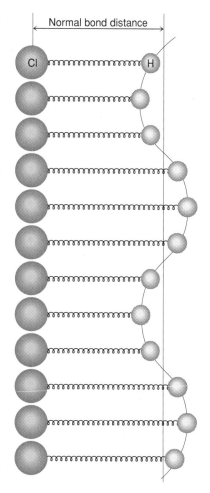

Figure 8-1
The vibrational motion of an HCl molecule involves alternately increasing and decreasing the bond distance between the hydrogen and chlorine nuclei.

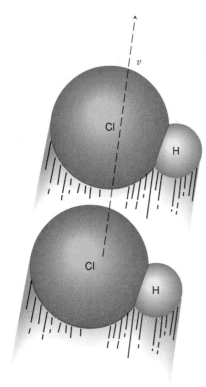

Figure 8-2
The translational energy of an HCl molecule is associated with the linear motion of the molecule through space. In this type of motion, the centre of gravity of the molecule moves.

cule, the bond between the hydrogen atom and the chlorine atom is analogous to a spring: attractive forces pull the two atoms together until repulsive forces cause them to spring away from each other. This alternating attraction and repulsion results in a vibrational motion of the molecule (Fig. 8-1 on page 313). As the vibrational energy increases, the distance through which the atoms vibrate increases, and the amplitude of the vibration increases. When the energy reaches a certain value, the amplitude of vibration becomes so great that the attractive forces between the atoms are no longer effective, and the atoms fly apart. As with other types of energy, vibrational energy is quantized. Vibrational quanta have a frequency that falls in the infrared region of the electromagnetic spectrum.

Translational energy (E_t) is a type of kinetic energy associated with gas molecules as they move linearly from one point to another. The translational energy of a molecule is expressed as $E_t = \frac{1}{2}mv^2$. At 0 K, the translational motion of a molecule becomes zero, and thus the translational energy is also zero at this temperature. The translational motion of an HCl molecule is shown in Fig. 8-2.

A molecule has ***rotational energy*** (E_r) if it is rotating about an axis through its centre of mass (Fig. 8-3). Both theory and experiment show that rotational energy is quantized; that is, there are only certain allowed rotational energy levels. Rotational quanta have a frequency that falls in the microwave region of the electromagnetic spectrum.

Within the hydrogen and chloride atoms that make up the HCl molecule, there are electrons moving about the atomic nuclei. The electron motion about the nuclei is a form of kinetic energy referred to as ***electron energy*** (E_e). Although vibrational, translational and rotational motion make up the kinetic energy of substances, calculations show that, at ordinary temperatures, the kinetic energy of molecules contributes little to the energy of a substance. In chemistry, we are mainly concerned with the electron energy (E_e) involved in the making and breaking of chemical bonds.

8-2
Potential Energy of a Molecule

The potential energy of a molecule is the energy stored in the bonds between the atoms and in the nuclear forces that hold the nucleus together.

The potential energy of a molecule results from the interaction between electrons and nuclei both within and between atoms. This interaction gives rise to chemical bonds. The energy associated

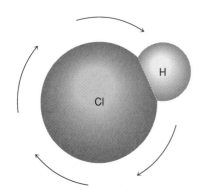

Figure 8-3
Rotational motion of an HCl molecule.

with this interaction between positive and negative charges is called ***bond energy*** (E_b).

We can also represent bond energy as H_{be}.

The energy changes that occur during a chemical reaction are, to a large extent, the result of the potential energy changes that occur during the breaking of chemical bonds in the reactants and the formation of new bonds in the products. The energy absorbed or emitted in the ultraviolet and visible range of the electromagnetic spectrum corresponds to electron transitions between energy levels. Thus, the wavelengths of the energy emitted or absorbed may be used to help identify the atoms that compose the molecule.

The category of ***miscellaneous energy*** (E_m) includes several types of energy that contribute to the total molecular energy. For example, nuclear energy is related to the forces that hold the nucleus together and is important when considering nuclear reactions. Furthermore, whenever externally applied electric or gravitational fields interact with a molecular system, additional energy effects arise and must be taken into account. The molecular energies discussed above are determined spectroscopically.

The total internal energy of a molecule is the sum of all of the molecular energies, both kinetic and potential:

$$\text{Total energy } (E) = E_v + E_t + E_r + E_e + E_b + E_m$$

It would be difficult to determine the total energy of a molecule or of a macroscopic system containing countless molecules. However, the energy that we measure experimentally is that associated with a system changing from an initial to a final state. In other words, we are interested in energy changes rather than in absolute total energy content. We are primarily concerned with energy in the form of heat that is absorbed or liberated by a reaction taking place in an open container at constant pressure. This quantity of energy is known as the *change in enthalpy* (heat content) of the chemical system and is symbolized by ΔH.

CHANGES IN ENTHALPY

In general, all reactions either liberate or absorb heat (Fig. 8-4). This heat is called the enthalpy (heat) of reaction and is defined as the difference between the enthalpy of products and the enthalpy of reactants. Thus,

$$\Delta H = H_{\text{products}} - H_{\text{reactants}}$$

The enthalpy of a reaction depends on whether the reaction is exothermic or endothermic.

Figure 8-4
An instant cold pack helps prevent swelling from athletic injuries and uses an endothermic reaction to lower the temperature of the pack.

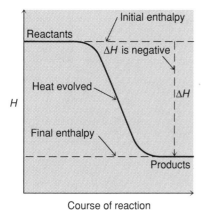

Figure 8-5
The enthalpy of a system decreases during an exothermic reaction. This indicates that the reactants have a greater enthalpy than the products. For all exothermic reactions, energy is liberated and Δ*H* is negative.

Exothermic Reactions

An exothermic reaction liberates energy in the form of heat and light to the surroundings.

There are many examples of exothermic processes in our everyday lives. When someone strikes a match, lights a Bunsen burner or burns fuel to heat a home, an exothermic reaction is taking place. The prefix *exo-* is from the Greek word for "outside," and *thermic* is from the Greek word for "heat." Consider the example of lighting a match. Before ignition, the match is at room temperature and has a certain amount of potential chemical energy. As it burns, the chemical energy is converted to heat and light. If the match is extinguished and allowed to return to room temperature, its potential energy is less than it was initially. In other words, the enthalpy of the reactants is greater than the enthalpy of the products (Fig. 8-5). Since

$$\Delta H = H_p - H_r$$

and the value of H_p is smaller than H_r for all exothermic reactions, the change in enthalpy is negative.

THE HALIFAX HARBOUR FIRE

O n December 6, 1917, one of the greatest non-nuclear explosions of this century occurred in the city of Halifax, Nova Scotia. The north end of the city was devastated and almost 2000 people were killed. The cause: human error and negligence.

It was at the height of World War I. Halifax, which was a major port at that time, was very busy as ships from around the world docked in its harbour, loading and unloading military materials. A French munitions carrier, the *Mont Blanc*, had pulled into harbour late in November. On board were stored three of the most powerful explosive materials developed at that time: trinitrotoluene (TNT), picric acid and guncotton. TNT was the newest and safest of these explosives. Picric acid was a conventional explosive used in shells; when in contact with most metals, it formed salts that were even more explosive. Guncotton, an explosive made from cotton fibres soaked in nitric acid and sulfuric acid, was used for making fuses. These three materials would have constituted the full load of the *Mont Blanc* except that steel drums of benzene had been added to its cargo and tied down to the decks at the last minute. Benzene is an extremely flammable liquid used to manufacture explosives.

In the early morning of December 6, the Belgian relief vessel *Imo* collided with the *Mont Blanc* in the narrowest part of Halifax harbour. Although neither vessel was seriously damaged, a few drums of benzene on the *Mont Blanc* were shaken loose and broke apart. Sparks generated by the collision ignited the benzene, which was now beginning to drip through the floor boards down into the lower decks. The captain and crew abandoned the burning ship, leaving it to float toward the city. The Halifax fire department was summoned and sent its new pumper to the scene.

Meanwhile, sailors from a nearby ship began to board the *Mont Blanc* to fight the fire, unaware of the explosive cargo below. They never stood a chance. At 9:06 AM, the *Mont Blanc* exploded and vanished in a column of smoke. The only recognizable parts of the ship ever found were the half-melted and twisted cannon and the shank of an anchor.

Much of Halifax's north end was destroyed; over two square kilometres of buildings were levelled, either from the blast itself or from the tidal wave caused by the explosion. The explosion shattered windows in Truro, 100 km away, and church bells began ringing for hundreds of kilometres around. Immediately after the shock wave, a rush of air came blasting back, causing more

buildings to collapse. Raging fires, ignited when buildings collapsed onto stoves and furnaces, began to consume any buildings that were still standing. As the fire moved toward the main military-supply depot, the city's surviving inhabitants were evacuated. Large pieces of debris—rocks, red-hot metallic parts of ships and pieces of trains and buildings—began raining down on the city. In total, 16 000 buildings were destroyed, 1600 people were killed and 9000 injured.

The damage came to $35 million. Help was sent from around the world, most notably from the state of Massachusetts, which sent a complete relief expedition of food, clothing, doctors and nurses. The Massachusetts Relief Commission continued its relief programs long after the disaster occurred. Relief funds were also raised across Canada and around the world. More than $30 million was administered by the Halifax Relief Commission between 1918 and 1976.

Today, Halifax is one of Canada's leading commercial and industrial centres. December 6, 1917 is a date that has burned itself into the city's history. The Halifax harbour fire was the result of human error and serves as a reminder of the potentially destructive energy that can result when certain chemicals are mixed together and the respect and caution with which they must be handled.

8-4

Endothermic Reactions

Endothermic reactions require a constant supply of energy from the surroundings in order for the reaction to occur.

The prefix *endo-* is from the Greek word for "within." Let us examine a simple endothermic reaction: the change from ice to water. An ice cube at room temperature will absorb energy from its surroundings. The water particles in the solid begin to move more rapidly, the bonds between the individual water molecules in the crystal lattice begin to break and the ice begins to melt. When ice melts at 0°C it forms water (also at 0°C), which has a greater enthalpy than the ice. The change in enthalpy (ΔH) is calculated as follows:

$$\Delta H = H_p - H_r$$

Because heat is absorbed, the enthalpy of the products is greater than the enthalpy of the reactants (Fig. 8-6) and the enthalpy of the reaction is positive. This is true for all endothermic reactions.

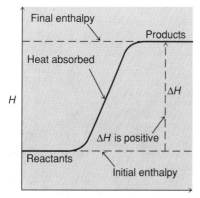

Course of reaction

Figure 8-6
The enthalpy of a system increases when an endothermic reaction takes place. This indicates that the products have a greater enthalpy than the reactants. For all endothermic reactions, energy is absorbed and ΔH is positive.

The thermal decomposition of bluestone ($CuSO_4 \cdot 5H_2O$), a blue crystalline solid, is another example of an endothermic reaction. A ***thermal decomposition*** is a reaction in which a substance is broken down into simpler substances by the application of heat. If the application of heat is stopped, the reaction ceases. The reaction is

$$heat + CuSO_4 \cdot 5H_2O \longrightarrow CuSO_4 + 5H_2O$$

The product of this reaction is anhydrous copper sulfate ($CuSO_4$), a white or grey powder. If water is added to the $CuSO_4$, the white powder turns blue and heat is produced:

$$CuSO_4 + 5H_2O \longrightarrow CuSO_4 \cdot 5H_2O + heat$$

This chemical process illustrates an important feature of enthalpy change in chemical processes: *when the forward reaction is endothermic, the reverse reaction is exothermic, and vice versa*. This is in agreement with the law of conservation of energy.

FOLLOW-UP PROBLEM

Identify each of the following processes as exothermic or endothermic:

a) The combustion of ethyne (acetylene) in an oxyacetylene torch.

b) $Ag_2O(s) \xrightarrow{\text{heat}} 2Ag(s) + \frac{1}{2}O_2(g)$

c) As solid $NaNO_3$ dissolves in water at 25°C, the temperature changes to 22°C.

d) When calcium is added to water at 22°C, the temperature slowly changes to 26°C.

e) $Mg(s) + \frac{1}{2}O_2(g) \longrightarrow MgO(s)$ + bright light

f) $2H_2(g) + O_2(g) \longrightarrow 2H_2O(l)$ $\quad \Delta H = -571.0$ kJ

g) $N_2(g) + O_2(g) \longrightarrow 2NO(g)$ $\quad \Delta H = 180.8$ kJ

Answers: a, d, e and f are exothermic.

8-5

Specific Heat

The specific heat capacity of a substance is the amount of energy required to raise the temperature of one gram of the substance by one kelvin. Specific heat capacities can be used to calculate the amount of energy absorbed or released by a chemical reaction.

Specific heat capacity is often called *specific heat* and is given the symbol c. The ***specific heat capacity*** is defined as the amount of energy required to raise the temperature of an object by one kelvin. For example, 4.18 J of energy is required to raise the temperature of 1.00 g of water 1.0°C or 1.0 K. This quantity of heat is specific to water and is referred to as the *specific heat of water*. Each substance has its own specific heat, measured in J/g·K (Table 8-1). Although specific heats vary with temperature and pressure, the amount is generally insignificant. Specific heat is calculated as follows:

$$\text{Specific heat} = \frac{\text{heat lost or gained}}{(\text{mass})(\text{temperature change})}$$

Molar heat capacity (C) is the amount of energy required to raise one mole of the substance by one kelvin and is measured in J/mol·K. Molar heat capacity is calculated as follows:

$$\text{Molar heat capacity} = (\text{specific heat})(\text{molar mass})$$
$$C = (c)(m)$$

For example, it has been experimentally found that 221.4 J of energy is needed to heat 30 g of ethanol from 15°C to 18°C. Thus,

$$\text{Specific heat of ethanol} = \frac{221.4\ J}{(30\ g)(3°C)}$$
$$= 2.46\ J/g·°C$$

Because one degree Celsius is equal to one kelvin, the specific heat of ethanol can be rewritten as 2.46 J/g·K.

The amount of heat gained or lost *(Q)* by a substance in some processes can be easily calculated with the following expression:

$$\text{Heat lost or gained} = (\text{specific heat})(\text{mass})(\Delta\ \text{temperature})$$
$$Q = (c)(m)(\Delta T)$$

The temperature change (ΔT) can also be calculated by

$$\Delta T = \text{final temperature} - \text{initial temperature}$$

For example, let us calculate the amount of energy lost by a pot of tea as it cools from 100°C to 45°C. If we assume that the pot contains 1 L of water and has a mass of 1 kg, and that the specific heat of tea is the same as water, we can calculate the temperature change as

$$\Delta T = 45°C - 100°C$$
$$= -55°C$$

Thus, the heat change can be calculated by

$$Q = (c)(m)(\Delta T)$$
$$= (4.18\ J/g·K)(1000\ g)(-55°C)$$
$$= -229.9\ kJ$$

TABLE 8-1
SPECIFIC HEAT CAPACITIES *(c)*

Substance	c (J/g·K)
copper	0.39
iron	0.45
steel	0.45
glass	0.84
aluminum	0.90
wood	1.76
water*(s)*	2.06
ethylene glycol	2.42
ethanol	2.46
water*(l)*	4.18
ammonia	4.70

Heat quantity *(Q)* is measured in J or kJ.

Note that the negative sign indicates that heat has been lost by the tea to its surroundings. Therefore, this is an exothermic reaction. If there had been an increase in the temperature from 45°C to 100°C, the heat change would have had a positive sign, indicating that the reaction was endothermic.

Figure 8-7
(a) A simple laboratory calorimeter for measuring heats of reaction (constant pressure). (b) A bomb (constant volume) calorimeter is used to measure the energy liberated or absorbed during a chemical reaction. The energy change can be measured by noting the temperature changes in a measured amount of water surrounding the reaction chamber. Note that in (a), there must be an opening in the cover so that the reaction chamber is open to the atmosphere.

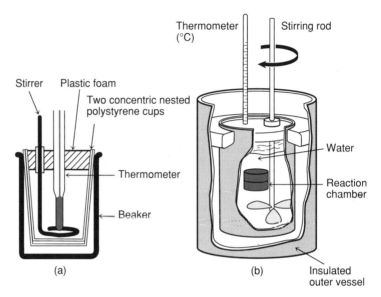

Quantitatively, the process of determining heat changes associated with chemical reactions is known as *calorimetry*. It is possible to experimentally determine how much heat is liberated during a reaction by allowing the reaction to take place in a *calorimeter* (Fig. 8-7), a well-insulated vessel containing a liquid that absorbs the heat evolved by the reaction. The reaction is carried out in the inner reaction vessel. Heat evolved by the reaction is transferred to the weighed amount of water in the insulated outer vessel. The original and final temperatures of the water are read on the thermometer. Of course, any heat transferred to the calorimeter must be taken into account.

EXAMPLE 8-1
Calculating the Molar Heat Capacity of a Compound
A student burns a 0.452 g sample of naphthalene ($C_{10}H_8$) in a bomb calorimeter. The combustion reaction causes a temperature increase of 2.961°C in the calorimeter. If the heat capacity of the calorimeter is 6.11×10^4 kJ/°C, calculate the enthalpy change per mole of naphthalene.

SOLUTION

1. Calculate the heat released by the combustion of the naphthalene:

$$\text{Heat released} = (\text{heat capacity})(\text{temperature change})$$
$$= (6.11 \times 10^4 \text{ kJ/}°\text{C})(2.961°\text{C})$$
$$= 1.81 \times 10^5 \text{ kJ}$$

2. Calculate the number of moles of naphthalene in the sample:

$$\text{Molar mass} = 128 \text{ g/mol}$$
$$\text{Number of moles} = \frac{0.452 \text{ g}}{128 \text{ g/mol}}$$
$$= 3.53 \times 10^{-3} \text{ mol}$$

3. Calculate the heat released per mole of naphthalene:

$$\text{Heat released} = \frac{1.81 \times 10^5 \text{ kJ}}{3.53 \times 10^{-3} \text{ mol}}$$
$$= 5.13 \times 10^7 \text{ kJ/mol}$$

Thus, the molar heat capacity of naphthalene is 5.13×10^7 kJ/mol.

FOLLOW-UP PROBLEMS

1. We wish to determine how much heat paraffin gives off on burning. We use a candle flame to heat some water in a calorimeter. The following data is obtained:

Mass of water in calorimeter	350 g
Initial mass of candle	150 g
Final mass of candle	112 g
Initial temperature of water	15°C
Final temperature of water	23°C

Calculate (a) the temperature rise, (b) the heat absorbed by the water in the calorimeter, (c) the mass of paraffin burned and (d) the approximate value of the heat of combustion of paraffin in J/g. Ignore the energy absorbed by the calorimeter.

2. A 0.2344 g sample of benzoic acid (C_6H_5COOH) is completely burned in a bomb calorimeter with a heat capacity of 2.674 kJ/°C. The temperature in the calorimeter rises from 15.42°C to 17.74°C. Calculate the amount of heat released by one mole of benzoic acid.

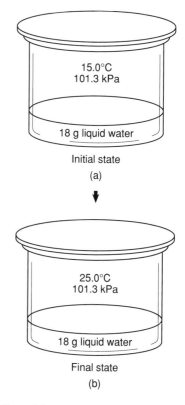

Figure 8-8
The two systems above are in different thermodynamic states. The final state (b) is fixed by specifying the following properties: chemical composition (H_2O), state of aggregation (liquid), quantity (18 g), temperature (25°C) and pressure (101.3 kPa).

Answers:
1. (a) 8.0°C, (b) 11.70 kJ, (c) 38 g, (d) 308 J/g
2. 3229 kJ/mol

Figure 8-9
In the systems represented here, assume there is no heat transferred between the system and its surroundings. Processes carried out under these conditions are called *adiabatic processes*. The same change in state (energy change) is observed in each system. In (a), vigorous stirring increases the energy content of the water. In (b), electric work, represented by a current flowing through a resistance, is used. In (c), energy is transferred by means of the work associated with the compression of a gas. In (d), the work done when two metal blocks are rubbed together is converted into energy. In (e), energy is transferred from the hot metal block by heat "flow" from the region of high temperature (the block) to one of lower temperature (the water). The change in state is independent of the method used to bring it about.

8-6

State Properties and Changes in State Properties

The value of the enthalpy of a system depends on the state of that system. Changes in state properties are independent of the path taken from the initial to the final state.

Enthalpy *(H)* is an example of a state property. This means that its value is determined by the state of the system. The state of a system is fixed when the temperature, pressure, number of moles, composition and other properties of the system are specified. Because of its higher temperature, the energy of the system in Fig. 8-8(b) on page 321 has a definite value that is greater than that of the system in Fig. 8-8(a). The value of the energy of the system in the final state does not depend on the method or the path by which the energy was transferred. The difference in energy between the two states can be the result of adding heat to the system, doing mechanical work such as vigorously stirring the water, or by using a combination of these or other methods (Fig. 8-9).

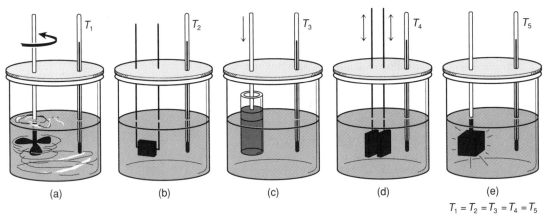

$T_1 = T_2 = T_3 = T_4 = T_5$

Changes in state properties are always independent of the path taken to change a system from some initial state to some final state (Fig. 8-10). This means that the net energy change must be the same, regardless of the path. If it were not, it would be possible to put one amount of energy into a system to reach a higher energy state and then return to the initial state by a different path, thus obtaining more energy than was put into the system. This would mean that energy could be created—a phenomenon that has never

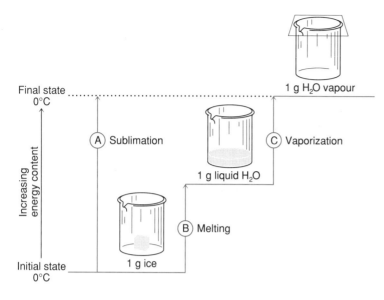

Figure 8-10
The conversion of ice at 0°C into satu-rated water vapour at 0°C can be accomplished by melting the ice and then vaporizing the water or by sub-liming the ice. The energy absorbed from the surroundings along path A is equal to the sum of the energies absorbed along paths B and C.

been observed and that would contradict the law of conservation of energy.

The quantity of heat absorbed or liberated during a reaction varies with the temperature. Scientists have, therefore, adopted 25°C and 101.3 kPa as *standard-state conditions* for reporting heat data. To calculate the enthalpy of a reaction, it is necessary to write an equation for the reaction, similar to that used to calculate quantities of products formed. The standard enthalpy change, designated by $\Delta H°$, for a given reaction is usually expressed in kilojoules and depends on how the equation is written. The standard enthalpy change of a reaction is also called the *heat of reaction*, and may be designated by $\Delta H_r°$. For example, we can write the equation for the reaction of hydrogen with oxygen in two ways:

$$H_2(g) + \tfrac{1}{2}O_2(g) \longrightarrow H_2O(g) \qquad \Delta H_r° = -242.0 \text{ kJ/mol} \qquad [8\text{-}1]$$
$$2H_2(g) + O_2(g) \longrightarrow 2H_2O(g) \qquad \Delta H_r° = -484.0 \text{ kJ} \qquad [8\text{-}2]$$

Experimentally, the change in enthalpy for the reaction ($\Delta H_r°$) is found to be −242.0 kJ/mol of $H_2O(g)$. The coefficients in Equation 8-2 are twice those in Equation 8-1 and represent the combustion of 2 mol of H_2. Therefore, the enthalpy change represented by Equation 8-2 is −484.0 kJ. Note that it is assumed that the initial and final states are measured at 25°C and 101.3 kPa, although the reaction occurs at a higher temperature.

The physical state of each participant is indicated in Equations 8-1 and 8-2. Because energy is involved in a phase change, *the energy related to a given reaction depends on the physical state of the participating reagents*. For example, when hydrogen gas and

Standard-State Conditions
In 1982, IUPAC adopted new values for standard-state conditions. Standard pressure is now considered to be 100.0 kPa (1 bar) instead of 101.325 kPa. Standard temperature is considered to be 298.15 K (25°C) for all standard values, including gas measurements, which formerly used 273.15 K (0°C) as standard temperature.

oxygen gas react and form one mole of liquid water, 285.5 kJ is liberated. In contrast, when hydrogen gas and oxygen gas react and form one mole of water vapour, only 242.0 kJ is liberated. The difference is the heat required to convert one mole of water from the liquid to the vapour phase. Because 43.5 kJ of energy is used to change the liquid water to vapour, only 242.0 kJ (285.5 kJ − 43.5 kJ) is liberated when the hydrogen and oxygen react and form water vapour directly.

The preceding example implies that two or more separate chemical equations and their heats of reaction can be manipulated like algebraic equations. This observation forms the basis for *Hess's law*.

FOLLOW-UP PROBLEM

How much heat is liberated when 40.0 g of $H_2(g)$ reacts with excess oxygen(g) to form water vapour?

Answer: 4.84×10^3 kJ/mol

8-7

Hess's Law

Chemical equations and their heats of reaction can be added together and manipulated algebraically. In this way, it is possible to determine heats of reaction for reactions that are difficult to obtain experimentally.

According to the law of conservation of energy, the total energy of the universe is constant and, thus, energy cannot be created or destroyed. Application of this law to the calculation of enthalpies (heats) of reactions means that the difference between the total enthalpy of specific reactants and specific products is constant, regardless of the path by which the products are obtained from the reactants. For example, no matter how many steps are involved, the enthalpy difference is constant, as long as the initial and final states of the reaction system are fixed.

Hess's law of heat summation, or *the principle of additivity of reaction heats*, is based on the first law of thermodynamics and states that *when a reaction can be expressed as the algebraic sum of two or more reactions, the heat of reaction is the algebraic sum of the heats of these reactions.*

Hess's law enables us to determine heats of reaction that cannot be easily determined by experiment. This can be accomplished by combining experimentally determined heats of reaction for related reactions. For example, it is relatively simple to measure the heats of reaction when one mole of carbon reacts with oxygen to form carbon dioxide, or when one mole of carbon monoxide reacts with oxygen to form carbon dioxide. The equations and heats of reaction are

$$C(s) + O_2(g) \longrightarrow CO_2(g) \qquad \Delta H^\circ_r = -393.5 \text{ kJ} \quad [8\text{-}3]$$
$$CO(g) + \tfrac{1}{2}O_2(g) \longrightarrow CO_2(g) \qquad \Delta H^\circ_r = -283.5 \text{ kJ} \quad [8\text{-}4]$$

Although the heat of reaction for the reaction in which carbon and oxygen form carbon monoxide cannot be accurately determined by experiment, it can be calculated by combining Equations 8-3 and 8-4 in such a way as to yield the desired equation:

$$C(s) + \tfrac{1}{2}O_2(g) \longrightarrow CO(g)$$

Since $CO(g)$ in the desired equation must be on the right-hand side, it is necessary to reverse Equation 8-4. This means that the sign of ΔH°_r must be changed. The negative sign indicates that the formation of CO_2 from CO is exothermic; therefore, the reverse reaction (decomposition of CO_2) must be endothermic and have a positive ΔH°_r. Thus,

$$C(s) + O_2(g) \longrightarrow CO_2(g) \qquad \Delta H^\circ_r = -393.5 \text{ kJ}$$
$$CO_2(g) \longrightarrow \tfrac{1}{2}O_2(g) + CO(g) \qquad \Delta H^\circ_r = +283.5 \text{ kJ}$$

Addition yields

$$C(s) + \tfrac{1}{2}O_2(g) \longrightarrow CO(g) \qquad \Delta H^\circ_r = -110.0 \text{ kJ}$$

The relationships are shown schematically in Fig. 8-11. Note again that it is assumed that all reactants and products are changed to standard state for purposes of evaluating ΔH°_r values.

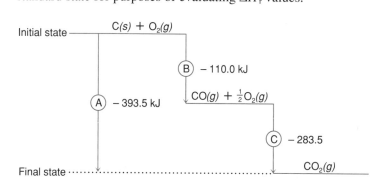

Figure 8-11
A change in the initial state of the system is accompanied by a definite change in its enthalpy, regardless of the pathway by which the change occurs. Thus, the sum of the enthalpy changes occurring along paths B and C equals the enthalpy change occurring along path A.

The following example also shows how chemical equations and ΔH°_r values can be manipulated algebraically. Our objective in this example is to combine the equations for the formation of one mole of gaseous water and one mole of liquid water to obtain an equation that represents the vaporization of one mole of liquid water. The equations are as follows:

$$H_2(g) + \tfrac{1}{2}O_2(g) \longrightarrow H_2O(g) \qquad \Delta H_r^\circ = -242.0 \text{ kJ} \qquad [8\text{-}5]$$
$$H_2(g) + \tfrac{1}{2}O_2(g) \longrightarrow H_2O(l) \qquad \Delta H_r^\circ = -285.5 \text{ kJ} \qquad [8\text{-}6]$$

Algebraically subtracting Equation 8-6 from Equation 8-5 yields

$$0 = H_2O(g) - H_2O(l) \qquad \Delta H_r^\circ = +43.5 \text{ kJ}$$

If we rearrange this equation to obtain a conventional expression for the reaction, we get

$$H_2O(l) \longrightarrow H_2O(g) \qquad \Delta H_r^\circ = +43.5 \text{ kJ}$$

This equation shows that 43.5 kJ is required to convert one mole of liquid water at 25°C into one mole of water vapour. This value agrees with the experimentally determined molar heat of vaporization for water at this temperature.

Rather than subtract one equation from another, it is more common practice to reverse one of the equations algebraically and then add them. This procedure prevents negative signs from appearing in the final equation. It must be remembered that when the equation for an exothermic reaction is reversed, the expression now represents an endothermic reaction. Therefore, the sign of ΔH_r° must be changed whenever the equation of a reaction is reversed. In the preceding example, reversing Equation 8-6,

$$H_2O(l) \longrightarrow H_2(g) + \tfrac{1}{2}O_2(g) \qquad \Delta H_r^\circ = +285.5 \text{ kJ}$$

and adding Equation 8-5,

$$H_2(g) + \tfrac{1}{2}O_2(g) \longrightarrow H_2O(g) \qquad \Delta H_r^\circ = -242.0 \text{ kJ}$$

yields

$$H_2O(l) + H_2(g) + \tfrac{1}{2}O_2(g) \longrightarrow H_2(g) + \tfrac{1}{2}O_2(g) + H_2O(g)$$
$$\Delta H_r^\circ = +43.5 \text{ kJ}$$

Simplification gives us the net equation for the vaporization of water:

$$H_2O(l) \longrightarrow H_2O(g) \qquad \Delta H_r^\circ = +43.5 \text{ kJ}$$

Figure 8-12
Energy diagram for the conversion of hydrogen gas and oxygen gas into liquid water by two different processes. The total heat evolved to the surroundings is the same for both pathways.

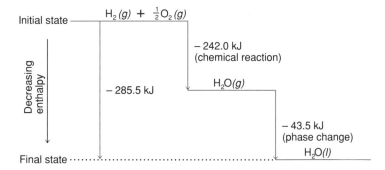

FOLLOW-UP PROBLEM

The standard heat of combustion of liquid ethanol (ethyl alcohol) is −1367 kJ/mol and that of ethanoic acid (acetic acid) is −874 kJ/mol. The equations are

$$C_2H_5OH(l) + 3O_2(g) \longrightarrow 2CO_2(g) + 3H_2O(l)$$
$$\Delta H_r^\circ = -1367 \text{ kJ}$$
$$CH_3COOH(l) + 2O_2(g) \longrightarrow 2CO_2(g) + 2H_2O(l)$$
$$\Delta H_r^\circ = -874 \text{ kJ}$$

What is the heat of reaction for the oxidation of one mole of ethyl alcohol to acetic acid?

$$C_2H_5OH(l) + O_2(g) \longrightarrow CH_3COOH(l) + H_2O(l)$$

Answer: $\Delta H_r^\circ = -493$ **kJ**

8-8
Standard Enthalpies of Formation

The molar enthalpy (heat) of formation of a compound is the enthalpy change that accompanies the formation of one mole of the compound directly from its elements or diatomic gases in the standard state.

Although many enthalpies of reaction have been measured experimentally and tabulated in handbooks, there are numerous reactions whose enthalpies have not been determined or are not readily available. A simple method of calculating reaction enthalpies from readily available data would be desirable. We will now develop the concept of enthalpy of formation of compounds and show how it can be used to calculate the enthalpy of a given reaction.

The molar enthalpy of formation for a compound is the enthalpy change that accompanies the formation of one mole of compound directly from its elements in their standard state. For example, the standard enthalpy of formation, designated as ΔH_f°, for calcium oxide is −635.5 kJ. This means that 635.5 kJ is liberated to the surroundings when one mole of calcium metal at standard state (25°C, 101.3 kPa) reacts with one-half mole of oxygen gas at standard state to form one mole of solid calcium oxide at standard state. The equation for the reaction is

$$Ca(s) + \tfrac{1}{2}O_2(g) \longrightarrow CaO(s) \qquad \Delta H_f^\circ = -635.5 \text{ kJ}$$

During the reaction, the product formed (CaO) is very hot and therefore not at standard state. The 635.5 kJ represents the heat that must be transferred from the system when one mole of calcium oxide is formed and cooled to 25°C, the temperature of the original reactants. In general, the enthalpy of formation for a compound containing n elements can be represented as

$$\Delta H_f^\circ = H_{compound}^\circ - [H_{element\ 1}^\circ + H_{element\ 2}^\circ + \cdots H_n^\circ] \quad [8\text{-}7]$$

At standard state, every substance has a characteristic enthalpy (heat content), designated as H°. Since it would be very difficult to determine absolute values of enthalpies, scientists use *relative enthalpies*. Relative enthalpies are based on the enthalpies of free elements that are arbitrarily assigned an enthalpy of zero at 25°C and 101.3 kPa pressure. This means that the bracketed term in Equation 8-7 is assigned a value of zero and that the relative enthalpy of a compound ($H_{compound}^\circ$), such as calcium oxide, is equal to its standard enthalpy of formation (ΔH_f°). Standard enthalpies of formation for a number of compounds are listed in Table 8-2.

A positive enthalpy of formation indicates that the enthalpy of the compound is greater than the sum of enthalpies of the elements from which it was formed. For example, when hydrogen gas and solid iodine react and form hydrogen iodide gas, 26.0 kJ of heat is absorbed from the surroundings. The equation for the reaction is

$$26.0\ \text{kJ} + \tfrac{1}{2}H_2(g) + \tfrac{1}{2}I_2(s) \longrightarrow HI(g)$$

Thus, the standard enthalpy of formation of one mole of $HI(g)$ is 26.0 kJ. This indicates that the enthalpy of one mole of $HI(g)$ at 25°C and 101.3 kPa is greater than the total enthalpy of one-half mole of $H_2(g)$ and one-half mole of I_2, also measured under these conditions. Thus, energy must be added to the reaction in order to form HI. The enthalpy of formation is positive because the chemical system gained energy in the formation of the compound. The positive value indicates a greater amount of energy is absorbed in breaking bonds than is liberated in the formation of bonds. The net result is an absorption of energy and an endothermic reaction.

A negative enthalpy of formation indicates that the enthalpy of the compound is less than the sum of the enthalpies of the elements from which it was formed. For example, the standard enthalpy of formation for $H_2O(g)$ is −242.0 kJ/mol (see Table 8-2). This indicates that the enthalpy of one mole of $H_2O(g)$ is less than the total enthalpy of one mole of H_2 plus one-half mole of O_2; thus, energy is liberated when H_2 and O_2 gas react to form $H_2O(g)$. The enthalpy of formation is negative because the chemical system loses energy in the formation of the compound. A negative value indicates that there are fewer and/or weaker bonds in the reactants than in the products. In other words, more energy is liberated when bonds are formed between H and O atoms than is absorbed when bonds are broken within the H_2 and O_2 molecules. The net result is the liberation of energy and an exothermic reaction.

If ΔH_f° is positive, the reaction is endothermic.

If ΔH_f° is negative, the reaction is exothermic.

The value of ΔH_f° depends on the relative numbers and strengths of the bonds in the reactant as compared with the molecules in the product. Now that we have related ΔH_f° qualitatively to bonding concepts, let us see how it can be used to calculate enthalpies of reactions.

TABLE 8-2
STANDARD ENTHALPIES OF FORMATION (25°C AND 101.3 kPa)

Compound	Formation Reaction	ΔH_f° (kJ/mol)
$Ag_2O(s)$	$2Ag(s) + \frac{1}{2}O_2(g) \longrightarrow Ag_2O(s)$	−31.1
$AgNO_3(s)$	$Ag(s) + \frac{1}{2}N_2(g) + \frac{3}{2}O_2(g) \longrightarrow AgNO_3(s)$	−124.0
$AgCl(s)$	$Ag(s) + \frac{1}{2}Cl_2(g) \longrightarrow AgCl(s)$	−127.1
$BaCO_3(s)$	$Ba(s) + C(s) + \frac{3}{2}O_2(g) \longrightarrow BaCO_3(s)$	−1219.0
$BaCrO_4(s)$	$Ba(s) + Cr(s) + 2O_2(g) \longrightarrow BaCrO_4(s)$	−1428.0
$Ba(OH)_2(s)$	$Ba(s) + O_2(g) + H_2(g) \longrightarrow Ba(OH)_2(s)$	−998.2
$Bi_2O_3(s)$	$2Bi(s) + \frac{3}{2}O_2(g) \longrightarrow Bi_2O_3(s)$	−576.0
$CCl_4(l)$	$C(s) + 2Cl_2(g) \longrightarrow CCl_4(l)$	−134.0
$CH_4(g)$	$C(s) + 2H_2(g) \longrightarrow CH_4(g)$	−74.9
$C_2H_2(g)$	$2C(s) + H_2(g) \longrightarrow C_2H_2(g)$	+227.0
$C_2H_4(g)$	$2C(s) + 2H_2(g) \longrightarrow C_2H_4(g)$	+51.9
$C_2H_6(g)$	$2C(s) + 3H_2(g) \longrightarrow C_2H_6(g)$	−84.5
$C_3H_8(g)$	$3C(s) + 4H_2(g) \longrightarrow C_3H_8(g)$	−104.0
$C_4H_{10}(g)$	$4C(s) + 5H_2(g) \longrightarrow C_4H_{10}(g)$	−126.0
$C_6H_6(g)$	$6C(s) + 3H_2(g) \longrightarrow C_6H_6(g)$	+82.8
$C_6H_6(l)$	$\longrightarrow C_6H_6(l)$	+49.0
$CH_3OH(l)$	$C(s) + 2H_2(g) + \frac{1}{2}O_2(g) \longrightarrow CH_3OH(l)$	−238.0
$C_2H_5OH(l)$	$2C(s) + 3H_2(g) + \frac{1}{2}O_2(g) \longrightarrow C_2H_5OH(l)$	−278.0
$CH_3COOH(l)$	$2C(s) + 2H_2(g) + O_2(g) \longrightarrow CH_3COOH(l)$	−487.0
$C_6H_5COOH(l)$	$6C(s) + 3H_2(g) + O_2(g) \longrightarrow C_6H_5COOH(l)$	−385.1
$CO(g)$	$C(s) + \frac{1}{2}O_2(g) \longrightarrow CO(g)$	−110.0
$CO_2(g)$	$C(s) + O_2(g) \longrightarrow CO_2(g)$	−393.5
$CaO(s)$	$Ca(s) + \frac{1}{2}O_2(g) \longrightarrow CaO(s)$	−635.5
$CaCO_3(s)$	$Ca(s) + C(s) + \frac{3}{2}O_2(g) \longrightarrow CaCO_3(s)$	−1207.0
$CuO(s)$	$Cu(s) + \frac{1}{2}O_2(g) \longrightarrow CuO(s)$	−155.0
$Cu_2O(s)$	$2Cu(s) + \frac{1}{2}O_2(g) \longrightarrow Cu_2O(s)$	−168.6
$CuSO_4(s)$	$Cu(s) + S(s) + 2O_2(g) \longrightarrow CuSO_4(s)$	−771.4
$Fe_2O_3(s)$	$2Fe(s) + \frac{3}{2}O_2(g) \longrightarrow Fe_2O_3(s)$	−822.2
$Fe_3O_4(s)$	$3Fe(s) + 2O_2(g) \longrightarrow Fe_3O_4(s)$	−1118.4
$HBr(g)$	$\frac{1}{2}H_2(g) + \frac{1}{2}Br_2(l) \longrightarrow HBr(l)$	−36.0
$HCl(g)$	$\frac{1}{2}H_2(g) + \frac{1}{2}Cl_2(g) \longrightarrow HCl(g)$	−92.5
$HF(g)$	$\frac{1}{2}H_2(g) + \frac{1}{2}F_2(g) \longrightarrow HF(g)$	−271.0
$HI(g)$	$\frac{1}{2}H_2(g) + \frac{1}{2}I_2(s) \longrightarrow HI(g)$	+26.0
$H_2O(g)$	$H_2(g) + \frac{1}{2}O_2(g) \longrightarrow H_2O(g)$	−242.0
$H_2O(l)$	$\longrightarrow H_2O(l)$	−285.5
$H_2S(g)$	$H_2(g) + S(s) \longrightarrow H_2S(g)$	−20.6
$H_2SO_4(aq)$	$H_2(g) + S(s) + 2O_2(g) \longrightarrow H_2SO_4(aq)$	−909.3
$HgO(s)$	$Hg(l) + \frac{1}{2}O_2(g) \longrightarrow HgO(s)$	−90.8
$KBr(s)$	$K(s) + \frac{1}{2}Br_2(l) \longrightarrow KBr(s)$	−393.8

TABLE 8-2 (continued)
STANDARD ENTHALPIES OF FORMATION (25°C AND 101.3 kPa)

Compound	Formation Reaction	ΔH_f° (kJ/mol)
$KCl(s)$	$K(s) + \frac{1}{2}Cl_2(g) \longrightarrow KCl(s)$	−436.8
$KF(s)$	$K(s) + \frac{1}{2}F_2(g) \longrightarrow KF(s)$	−567.3
$MgO(s)$	$Mg(s) + \frac{1}{2}O_2(g) \longrightarrow MgO(s)$	−601.7
$MgCO_3(s)$	$Mg(s) + C(s) + \frac{3}{2}O_2(g) \longrightarrow MgCO_3(s)$	−1113.0
$MgSO_4(s)$	$Mg(s) + S(s) + 2O_2(g) \longrightarrow MgSO_4(s)$	−1170.6
$NaBr(s)$	$Na(s) + \frac{1}{2}Br_2(l) \longrightarrow NaBr(s)$	−360.0
$NaCl(s)$	$Na(s) + \frac{1}{2}Cl_2(g) \longrightarrow NaCl(s)$	−413.0
$NaClO_3(s)$	$Na(s) + \frac{1}{2}Cl_2(g) + \frac{3}{2}O_2(g) \longrightarrow NaClO_3(s)$	−358.2
$NaF(s)$	$Na(s) + \frac{1}{2}F_2(g) \longrightarrow NaF(s)$	−571.0
$NaI(s)$	$Na(s) + \frac{1}{2}I_2(s) \longrightarrow NaI(s)$	−288.0
$Na_2SO_4(s)$	$2Na(s) + S(s) + 2O_2(g) \longrightarrow Na_2SO_4(s)$	−1384.5
$NH_3(g)$	$\frac{1}{2}N_2(g) + \frac{3}{2}H_2(g) \longrightarrow NH_3(g)$	−46.0
$NH_4Cl(s)$	$\frac{1}{2}N_2(g) + 2H_2(g) + \frac{1}{2}Cl_2(g) \longrightarrow NH_4Cl(s)$	−314.4
$NO(g)$	$\frac{1}{2}N_2(g) + \frac{1}{2}O_2(g) \longrightarrow NO(g)$	+90.4
$NO_2(g)$	$\frac{1}{2}N_2(g) + O_2(g) \longrightarrow NO_2(g)$	+34.0
$PCl_3(l)$	$P(s) + \frac{3}{2}Cl_2(g) \longrightarrow PCl_3(l)$	−319.5
$PCl_5(s)$	$P(s) + \frac{5}{2}Cl_2(g) \longrightarrow PCl_5(s)$	−443.5
$SiO_2(s)$	$Si(s) + O_2(g) \longrightarrow SiO_2(s)$	−910.0
$SnCl_4(l)$	$Sn(s) + 2Cl_2(g) \longrightarrow SnCl_4(l)$	−511.3
$SnO(s)$	$Sn(s) + \frac{1}{2}O_2(g) \longrightarrow SnO(s)$	−285.8
$SnO_2(s)$	$Sn(s) + O_2(g) \longrightarrow SnO_2(g)$	−580.7
$SO_2(g)$	$S(s) + O_2(g) \longrightarrow SO_2(g)$	−297.0
$SO_3(g)$	$S(s) + \frac{3}{2}O_2(g) \longrightarrow SO_3(g)$	−395.8

8-9

Calculating Enthalpies of Reaction

Using Hess's law and the heats-of-formation equations and values, we can calculate the enthalpies (heats) of reaction for various reactions.

We can calculate the heats of reaction for any reaction using Hess's law, along with the heats-of-formation data from Table 8-2. This technique is illustrated in Example 8-2.

EXAMPLE 8-2
Calculating the Heat of Reaction
Using Heats of Formation

Calculate the standard heat of reaction (ΔH_r°) when ammonia is oxidized according to the following equation:

$$4NH_3(g) + 7O_2(g) \longrightarrow 4NO_2(g) + 6H_2O(g)$$

SOLUTION

1. Write the heats-of-formation equations and ΔH_f° values from Table 8-2 for each of the compounds in the equation:

$$\tfrac{1}{2}N_2(g) + \tfrac{3}{2}H_2(g) \longrightarrow NH_3(g) \qquad \Delta H_f^\circ = -46.0 \text{ kJ}$$
$$\tfrac{1}{2}N_2(g) + O_2(g) \longrightarrow NO_2(g) \qquad \Delta H_f^\circ = +34.0 \text{ kJ}$$
$$H_2(g) + \tfrac{1}{2}O_2(g) \longrightarrow H_2O(g) \qquad \Delta H_f^\circ = -242.0 \text{ kJ}$$

Note that while $O_2(g)$ appears in the equation, a heat-of-formation reaction is not written for it since the heat of formation of diatomic gases (as well as elements) is assumed to be zero.

2. The reactants and products in the heats-of-formation equations (from Table 8-2) must correspond to the reactants and products in the original equation. If they do not, the equation and the signs of ΔH_f° must be reversed. For example, in the original equation, $NH_3(g)$ is a reactant, whereas in the heat-of-formation equation, $NH_3(g)$ is a product. Thus, the equation for $NH_3(g)$ must be reversed:

$$NH_3(g) \longrightarrow \tfrac{1}{2}N_2(g) + \tfrac{3}{2}H_2(g) \qquad \Delta H_r^\circ = +46.0 \text{ kJ}$$

Because $H_2O(g)$ and NO_2 are products in the original equation as well as in the heats-of-formation equations, they do not need to be reversed.

3. Multiply the heats-of-formation equations of the compounds by the coefficients in the original equation. For example, in the original equation, $NH_3(g)$ has a coefficient of four; thus, the heat-of-formation equation for NH_3 must also be multiplied by four. Similarly, the heat-of-formation equation for $H_2O(g)$ must be multiplied by six and the equation for $NO_2(g)$ by four. Perform these multiplications and add the three equations algebraically:

$$4NH_3(g) \longrightarrow 2N_2(g) + 6H_2(g) \qquad \Delta H_r^\circ = +184.0 \text{ kJ}$$
$$2N_2(g) + 4O_2(g) \longrightarrow 4NO_2(g) \qquad \Delta H_r^\circ = +136.0 \text{ kJ}$$
$$6H_2(g) + 3O_2(g) \longrightarrow 6H_2O(g) \qquad \Delta H_r^\circ = +136.0 \text{ kJ}$$

$$4NH_3(g) + 2N_2(g) + 6H_2(g) + 7O_2(g) \longrightarrow$$
$$2N_2(g) + 6H_2(g) + 4NO_2(g) + 6H_2O(g)$$
$$\Delta H_r^\circ = -1132.0 \text{ kJ}$$

Simplify the above reaction:

$$4NH_3(g) + 7O_2(g) \longrightarrow 4NO_2(g) + 6H_2O(g)$$
$$\Delta H_r^\circ = -1132.0 \text{ kJ}$$

Note that after the equations from Table 8-2 have been added, the final equation should match the original equation exactly.

FOLLOW-UP PROBLEMS

1. Calculate $\Delta H°$ for the reaction

$$CO_2(g) + H_2(g) \longrightarrow CO(g) + H_2O(g)$$

2. Calculate the standard molar heat of combustion of ethanol (ethyl alcohol):

$$C_2H_5OH(l) + 3O_2(g) \longrightarrow 2CO_2(g) + 3H_2O(l)$$

3. Calculate the standard molar heat of combustion of ethane $(C_2H_6)(g)$:

$$C_2H_6(g) + \tfrac{7}{2}O_2(g) \longrightarrow 2CO_2(g) + 3H_2O(l)$$

Answers:

1. $\Delta H° = 41.5$ kJ

2. $\Delta H_r° = -1.365 \times 10^3$ kJ/mol

3. $\Delta H_r° = -1.559 \times 10^3$ kJ/mol

A simpler method for calculating the enthalpies of reaction is based on the definition of $\Delta H_r°$: *The enthalpy change is equal to the difference between the total enthalpies of the reactants and products.* Because the enthalpies of formation are equal to the relative enthalpies of the compounds, we can say that at constant pressure, the enthalpy of a reaction $(\Delta H_r°)$ is equal to the sum of the heats of formation $(\Delta H_f°)$ of the products minus the sum of the heats of formation of the reactants. This is more simply referred to as the ***summation method***. For the general reaction,

$$a\text{A} + b\text{B} \longrightarrow c\text{C} + d\text{D}$$

this relationship can be expressed as

$$\Delta H_r° = \Sigma\Delta H_f° \text{ products} - \Sigma\Delta H_f° \text{ reactants} \qquad [8\text{-}8]$$

or as

$$\Delta H_r° = [c(\Delta H_f°)\text{C} + d(\Delta H_f°)\text{D}] - [a(\Delta H_f°)\text{A} + b(\Delta H_f°)\text{B}]$$

The use of the summation method is illustrated in the following examples.

EXAMPLE 8-3
Calculating the Heat of Reaction Using the Summation Method

Propane (C_3H_8) is a popular fuel commonly used in gas barbecues. Calculate the heat of reaction (ΔH_r°) for the burning of one mole of propane. The combustion reaction is

$$C_3H_8(g) + 5O_2(g) \longrightarrow 3CO_2(g) + 4H_2O(l)$$

SOLUTION

1. From Table 8-2, obtain the enthalpies of formation for the species involved in the reaction:

$$C_3H_8(g) \quad \Delta H_f^\circ = -104.0 \text{ kJ/mol}$$
$$CO_2(g) \quad \Delta H_f^\circ = -393.5 \text{ kJ/mol}$$
$$H_2O(l) \quad \Delta H_f^\circ = -285.5 \text{ kJ/mol}$$

2. Substitute these enthalpies of formation into Equation 8-8:

$$\Delta H_r^\circ = [3(\Delta H_f^\circ)CO_2 + 4(\Delta H_f^\circ)H_2O] -$$
$$\qquad [(\Delta H_f^\circ) C_3H_8 + 5(\Delta H_f^\circ)O_2]$$
$$= [3 \text{ mol } (-393.5 \text{ kJ/mol}) +$$
$$\qquad 4 \text{ mol } (-285.5 \text{ kJ/mol})] -$$
$$\qquad [1 \text{ mol } (-104.0 \text{ kJ/mol}) + 5 \text{ mol } (0 \text{ kJ/mol})]$$
$$= [(-1180.5 \text{ kJ}) + (-1142.0 \text{ kJ})] - [(-104.0 \text{ kJ})]$$
$$= -2218.5 \text{ kJ}$$

Therefore, the heat of reaction, or heat of combustion, for one mole of propane is −2218.5 kJ.

EXAMPLE 8-4
Calculating the Heat of Formation of an Unknown Compound

Propanone (acetone, CH_3COCH_3) is a common organic solvent. This compound is highly flammable and burns according to the following reaction:

$$CH_3COCH_3(l) + 4O_2(g) \longrightarrow 3CO_2(g) + 3H_2O(l)$$

Experimental evidence shows that when one mole of CH_3COCH_3 is burned, 1788.9 kJ of heat is released. Calculate the heat of formation of CH_3COCH_3 in kJ/mol.

SOLUTION

1. From Table 8-2, obtain the enthalpies of formation for the species involved in the reaction:

$$CO_2(g) \quad \Delta H_f^\circ = -393.5 \text{ kJ/mol}$$
$$H_2O(l) \quad \Delta H_f^\circ = -285.5 \text{ kJ/mol}$$

2. Substitute these enthalpies of formation into Equation 8-8. Because heat is released during this reaction, the heat of reaction is negative (−1788.9 kJ).

$$\Delta H_r^\circ = [3(\Delta H_f^\circ)CO_2 + 3(\Delta H_f^\circ)H_2O] - [(\Delta H_f^\circ)CH_3COCH_3 + 4(\Delta H_f^\circ)O_2]$$

$$-1788.9 \text{ kJ} = [3 \text{ mol } (-393.5 \text{ kJ/mol}) + 3 \text{ mol } (-285.5 \text{ kJ/mol})] - [1 \text{ mol } (\Delta H_f^\circ)CH_3COCH_3 + 4 \text{ mol } (0 \text{ kJ/mol})]$$

$$-1788.9 \text{ kJ} = [(-1180.5 \text{ kJ}) + (-856.5 \text{ kJ})] - [1 \text{ mol } (\Delta H_f^\circ)CH_3COCH_3]$$

$$1 \text{ mol } (\Delta H_f^\circ)CH_3COCH_3 = -2037.0 \text{ kJ} + 1788.9 \text{ kJ}$$

$$(\Delta H_f^\circ)CH_3COCH_3 = \frac{-248.1 \text{ kJ}}{1 \text{ mol}} = -248.1 \text{ kJ/mol}$$

Thus, the heat of formation of acetone is −248.1 kJ/mol.

EXAMPLE 8-5

Calculating the Enthalpy of Formation of a Compound Using Thermochemical Data

In an experiment that uses a bomb calorimeter with a heat capacity of 10.42 kJ/°C, a 0.46 g sample of ethanol (ethyl alcohol, C_2H_5OH) is burned in the presence of excess oxygen to produce $CO_2(g)$ and $H_2O(l)$. The combustion reaction causes a temperature increase from 21.48°C to 22.79°C. Calculate the enthalpy of formation of ethanol.

SOLUTION

1. Write a balanced reaction for this combustion reaction:

$$C_2H_5OH(l) + 3O_2(g) \longrightarrow 2CO_2(g) + 3H_2O(l)$$

2. Calculate the heat of combustion for one mole of ethanol:

Heat evolved = (heat capacity)(temperature change)
= (10.42 kJ/°C)(22.79°C − 21.48°C)
= (10.42 kJ/°C)(1.31°C)
= 13.65 kJ

Molar mass = 46 g/mol

$$\text{Number of moles} = \frac{0.46 \text{ g}}{46 \text{ g/mol}}$$
$$= 0.01 \text{ mol}$$
$$\text{Heat evolved per mole} = \frac{13.65 \text{ kJ}}{0.01 \text{ mol}}$$
$$= 1365 \text{ kJ/mol}$$

Since this is an exothermic reaction, the heat of reaction (ΔH_r°) is -1365 kJ/mol.

3. Using the thermochemical data above and the enthalpies of formation of CO_2 and $H_2O(l)$ from Table 8-2, calculate the enthalpy of formation of ethanol:

$$\Delta H_r^\circ = [2(\Delta H_f^\circ)CO_2 + 3(\Delta H_f^\circ)H_2O] -$$
$$[(\Delta H_f^\circ)C_2H_5OH + 3(\Delta H_f^\circ)O_2]$$
$$-1365 \text{ kJ} = [2 \text{ mol} (-393.5 \text{ kJ/mol}) +$$
$$3 \text{ mol} (-285.5 \text{ kJ/mol})] -$$
$$[1 \text{ mol} (\Delta H_f^\circ)C_2H_5OH +$$
$$3 \text{ mol} (0 \text{ kJ/mol})]$$
$$-1365 \text{ kJ} = -1643.5 \text{ kJ} - 1 \text{ mol} (\Delta H_f^\circ)C_2H_5OH$$
$$278.5 \text{ kJ} = -1 \text{ mol} (\Delta H_f^\circ)C_2H_5OH$$
$$(\Delta H_f^\circ)C_2H_5OH = \frac{-278.5}{1 \text{ mol}} = -278.5 \text{ kJ/mol}$$

Thus, the enthalpy of formation of ethanol is -278.5 kJ/mol.

FOLLOW-UP PROBLEMS

1. Use the standard enthalpies of formation from Table 8-2 to determine the change in enthalpy (heat of reaction) for each of the following reactions.
   $\Delta H_f^\circ N_2O(g) = +81.5$ kJ/mol.

   a) $2CO(g) + O_2(g) \longrightarrow 2CO_2(g)$

   b) $CH_4(g) + 2O_2(g) \longrightarrow CO_2(g) + 2H_2O(l)$

   c) $2H_2S(g) + 3O_2(g) \longrightarrow 2H_2O(l) + 2SO_2(g)$

   d) $10N_2O(g) + C_3H_8(g) \longrightarrow$
   $$10N_2(g) + 3CO_2(g) + 4H_2O(l)$$

2. Given that a total of 133.5 kJ of energy is released by the reaction below, calculate the enthalpy of formation for urea $(CO(NH_2)_2)$.

   $$2NH_3(g) + CO_2(g) \longrightarrow CO(NH_2)_2(g) + H_2O(l)$$

Answers:
1. (a) −567 kJ, (b) −889.6 kJ, (c) −1123.8 kJ,
   (d) −3033.5 kJ
2. −533.5 kJ/mol

Earlier in this chapter we noted that energy changes accompanying a chemical reaction are the result of making and breaking chemical bonds. Furthermore, it was implied that the magnitude and sign of ΔH_r° were related to the relative strength and number of bonds broken and the relative strength and number of bonds formed. This relationship suggests that bond energies can be used to approximate enthalpy changes in chemical reactions. We will now look at these concepts in more detail.

BOND DISSOCIATION ENERGY

Chemical reactions involve the breaking and formation of chemical bonds. Thus, a knowledge of bond strengths is necessary if we are to estimate the energies of reactions. The strength of the forces holding atoms together in a gaseous molecule is measured in terms of bond dissociation energy, or bond energy.

8-10
Principle of Additivity of Bond Energies

The bond energy of a molecule is the sum of the bond energies between the individual atoms making up the molecule.

Bond energy is the energy required to break all bonds in one mole of gaseous molecules that are in their lowest energy states. For example, 436 kJ is required to break the bonds in one mole of hydrogen molecules. Therefore, the H—H bond energy is said to be 436 kJ/mol. In other words, the bond energy per mole of H_2 is the enthalpy change for the reaction represented by the equation

$$H_2(g) \longrightarrow H(g) + H(g) \qquad \Delta H_r^\circ = 436 \text{ kJ/mol}$$

Table 8-3 lists the average experimental bond energies required to break a bond between atoms. Note that these values are for gaseous molecules and are always positive. These values can change, however, depending on the neighbouring atoms. For example, the C—H bond is listed as having a bond energy of 412 kJ/mol. However, the C—H bond of methane (CH_4) has a different bond energy than the C—H bond in ethyne (CH≡CH). Thus, the 412 kJ/mol listed is an average of different C—H bonds in

TABLE 8-3
AVERAGE BOND ENERGIES

Bond	Energy (kJ/mol)
O—O	138
I—I	151
N—N	159
Br—Br	192
Cl—Cl	242
H—I	299
C—C	348
C—O	360
H—Br	366
N—H	389
C—H	412
H—Cl	431
H—H	436
O—H	464
O=O	498
H—F	565
C=C	612
C=O	740
C≡C	836
N≡N	940

different molecules. This is true for all the bond energies listed in Table 8-3.

For substances whose molecules have more than one bond, the total bond energy is the sum of the contributions from each bond in each of the molecules. For example, the bond energy of ethane (see margin) is the sum of the energy of six C—H bonds and one C—C bond. This illustrates the *principle of additivity of bond energies*, which states that *the bond energy of a substance is the sum of all the bond energies of the bonds that make up the substance*. If we apply the principle of additivity, we can calculate the bond energy (H_{be}) for ethane:

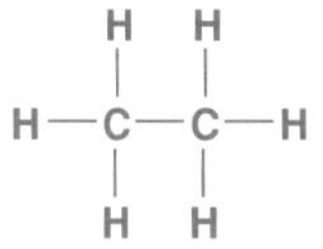

ethane

$$H_{be} = 6E_{C-H} + E_{C-C} = 6(412 \text{ kJ/mol}) + 1(348 \text{ kJ/mol})$$
$$= 2820 \text{ kJ/mol}$$

FOLLOW-UP PROBLEM

Calculate the value of the H_{be} for (a) methane and (b) propane.

Answers: (a) 1648 kJ/mol, (b) 3992 kJ/mol

8-11
Calculating Enthalpy Changes From Bond Energies

The approximate enthalpy change of a reaction can be calculated using average bond-energy values.

The average bond-energy values listed in Table 8-3 show relatively little variation from actual values and may be used to give good approximations when actual values are not available. For example, consider the reaction between hydrogen gas and chlorine gas, which produces hydrogen chloride:

$$H_2(g) + Cl_2(g) \longrightarrow 2HCl(g)$$

Once initiated, this reaction is observed to be spontaneous and highly exothermic. The enthalpy change in this reaction represents the difference between the total energy required to break the bonds in one mole of hydrogen molecules and one mole of chlorine molecules and the energy liberated when new bonds are formed in the two moles of hydrogen chloride molecules. The bond energies of chlorine molecules and hydrogen molecules are, respectively, 242 and 436 kJ/mol. The bond energy of HCl is 431 kJ/mol. This data indicates that 678 kJ/mol of energy should be absorbed in breaking bonds and 862 kJ/mol should be liberated by bond formation. This information is summarized as follows:

Bonds Broken	Energy Absorbed	Bonds Formed	Energy Evolved
H—H	436 kJ/mol		–
Cl—Cl	242 kJ/mol	2H—Cl	862 kJ/mol
Totals	678 kJ/mol		862 kJ/mol

The difference between the energy evolved and the energy absorbed in this reaction is

$$\Delta H_r^\circ = -862 \text{ kJ/mol} + 678 \text{ kJ/mol}$$
$$= -184 \text{ kJ/2 mol}$$

This approximates the net energy evolved in the formation of two moles of HCl. Accordingly, the enthalpy of formation for HCl, calculated from bond energies, is

$$\Delta H_f^\circ = -184 \text{ kJ/2 mol}$$
$$= -92 \text{ kJ/mol}$$

This calculated value agrees closely with the experimentally determined enthalpy of formation for HCl given in Table 8-2.

In general, single bonds between dissimilar atoms are stronger than those between similar ones. In our example, the H—Cl bond is stronger than the average of H—H and Cl—Cl bonds. We could, therefore, predict qualitatively that the reaction would be exothermic and that ΔH_r° has a negative value.

Figure 8-13
Diagram representing the net energy liberated when two moles of HCl are formed.

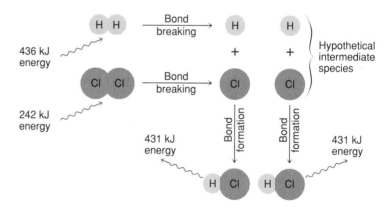

Bond energies can be used in more complicated situations to give us approximations of expected results in an experimental situation. For example, we can use bond energies to determine the approximate enthalpy change during the combustion of a gaseous fuel. Such a problem is illustrated in Example 8-6.

EXAMPLE 8-6
Calculating the Heat of Combustion
Using Bond Energies

Propane undergoes combustion according to the following reaction:

$$C_3H_8(g) + 5O_2(g) \longrightarrow 3CO_2(g) + 4H_2O(g)$$

Using bond energies, calculate the approximate enthalpy change (heat of combustion) when one mole of propane is burned.

SOLUTION

1. Draw the structural formulas for the compounds involved:

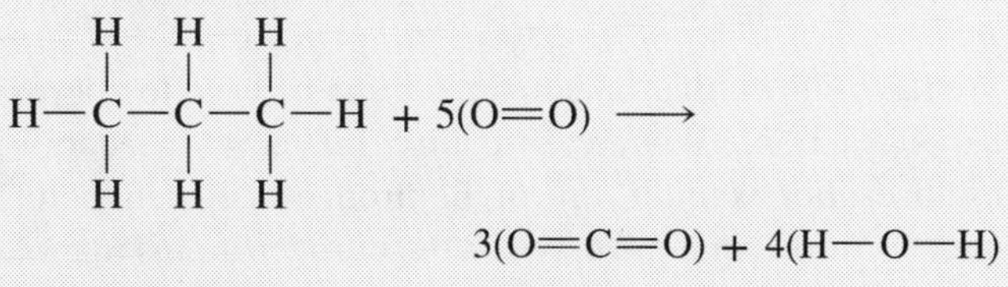

$$\begin{array}{ccc} H & H & H \\ | & | & | \\ H-C-C-C-H \\ | & | & | \\ H & H & H \end{array} + 5(O{=}O) \longrightarrow$$

$$3(O{=}C{=}O) + 4(H{-}O{-}H)$$

2. Using the principle of additivity, calculate the amount of energy required to break the bonds of the reactants and the amount of energy released in the formation of the new bonds of the products.

Bonds Broken	Energy Absorbed	Bonds Formed	Energy Evolved
2(C—C)	2(348 kJ/mol) = 696 kJ/mol	6(C=O)	6(−740 kJ/mol) = −4440 kJ/mol
8(C—H)	8(412 kJ/mol) = 3296 kJ/mol	8(O—H)	8(−464 kJ/mol) = −3712 kJ/mol
5(O=O)	5(498 kJ/mol) = 2490 kJ/mol		
Totals	+6482 kJ/mol		−8152 kJ/mol

3. Calculate the net enthalpy change for the reaction. The net change is

$$\Delta H_r^\circ = +6482 \text{ kJ/mol} - 8152 \text{ kJ/mol}$$
$$= -1670 \text{ kJ/mol}$$

Thus, the heat of combustion of one mole of propane is −1670 kJ/mol. Note that in Example 8-3, the heat of combustion of propane was determined to be −2218.5 kJ/mol, using experimentally determined heats of formation. Bond energies do not give the same result because they are only average values.

FOLLOW-UP PROBLEM

1. Using the data in Table 8-3, calculate the heat of reaction (ΔH_r°) for the reaction,

$$N_2(g) + O_2(g) \longrightarrow 2NO(g)$$

The bond energy for the N—O bond is 627 kJ/mol.

2. Using bond energy data, calculate the heat of combustion of one mole of gaseous ethanol:

$$C_2H_5OH(g) + 3O_2(g) \longrightarrow 2CO_2(g) + 3H_2O(g)$$

Answers:
1. **184 kJ/mol**
2. **−1018 kJ**

We have shown that bond energies can be used to approximate heats of reaction. They are, of course, related to the stabilities of substances. For example, one of the strongest covalent bonds (940 kJ/mol) is the triple bond between the nitrogen atoms in molecular nitrogen. As a result, molecular nitrogen (N_2) is unusually stable and relatively unreactive. On the other hand, one of the weakest covalent bonds is that between fluorine atoms in molecular fluorine (F_2). This explains why elemental fluorine is the most reactive nonmetallic element known.

8-12
Lattice Energy of an Ionic Crystal

The lattice energy of an ionic crystal is a measure of the stability of the ionic crystal; as the lattice energy increases, the crystal becomes more stable.

In ionic crystals, bond energy is expressed in terms of crystal-lattice energy. *Crystal-lattice energy* is defined as *the energy liberated when one mole of an ionic crystal is formed from gaseous ions*. This quantity has been measured experimentally for only a few substances. The value can be calculated from experimentally determined enthalpies of formation (ΔH_f°) plus other experimental data. We will illustrate the calculation of crystal-lattice energy for NaCl(s). The enthalpy of formation (ΔH_f°) for NaCl is −413.0 kJ/mol.

$$Na(s) + \tfrac{1}{2}Cl_2(g) \longrightarrow NaCl(s) + 413.0 \text{ kJ} \qquad [8\text{-}9]$$

When solid sodium and gaseous chlorine are mixed under proper conditions, the reaction appears to take place in one simple step, even though the reaction is probably very complicated. Although the actual steps are not known, we can represent the formation of sodium chloride from its elements by a series of five hypothetical steps. All steps but one involve energy transfers that have been measured experimentally. To conform to the law of conservation of energy, the five-step sequence must be energetically equal to the one-step process represented by Equation 8-9. This hypothetical sequence is known as the ***Born-Haber cycle*** and is represented in Fig. 8-14.

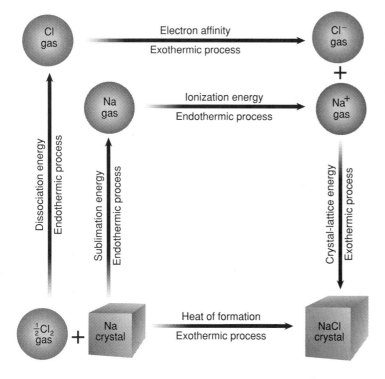

Figure 8-14
The Born-Haber cycle. When five of the six energy factors in the cycle are known, the sixth can be calculated. This is an application of the law of conservation of energy.

By equating the enthalpy of formation to the sum of the enthalpy changes for each step in the cycle, we can calculate the crystal-lattice energy. Thus, the analysis of the enthalpy of formation gives us a measure of the stability of the crystal lattice. It will also provide an insight into the driving force that accounts for the formation of ionic bonds. Let us examine in detail the energetics of each step in the Born-Haber cycle.

Step 1: *The conversion of sodium atoms from the solid to the gaseous phase* (Fig. 8-15). This process, called ***sublimation***, absorbs energy (endothermic). The energy absorbed per mole, called the ***enthalpy of sublimation*** (ΔH_s°), has a value of 109 kJ/mol. The thermochemical equation representing the process is

$$109 \text{ kJ} + \text{Na}(s) \longrightarrow \text{Na}(g)$$

Figure 8-15
Sublimation of sodium metal. In order to convert one mole of metallic sodium crystals into sodium vapour, 109 kJ/mol is required.

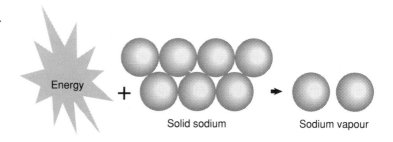

Solid sodium   Sodium vapour

Step 2: *The conversion of gaseous chlorine molecules into gaseous chlorine atoms* (Fig. 8-16). This process, called ***dissociation***, absorbs energy. The energy required to break the bonds holding the chlorine atoms together in the molecule is called ***dissociation energy*** (ΔH_d°). The dissociation energy has a value of 242 kJ/mol of Cl_2. The following equation shows that only 0.5 mol of chlorine is involved, so ΔH_d° for this reaction is 121 kJ per 0.5 mol of Cl_2. The thermochemical equation for the reaction is

$$121 \text{ kJ} + \tfrac{1}{2}Cl_2(g) \longrightarrow Cl(g)$$

Figure 8-16
Energy is required to overcome the force of attraction (chemical bond) binding two chlorine atoms together in a molecule. The separate chlorine atoms are, therefore, in a higher energy state than the bound atoms.

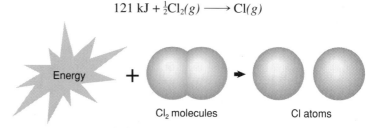

Cl_2 molecules   Cl atoms

Step 3: *The conversion of sodium atoms in the gaseous phase into gaseous sodium ions* (Fig. 8-17). This process is called ***ionization***. As you have already learned, this energy is known as the ***first ionization energy*** (ΔH_i°) and is the energy required to remove the most loosely bound electrons from one mole of sodium atoms. The value of ΔH_i° for the reaction represented below is 493 kJ/mol. The thermochemical equation is

$$493 \text{ kJ} + Na(g) \longrightarrow Na^+(g) + e^-$$

Figure 8-17
To remove one electron from a sodium atom, 5.14 eV is required; 5.14 eV per atom is equivalent to 493 kJ/mol of atoms. Can you determine the conversion factor?

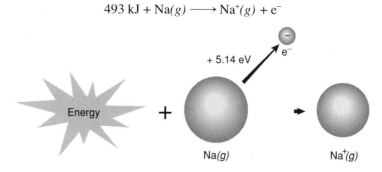

+ 5.14 eV

$Na(g)$ $Na^+(g)$

Step 4: *The conversion of gaseous chlorine atoms into gaseous chloride ions* (Fig. 8-18). This process is exothermic. The addition of an electron to a neutral atom involves attractive forces that result in a decrease in energy for this system. Therefore, energy is released to the surroundings. As discussed in Chapter 3, the energy released is known as the **electron affinity** (ΔH_e°). The electron affinity of an atom is the energy released when an electron is added to a gaseous atom in the ground state. The value of ΔH_e° for the equation below is -364 kJ/mol. The thermochemical equation is

$$Cl(g) + e^- \longrightarrow Cl^-(g) + 364 \text{ kJ/mol}$$

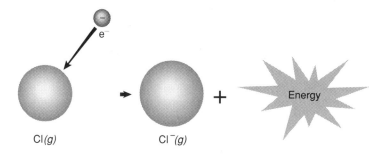

Cl(g)   Cl⁻(g)   + Energy

Figure 8-18
The potential energy of the system decreases when the chlorine atom acquires an electron to form the chloride ion.

Step 5: *The combining of positive sodium ions and negative chloride ions to form solid sodium chloride as a crystal* (Fig. 8-19). Attractive forces lower the energy of the system. The reaction is exothermic and releases energy. The process is represented as

$$Na^+(g) + Cl^-(g) \longrightarrow Na^+Cl^-(s) + \text{energy}$$

The energy released in this reaction is called the *crystal-lattice energy* (ΔH_c°). The value of ΔH_c° is a measure of the energy required to separate the ions in the crystal so that they can enter the gaseous phase. Thus, a substance with a large crystal-lattice energy is a solid with a relatively low vapour pressure.

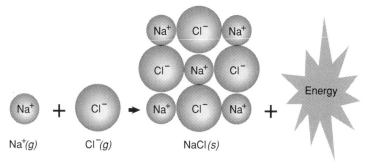

Na⁺(g)   Cl⁻(g)   NaCl(s)

Figure 8-19
When oppositely charged ions in the gaseous phase condense to form a solid crystal, crystal-lattice energy is released.

If we apply Hess's law to the Born-Haber cycle (Fig. 8-14), we can write

$$\Delta H_f^\circ = \Delta H_s^\circ + \Delta H_d^\circ + \Delta H_i^\circ + \Delta H_e^\circ + \Delta H_c^\circ$$

Solving this equation for ΔH_c°, we obtain

$$\Delta H_c^{\circ} = \Delta H_f^{\circ} - \Delta H_s^{\circ} - \Delta H_d^{\circ} - \Delta H_i^{\circ} - \Delta H_e^{\circ}$$

Substituting experimentally determined values for the terms on the right side of the preceding equation yields

$$\Delta H_c^{\circ} = (-413.0 \text{ kJ}) - (109 \text{ kJ}) - (121 \text{ kJ}) - (493 \text{ kJ}) - (-364 \text{ kJ})$$
$$= -1136 \text{ kJ} + 364 \text{ kJ}$$
$$= -772 \text{ kJ}$$

This relatively high value for the crystal-lattice energy of NaCl is consistent with the fact that NaCl is thermally stable and has a low vapour pressure.

Analysis of the steps in the Born-Haber cycle shows that the gaseous ions with octet structures have a greater potential energy (129 kJ/mol) and, thus, less stability than the gaseous atoms. The 129 kJ/mol represents the difference between the ionization energy for sodium and the electron affinity for chlorine (493–364). Because there is no significant entropy increase, this process would not occur spontaneously unless there were a simultaneous exothermic change that lowers the potential energy of the system. *It is the force of attraction between the ions in the crystal that supplies the required stability.* This reasoning implies that the ionic bond is formed in response to the attractive forces between ions rather than in response to a tendency to form an octet structure.

Analysis of the individual steps of the cycle also suggests that an ionic substance such as Na^+Cl^- has a unique formula. The second ionization energy for sodium is over 4200 kJ/mol. The formation of Na^{2+} would require the absorption of this amount of energy and would produce an extremely high-energy, unstable system. The relatively similar amount of crystal-lattice energy that would be evolved when the ions condensed and formed a crystal of Na^+Cl^- would not be sufficient to reduce the energy to form a stable system.

FOLLOW-UP PROBLEM

a) Using the data below, calculate the net energy liberated in the formation of one mole of solid potassium fluoride from its elements (heat of formation).

b) What is the value of ΔH_f°?

c) Write an equation for the formation of one mole of solid KF, showing the heat term on the right-hand side of the equation.

Heat of sublimation (ΔH_s°) of potassium = 87.78 kJ/mol
Ionization energy (ΔH_i°) of potassium = 414 kJ/mol
Heat of dissociation (ΔH_d°) of fluorine (F_2) = 159 kJ/mol
Electron affinity (ΔH_e°) of fluorine = −334 kJ/mol
Crystal-lattice energy (ΔH_c°) of KF = −807 kJ/mol

Answers:
a) **560 kJ/mol is liberated.**
b) $\Delta H_f^\circ = $ **−560 kJ/mol**
c) $K(s) + \frac{1}{2}F_2(g) \longrightarrow KF(s) + 560 \text{ kJ}$

In the previous sections, we discussed energy changes associated with chemical reactions. We are now ready to investigate reactions in which the nuclei of atoms undergo a change.

HYDROGEN: THE IDEAL FUEL AND ENERGY CARRIER

The Space Shuttle is famous worldwide for its dramatic lift-offs. What is less known is that the fuel responsible for those earth-shaking take-offs is liquid hydrogen.

Hydrogen has a number of advantages over traditional fuels. Fossil fuels, such as coal, petroleum and gas, are costly to find and develop. Moreover, the combustion of such fuels produces carbon dioxide, which contributes to the greenhouse effect, as well as nitrogen oxides and sulfur dioxide, which aggravate the problem of acid rain. In contrast, the combustion of hydrogen with air produces water vapour and energy, and is thus non-polluting:

$$2H_2 + O_2 \longrightarrow 2H_2O + energy$$

No toxic products such as carbon monoxide or organic acids are produced. Because hydrogen has a high flame speed, wide flammability limits and a high detonation temperature, it is also a very efficient fuel. More energy can be derived from burning one kilogram of hydrogen than from the same mass of any other chemical fuel. For example, one tonne of coal converted to hydrogen will supply 50% more energy than the same amount of coal converted to gasoline. As well, because hydrogen is a gas at −253°C, it does not cause problems associated with liquid fuels, such as vapour lock and poor mixing; for Canadians, this means instant start-up for car engines in the winter. Most important, hydrogen is readily available, since it is present in water. Unfor-

tunately, hydrogen does not exist in pure form on earth. Energy from fossil and non-fossil sources must be added to water or other substances to liberate the hydrogen in a usable form. For example, hydrogen can be produced from the electrolysis of water,

$$2H_2O \longrightarrow 2H_2 + O_2$$

or through the thermal cracking of water,

$$H_2O \xrightarrow{\text{2000°C, pressure}} H_2 + O_2$$

Most hydrogen, however, is obtained by reacting natural gas with steam,

$$CH_4 + H_2O \longrightarrow 3H_2 + CO$$

by coal gasification,

$$coal + H_2O \longrightarrow CO + H_2$$
$$CO + H_2O \longrightarrow CO_2 + H_2$$

or through gasification of solid wastes. This last process is a recent innovation and holds promise both as a new source of hydrogen and as a method for disposing of waste:

$$solid \ waste + air \longrightarrow CO + H_2$$

Hydrogen could eventually replace gasoline, diesel fuel and propane as a source of fuel. It may one day heat our homes and operate equipment. Already used experimentally as a jet fuel, hydrogen may ultimately fuel trains, trucks, ships and planes.

Many countries are presently involved in research into hydrogen fuel: Germany is a leader in the production and handling of liquid hydrogen and has developed a prototype storage tank for cars and buses; Japan has devised a high-powered automobile engine fueled by liquid hydrogen; Canada is doing research into hydrogen-fueled locomotives and buses and is a leader in the production of hydrogen from water electrolysis.

Developing hydrogen into a cheap and efficient fuel has its problems. One of these is storage. Since hydrogen is highly flammable, it is difficult to store and transport. One solution to this problem is to store the hydrogen in a tank as a compound with metal-alloy particles, such as magnesium, magnesium-nickel alloys and iron-titanium alloys. These metal alloys act as sponges to absorb the hydrogen and form metal hydrides. Metal hydride systems cannot burn or explode and are considered safer than conventional gasoline or diesel fuel. Because the hydrogen is chemically bound to the metal, the gas is stored in the metal until energy is applied to release the hydrogen; this energy is provided by the engine exhaust, which, in a conventional engine, is usually wasted. The chief drawback of using metal hydrides is the size of the storage tank required. For example, an 860 kg tank would be needed to provide fuel for a car for 180 km.

Producing hydrogen is still relatively expensive. For example, the cost of the electricity to produce hydrogen is still much higher than the cost of obtaining fossil fuels. However, electrolytic cells, which produce hydrogen and oxygen from water, are becoming more efficient and less expensive.

Although car owners will not be pulling their vehicles into hydrogen-fueling stations in the immediate future, technological developments are helping the dream of hydrogen fuel become an achievable reality.

NUCLEAR ENERGY

"Looking behind the possible loss of harnessed energy, we see that mankind can be destroyed by something much smaller to propagate, namely mistrust."
W. B. Lewis (1908–1987)
Father of the CANDU power plant

Much of our energy today still comes from chemical sources such as the burning of fossil fuels. Fortunately, we no longer have to depend solely on fossil fuels to supply all of our energy needs. In 1942, Enrico Fermi and his co-workers made available a new source of energy when they unlocked some of the energy stored in the nuclei of atoms. Their discovery heralded the start of the nuclear age.

In this part of the chapter, we will investigate the structure and properties of nuclei and then consider the different kinds of nuclear reactions.

8-13

Factors Affecting the Stability of a Nucleus

The stability of the nucleus of an isotope depends on the number of protons and neutrons.

The fundamental particles in the atomic nucleus are protons and neutrons, collectively known as *nucleons*. As we saw in Chapter 1, protons carry a positive charge of one, while neutrons have no charge. *Isotopes* are different forms of an element that have the same number of protons and a different number of neutrons.

Because of the close packing of positively charged and neutral particles, it might appear that forces of repulsion would cause the nuclei of all atoms to be unstable and, therefore, to disintegrate spontaneously. It is true that a proton does repel other protons with a strong, long-range force of repulsion. This electrostatic repulsive force tends to decrease the stability of the nucleus and helps explain the instability of the heavier elements whose nuclei have large numbers of protons.

It is apparent that there must be another force, called a ***nuclear force***, that holds the protons and neutrons together. Since positive charges repel, this nuclear force must be greater than the force of electrostatic repulsion and must act at very short distances, since the diameter of a nucleus is approximately 10^{-15} m.

If the nuclear force is responsible for nuclear stability, why are many nuclei unstable? Figure 8-20 on the next page shows a graph of the number of neutrons plotted against the number of protons for elements with atomic numbers 1 through 83. The belt of stable nuclei is called the *band of stability*. Close examination of Fig. 8-20 reveals the following observations:

1. Stable nuclei, up to and including those in which the atomic number *(Z)* equals 20, have the same number of protons and neutrons.
2. The number of neutrons is greater than the number of protons for atoms whose atomic number falls between 20 and 83.
3. The nuclei of atoms with atomic numbers greater than 83 are unstable.
4. Atoms with even numbers of protons *(Z)* have more stable isotopes than those with an odd number of protons.
5. Many more stable isotopes have an even number of neutrons than an odd number.

Observations 1 through 3 show that as the atomic number increases, the number of neutrons increases. This is because the neutrons contribute to the nuclear force that holds the nucleus together but are unaffected by the electrostatic forces repelling the protons from each other. We can see from observations 4 and 5 that nuclei with odd numbers of protons or neutrons are less stable than

In 1947, scientists discovered a sub-nuclear particle called a *pi meson*. A pi meson (pion) has a mass about 270 times that of an electron. It is thought that protons and neutrons exchange pi mesons continuously and that this exchange is responsible for the nuclear force. In other words, the pi mesons carry the nuclear force.

The atomic number *(Z)* represents the number of protons.

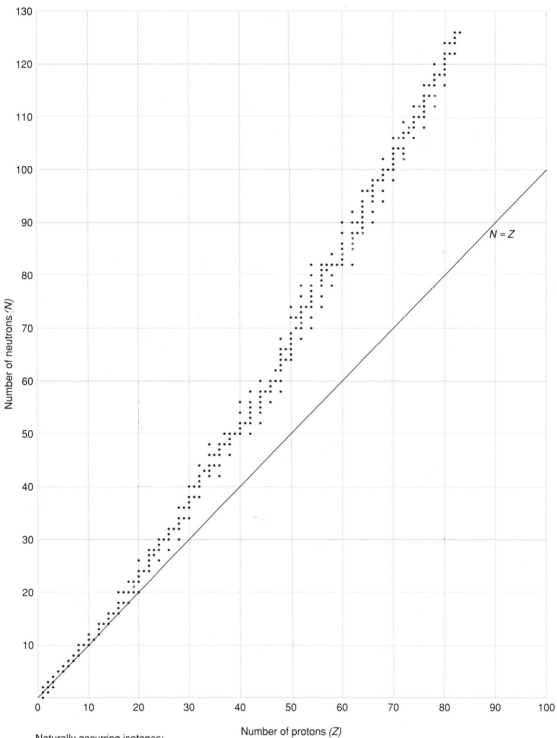

Naturally occurring isotopes:
- stable nuclei
- unstable nuclei

those with even numbers of protons or neutrons. This is because nucleons, like electrons, have a spin. When two protons or two neutrons have opposite spins, they become paired and have less combined energy than they would if they were not paired. Unpaired protons and neutrons increase the energy of the system, thus decreasing its stability.

By noting relationships between the number of protons and neutrons and the stability of the nucleus, scientists have developed the *magic-number concept* to explain the trend in nuclear stability: Atoms with the greatest stability have certain "magic" numbers of neutrons and protons. These magic numbers, which represent full nuclear shells, are 2, 8, 20, 28, 50, 82 and 126. For example, the isotope of lead ($^{208}_{82}$Pb) is very stable because it contains two of the magic numbers (82 protons and 126 neutrons, which add to 208) and, thus, contains a full nuclear shell of protons and neutrons. These factors determine the bond energy of the nucleus and, hence, its stability.

Maria Goeppert Mayer (1906–1972) was born in Kattowitz, Germany, and received her PhD from the University of Göttingen. She later moved to the United States, where she spent the rest of her life. Mayer was the first to suggest the idea of magic numbers, and developed a nuclear shell model to explain the properties of atomic nuclei. Mayer shared the 1963 Nobel Prize in physics with J. Hans Daniel Jensen and Eugene P. Wigner for their explanation of the shell structure of nuclei.

8-14
Binding Energy

Binding energy is the energy required to separate a nucleus into its component protons and neutrons.

Nuclear reactions involve energies that are a million times greater than those of chemical reactions. The reason for this is that the binding energy per nuclear particle (the energy required to separate the nucleus into individual particles) is much greater than the bond energy per molecule (the energy required to break chemical bonds). Binding energy is a measure of the stability of the nucleus; the greater the binding energy, the more stable is the nucleus.

Using precisely determined masses, we can show that the sum of the masses of the individual particles in the nucleus is not equal to the actual mass of the nucleus. For example, a precise calculation shows that mass is transformed or lost when protons and neutrons combine to form a helium nucleus:

Mass of 2 moles neutrons = 2(1.008 66 g/mol) = 2.017 32 g/mol
Mass of 2 moles protons = 2(1.007 28 g/mol) = 2.014 56 g/mol

Total mass = 4.031 88 g/mol

However, the actual mass of one mole of helium is 4.001 50 g/mol. Thus, the difference in mass (Δm) is

$$\Delta m = 4.031\ 88\ \text{g/mol} - 4.001\ 50\ \text{g/mol}$$
$$= 3.04 \times 10^{-5}\ \text{kg/mol}$$

Note that the mass of the nucleus is less than the sum of the masses of the individual protons and neutrons. This transformed mass is called the *mass defect* and is equivalent to the binding energy that was released in forming the nucleus. We can calculate the binding energy of the nucleus by using a modification of Einstein's mass-energy equivalence law:

$$\Delta E = \Delta mc^2$$
$$\Delta E = (3.04 \times 10^{-5} \text{ kg/mol})(3 \times 10^8 \text{ m/s})^2$$
$$\Delta E = 2.74 \times 10^{12} \text{ kg·m}^2/\text{mol·s}^2$$
$$= 2.74 \times 10^{12} \text{ J/mol}$$
$$= 2.74 \times 10^9 \text{ kJ/mol}$$

If we compare this binding energy with the bond energies given in Table 8-3, we can see that the energy available from nuclear reactions is much greater than the energy available from chemical reactions.

We can plot the binding energy per nucleon against the mass number to obtain the graph shown in Fig. 8-21, which shows the relative stabilities of various nuclei. We can see from Fig. 8-21 that iron, with a mass number of 56, is the most stable nucleus. Therefore, more energy is required to separate two nucleons in an iron nucleus than for any other nucleus; that is, the formation of an iron nucleus from component particles liberates more energy than the formation of any other nucleus. Figure 8-21 also shows that the binding energy per nucleon in the nuclei of very light elements is much less than that of iron and its neighbouring elements. Therefore, a large amount of energy is released when very light nuclei merge to form nuclei having mass numbers around 56. Nuclear reactions in which small nuclei merge to form more massive

Figure 8-21
Binding-energy curve.

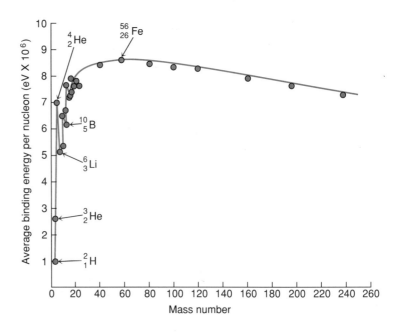

nuclei are called *nuclear-fusion, or thermonuclear, reactions*.

Figure 8-21 further reveals that the nuclei of very heavy elements have binding energies that are somewhat less than those of the intermediate elements. The difference is not as great as in the case of the very light nuclei, thus indicating that less energy will be released when very heavy nuclei split into smaller fragments. This type of nuclear reaction is known as *nuclear fission*. The energy evolved from fission reactions is used to generate electricity. We will discuss power generation from both nuclear fission and nuclear fusion in later sections.

FOLLOW-UP PROBLEM

Calculate the binding energy for one mole of $^{12}_{6}C$ nuclei. The actual mass of one mole of $^{12}_{6}C$ is 12.011 15 g.

Answer: 7.6×10^{12} J/mol

8-15
Nuclear Reactions and Radioactivity

Nuclear reactions involve changes in the nuclei of isotopes. Radioactivity is the emission of alpha and beta particles and gamma radiation from nuclei, which increases the stability of the nucleus.

Nuclear reactions are reactions that lead to changes in the atomic number, mass or energy state of nuclei. Nuclear reactions are caused by the spontaneous decay of radioisotopes, bombardment of nuclei with fast-moving particles, fission of heavy, unstable nuclei or fusion of light nuclei. During a nuclear reaction, the atom attains a more stable state by losing energy.

When writing nuclear equations, it is important to write the mass numbers and atomic numbers for all reactants and products. Note that the sum of the protons and neutrons of the products must equal the sum of the protons and neutrons of the reactants. Thus, the total nuclear charge (given by the atomic number) of the products must also equal the total nuclear charge of the reactants.

The radiation emitted by unstable nuclei during nuclear reactions is called *radioactivity*. Radioactivity was discovered by the French physicist Henri Becquerel (1852–1908) in 1896. Becquerel, who had been studying X rays, serendipitously discovered that a uranium salt was radioactive. Becquerel's discovery attracted the attention of Marie Curie (1867–1934) and her husband Pierre Curie (1859–1906), who began to study the mineral pitchblende, which has a specific activity that is higher than uranium. Marie

Nuclides that spontaneously decay are called radioactive isotopes, radioisotopes or radionuclides.

The first unit for measuring the activity of a radioisotope was the curie (Ci), named after Marie Curie. This unit was defined as the activity of a 1 g sample of radium-226. 1 Ci = 3.7×10^{10} Bq.

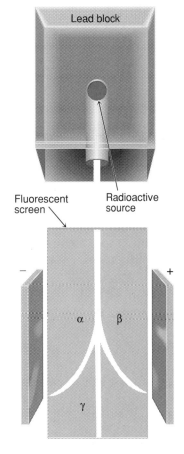

Lead block

Fluorescent screen

Radioactive source

Figure 8-22
When a beam from a radioactive source passes between oppositely charged plates, alpha particles are bent toward the negative plate, beta particles are bent toward the positive plate and gamma radiation is undeflected.

Curie knew that this activity could only be explained by the presence of small quantities of an unknown substance of very high activity. This led to their discovery of polonium and radium. The Curies were able to prove that the radiation emitted by radium consisted of positive, negative and neutral particles. Ernest Rutherford later called these particles alpha, beta and gamma rays (Fig. 8-22).

Further information about radioactivity was revealed by Rutherford and Frederick Soddy (1877–1956). They concluded in 1902 that, in the process of emitting radiation, one element is transformed into another. They recognized that radium-226 decays to an alpha particle and an atom of radon-222:

$$^{226}_{88}\text{Ra} \longrightarrow {}^{4}_{2}\text{He} + {}^{222}_{86}\text{Rn}$$

In 1919, Rutherford artificially transformed a nitrogen atom into an oxygen atom:

$$^{14}_{7}\text{N} + {}^{4}_{2}\text{He} \longrightarrow {}^{17}_{8}\text{O} + {}^{1}_{1}\text{p}$$

In 1934, Irène Joliot-Curie (1897–1956) and her husband Frédéric Joliot-Curie (1900–1958) discovered that they could create artificial radioactive elements by bombarding stable nuclei with alpha particles (Fig. 8-23).

Any unstable nucleus emits some form of radiation and is said to be radioactive. Radiation represents a decrease in the energy of a nucleus and results in an increase in its stability. The three types of nuclear radiation that we will consider are alpha-particle emission, beta-particle emission and gamma rays. These and other particles can be detected by photographic film or bubble chambers (Figs. 8-24 and 8-25). Let us examine each of these types of radiation in detail.

Figure 8-23
Irène and Frédéric Joliot-Curie won the 1935 Nobel Prize for chemistry for their discovery of new radioactive elements that could be artificially prepared.

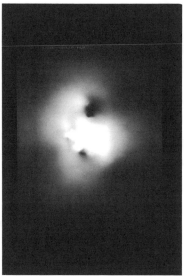

Figure 8-24
Photographic film is an excellent detector of radioactive rays. The photographic film was protected from ordinary light by black paper wrapping (left). The radioactive rays from the sample of uranite ore penetrated the paper and exposed the film (right).

Figure 8-25
Tracks made by high-energy protons and other nuclear particles in a liquid-hydrogen bubble chamber.

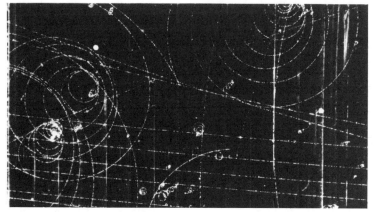

Alpha-Particle Emission (α)

An alpha particle is a helium nucleus ($_2^4$He) with a charge of 2+ and a mass number of 4. The emission of a helium nucleus by a radioactive nucleus is known as *alpha-particle decay*. For example, the following equation represents the nuclear decay of radium to form radon:

$$^{226}_{88}\text{Ra} \longrightarrow {}^{4}_{2}\text{He} + {}^{222}_{86}\text{Rn} \qquad [8\text{-}10]$$

Equation 8-10 indicates that radium decays to a nucleus of radon with the emission of an alpha particle.

Alpha particles have high ionizing ability and low penetrating power. Alpha particles are relatively massive radioactive particles that travel at about one-tenth the speed of light. A moving massive alpha particle easily dislodges electrons from atoms and molecules and produces what are known as *ion pairs*. An ion pair consists of

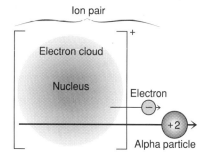

Figure 8-26
When a positively charged alpha particle passes near an atom, it dislodges an electron from the atom, producing an ion pair.

MARIE CURIE   **PIERRE CURIE**
1867–1934   **1859–1906**
**Marie Curie was born Manya
Sklodowska in Warsaw, Poland. She
studied physics and chemistry at the
Sorbonne in Paris, where she met
Pierre Curie.**
  **Pierre Curie was born in Paris and
attended the Sorbonne, where he
became a laboratory assistant in
1878. There he studied crystals with
his brother Jacques, and together
they discovered the concept of piezo-
electricity. In 1882, Curie was
appointed head of the laboratory of
the École de Physique et Chimie and
began his studies of magnetism.**
  **In 1895, Pierre and Marie married
and began their famous research
partnership. Together they discovered radium and polonium (which
Marie named after her native Poland)
and studied the radioactivity of pitchblende. In 1903, the Curies shared the
Nobel Prize for physics with Henri**

the electron that is dislodged (the negative half of the ion pair) and the charged particle that remains after an electron has been removed (positive half). It has been estimated that the average alpha particle produces more than 100 000 ion pairs during its existence. The process of ionization robs the alpha particle of energy so that it slows down and finally captures a pair of electrons, thereby becoming a neutral helium atom.

An alpha particle has relatively little penetrating power compared with other types of radiation. In air, its range may only be a few centimetres, because it quickly collides with air molecules and picks up two electrons to become a helium atom. A sheet of paper or the outside layer of human skin are capable of stopping alpha particles. This means that alpha particles present no appreciable external hazard to humans. On the other hand, because of its high ionization ability, alpha radiation can pose serious internal hazards: if sources of alpha particles are ingested or inhaled, the soft tissues of the intestines and lungs can be seriously damaged.

Beta-Particle Emission (β)

A beta particle is a high-energy electron. Because an electron is not a fundamental particle of a nucleus, a beta particle results from the transformation of a neutron into a proton and an electron:

$$_0^1 n \longrightarrow {}_1^1 p + {}_{-1}^0 e$$

The process of beta-particle emission takes place when a nucleus has an unusually high ratio of neutrons to protons. Any nucleus emitting a beta particle becomes a new nucleus with the same mass number but with an atomic number one greater than the original. This reduces the neutron-to-proton ratio, and the nucleus falls into the band of stability shown in Fig. 8-20. The beta decay of phosphorus-22 is an example of this process:

$$_{15}^{32} P \longrightarrow {}_{16}^{32} S + {}_{-1}^0 e$$

When the ratio of neutrons to protons is too low, a nucleus can increase the number of neutrons by transforming a proton into a neutron. This can take place in two different ways:

– The nucleus can capture an orbital electron from the first quantum level. When this happens, an electron from the second major energy level gives off energy in the form of an X ray as it drops into the lower vacancy. This process, known as *K-electron capture*, reduces the nuclear charge by one unit.

– If the excess energy of the excited state has the mass equivalent of two beta particles, then the energy can be transformed into two particles—a beta particle and a positron. The negative beta transforms the proton into a neutron, and the positron is emitted. Thus, the number of neutrons is increased.

Unlike an alpha particle, a beta particle has a very small mass. Thus, its ionizing power is about 0.01 that of the alpha particle. Also, because of its small size and high speed, a beta particle has a penetrating power of approximately 100 times that of an alpha particle and, consequently, presents more of an external radiation hazard. As it moves along, a beta particle loses energy whenever it ionizes atoms or molecules in its path. At the end of its range, it combines with some positive particle. The range of a beta particle varies with its energy, but in air the range is not more than a few metres. It can usually be stopped by thin sheets of aluminum.

Gamma Rays (γ)

A gamma ray is a form of electromagnetic radiation. Whenever a nucleus is left in an excited state by particle emission or bombardment, gamma rays are emitted as the nucleus goes from an excited state to a ground state. The energy of the gamma ray is equal to the difference in energy between the initial excited state and the final state. For example, the isotope cesium-137 decays to barium by emitting an electron and a gamma ray:

$$^{137}_{55}\text{Cs} \longrightarrow {}^{0}_{-1}\text{e} + {}^{0}_{0}\gamma + {}^{137}_{56}\text{Ba}$$

Gamma radiation has a shorter wavelength and is much more energetic than visible light. Since it has no rest mass and no charge, a gamma ray causes no change in the mass number or the atomic number of a nucleus. It has less ionizing ability but far greater penetrating power than an alpha particle. When a gamma-ray photon passes through matter, it may interact with matter by dislodging electrons from the atoms or molecules. The ejected electrons generally have a considerable amount of energy and, in turn, produce additional ionization. Only those photons that are absorbed by the body produce harmful effects. A certain number of the photons pass through the body without dislodging electrons. Sheets of lead or thick concrete walls are effective absorbers of gamma rays.

Becquerel for their discovery of radioactivity.

In 1906, Pierre Curie was run over by a horse-drawn cart and died instantly. After his death, Marie took over his teaching post at the Sorbonne, becoming the first woman to teach there. In 1911, she received the Nobel Prize for chemistry for the isolation of pure radium.

During World War I, Marie Curie worked on the development of X-radiography. She also helped equip ambulances with X-ray equipment, teaching doctors how to use the new technology.

Because of her continued exposure to radiation in her work, Marie Curie developed leukemia in the late 1920s and died of cancer in 1934.

Electrons that carry a positive charge are called *positrons* and are symbolized as ${}^{0}_{+1}\text{e}$.

A particle called a *neutrino* is emitted along with a beta particle when a neutron is transformed into a proton. A neutrino is not usually shown in the nuclear equation.

FOLLOW-UP PROBLEMS

1. Complete the following nuclear reaction:

$$^{238}_{92}\text{U} \longrightarrow {}^{4}_{2}\text{He} + ?$$

(Hint: to identify the element, use the atomic number.)

2. The isotope radon-222 is an alpha-particle emitter. Complete the following nuclear reaction:

$$^{222}_{86}\text{Rn} \longrightarrow {}^{4}_{2}\text{He} + ?$$

3. Complete the following nuclear reactions:
    a) $^{86}_{34}\text{Se} \longrightarrow 2{}^{0}_{-1}\text{e} + ?$
    b) $^{16}_{8}\text{O} + ? \longrightarrow {}^{13}_{6}\text{C} + {}^{4}_{2}\text{He}$
    c) $^{93}_{42}\text{Mo} \longrightarrow {}^{93}_{42}\text{Mo} + ?$
    d) $^{93}_{43}\text{Tc} \longrightarrow {}^{93}_{42}\text{Mo} + ?$
    e) $^{40}_{18}\text{Ar} + ? \longrightarrow {}^{43}_{19}\text{K} + {}^{1}_{1}\text{H}$

Answers:
1. $^{234}_{90}\textbf{Th}$
2. $^{218}_{84}\textbf{Po}$
3. a) $^{86}_{36}\textbf{Kr}$
   b) $^{1}_{0}\textbf{n}$ (**Note that some nuclei emit neutrons directly.**)
   c) $^{0}_{0}\boldsymbol{\gamma}$
   d) $^{0}_{+1}\textbf{e}$

TABLE 8-4

HALF-LIFE AND MODE OF DECAY FOR SELECTED RADIOISOTOPES

Isotope	Half-Life	Mode of Decay
$^{1}_{0}$n	12 min	β
$^{3}_{1}$H	12.3 a	β
$^{14}_{6}$C	5730 a	β
$^{24}_{11}$Na	15.0 h	β
$^{32}_{15}$P	14.3 d	β
$^{36}_{17}$Cl	3.1×10^{5} a	β
$^{40}_{19}$K	1.3×10^{9} a	β
$^{55}_{26}$Fe	2.6 a	e^{-} capture
$^{60}_{27}$Co	5.27 a	β
$^{90}_{38}$Sr	28.1 a	β
$^{131}_{53}$I	8.07 d	β
$^{210}_{82}$Pb	21 a	β
$^{214}_{82}$Pb	26.8 min	β
$^{210}_{83}$Bi	5.01 d	β
$^{214}_{83}$Bi	19.7 min	β
$^{210}_{84}$Po	138.4 d	α
$^{214}_{84}$Po	1.6×10^{-4} s	α
$^{218}_{84}$Po	3.05 min	α
$^{222}_{86}$Rn	3.82 d	α
$^{226}_{88}$Ra	1600 a	α
$^{234}_{90}$Th	24.5 d	β
$^{234}_{91}$Pa	6.66 h	β
$^{234}_{92}$U	2.48×10^{5} a	α
$^{236}_{92}$U	2.39×10^{7} a	α
$^{238}_{92}$U	4.5×10^{9} a	α
$^{239}_{92}$U	23.5 min	β

8-16
Rate of Decay

The rate of decay of a radioisotope is given by the fraction of nuclei that disintegrate per unit time.

The rate at which different substances decay is a measure of their relative stabilities. Decay rates can be measured by Geiger counters or other counting devices. Measurements show that every radioactive substance decays at a characteristic rate that is expressed in terms of a quantity called the *half-life*. *The half-life of a radioisotope is the time it takes for one-half of the nuclei in a given sample to decay to form other nuclei.* The more unstable the nuclei are, the shorter the half-life. As an example, compare uranium-238, which has a half-life of 4.5 billion years, with radon-222, which has a half-life of only 3.8 days. After 4.5×10^{9} years, a 1 g sample of uranium-238 will have disintegrated to 0.5 g of uranium, plus an assortment of its decay products. It would take only 3.8 days, however, for a 1 g sample of radon-222 to disintegrate to 0.5 g of radon-222. A number of radioisotopes, their half-lives and modes of decay are shown in Table 8-4.

The rate of decay of a radioisotope can be expressed as its activity, which is the number of disintegrations in a given unit of time. The SI unit of activity is the *becquerel* (Bq), which is defined as one disintegration per second. The rate of radioactive decay has been found to be proportional to the number of radioactive nuclei *(N)* in the sample:

$$rate = kN \qquad [8\text{-}11]$$

where k is the *rate constant*, or *proportionality constant*, and has the unit t^{-1}. The rate constant is characteristic of each radioisotope. We can rewrite Equation 8-11 as

$$\ln\left(\frac{N_t}{N_0}\right) = -kt \qquad [8\text{-}12]$$

where N_0 is the initial number of nuclei undergoing disintegration in the sample and N_t is the number of nuclei at time t. We can use Equation 8-12 to determine the half-life of a radioisotope. By definition, at the half-life time of an isotope $(t_{\frac{1}{2}})$, N_t will be exactly one-half of N_0. Thus,

> The ratio of N_t (at time t) to N_0 (at time 0) is the same as the ratio of activity at time, t, to the activity at time 0.

$$\ln\left(\frac{\frac{1}{2}N_0}{N_0}\right) = -k\,t_{\frac{1}{2}}$$

$$\ln \tfrac{1}{2} = -k\,t_{\frac{1}{2}}$$

Solving mathematically, we can derive an expression for the half-life of a radioisotope. The expression,

$$t_{\frac{1}{2}} = \frac{0.693}{k} \qquad [8\text{-}13]$$

can be applied to the disintegration of a radioactive substance.

EXAMPLE 8-7
Calculating the Rate Constant for Radioisotopes
Calculate the rate constant for the decay of strontium-90.

SOLUTION
1. Determine the half-life of strontium-90 from Table 8-4:

$$t_{\frac{1}{2}} = 28.1 \text{ a}$$

2. Substitute the half-life value into Equation 8-13:

$$t_{\frac{1}{2}} = \frac{0.693}{k}$$

$$k = \frac{0.693}{t_{\frac{1}{2}}}$$

$$= \frac{0.693}{28.1 \text{ a}}$$

$$= 2.5 \times 10^{-2} \text{ a}^{-1}$$

Therefore, the rate constant for strontium-90 is $2.5 \times 10^{-2} \text{ a}^{-1}$.

Harriet Brooks and Radon
Harriet Brooks (1876–1933) was born in Exeter, Ontario. She studied under Ernest Rutherford at McGill University and later worked with J. J. Thompson and Marie Curie. Brooks was one of the first researchers to identify radon and made the first attempt to measure its atomic mass. She did most of her work on the products of radon decay.

Radon is produced by the radioactive decay of heavy elements in many rock formations. Radon can leak through foundations and build up in poorly ventilated houses that are built over these formations. The radon decays into solid polonium-218, which decays inside the lungs to lead and helium nuclei (alpha particles):

$$^{218}_{84}Po \longrightarrow {}^{214}_{82}Pb + {}^{4}_{2}He$$

There is some concern that this alpha radiation may promote lung cancer. The accumulation of radon and other potentially harmful substances in our homes can be avoided by maintaining proper ventilation.

EXAMPLE 8-8
Determining the Half-Life of a Radioisotope

Assume that a small sample of radioisotope has an initial activity of 5.9×10^{12} Bq. This isotope is stored in a concrete container for 25 years. If we assume that the activity of the isotope after 25 years is 2.6×10^{12} Bq, what is the half-life of the isotope?

SOLUTION

1. Determine the value of the rate constant using Equation 8-12:

$$N_0 = 5.9 \times 10^{12} \text{ Bq}$$
$$N_t = 2.6 \times 10^{12} \text{ Bq}$$
$$t = 25 \text{ a}$$

$$\ln\left(\frac{2.6 \times 10^{12}}{5.9 \times 10^{12}}\right) = -k(25)$$
$$k = 3.28 \times 10^{-2} \text{ a}^{-1}$$

2. Calculate the half-life of the isotope using Equation 8-13:

$$t_{\frac{1}{2}} = \frac{0.693}{3.28 \times 10^{-2}}$$
$$= 21.1 \text{ a}$$

Therefore, this isotope has a half-life of 21.1 years. Referring to Table 8-4, we can assume that this isotope is $^{210}_{82}Pb$.

FOLLOW-UP PROBLEMS

1. Calculate the rate constant for the decay of cobalt-60.

2. Assume that scientists at Atomic Energy of Canada Limited have discovered a new radioisotope that might be used in the treatment of malignant tumours. The initial activity of this isotope is 2000 Bq. After six hours, the isotope has an activity of 1500 Bq. What is the half-life of this isotope?

Answers:
1. 0.131 a^{-1}
2. 14.4 h

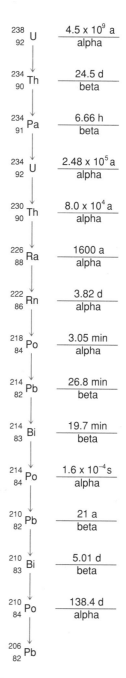

Figure 8-27
The uranium disintegration series.
Half-lives of the products are given.

8-17
Radioisotope Dating

Uranium-238 and radiocarbon dating are two methods used to determine the age of ancient inorganic and organic objects, respectively.

Radioactivity can be used to determine the ages of certain minerals and other materials that have existed since prehistoric times. For example, uranium-238 is present in many minerals. All naturally occurring uranium-238 decays in a series of disintegrations to eventually form lead-206: uranium-238 loses an alpha particle and becomes thorium ($^{234}_{90}$Th); thorium loses a beta particle and becomes protactinium ($^{234}_{91}$Pa); and protactinium, through a few more transmutations, forms the stable, non-radioactive isotope lead-206 (Fig. 8-27). Scientists believe that this is the only way lead-206 is formed in nature. Thus, every mineral containing uranium-238 also contains some lead-206. Because the rate of disintegration for each step is known, it is possible to calculate the age of a mineral by determining the proportion of uranium-238 atoms to lead-206 atoms. Through the use of radioisotope dating, scientists have established the age of the earth to be 4.5×10^9 years.

Radiocarbon dating is used to determine the age of organic materials such as plant and animal remains. However, radiocarbon dating is limited to materials that are less than 50 000 to 75 000 years old, because the activity in older objects is too low to be detected. Radiocarbon dating has proved useful in many situations. It was by this process that the Dead Sea Scrolls were shown to be over 1900 years old and, therefore, authentic. Let us briefly examine the principle underlying the process of radiocarbon dating.

The sequence of events that makes radiocarbon dating possible begins when high-energy cosmic rays bombard the upper atmosphere, producing large numbers of neutrons. These neutrons collide with the nitrogen in the air, changing some of it into carbon-14:

$$^{14}_{7}\text{N} + ^{1}_{0}\text{n} \longrightarrow ^{14}_{6}\text{C} + ^{1}_{1}\text{H}$$

Carbon-14 is radioactive and has a half-life of 5730 years. It combines with oxygen in the upper atmosphere and forms a small concentration of $^{14}\text{CO}_2$, which diffuses down to earth and is absorbed by plants during photosynthesis. Thus, there is a small concentration of carbon-14 in all plant and animal tissues. When the organism dies, the intake of carbon-14 stops, and the amount of carbon-14 in the tissues decreases (Fig. 8-28). By comparing

Willard F. Libby (1908–1980) was awarded the Nobel Prize for chemistry in 1960 for developing the technique of radiocarbon dating.

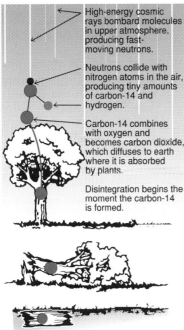

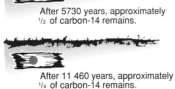

After 5730 years, approximately ¹/₂ of carbon-14 remains.

After 11 460 years, approximately ¹/₄ of carbon-14 remains.

After 17 190 years, approximately ¹/₈ of carbon-14 remains.

After 70 000 years, practically no carbon-14 remains.

Figure 8-28
Formation, absorption and disintegration of carbon-14.

the activity of carbon-14 in any organic material with present-day carbon-14 activity, scientists can determine the age of the organic material.

EXAMPLE 8-9
Determining the Age of an Ancient Object

Archaeologists excavating an ancient city in Egypt found the partial remains of a mummy. A small piece of the mummy was sent to a laboratory where the carbon-14 activity in the sample was found to be 8.5 disintegrations per minute for each gram of carbon. What was the approximate age of the Egyptian mummy? Carbon-14 has a half-life of 5730 years.

SOLUTION

1. Determine the value of k using Equation 8-13 and the half-life of carbon from Table 8-4:

$$t_{\frac{1}{2}} = \frac{0.693}{k}$$

$$k = \frac{0.693}{5730 \text{ a}}$$

$$k = 1.2 \times 10^{-4} \text{ a}^{-1}$$

2. Determine the age of the mummy using Equation 8-12:

$$N_0 = 14 \text{ disintegrations/min·g}$$
$$N_t = 8.5 \text{ disintegrations/min·g}$$
$$k = 1.2 \times 10^{-4} \text{ a}^{-1}$$

$$\ln \frac{N_t}{N_0} = -k t_{\frac{1}{2}}$$

$$\ln \frac{(8.5 \text{ dis/min·g})}{(14 \text{ dis/min·g})} = -(1.2 \times 10^{-4} \text{ a}^{-1}) t_{\frac{1}{2}}$$

$$\ln 0.607 = -(1.2 \times 10^{-4} \text{ a}^{-1}) t_{\frac{1}{2}}$$

$$-0.5 = -(1.2 \times 10^{-4} \text{ a}^{-1}) t_{\frac{1}{2}}$$

$$t_{\frac{1}{2}} = 4167 \text{ a}$$

Thus, the Egyptian mummy is 4167 years old.

8-18

Nuclear Fission

Nuclear fission is the process in which a heavy nucleus is split into smaller fragments.

The discovery and control of nuclear fission is one of the significant events in the history of science. The story of the effort to release and control the energy of the nucleus began with James Chadwick's discovery of the neutron in 1932. Soon after Chadwick's discovery, scientists recognized that this neutral particle would make an excellent projectile for bombarding the nuclei of other atoms; because the neutron carries no charge, it is not repelled by positively charged nuclei.

One of the first to recognize the value of the neutron as an atomic bullet was a young Italian physicist, Enrico Fermi. He and his co-workers bombarded practically every known element with neutrons and succeeded in producing a large number of radioactive isotopes. When Fermi bombarded uranium with neutrons and obtained radioisotopes, he incorrectly assumed that the uranium was absorbing a neutron and changing into elements with atomic numbers 93 and 94. His assumption was a natural one, since it was known that elements with a high neutron-to-proton ratio emitted beta particles and formed elements with higher atomic numbers. Although he was unaware of it at the time, Fermi was probably the first person to achieve nuclear fission.

Three German scientists—Lise Meitner (1878–1968), Otto Hahn (1879–1968) and Fritz Strassman (1902–)—followed Fermi's work with great interest and decided to repeat his experiments. In 1939, they reported that the products of the bombardment of uranium with neutrons were not elements with atomic numbers greater than 92. Rather, they said that the uranium nuclei had split (fissioned), thus forming lighter nuclei (Fig. 8-29). One of the products that Hahn identified was barium, a middle-sized atom. Meitner suggested that when uranium absorbs a neutron, it splits into two approximately equal fragments. Meitner and Hahn called this process *fission*.

These experiments were quickly reproduced and verified by scientists in other countries, who also found that uranium fission was accompanied by the release of neutrons as well as large amounts of energy. Scientists realized the possibility of obtaining and using large amounts of energy from the nucleus and producing a self-sustaining chain reaction that could release a tremendous amount of energy. When a neutron is absorbed by a uranium-235 atom, the uranium nucleus splits into fragments and releases energy and more neutrons. These neutrons might then split other uranium atoms and again release more energy and more neutrons. This process is known as a *chain reaction* and is shown in Fig. 8-30 on the next page.

Since the 1930s and 1940s, great advances have been made in harnessing nuclear energy. Canada has developed and used the CANDU (CANada Deuterium Uranium) reactor, which uses deuterium oxide (heavy water) as a neutron moderator and natural uranium as a fuel. Graphite, also a good moderator, was used at the

ENRICO FERMI
1901–1954
Enrico Fermi was born in Rome and earned his PhD in physics from the University of Pisa at the age of 21.

In 1934, Fermi began experimenting with neutron bombardment of atomic nuclei. He discovered that heavy nuclei such as uranium can absorb a neutron and subsequently lose an electron, producing a new element—in this case, neptunium. He also discovered that placing graphite, paraffin or water between the neutron source and the target slowed the neutrons and increased the nuclear effect.

For this research, Fermi won the Nobel Prize for physics in 1938. After the award ceremony in Sweden, he refused to return to Fascist Italy and went to the United States. In 1939, he became a professor of physics at Columbia University.

The first nuclear reactor was built and operated by Fermi at the University of Chicago in 1942. Fermi predicted the existence of the neutrino in order to account for conservation of spin during radioactive emissions. Element 100, fermium, was named in his honour.

Fermi died in 1954, only a few years after he helped usher in the nuclear age.

Figure 8-29
A uranium-235 nucleus absorbs a neutron and forms a uranium-236 nucleus, which is highly unstable. This immediately splits into two fragments of roughly equal size and produces several neutrons and yields a relatively large amount of energy in the form of gamma rays.

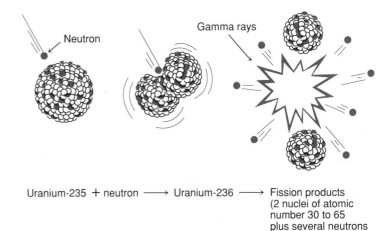

Uranium-235 + neutron ⟶ Uranium-236 ⟶ Fission products
(2 nuclei of atomic number 30 to 65 plus several neutrons and energy)

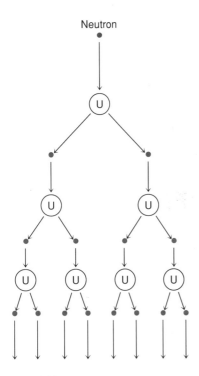

Figure 8-30
Schematic diagram of a chain reaction.

A CANDU reactor was used by India to produce fissile material to build a nuclear weapon in 1974. The Canadian government has since established a policy of not selling CANDU reactors to countries that may use them to build nuclear weapons.

nuclear power plant in Chernobyl, USSR. In the CANDU reactor, the calandria, or reactor vessel, is filled with the moderator to slow down the neutrons so that they will be more easily absorbed by uranium. The fast neutrons that are released by the fission reaction are also slowed down by the moderator. Several hundred pressure tubes containing the uranium fuel penetrate into the calandria. Control rods are distributed throughout the reactor vessel to control the rate of the fission reaction. A coolant (heavy water under pressure) is pumped past the uranium fuel within the pressure tubes. The heat from the fission reaction is transferred to the coolant, which then flows on to boilers or steam generators where it gives up its energy to heat ordinary water. This water is converted to steam and used to drive the giant turbines that produce much of our electricity. CANDU reactors can be refueled while the reactor is running. Figure 8-31 shows a cross-section of the CANDU reactor.

Canada's nuclear power plants are located in Ontario, Quebec and New Brunswick. In 1988, Ontario's 16 CANDU reactors produced 50% of the province's electricity needs.

Despite the nuclear power industry's excellent safety record, there exists widespread public misunderstanding about the risks and benefits of nuclear power generation. Two accidents at nuclear-power reactors have intensified people's concerns about the safety of nuclear energy. In 1979, at Three Mile Island, Pennsylvania, operator error caused a loss of water from the cooling system, raising the temperature of the reactor core. The emergency cooling system, however, worked as designed, cooling the core until the reactor could be shut down. The cleanup was expensive, and it was several years before the plant could operate again. Little radiation was released and no lives were lost. As a result of the Three Mile Island incident, improvements in reactor

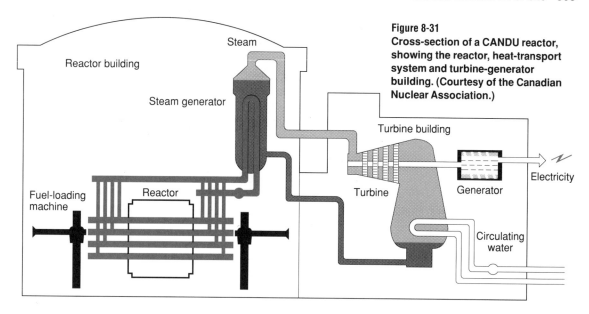

Figure 8-31
Cross-section of a CANDU reactor, showing the reactor, heat-transport system and turbine-generator building. (Courtesy of the Canadian Nuclear Association.)

design have reduced the possibility of future accidents.

On April 26, 1986, an explosion occurred in a nuclear reactor in Chernobyl in the Soviet Union. As a result of the reactor's poor design and the violation of numerous safety rules by the plant operators, the core of the reactor overheated and exploded. The graphite moderator caught fire, making attempts at control very difficult. The Soviet reactor lacked an adequate containment building that would have contained the initial explosion and prevented the release of radioactive material. Such a structure is used on all reactors in the West. Radioactive fallout from Chernobyl spread over much of northern Europe, poisoning the reindeer herds of northern Finland, Sweden and Norway and contaminating Soviet foodstuffs, such as meat and milk, with unsafe levels of radiation. At least 25 people were killed and thousands more may die of cancer in the years to come.

Although nuclear reactors release radioactive material into the atmosphere, this radiation normally adds only 0.01 mSv per year to the average annual human exposure of about 2 mSv (Table 8-5). In comparison, a single whole-body dose of 300 mSv is required to produce mild radiation sickness in humans; 6000 mSv can cause death.

Another concern of the nuclear age is the safe storage and disposal of nuclear-reactor wastes. Much of the radioactive waste produced by nuclear reactors is non-fissile uranium-238, which can be converted in *breeder reactors* into fissile plutonium-239. Although breeder reactors are not considered economically viable, they may someday be able to use nuclear waste as fuel.

Some nuclear waste products have short half-lives and can be

The Manhattan Project
In 1939, U.S. President Franklin D. Roosevelt received a letter drafted by a group of famous physicists and signed by Albert Einstein. The letter suggested that the energy produced by the fission of uranium might be used to build a very powerful bomb and that Nazi Germany might be well on its way to producing one.

Little was done about the letter until the United States entered World War II in December 1941. Research into nuclear weapons began at Manhattan's Columbia University and was soon taking place around the country. The bomb itself was designed by a team led by J. Robert Oppenheimer (1904–1967) in Los Alamos, New Mexico.

The first fission bomb was tested on July 16, 1945. On August 6 and 9, two bombs were dropped on the Japanese cities of Hiroshima and Nagasaki.

The symbol Sv is short for *sievert* and is the SI unit for the dose equivalent of ionizing radiation equal to one joule per kilogram.

TABLE 8-5

AVERAGE ANNUAL HUMAN RADIATION EXPOSURE FROM SOME COMMON SOURCES

	Dose (μSv/year)
Naturally occurring radiation	
Cosmic rays	350
Terrestrial radiation (rocks, buildings)	500
Radioisotopes ($^{40}_{19}K$ and $^{226}_{88}Ra$) in bones	300
Radon in the air	250
Total	1400
Artificial radiation	
Medical sources	
Diagnostic X rays	500
Therapeutic and radioisotopes	70
Fallout from nuclear tests	20
Nuclear power plants	10
Total	600

stored on site until their radioactivity drops to safe levels. Low-level wastes, with their longer half-lives, must be safely isolated for hundreds of years. One proposed method of doing this is to seal the wastes into glass-concrete mixtures in steel barrels and bury them in geologically stable formations in the Canadian Shield.

Although the CANDU reactor is considered as safe as any reactor in the world, no method of generating power can ever be completely safe. Hydro-dam failures, oil spills, pollution from burning coal and oil, refinery fires and natural-gas explosions are all proven threats to human health and the environment. Nuclear power is one of the safest and most reliable methods of generating electricity and is likely to become more important in the future.

8-19

Nuclear Fusion

Nuclear fusion is a thermonuclear reaction in which hydrogen nuclei are fused together to form a helium nucleus.

Even before the discovery of radioactivity, people marvelled at the seemingly limitless source of energy from the sun. Sir Arthur Eddington (1882–1944) suggested in 1920 that the sun produced all of its energy by fusing light nuclei into more complex nuclei. With the help of Einstein's mass-energy equation ($E = mc^2$), Eddington reasoned that this process produced a million times more heat per atom than any ordinary burning process.

In 1930, Dr Hans A. Bethe (1906–) postulated that the hydrogen nuclei (protons) in the sun's interior fused together, under great pressure and at a temperature of 1.5×10^7 K, to form a single helium nucleus as a result of a series of nuclear reactions:

$$^1_1H + ^1_1H \longrightarrow ^2_1H + ^0_1e$$
$$^1_1H + ^2_1H \longrightarrow ^3_2He$$

The fusion of hydrogen nuclei yields energy equivalent to the difference between the sum of the masses of the reactants and that of the fusion products. The net equation for the nuclear fusion reaction in the sun is

$$4^1_1H \longrightarrow ^4_2He + 2^0_1e$$

Continuous nuclear fusion has only been observed in the sun and stars, although research is underway to produce the temperatures needed for thermonuclear reactions on earth. The problems of igniting, controlling and maintaining a fusion reaction in a power plant have been called the greatest scientific challenge today. These problems must be solved before fusion power becomes a practical source of energy.

The series of reactions likely to be used in a fusion reactor uses only deuterium as a fuel:

$$_1^2H + _1^2H \longrightarrow _1^3H + _1^1H + 4.0 \text{ MeV}$$
$$_1^2H + _1^2H \longrightarrow _2^3He + _0^1n + 3.3 \text{ MeV}$$
$$_1^2H + _1^3H \longrightarrow _2^4He + _0^1n + 17.6 \text{ MeV}$$

$$5_1^2H \longrightarrow _2^4He + _2^3He + _1^1H + 2_0^1n + 24.9 \text{ MeV}$$

Isotopes of hydrogen are preferred for fusion reactions because the neutrons reduce the electrostatic repulsion between the hydrogen nuclei (protons). Even so, a very high temperature, around 10^8 K, is needed to overcome this electrostatic repulsion and fuse the nuclei together, releasing a substantial amount of energy.

Since no ordinary container could withstand this amount of heat, new ways of confining fusion reactions must be developed. At present, two methods show promise. The first involves the use of a *Tokamak*, a toroidal-shaped (doughnut-shaped) machine that sets up a magnetic field to contain the fusion reaction. The largest of these machines are the Tokamak Fusion Test Reactor (TFTR) at Princeton University, the Joint European Torus (JET) in England and the JT 60 in Japan.

The second form of confinement is *inertial confinement*. In this method, the tritium and deuterium are confined within a small pellet, 1 mm in diameter. The pellet, usually made of glass, plastic or metal, is heated with lasers. The heat causes the outside of the pellet to vaporize explosively and the interior to collapse, or fuse. As the quality of lasers improves, this method of containment will become more efficient.

The Hydrogen Bomb

The idea of the hydrogen, or thermo-nuclear, bomb originated in a conversation in 1942 between Enrico Fermi and Edward Teller. The hydrogen bomb uses a fission bomb to set off a much more powerful fusion reaction:

$$\text{fission reaction} \longrightarrow \text{heat + neutrons}$$

$$_3^6Li + _0^1n \longrightarrow _2^4He + _1^3H + 4.8 \text{ MeV}$$

$$_1^2H + _1^3H \longrightarrow _2^4He + _0^1n + 17.6 \text{ MeV}$$

The first hydrogen bomb was exploded on Bikini Atoll in the Pacific Ocean on November 2, 1952. It has since replaced the fission bomb as the explosive used in nuclear weapons.

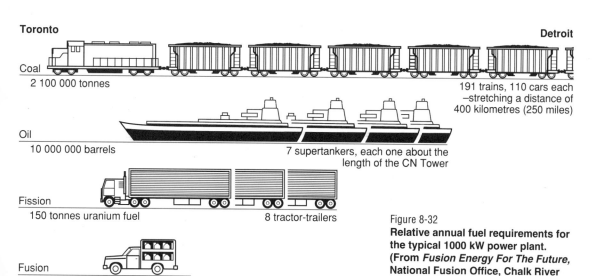

Toronto

Detroit

Coal
2 100 000 tonnes

191 trains, 110 cars each
–stretching a distance of
400 kilometres (250 miles)

Oil
10 000 000 barrels

7 supertankers, each one about the
length of the CN Tower

Fission
150 tonnes uranium fuel

8 tractor-trailers

Fusion
0.6 tonne fusion fuel   1 pickup truck

Figure 8-32
Relative annual fuel requirements for the typical 1000 kW power plant. (From *Fusion Energy For The Future*, National Fusion Office, Chalk River Laboratories, Chalk River, Ontario.)

Cold Fusion

March 23, 1989 could have marked the beginning of a new era of unlimited energy. More likely it will be remembered as an illustration of bad science. Two chemists, Stanley Pons and Martin Fleishmann, announced at a press conference that they had produced fusion in a test tube at room temperature, and that their process produced significantly more energy than it consumed. Their experiment has since been criticized as having been poorly done, and their results have not been replicated. What was thought to be a critical scientific breakthrough that would end energy problems forever is now considered to be a cold issue.

If fusion power becomes economically feasible, it will have a number of advantages over other power sources. Deuterium, the basic fuel, can easily be extracted from seawater and is, for all practical purposes, inexhaustible. In addition, fusion reactions produce no radioactive by-products or other pollutants. The fuel used to produce fusion power is much more compact than other fuels, reducing transportation expenses (Fig. 8-32). Dangerous fusion-plant accidents would be unlikely, since little energy is stored at any one time.

In this chapter we have investigated chemical and nuclear energy. We have looked at the energy possessed by chemical compounds and the energy changes associated with a chemical reaction. We have also discussed the origin and characteristics of nuclear reactions as well as the uses of different forms of radiation.

We noted that reactions that appear to take place in a single step may actually involve a series of simpler steps. The study of reaction rates is known as *chemical kinetics*. A discussion of reaction mechanisms and reaction rates follows in Chapter 9.

RADIOISOTOPES: A MEDICAL TOOL

When most people think of radiation, they think of nuclear weapons and nuclear power plant accidents; they see radiation as a cause of death and disease. What is often overlooked is the importance of radiation as a tool in combating deadly diseases—the foremost being cancer.

Radioisotopes can be used both to identify and treat diseases. The field of *nuclear medicine* involves injecting radioisotopes and examining their patterns of dispersal in order to detect the presence of disease. In *radiation therapy*, a large amount of radioisotope is placed near the patient's body or directly into affected tissues where it emits radiation and kills diseased cells, thus helping to cure the illness.

In nuclear medicine, sensitive radiation detectors are used to detect radiation emitted from radioisotopes that have been injected into the body. Technetium-99M is the most common radioisotope used, although iodine-131, chromium-51 and gallium-67 are also used. For medical applications, a radioisotope must have a half-life short enough to allow the isotope to decay rapidly in the body but not so short that it decays during transportation to the hospital. Technetium-99M, for example, has a half-life of 6 hours. The radioisotope should also emit a gamma ray of a single energy. This is because only one energy contributes to the image. All of

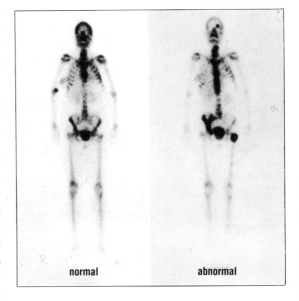

normal   abnormal

the gamma rays from technetium-99M have an energy value of 140 keV.

When an isotope is injected into a healthy body, it disperses to various organs in predictable patterns. After a period of time, the isotope decays or is excreted from the body. In a diseased body, the injected isotope does not disperse in a regular pattern. The location of the radioisotope within the body is detected by use of a gamma camera. When an injected isotope emits radiation, the gamma ray passes through the body and strikes one of a series of radiation detectors that are located inside the camera. Each detector counts the gamma rays that it collects and an image is formed, indicating where the radioisotope has collected. On such images, abnormally dark regions in bones, for example, may indicate bone cancer.

These images can also be used to detect damage to the heart. One image is collected every second after a radioisotope is injected and the speed with which it passes through the heart is examined.

Abnormalities in the thyroid glands can be detected by having the patient swallow about 2 MBq of iodine-131 and then measuring the amount that collects in the thyroid.

One of the newest areas of nuclear-medicine imaging is *positron emission tomography* (PET), which can provide insights into physiological processes in such organs as the brain. Certain radioisotopes such as oxygen-15, carbon-11 and nitrogen-13 emit positrons that quickly combine with electrons to produce gamma-ray photons simultaneously in opposite directions. These gamma rays are detected by a PET scanner, which accurately pinpoints their locations. These isotopes are produced by a cyclotron and usually have very short half-lives.

A typical nuclear-medicine procedure exposes target tissues to about 4 mSv of radiation, which is low compared with the annual recommended whole-body limit of 5 mSv for the general public. The risks from radiation must always be balanced against the opportunity for successful diagnosis and treatment of disease.

Once a disease has been identified, it can be treated by means of radiation therapy, chemotherapy or surgery. The use of isotopes in radiation therapy began shortly after Marie and Pierre Curie discovered radium-226 in 1898. Since then, radioisotopes such as cobalt-60, iridium-192, cesium-137, gold-198 and iodine-125 have replaced radium in radiation therapy.

One of the drawbacks of radiation therapy is that it kills cells indiscriminately—normal cells are destroyed along with diseased cells. One solution is to direct the radiation only at tumours to spare as much normal tissue as possible. One of the most widely used devices for this purpose is the cobalt machine, shown above, which was developed by Canadian physicist Harold Johns (1915–) in 1951. The cobalt machine uses a very strong (2×10^8 MBq) source of cobalt-60 placed about 80 cm from the patient's skin. The source is surrounded by lead, which absorbs all radiation

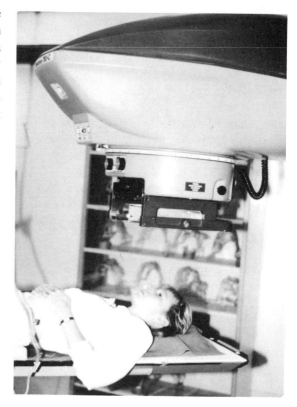

except for a small hole through which the gamma radiation passes into the patient's body. Cobalt-60 is used because it can be made into small, strong sources. Its gamma rays have energies close to 1.25 MeV and its half-life of five years implies that it must be replaced every five years. The cobalt machine is the simplest and most widely used device for radiation therapy.

Radiation can also be delivered directly into the tumour in a technique called *brachytherapy*. Long, hollow needles containing small, solid pellets of radioisotope can be inserted through the skin and into the tumour. Most of the radiation emitted by these pellets is absorbed by the tumour, and damage to normal cells is minimized. Iridium-192, cesium-137, iodine-125 and gold-198 can all be made into small pellets for this purpose. The total activity of the radioisotope is usually about 3700 MBq, which is much less than that needed in the cobalt machine. The pellets are usually left in the body for a few days while the patient is kept in hospital and are then removed.

In recent years, there has been much concern about the harmful effects of radiation. When used carefully, however, radioisotopes can be a highly beneficial tool in the detection and treatment of life-threatening diseases.

QUESTIONS

1. Discuss the idea that the standard of living in a society might be measured in units of kJ/person available in that society.

2. (a) List five ways in which energy can be stored in a molecule. (b) Which of these are potential? (c) Which are kinetic?

3. Explain why the energy stored in chemical bonds is mostly potential rather than kinetic.

4. What is meant by *state property*?

5. Why is it difficult to measure the total energy of a chemical system?

6. Indicate how each of the following affects the total energy, E, of a system. (a) Heat is transferred from the surroundings to the system. (b) Heat is transferred from the system to the surroundings. (c) Light energy is absorbed by the system. (d) Electric work is done by the system. (e) Mechanical work is done by the system. (f) The system contracts in response to external pressure. (g) Externally applied electric energy is used to decompose substances within the system. (h) The system expands against the atmosphere.
   Answers: (a) increases, (d) decreases, (f) increases, (h) decreases

7. For the reaction,

   $$N_2(g) + O_2(g) \longrightarrow 2NO(g)$$

   $\Delta H_r^\circ = 181$ kJ. (a) Which is greater, the total value of ΔH_f° for the reactants or ΔH_f° of the product? (b) Calculate ΔH_f° for the product. (c) How do the strengths of the bonds in an NO molecule compare with those in $N_2(g)$ and $O_2(g)$?

8. Describe the changes in enthalpy, ΔH°, when ice melts spontaneously.

9. Which of the following are exothermic reactions?
   a) $N_2 + 3H_2 \longrightarrow 2NH_3 \qquad \Delta H_r^\circ = -92$ kJ
   b) $2HgO + 181$ kJ $\longrightarrow 2Hg + O_2$
   c) $Fe_2O_3 + 3CO \longrightarrow 2Fe + 3CO_2 + 27.6$ kJ
   d) $N_2 + O_2 \longrightarrow 2NO - 181$ kJ

10. Rewrite each of the equations above so that the coefficient in front of the first formula to the right of the arrow is 1. Show the enthalpy change associated with one mole of this substance.

11. Which substance in each of the following pairs is the more thermally stable:
    a) N_2 with $H_{bc} = +940$ kJ or NCl_3 with $\Delta H_f^\circ = +464$ kJ?
    b) F_2 with $H_{be} = +155$ kJ or HF with $\Delta H_f^\circ = -564.3$ kJ?

12. Table 8-2 gives the ΔH_f° of the hydrogen halides (HF, HCl, HBr and HI). (a) Account for the change in ΔH_f° as the atomic number of the halogen increases. (b) Which of the halogens forms the strongest bond with hydrogen? (c) Which hydrogen halide most readily gives up hydrogen atoms in a chemical reaction?

13. Is it possible for a reaction to be spontaneous (probable) and yet undergo no observable changes when the reactants are mixed? Give an example and explain your answer.

14. Contrast the source and magnitude of energies liberated in chemical reactions and nuclear transformations.

15. (a) What is the meaning of *binding energy*? (b) Which elements in the periodic table have the greatest binding energy per nucleon? (c) Which elements have the most stable nuclei?

Colour Plates I and IV represent various fields in which chemistry is applied. (Above) Nuclear power: the New Brunswick Nuclear Generating Station at Point Lepreau. (Right) Horticulture: a study of hydroponic gardening conducted at the Bruce Energy Centre. (Below) Food science: preservatives being used at a food-processing plant in Vancouver, British Columbia.

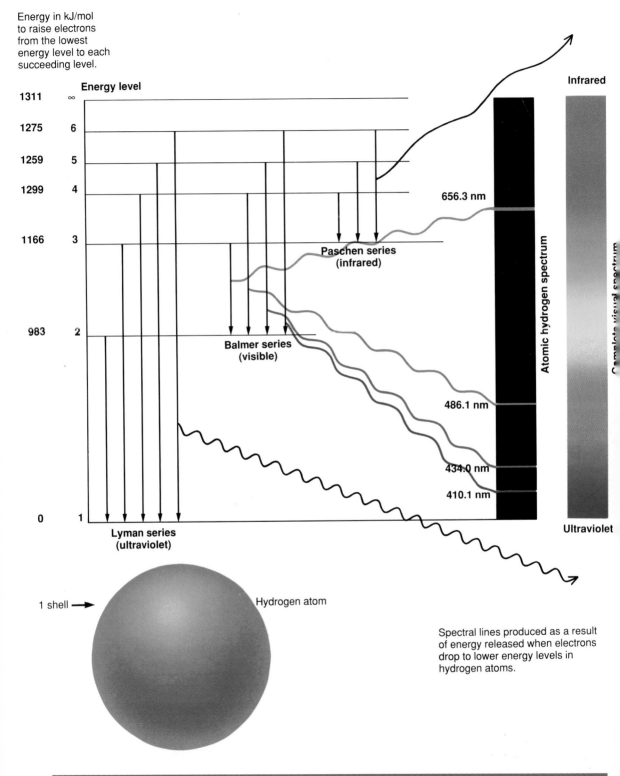

Energy in kJ/mol to raise electrons from the lowest energy level to each succeeding level.

Energy level

1311	∞
1275	6
1259	5
1299	4
1166	3
983	2
0	1

656.3 nm

Paschen series (infrared)

Balmer series (visible)

486.1 nm

434.0 nm

410.1 nm

Lyman series (ultraviolet)

Atomic hydrogen spectrum

Infrared

Ultraviolet

1 shell →

Hydrogen atom

Spectral lines produced as a result of energy released when electrons drop to lower energy levels in hydrogen atoms.

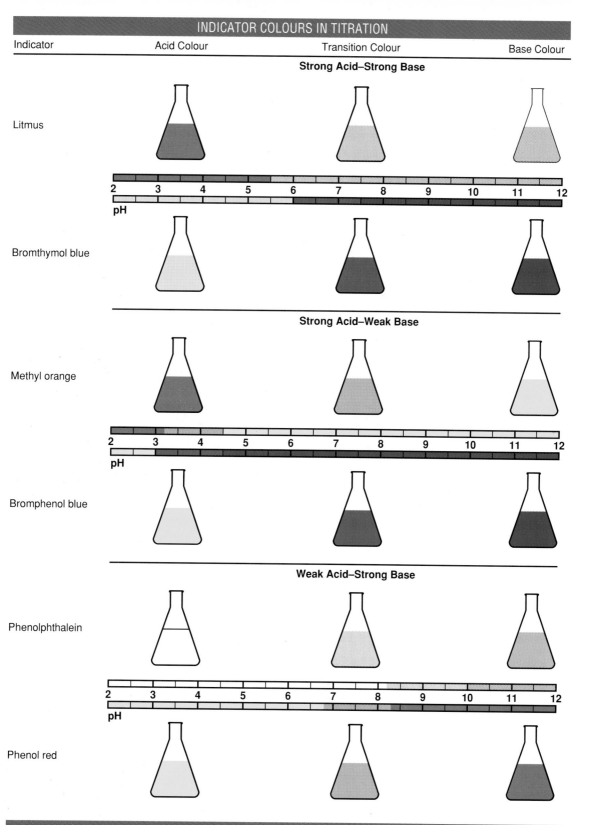

INDICATOR COLOURS IN TITRATION

| Indicator | Acid Colour | Transition Colour | Base Colour |

Strong Acid–Strong Base

Litmus

2   3   4   5   6   7   8   9   10   11   12
pH

Bromthymol blue

Strong Acid–Weak Base

Methyl orange

2   3   4   5   6   7   8   9   10   11   12
pH

Bromphenol blue

Weak Acid–Strong Base

Phenolphthalein

2   3   4   5   6   7   8   9   10   11   12
pH

Phenol red

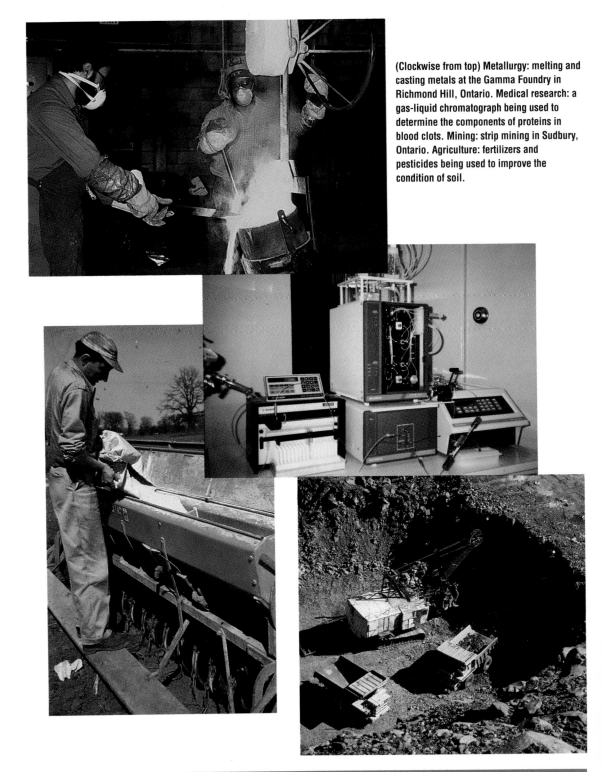

(Clockwise from top) Metallurgy: melting and casting metals at the Gamma Foundry in Richmond Hill, Ontario. Medical research: a gas-liquid chromatograph being used to determine the components of proteins in blood clots. Mining: strip mining in Sudbury, Ontario. Agriculture: fertilizers and pesticides being used to improve the condition of soil.

16. The equation representing the sublimation of I_2 is

$$I_2(s) \longrightarrow I_2(g) \qquad \Delta H_s^\circ = 62.3 \text{ kJ}$$

a) Is the sublimation or crystallization of I_2 favoured by the tendency of a system to achieve a state of maximum entropy?
b) Is the sublimation or crystallization of I_2 favoured by the tendency of a system to achieve a condition of minimum enthalpy?
c) At a given temperature, would solid iodine have a greater or lesser tendency than X_2 to vaporize if the ΔH_s° for X_2 is 78.2 kJ? Assume entropy changes are the same for both substances.

17. Explain the fact that the force of repulsion between two protons in an atomic nucleus does not disrupt the nucleus.

18. (a) How is nuclear stability related to the neutron-proton ratio? (b) Give evidence.

19. (a) What is meant by *radioactivity*? (b) How is it detected? (c) What particles are emitted during radioactive decay? (d) How do you distinguish between the particles in (c)?

20. Why are gamma rays more likely to be dangerous than alpha particles?

21. Copy and complete the following table. *Do not write in this text.*

STRUCTURE OF THE NUCLEUS

Symbol	Z	N	Symbol	Z	N
^1_1H			$^{17}_8O$		
^2_1H	1	1	$^{39}_{19}K$	19	20
^4_2He			$^{40}_{19}K$		
^5_2He			$^{235}_{92}U$		
^6_3Li	3	3	$^{239}_{92}U$	92	147
^7_3Li			$^{239}_{93}Np$		
$^{16}_8O$			$^{239}_{94}Pu$		

22. Identify the particle resulting from the following natural decay processes:
a) $^{238}_{92}U \longrightarrow ? + ^4_2He$
b) $^{214}_{83}Bi \longrightarrow ? + ^0_{-1}e$
c) $^{239}_{93}Np \longrightarrow ? + ^0_{+1}e$
d) $^{226}_{88}Ra \longrightarrow ^{222}_{86}Rn + ?$
e) $^{239}_{92}U \longrightarrow ^{239}_{93}Np + ?$
f) $^{234}_{91}Pa \longrightarrow ^{234}_{92}U + ?$
Answer: (b) $^{214}_{84}Po$

23. Uranium-228 has a half-life of 10 min and undergoes alpha (α) emission when it decays. (a) Write the nuclear equation for the decay of uranium-228. (b) If you had a 1 g sample, how much uranium-228 would you have after 10 min, 20 min, 1 h, 1 d? (c) Write a generalized formula for the answer to part b.

24. What are the characteristics of the following particles emitted by radioactive nuclei: (a) α particle, (b) β particle, (c) γ ray?

25. If radioactive wastes must be stored for seven half-lives before disposal, (a) how long must $^{32}_{15}P$ be stored (see Table 8-4)? (b) what fraction of the $^{32}_{15}P$ originally set aside remains after this time?

26. If $^{32}_{16}S$ is exposed to a neutron field, it captures a neutron and disintegrates, forming radioactive $^{32}_{15}P$. Write a nuclear equation for the reaction.

27. The carbon-nitrogen cycle has been used to explain the source of the sun's energy. It is

$$^{12}_6C + ^1_1H \longrightarrow ^{13}_7N + \gamma$$
$$^{13}_7N \longrightarrow ^{13}_6C + ^0_{+1}e$$
$$^{13}_6C + ^1_1H \longrightarrow ^{14}_7N + \gamma$$
$$^{14}_7N + ^1_1H \longrightarrow ^{15}_8O + \gamma$$
$$^{15}_8O \longrightarrow ^{15}_7N + ^0_{+1}e$$
$$^{15}_7N + ^1_1H \longrightarrow ^{12}_6C + ^4_2He$$

Show that this sequence is equivalent to

$$4^1_1H \longrightarrow ^4_2He + 2^0_{+1}e$$

PROBLEMS

1. A calorimeter containing 1.00 L of water at 23°C is warmed to 68°C when 5.00 g of butter is burned. Calculate (a) the heat absorbed by the water, (b) the heat given off by the oxidation of butter fat in J/g and kJ/g. **Answers: (a) 1.88×10^5 J, (b) 37 620 J/g, 37.6 kJ/g**

2. A man is immersed in a tub containing 60.0 L of water. The heat of his body raises the temperature of the water from 30.0°C to 31.5°C in one hour. (a) At what rate is the man giving off heat? (b) How many kJ would he give off in a day? (c) How many grams of fat ($\Delta H_{combustion\ of\ fat} = 39.7$ kJ/g) would he need per day to supply this much energy? **Answers: (a) 376.2 kJ/h, (b) 9029 kJ/d, (c) 227 g**

3. Use the following data to determine the heat of combustion of a candle made of paraffin:

Mass of water in calorimeter	340 g
Temperature of water at start	15.0°C
Temperature of water at end	31.2°C
Mass of candle at start	24.7 g
Mass of candle at end	23.6 g

4. (a) How many kJ of heat are evolved when 6.0 g of pure carbon is completely burned? (b) How many grams of carbon must be burned to furnish 39.3 kJ of heat? The combustion of carbon is:

$$C(s) + O_2(g) \longrightarrow CO_2(g) \quad \Delta H_r^\circ = -393.5 \text{ kJ}$$

5. How many grams of carbon would have to be burned in order to heat 1000 L of water from 20.0°C to 100°C?

$$\text{Specific heat capacity of water} = \frac{4.18 \text{ J}}{\text{gH}_2\text{O°C}}$$

Assume the density of water is 1.0 g/mL. **Answer: 1×10^4 g**

6. When 1.37 g of barium reacts with oxygen gas at 25°C and atmospheric pressure, there is a net release of 5.56 kJ after the BaO cools to a temperature of 25°C. What is ΔH_f° for BaO?

$$Ba(s) + \tfrac{1}{2}O_2(g) \longrightarrow BaO(s)$$

7. Given the following equation, answer the questions below.

$$H_2(g) + \tfrac{1}{2}O_2(g) \longrightarrow H_2O(g) + 241.6 \text{ kJ}$$

(a) How much heat is evolved in the formation of 2.5 mol of H_2O? (b) How much heat is liberated when 1.75 mol of H_2 burns in excess oxygen? (c) Write a thermochemical equation corresponding to the reaction above for the combustion of 2 mol of H_2. (d) How much heat is absorbed when 4 mol of H_2O decomposes in the reverse reaction? (e) How much heat is evolved for each gram of hydrogen burned? **Answer: (a) 606 kJ**

8. Using Table 8-2, calculate ΔH_r° for the following reactions. In each case, (i) state whether the reaction is exothermic or endothermic, (ii) rewrite the equation as a thermochemical equation to include the heat term and (iii) indicate whether the products have a greater or smaller enthalpy than the reactants.
ΔH_f° for $Ca(OH)_2 = -986.6$ kJ/mol.
a) $SO_2(g) + \tfrac{1}{2}O_2(g) \longrightarrow SO_3(g)$
b) $CaO(s) + H_2O(l) \longrightarrow Ca(OH)_2(s)$
c) $N_2(g) + 3H_2(g) \longrightarrow 2NH_3(g)$
d) $C_6H_6(l) + \tfrac{3}{2}O_2(g) \longrightarrow 6C(s) + 3H_2O(l)$
e) $NH_3(g) + HCl(g) \longrightarrow NH_4Cl(s)$
Answers: (a) −98.8 kJ, (b) −65.6 kJ, (c) −92.0 kJ, (d) −905.5 kJ, (e) −175.9 kJ

9. Calculate the heat of reaction, ΔH_r°, for each of the following reactions, using the data from Table 8-2.

a) $CH_4(g) + 2O_2(g) \longrightarrow CO_2(g) + 2H_2O(l)$

b) $C_2H_2(g) + 2H_2(g) \longrightarrow C_2H_6(g)$

c) $C_3H_8(g) + 5O_2(g) \longrightarrow$
$$3CO_2(g) + 4H_2O(l)$$

d) $H_2O(g) + C(s) \longrightarrow CO(g) + H_2(g)$

Answers: (b) −311.5 kJ, (d) +132.0 kJ

10. Calculate ΔH_r° for

$$SO_2(g) + \tfrac{1}{2}O_2(g) \longrightarrow SO_3(g)$$

from the following equations:

$S(s) + O_2(g) \longrightarrow SO_2(g) \qquad \Delta H_f^\circ = -296.6 \text{ kJ}$

$S(s) + \tfrac{3}{2}O_2(g) \longrightarrow SO_3(g) \qquad \Delta H_f^\circ = -394.8 \text{ kJ}$

11. ΔH_r° for the complete combustion of ethyl-ene (C_2H_4) is −1410 kJ:

$C_2H_4(g) + 3O_2(g) \longrightarrow 2CO_2(g) + 2H_2O(l)$
$$\Delta H_r^\circ = -1410 \text{ kJ}$$

Use this information and the data in Table 8-2 to calculate the heat of formation, ΔH_f°, for ethylene.

12. Calculate ΔH_r° for

$$C(s) + H_2O(g) \longrightarrow CO(g) + H_2(g)$$

from the following equations:

$C(s) + O_2(g) \longrightarrow CO_2(g) \quad \Delta H_f^\circ = -393.5 \text{ kJ}$

$CO(g) + \tfrac{1}{2}O_2(g) \longrightarrow CO_2(g)$
$$\Delta H_f^\circ = -283.0 \text{ kJ}$$

$H_2(g) + \tfrac{1}{2}O_2(g) \longrightarrow H_2O(g)$
$$\Delta H_f^\circ = -242.0 \text{ kJ}$$

Answer: 132 kJ

13. The heat of combustion, ΔH_c°, for ethylene glycol $((CH_2OH)_2)$ is −1178.0 kJ:

$(CH_2OH)_2(l) + 2\tfrac{1}{2}O_2(g) \longrightarrow$
$$2CO_2(g) + 3H_2O(l)$$

Use this information and the data in Table 8-2 to calculate ΔH_f° for $(CH_2OH)_2(l)$.

14. Calculate the heat of combustion for C_2H_6 from the following information:

$C_2H_4 + 3O_2 \longrightarrow 2CO_2 + 2H_2O$
$$\Delta H_f^\circ = -1409.5 \text{ kJ}$$

$C_2H_4 + H_2 \longrightarrow C_2H_6 \qquad \Delta H_f^\circ = -136.7 \text{ kJ}$

$H_2 + \tfrac{1}{2}O_2 \longrightarrow H_2O \qquad \Delta H_f^\circ = -285.5 \text{ kJ}$

15. Calculate the heat of formation, ΔH_f°, for ethane (C_2H_6) from the following data:

ΔH_c° for $C_2H_6 \quad = -1555.0 \text{ kJ}$

ΔH_f° for $CO_2 \quad = -393.0 \text{ kJ}$

ΔH_f° for $H_2O(l) = -285.5 \text{ kJ}$

16. Use the bond energies listed in Table 8-3 to calculate H_{be} for the reaction

$$2H_2(g) + O_2(g) \longrightarrow 2H_2O(g)$$

17. Use the bond energies listed in Table 8-3 to calculate the approximate heat of reaction for the combustion of ethene gas.

$$C_2H_4(g) + 3O_2(g) \longrightarrow 2CO_2(g) + 2H_2O(g)$$

Answer: −1062 kJ

18. It has been found by experiment that the molar mass of the $^{222}_{86}Rn$ nuclide is 221.9703 g and that of the $^{218}_{83}Po$ nuclide is 217.9630 g. As you may remember from Section 8-14, the molar mass of helium is 4.001 50 g. Given this information, calculate the energy evolved (in kJ) for the following nuclear reaction:

$$^{222}_{86}Rn \longrightarrow {}^{218}_{83}Po + {}^{4}_{2}He$$

Answer: 5.2×10^8 kJ

19. Let us assume that archaeologists have just found remnants from an early culture that existed in northern Canada thousands of years ago. If the artifact is analysed and found to give off 10.8 disintegrations per minute per gram of carbon-14, how old is the artifact?

In 1937, the airship *Hindenburg* caught fire while approaching Lakehurst, New Jersey. The tragedy effectively ended the use of hydrogen in passenger airships.

Rates of Chemical Reactions

Chemical processes occur at different rates. Sometimes we wish to increase the rate of a reaction so that the process is more efficient, practical and economical. This is usually the objective of the chemical industry, which produces thousands of substances that enhance our standard of living and add to our well-being. In our daily activities, we also try to make many processes more quick and efficient, such as cooking, cleaning, drying paints and finishes, or relieving pain. On the other hand, we sometimes wish to decrease the rate of undesirable processes such as spoilage of food, spontaneous ignition or explosion of fuels, and corrosion of metals.

Much progress has been made in the study of reaction rates. Scientists, however, do not always know exactly how or why a particular substance increases the rate of a certain chemical reaction, because they do not know the exact paths or sequence of steps involved in the reaction. The study of reaction rates helps to determine the steps in a reaction path. This study, called *chemical kinetics*, is one of the frontiers of chemistry and provides an almost unlimited supply of problems and opportunities for those interested in chemical research.

The primary objective of a scientist who does basic research on

Figure 9-1
In the lab, students react magnesium with hydrochloric acid and measure the volume of hydrogen gas produced at regular time intervals. A graph of the results will show how the concentrations of the product (hydrogen) varies with time.

reaction rates is to explain and describe macroscopic observations of these rates at the microscopic level in terms of atoms, molecules and ions. Since events on the microparticle level cannot be observed directly, the task of identifying the steps in a reaction is very difficult.

The identification and analysis of the intermediate steps of a reaction are extremely complex and beyond the scope of this text. In this chapter, we will focus primarily on
– how reaction rates are measured
– the factors that affect the rate of a reaction
– the use of the molecular theory to explain why reaction rates differ
– the energy changes that occur during a reaction
– the meaning of reaction mechanisms

THE MEANING AND MEASUREMENT OF REACTION RATES

The rate of a reaction refers to the speed at which the reactant molecules change to product molecules. Reaction rates range from the extremely slow processes in the weathering of rocks or the formation of stalagmites and stalactites in limestone caves to the instantaneous explosive reaction in the detonation of dynamite. For some laboratory reactions, we are able to qualitatively measure the relative rate of a reaction by observing how quickly a product appears or a reactant disappears. For example, when a piece of magnesium ribbon is placed in a beaker of dilute hydrochloric acid, an extremely rapid evolution of hydrogen gas (product) takes place as the magnesium (reactant) rapidly disappears (Fig. 9-1). When a piece of iron is placed in the same acid, hydrogen gas is evolved slowly, and the iron disappears at a relatively slow rate. Evidently, the rate of the first reaction is much faster than that of the second.

9-1
Rate of Reaction

The rate of a chemical reaction is defined as the change in concentration of a reactant or a product per unit time.
The magnitude of the reaction rate depends on the unit of time. The rate of a reaction tells how the concentration of a product or a reactant changes over time. In the reaction rate, the units of concentration are divided by time, for example, mol/L·s. For very slow reactions, the time can be in minutes, hours, days or years.

The rate of formation of a product is always positive; the rate of disappearance of a reactant is always negative. However, the rate of a reaction is always positive.

Let us consider a reaction represented by the equation

$$A + B \longrightarrow AB$$

In this reaction, one mole of A reacts with one mole of B to form one mole of AB. Suppose we measure the concentration of reactant A and the concentration of the product AB periodically as the reaction proceeds and plot a graph, as shown in Fig. 9-2. We can calculate the average rate of reaction over any particular time interval in terms of the decrease in concentration of reactant A. For example, during the first 40 s of the reaction, reactant A decreases in concentration from 1.0 mol/L to 0.50 mol/L. The rate of reaction can be calculated as follows:

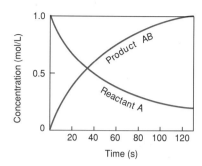

$$\text{rate} = \frac{\text{decrease in } [A]}{\text{time}}$$
$$= \frac{1.0 - 0.50}{40 \text{ s}}$$
$$= 0.012 \text{ mol/L·s}$$

Alternatively, the product AB increases in concentration from 0 to 0.50 mol/L during the first 40 s. Thus, the rate of reaction is

$$\text{rate} = \frac{\text{increase in } [AB]}{\text{time}}$$
$$= \frac{0.50 - 0}{40 \text{ s}}$$
$$= 0.012 \text{ mol/L·s}$$

Figure 9-2
Graph showing how the concentrations of reactant A and product AB vary with time. The steepness of the curve (slope of tangent to the curve) at any point is a measure of the rate of the reaction at that point and is called the *instantaneous rate*.

Note that since one mole of A yields one mole of AB, the rate at which A disappears is the same as the rate at which AB appears.

Experiments show that for most reactions, the concentrations of all participants change most rapidly at the beginning of the reaction. That is, the concentration of the products increases most rapidly and the concentration of the reactants decreases most rapidly at the beginning of the reaction. This means that *the rate of a reaction changes with time*. Therefore, a rate must be identified with a specific time.

If we calculate the rate of reaction over different time intervals using the data from Fig. 9-2, we can obtain the average rate of reaction for each specific time interval. We can also use the graph to determine the rate of reaction at any specific point by drawing a tangent to the curve and finding its slope. This gives us the ratio of the change in concentration to the change in time, which is equivalent to the reaction rate.

When referring to the rate of a reaction, it is important to specify the species for which the rate is being considered. For example, look at the following reaction:

$$2A + B \longrightarrow A_2B$$

The rate of most reactions is greatest at the beginning of the reaction. At this stage, the concentrations of the reactants are at their highest and, thus, more collisions between reactant molecules occur.

Note that a reaction rate is not constant.

Since two moles of A yield one mole of A_2B, the rate at which A disappears is twice the rate at which A_2B appears; the rate at which B disappears is the same as the rate at which A_2B appears.

9-2
Measuring Reaction Rates

Reaction rates can be measured by directly measuring changes in concentrations of the components or by measuring changes in concentration-related properties such as colour, density, electric conductivity and pressure.

Since the rate of a reaction is defined as the change in concentration per unit time, we need to measure the concentrations of the reactants at different times to determine this rate. The techniques used to determine the difference in concentrations vary with the reaction and the available apparatus. For reactions in solution, small samples may be periodically withdrawn from the reaction mixture in order to determine the concentration by methods of quantitative analysis (titration). For reactions involving coloured substances, changes in the colour can be measured with special instruments and related to changes in concentration of the coloured substances. A number of other properties such as density and electric conductivity may vary with concentration. These also can be measured and related to changes in concentration.

For many reactions involving gases in a closed system, changes in pressure may be related to changes in the quantity of reactants or products. The development of instruments that enable scientists to rapidly identify and measure the components of a reaction has facilitated research in the field of chemical kinetics. Absorption spectrometers and gas chromatographs are two instruments widely used to identify and analyse reaction mixtures.

FACTORS AFFECTING REACTION RATES

For homogeneous reactions there are four general factors that affect the rate of a reaction:
– the nature of the reactants
– the concentrations of the reactants
– temperature
– catalysts

For heterogeneous reactions, a fifth factor can also affect the rate of reaction: the surface area that lies between the two phases of the system. The experiments described in the following sections illustrate how these five factors affect reaction rates.

Gunpowder
Gunpowder, or black powder, was first developed in China around the seventh century. It is a mixture of charcoal, sulfur and saltpeter (potassium nitrate).

There are many factors that affect the rate of reaction of gunpowder. Thorough mixing is essential so that the ingredients can react with each other. If non-reactive ingredients are present, or if there is too much of a reactive ingredient, the reaction will be impeded, producing a "fizz" instead of a "bang." If the gunpowder is not packed tightly into its container, the reaction will not spread rapidly enough and the powder will burn instead of exploding. The fineness of the granules is also important. Finer granules have a greater total surface area, which allows for a faster reaction and produces a more effective explosion.

A heterogeneous reaction is a reaction in which there is more than one phase present in the system.

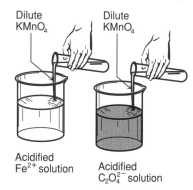

9-3
Nature of the Reactants

Reactions between simple ions are almost instantaneous; reactions between more complex ions take longer.

Let us conduct an experiment to compare the rate of the reaction between permanganate ions (MnO_4^-) and iron(II) ions (Fe^{2+}) in acid solution, and the rate of the reaction between permanganate ions and oxalate ions ($C_2O_4^{2-}$) in acid solution (Fig. 9-3). We can qualitatively estimate the relative rates of reaction by noting the time required for the purple colour of the permanganate solution to disappear. Observations reveal that in the first procedure, the permanganate solution loses its colour almost instantly. In the second procedure, the colour remains for a relatively long period of time. This means that permanganate ions react rapidly with iron(II) ions but slowly with oxalate ions. The only difference in the two reactions is the nature of one reagent; iron(II) (Fe^{2+}) is a simple ion, whereas an oxalate ion ($C_2O_4^{2-}$) is polyatomic and contains covalent bonds that must be broken or weakened in the reaction process. In general, reactions between simple ions such as Ag^+ and Cl^- ions, which combine in a one-to-one mole ratio, are almost instantaneous. Experimental measurements show that most of these reactions occur in about one-millionth of a second. On the basis of these experiments, we can conclude that the nature of the reactants affects the rate of a reaction and that complex species generally react more slowly than simple ions. You will find that there are several reasons why reactions between complex molecules are usually slow compared with those between simple ions.

Figure 9-3
The KMnO$_4$ solution is purple and is decolorized quickly in the Fe^{2+} ion solution. A relatively large time interval is required for the same number of KMnO$_4$ drops to be decolorized in the oxalate ion solution.

9-4
Concentrations of the Reactants

The rate of a reaction increases as the concentrations of the reactants increase.

When solutions of potassium iodate (KIO_3) and sodium sulfite (Na_2SO_3) are mixed, a reaction occurs, and iodine (I_2) is produced. If we add starch to the reaction mixture at the start of the experiment, we can detect the production of I_2, which forms a deep blue compound with starch. The time taken for the blue colour to appear indicates the rate of the reaction between KIO_3 and Na_2SO_3. The faster the reaction, the shorter the time required for the blue compound to appear. By adding diluted solutions of KIO_3, we can see how changing the concentration of a reactant affects the rate of the reaction (Fig. 9-4). In this case, decreasing the concentration decreases the rate of reaction. Conversely, we find that increasing the concentration of KIO_3 increases the rate of reaction.

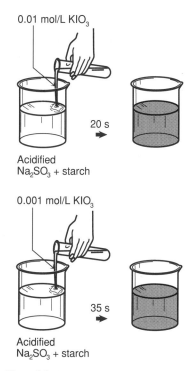

Figure 9-4
Reducing the concentration of a reactant reduces the rate of the reaction and increases the time required for its completion.

Fever and Hypothermia
The human body must maintain a constant temperature of 37°C, since temperature affects the rate of metabolic reactions.

Fever is a mechanism the body uses to fight infection; an increase of 1 to 3°C raises the rate of reactions within the body. An increase of 4°C or more can damage the brain and cause death.

Hypothermia is an abnormal lowering of body temperature. During heart surgery, the patient's body temperature is sometimes lowered to 28 to 30°C. At this temperature, reactions within the body slow down.

Accidental hypothermia is caused by immersion in cold water or by prolonged environmental exposure. As the body temperature drops, pulse and respiration rates and blood pressure are lowered. At body temperatures below 32°C, immediate warming is necessary or the brain will fail from lack of oxygen, and death will result. There are, however, cases of children who have survived long periods of immersion in cold water. They survived because their bodies were cooled rapidly enough for their metabolisms to slow down without causing damage to the brain.

Figure 9-5
A sugar cube treated with ashes readily ignites. The oxidation is catalyzed by the oxides in the ashes. An untreated sugar cube does not burn when placed in the flame of a match.

The effect of an increase or decrease in the concentration of oxygen on the rate of burning is familiar to most people. A piece of steel wool heated in air (21% oxygen by volume) burns slowly, but when heated in pure oxygen, undergoes rapid combustion as evidenced by a dazzling shower of sparks.

9-5
Temperature

Reactions occur faster at higher temperatures.

We can use the reaction between a KIO_3 solution and an Na_2SO_3 solution to study the effect of changing temperature on the rate of a reaction. We can do this by warming the solutions and measuring the time required for the blue colour of the compound to appear at different temperatures.

Experiments have shown that the time required for the blue colour to appear decreases as the temperature of the KIO_3 solution is increased. This is evidence that the rate of the reaction increases as the temperature rises.

The relationship between the reaction rate and temperature can be seen in many household applications. For example, a refrigerator is used to store foods, such as meat and milk, at low temperatures to slow down reactions that may result in spoilage. Pressure cookers are used to obtain higher temperatures in order that the reactions involved in cooking food will take place at a faster rate. In general, a 10°C rise in temperature doubles or sometimes triples the rate of a reaction. It should be noted that there are a few reactions whose rates decrease with increasing temperature. However, the explanations for these exceptions are beyond the scope of this text.

9-6
Catalysts

A catalyst is any reagent that increases the rate of reaction but is not consumed during the reaction.

In many reactions, it may be possible to introduce a *catalyst*, that is, a chemical substance that can increase the rate of the reaction without being consumed during the reaction. In some cases, a catalyst may be consumed during an intermediate step of a reaction but is regenerated in subsequent steps so that, overall, there is no net consumption.

We can study the effect of a catalyst on the reaction between the MnO_4 and $C_2O_4^{2-}$ ions described in Section 9-3. By adding a small quantity of a manganese(II) compound to the $C_2O_4^{2-}$ solution, we find that the purple colour of the MnO_4^- disappears much more rapidly than without the manganese salt. Thus, the manganese(II) compound is a catalyst for the reaction.

Enzymes produced by living organisms catalyze digestive and other biochemical processes. For example, ptyalin in human saliva increases the rate at which starch is converted to maltose. Without this catalyst, the conversion would take weeks and would be of little biological value.

There are two types of catalysts: homogeneous and heterogeneous. Homogeneous catalysts are in the same phase as the reactants. Heterogeneous catalysts are in phases different from the reactants.

ENZYMES: BIOLOGICAL CATALYSTS

When you chew a cracker and hold it in your mouth, you notice a sweet taste. This sensation is the result of salivary enzymes breaking down the starch in the cracker to sugar. Enzymes are important components of the body; without them, you would be unable to digest food and repair damaged tissues.

Enzymes are true catalysts: they enhance chemical reactions that would otherwise proceed very slowly and are not consumed during the reaction. Enzymes speed up reactions by combining with a reactant to produce a new complex that has a lower activation energy. Enzymes are far more active and have a higher degree of specificity than non-biological catalysts. They also function under relatively mild temperatures and pH conditions. Unlike inorganic catalysts, enzymes only accelerate one pathway of a reaction; thus, no toxic by-products are formed.

The existence of biological catalysts was first proposed in the early 1800s when it was observed that secretions of the stomach digested meat and that saliva broke down starch into sugar. French chemist Louis Pasteur used the term "ferments" to describe the agents in yeast responsible for the transformation of sugar into alcohol. He believed that they were an integral part of the yeast cells. It was not until 1897 that the enzymes in yeast were isolated in soluble active form by German chemist Eduard Buchner. Buchner's work spurred further research into the isolation and study of enzymes. In 1926, the American biochemist James Sumner isolated the first pure enzyme crystal, urease, and suggested that all enzymes were proteins. This conclusion was not generally accepted until the 1930s, when other enzymes were crystallized and found to be proteins.

There is still much that is unknown about enzymes, including their specific reaction mechanisms. However, chemists have developed a general explanation to describe how enzymes work. Recently, Sidney Altman (1939–), a Canadian-born biology professor at Yale University, shared the 1989 Nobel Prize for biochemistry with Thomas Cech for their discovery of the catalytic properties of ribonucleic acid (RNA). Altman's and Cech's work disproved the concept that all enzymes are proteins. Most enzymes are large protein molecules of high molecular mass, generally ranging from 12 000 to over 1 000 000. It is believed that enzymes are so large because they must change shape in order to function; only large proteins have the ability to change their shape. The complexity of enzymes means that their surfaces have highly specific *active sites* into which the reactant molecules fit exactly. In 1894, German chemist Emil Fischer suggested that many enzymes work by a lock-and-key mechanism, as shown below:

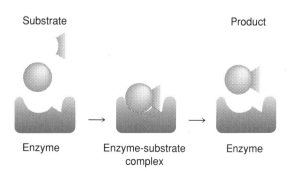

Substrate		Product
Enzyme	Enzyme-substrate complex	Enzyme

The enzyme's active site has the correct shape and polarity needed to attract and hold the reactant in position for the reaction to occur. Once the reactant, or *substrate*, reaches the active site, the enzyme changes shape to accommodate it. Subsequently, the enzyme changes the shape of the substrate and lowers the activation energy of the enzyme-substrate complex. This situation is called the *induced-fit model* and can be likened to the change in shape of a glove when a hand is inserted into it.

Many enzyme-catalyzed reactions have more than two different substrate molecules that bind to the enzyme and participate in a reaction. For example, in the reaction,

$$\text{ATP} + \text{glucose} \xrightarrow{\text{hexokinase}} \text{ADP} + \text{glucose 6-phosphate}$$
$$\text{(adenosine} \qquad\qquad\qquad \text{(adenosine}$$
$$\text{triphosphate)} \qquad\qquad\qquad \text{diphosphate)}$$

hexokinase catalyzes the reaction. Reactions that involve more than one substrate proceed by two different pathways. In *single-displacement reactions*, the two substrates are bound to the enzyme to form a complex, which then reacts to form the desired products. In the second pathway, called *double-displacement reactions*, one substrate is bound to the enzyme, followed by the transfer of its functional group to the enzyme. After the first substrate leaves the enzyme, the second substrate becomes bound to the enzyme and accepts the functional group. The reaction shown above is an example of a double-displacement reaction in which the ATP molecule is attracted to the enzyme and transfers a phosphate group to hexokinase. The resulting ADP is released, and a glucose molecule takes its place. The phosphate group then bonds to the glucose to form glucose 6-phosphate.

Enzymes are named by adding the suffix *-ase* to the name of the substrate they are modifying. Hence, urease catalyzes reactions involving urea. Because the same enzyme can have two different names, enzymes are systematically named according to the reactions they catalyze. Each enzyme is classified into six major classes: *oxidoreductases*, which transfer electrons; *transferases*, which transfer groups; *hydrolases*, which transfer groups to water; *lysases*, which add groups to or remove groups from double bonds; *isomerases*, which yield isomeric forms; and *ligases*, which form C—C, C—S, C—O and C—N bonds by condensation reactions. For example, hexokinase is systematically named *ATP: glucose phosphotransferase* because it catalyzes the transfer of a phosphate group from ATP to glucose.

Many enzymes need an inorganic ion, known as a *cofactor*, to function. This is why all living organisms require trace amounts of elements such as iron, copper, magnesium, manganese, potassium, nickel, molybdenum and selenium. For example, DNA polymerase, which is essential to the replication of bacteria, requires a Zn^{2+} ion. Similarly, hexokinase requires an Mg^{2+} ion as a cofactor. Some enzymes require complex organic molecules, called *coenzymes*, in order to act.

Enzymes can be inhibited or poisoned by molecules that are similar in shape or function to the normal substrate. There are two types of inhibitors: irreversible and reversible. *Irreversible inhibitors* combine with and destroy a functional group on the enzyme molecule necessary for its activity. For example, the enzyme acetylcholinesterase is important in the transmission of nerve impulses. The insecticide malathion is converted by insects into diisopropylfluorophosphate, a chemical that irreversibly inhibits acetylcholinesterase. Penicillin, discovered by Sir Arthur Fleming in 1929, inhibits the enzyme transpepsidase, required by bacteria to make cell walls rigid. Without this enzyme, the cell walls break down and the bacteria die. The toxicity of heavy metals such as lead and arsenic is due to their ability to poison important enzymes.

Reversible inhibitors compete with the substrate for binding to the active site on the enzyme; once attached to the enzyme, the inhibitor cannot be transformed. Sulfa drugs are effective against bacteria because they compete with para-aminobenzoic acid in the synthesis of folic acid, an important co-enzyme. The fake folic acid inhibits the action of the co-enzyme, eventually killing the bacteria.

Genetic disorders can affect the structure and function of particular enzymes; in some cases there may be an absence of an enzyme in the tissues. For example, the genetic disease, phenyl ketonuria, is caused by a defect in the gene that codes for the manufacture of the enzyme, phenylalanine 4-mono-oxygenase. This enzyme is required for one of the stages in the breakdown of the amino acid, phenylalanine. If it does not function properly, phenylalanine will not be broken down and will build up in the body, eventually causing brain damage. Screening for phenylketonuria at birth is now standard; the only treatment for this disease is to avoid foods that contain large amounts of phenylalanine, such as diet soft drinks containing the artificial sweetener Aspartame.

Genetic alterations in enzymes need not always be harmful to the organism. Sometimes an alteration in an enzyme can provide the organism with a special advantage over other organisms in its struggle for survival in an ever-changing world.

Surface Area

Increasing the surface area of the solid phase of a heterogeneous reaction increases the rate of the reaction.

The burning of wood is a heterogeneous reaction between solid carbon and oxygen gas (O_2). You have probably observed that wood chips burn much faster than logs. This is because the wood chips have a much larger surface area at which the reaction between carbon and oxygen can take place. As the surface area increases, the rate of the reaction increases.

A finely divided reactant has a greater surface area than a solid mass and reacts faster. If, for example, dilute hydrochloric acid (HCl) is added to a mass of powdered zinc (Zn) in one test tube and to a solid piece of zinc of the same mass in another test tube, we find that the powdered zinc reacts and disappears much faster than the solid piece. Similarly, if a glowing splint is lowered into a beaker containing grain dust particles, it will burst into flames (Fig. 9-6). However, if a glowing splint is put into a beaker containing a solid mass of grain, no burning is observed. Grain elevators, such as the one in Olds, Alberta (Fig. 9-7), have exploded because a spark ignited the grain dust. The reaction rate in such an explosion is so rapid that the heat generated by the explosion is not dissipated, and much damage can result; the explosion in Fig. 9-7, for example, levelled many buildings.

We now need a model that will help us explain our macroscopic observations of reaction rates at the microscopic level of atoms, molecules and ions. The model we will use is known as the *collision theory of reaction rates*.

COLLISION THEORY OF REACTION RATES

We can explain our observations of reaction rates using the collision theory of reaction rates. This theory assumes that the particles of a reaction mixture are in constant motion and that for a reaction to occur, there must be collisions between the reacting particles. If the molecules do not collide, no reaction occurs. In the case of the decomposition of a single species, the collision theory assumes that the species must have absorbed light or gained energy by contact with another microparticle.

According to the collision theory, the rate of a reaction depends on two factors: the number of collisions per unit time between the reacting molecules and the fraction of these collisions that are successful or effective in producing new product molecules.

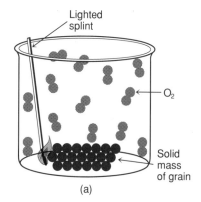

(a)

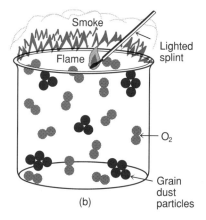

(b)

Figure 9-6
A heterogeneous reaction. The solid mass of grain represented in (a) has a small surface area compared with the finely divided grain dust represented in (b). The reaction between the grain dust and oxygen in (a) takes place very slowly compared with (b).

Figure 9-7
This grain elevator in Olds, Alberta, exploded in 1982.

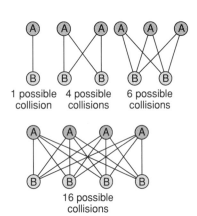

1 possible   4 possible   6 possible
collision   collisions   collisions

16 possible
collisions

Figure 9-8
The number of possible collisions between reactant molecules A and B is proportional to the product of the number of molecules present.

We will first examine the collision theory in terms of the concentrations of the reactants. Note that more collisions will occur between reacting molecules when the concentrations of the reactants are high. As the concentrations of the reactants decrease, collisions between reactant molecules occur less frequently and the reaction slows down.

9-8
Concentrations of Reactants and Number of Molecular Collisions

The number of molecular collisions depends directly on the concentrations of the reactants.

Let us investigate the relationship between the concentrations of the reactants and the number of collisions between them by considering a hypothetical reaction in which A and B form AB according to the equation

$$A + B \longrightarrow AB$$

Let us put one molecule of A and one of B in a unit volume and assume that there is a chance for one collision to take place in unit time. If two molecules of A and one of B are placed in the container, there will be two chances for a collision between A and B to occur in the same time interval. When three molecules of A and one of B are placed in the container, each A has a chance to collide with the B molecule. Therefore, there are three possible A-B collisions per unit time. When two B molecules are placed in the container with three A molecules, each of the three A molecules has a chance of colliding with each of the two B molecules. Therefore, there are six chances of A-B collisions.

The possible collisions are illustrated in Fig. 9-8. It can be seen that the number of collisions between A and B per unit time is proportional to the product of the number of molecules of A and the number of molecules of B. The number of molecules per unit volume can be expressed as a concentration term; thus, we can say that the rate of collision (number per unit time) is proportional to the product of the concentrations of reactants A and B; that is,

$$rate \propto [A][B]$$

This agrees with our experimental observations that increasing the concentration of either reactant increases the rate of the reaction.

Let us now explore the reason why so many reactions are slow and do not take place appreciably until external energy is supplied. We will seek an answer to this problem in terms of the collision theory of reaction rates.

9-9

Activation Energy

The activation energy is the minimum kinetic energy that reacting molecules must possess in order to react.

At room temperature, hydrogen gas (H_2) and oxygen gas (O_2) can be mixed and allowed to stand indefinitely without undergoing any apparent reaction, regardless of their concentrations. As soon as a certain amount of energy is added to the system, however, the gases react violently and exothermically. Why do so many reactions require energy in order to take place?

In any sample of gas, an enormous number of collisions take place between reactant molecules. For example, if each molecule in a mole (6.02×10^{23} molecules) of gas averages one billion (10^9) collisions per second, there would be 10^{32} collisions per second per mole of gas. If the rate of collisions per second were equal to the rate of reaction, every reaction would be extremely rapid. However, since many gaseous reactions are slow, it is apparent that only a fraction of the total collisions results in a reaction.

The tremendous number of collisions results in a wide range of velocities and kinetic energies. The distribution of kinetic energies is shown in Fig. 9-9. The area under the curve represents the total number of molecules. The activation energy (E_a) represents the minimum kinetic energy that a molecule must possess in order for it to react. From the shape of the curve it can be seen that only a few molecules in a given sample have kinetic energies greater than E_a. The collision theory assumes that only collisions between molecules having a minimum kinetic energy of E_a are energetic enough to overcome repulsive forces between the electron clouds of the interacting molecules and to weaken or break bonds, resulting in a reaction. Therefore, the main reason that H_2 and O_2 molecules react so slowly at room temperature is that relatively few of them have energies greater than E_a.

If we look at Fig. 9-9, we see that at a higher temperature (T_2), there is a large increase in the number of molecules with energy E_a or greater. Thus, at a higher temperature, there is an increase in the number of effective collisions and a faster rate of reaction.

So far, we have seen that molecules must collide and possess a

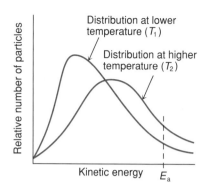

Figure 9-9
Distribution of molecular energies. As the temperature is increased, the number of molecules with energies greater than E_a is increased.

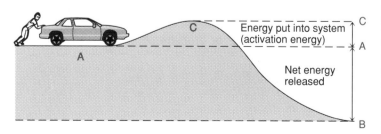

Figure 9-10
Activation-energy analogy. When enough energy has been expended to reach crest C, the car rolls to the bottom of the hill B and releases energy. The energy put into the system (activation energy) is regained as the car rolls from level C to level A. The energy released as the car goes from level A to level B is analogous to the net energy evolved by an exothermic reaction.

minimum amount of energy (activation energy) in order for a reaction to occur. Chemists have introduced a third factor, called *collision geometry*, to further explain observed reaction rates.

Collision Geometry

The shapes and orientations of molecules help to determine if a molecular collision will result in a reaction.

Molecules that possess the activation energy associated with a given reaction do not necessarily react when they collide. Even very high-speed collisions may not be effective if the colliding molecules are not oriented properly. For example, carbon dioxide molecules react with water molecules only when the two molecules come together in such a way that the carbon atom on a carbon dioxide molecule collides with the oxygen atom of a water molecule, as shown in Fig. 9-11(a).

$$CO_2 + H_2O \longrightarrow H_2CO_3 \longrightarrow HCO_3^- + H^+$$

When the oxygen atoms of CO_2 approach the oxygen atom of H_2O, as in Fig. 9-11(b), the collision geometry is totally unfavourable. Hence, no reaction occurs. Thus, the geometric shape and the collision geometry of reacting molecules affect reaction rates.

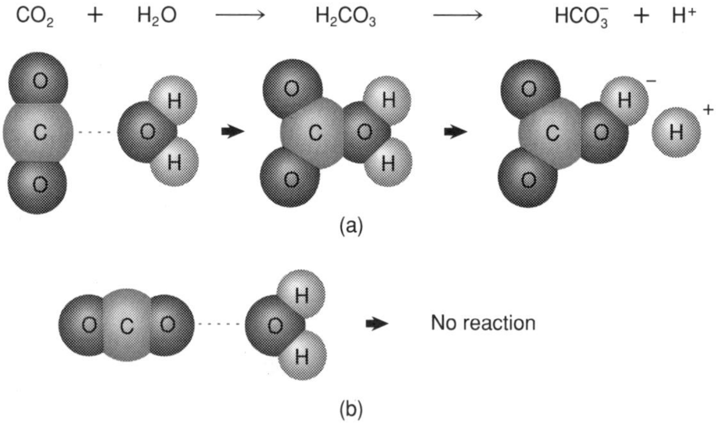

Figure 9-11
Orientation and reaction rate. In (a), the reaction occurs because the molecules have the "correct" collision geometry and sufficient energy. In (b) , there is no reaction because the molecules are not properly oriented.

$$CO_2 \quad + \quad H_2O \quad \longrightarrow \quad H_2CO_3 \quad \longrightarrow \quad HCO_3^- + H^+$$

(a)

(b)

As an analogy, shooting a basketball into a basket is similar to a molecular collision that succeeds in a reaction. Not only must the ball be given a sufficient amount of energy to reach above the level of the basket, it must also be properly oriented to go through the basket.

It might be useful to look at what actually happens during the moments of collision between reactant molecules. We can use the *transition-state theory*, or the *activated-complex theory*, to explain the collision in terms of an *activated complex*.

9-11
The Activated Complex

The transition-state theory was developed by American chemist Henry Eyring (1901–).

An activated complex is a short-lived, high-energy, unstable intermediate that is formed during a reaction.

When collision geometry is favourable and the colliding reactant molecules have kinetic energy at least equal to E_a, the molecules interact to form a high-energy, unstable, transitory species known as an activated complex. To illustrate this process, consider the following reaction:

$$A_2(g) + B_2(g) \longrightarrow 2AB(g)$$

As the reactant molecules interact, energy is absorbed and the bonds in A_2 (A—A) and B_2 (B—B) lengthen and weaken. At the same time, new bonds form between A and B and release energy. More energy is absorbed than liberated, and the potential energy of the system increases. Eventually, the potential energy reaches a maximum when the unstable activated complex A_2B_2 is formed. Beyond this point, more energy is released than is absorbed as the A—B bonds strengthen to form the product AB (Fig. 9-12). Thus, molecules involved in chemical reactions must have a certain

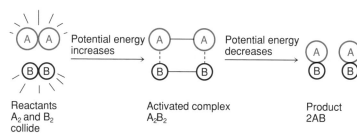

Reactants
A_2 and B_2
collide

Activated complex
A_2B_2

Product
2AB

Figure 9-12
Formation of the activated complex.

minimum kinetic energy that can be converted to the greater potential energy of the activated complex. They must also be properly oriented and be able to enter into high-energy, unstable bonding configurations before forming stable products. In the next section we will illustrate graphically the relationship of the activated complex to the reactant and product molecules.

ENERGY CHANGES DURING A REACTION

9-12
Graphical Representation of Energy Changes

A reaction can be better understood by graphing the energy changes that occur during the reaction.

Let us examine the changes in potential energy that take place when diatomic molecules A_2 and B_2 react to form AB in the single-step reaction

$$A_2(g) + B_2(g) \longrightarrow 2AB(g) \qquad [9\text{-}1]$$

These changes are represented graphically in Fig. 9-13. The total potential energy of the system is shown along the vertical axis. The horizontal axis is called the *reaction co-ordinate*. The points along this axis represent different stages during the progress of the reaction. At each point, the interatomic distances of the interacting atoms change, and so does the potential energy.

We will start at the left side of the curve and follow the path of the reaction through the formation of the products. The height of the plateau at the left represents the total potential energy, or enthalpy, of the starting A_2 and B_2 molecules. Along this part of the path, the reactant molecules have kinetic energy but are so far apart that no potential energy changes occur.

When the A_2 and B_2 molecules are close enough for their electron clouds to exert a significant repelling effect, the molecules slow down, lose kinetic energy and gain potential energy with an accompanying increase in enthalpy. As kinetic energy is converted to potential energy, the curve shows a rise. From this point to the peak, the A—A and B—B bonds are lengthening and weakening as energy is absorbed. At the same time, new bonds are forming between A and B, a process that evolves energy. The continued rise of the curve shows that more energy is absorbed than liberated. At the peak where the potential energy is at a maximum, the activated complex A_2B_2 is formed.

The potential energy of the activated complex determines the activation energy for the reaction. It can be seen from Fig. 9-13 that the activation energy of 160 kJ/mol is the difference between the total potential energy of the separate reactant molecules and that of the activated complex. Activation energy always increases the potential energy of a reaction system.

Once formed, the activated complex either reverts to the original reactant molecules or follows the path to the right. From the peak down to the right plateau, A—A bonds and B—B bonds continue to lengthen, and the A—B bonds become shorter and stronger. Bond formation now predominates so that more energy is liberated than absorbed. The potential energy of the system decreases as the potential energy of the activated complex is converted to the kinetic energy of the product molecules. When the plateau on the right side is reached, most of the potential energy of the complex has been converted to the kinetic energy of the products. The height of the right plateau represents the total

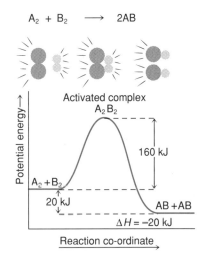

Figure 9-13
Changes in potential energy that occur in a chemical system during an exothermic reaction.

potential energy, or enthalpy, of the products.

The difference of 20 kJ/mol between the total potential energy of the products and that of the reactants is called the *enthalpy change*, or *heat of reaction* (ΔH). Since the enthalpy of the products is less than that of the reactants, the reaction is exothermic (ΔH is negative). It should be noted that the *net energy liberated* is independent of the activation energy. Experiments show that the activation energy is usually less than the bonding energy of the reacting molecules. This is attributed to the fact that new bonds are forming at the same time that old ones are weakening. This implies that it is not absolutely necessary for molecules to undergo violent collisions and break into individual atoms before a reaction can occur.

9-13

Relationship Between Activation Energies of Opposing Reactions

The activation energy of an endothermic reaction is always greater than the activation energy of the opposing exothermic reaction.

It is observed that slow reactions generally have high activation energies and that fast reactions have relatively low activation energies. An endothermic reaction always has a greater activation energy and a slower rate than the opposing exothermic reaction. Figure 9-14 shows the path for the reaction between AB molecules in the formation of A_2 and B_2 molecules.

$$2AB(g) \longrightarrow A_2(g) + B_2(g) \qquad [9\text{-}2]$$

This reaction is the reverse of the reaction illustrated in Fig. 9-13. Note that the AB molecules must collide with a favourable orientation in order to form the same activated complex as A_2 and B_2 in the reverse reaction. The total potential energy of two AB molecules, however, is less than that of A_2 + B_2 (Fig. 9-13). The activation energy for Equation 9-2 is, therefore, greater than that for the reverse reaction (Equation 9-1).

If we compare Fig. 9-13 with Fig. 9-14, we can see that the reactants AB have a higher barrier to surmount than the reactants A_2 and B_2. Thus, we would expect a smaller fraction of the AB molecules to get "over the top." In other words, there would be a smaller fraction of effective collisions between AB molecules than between A_2 and B_2 molecules per unit time.

Since the reactant AB molecules are at a lower potential-energy level than the product molecules, Equation 9-2 represents an endothermic reaction. Endothermic reactions always have a higher

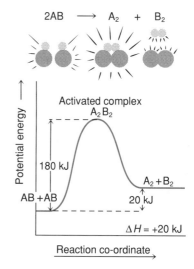

Figure 9-14
Changes in potential energy that occur in a chemical system during an endothermic reaction.

Note that as the temperature increases, the number of molecules with more than the minimum required amount of kinetic energy increases as well. Thus, at a higher temperature, more of the collisions that occur will result in a chemical change.

activation energy and, thus, are always slower at a given temperature than opposing exothermic reactions. Increasing the temperature increases the rate of both endothermic and exothermic reactions. Experiments show, however, that *an increase in temperature affects the rate of the endothermic reaction more than that of the exothermic reaction*.

The fact that catalysts increase the rate of a reaction suggests that more of the lower-energy molecules become able to react. Let us briefly examine the role of a catalyst in chemical reactions.

9-14
Effect of Catalysts on Activation Energy

Catalysts increase reaction rates by providing a lower-activation-energy pathway for the reactions.

Increasing the temperature of a reaction system will usually increase the rate of the reaction, but it may also cause the decomposition of the reactants before they can react. In addition, an increased temperature may result in the formation of unwanted products. Fortunately, scientists have known for many years that certain catalysts are able to increase the rate of a reaction. For example, platinum gauze causes a reaction between hydrogen and oxygen gas to take place at room temperature. Without the platinum catalyst, there is no apparent reaction under these conditions. The discovery and use of catalysts have been significant factors in the growth of the petroleum and most other chemical industries. Research chemists are constantly working on the development of new catalytic agents.

Figure 9-15
A catalyst provides an alternate pathway between the reactants and products. It is assumed that the catalyst forms an intermediate activated complex that has a lower activation energy.

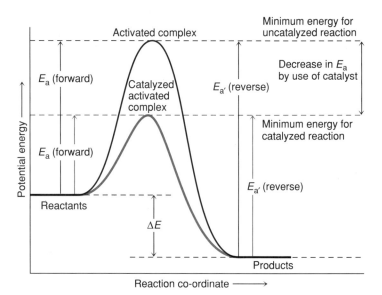

In general, catalysts provide a new reaction path in which a different, lower-energy activated complex can form; the path has a lower activation energy and thereby increases the rate of the reaction. Figure 9-15 shows the difference in activation energy between a catalyzed and a non-catalyzed reaction. The graph shows that both the forward and reverse reactions follow the same path. The activation energy is reduced to the same extent for both forward and reverse reactions.

REACTION MECHANISMS

A balanced chemical equation tells us the number of moles of reactants and products produced during a chemical reaction; however, it does not tell us how the reaction occurs. As a result of rate studies, we can predict the series of steps by which the reactants are transformed into products. Such a series of steps is called a *reaction mechanism*.

The simplest chemical reactions occur in a single step. The oxidation of nitrogen monoxide (NO) by ozone (O_3) is an example of a single-step reaction. The equation for this reaction is

$$NO(g) + O_3(g) \longrightarrow NO_2(g) + O_2(g)$$

This reaction occurs on the collision of two reactant molecules, NO and O_3, in a single-step reaction mechanism. Single-step reactions that occur on the collision of two molecules are called *bimolecular reactions*. Reactions that involve the decomposition or internal structural rearrangement of one single molecule constitute *unimolecular reactions*. Single-step reactions that occur on the collision of three molecules are called *termolecular reactions* and are very rare.

Many reactions proceed by a more complicated process involving two or more successive steps. Each of these steps is called an *elementary process*.

JOHN POLANYI
1929–
John Charles Polanyi was born in Berlin and educated in Manchester, England, where his family settled after leaving Germany in 1934. As a student, Polanyi was interested in politics and writing. However, he decided to follow the footsteps of his father and studied chemistry. Polanyi was appointed lecturer at the University of Toronto in 1956 and professor of chemistry in 1962.

Polanyi's major area of research is the dynamics of chemical reactions. In 1958, Polanyi and J.K. Cashion found that when they mixed atomic hydrogen and chlorine gas, the reaction vessel produced an infrared spectrum indicating the presence of hydrogen chloride. This method became known as infrared chemiluminescence. Eventually, Polanyi used this method to quantitatively determine product excitation and to measure the effects that different states of vibrational and rotational excitation in reagents had on reaction probability. For this work, Polanyi shared the 1986 Nobel Prize in chemistry with D.R. Hershbach and Y.T. Lee.

Currently, Polanyi is developing new spectroscopic methods for studying the reactive transition state. Polanyi likens this to watching the molecular dance of a chemical reaction while the partners are on stage rather than before or after the dance is over.

Polanyi has also written many articles on the control of nuclear armaments.

9-15
Elementary Processes

Elementary processes are one-step processes that make up a reaction mechanism.

In most cases, an elementary process is a one-step process in which the product particles are the direct result of the collision of only two reactant particles. Three particle collisions are known but are rare. Elementary processes cannot be observed directly, but must be deduced from macroscopic observations made during studies of reaction rates.

GERALDINE KENNEY-WALLACE
1943–
Geraldine Kenney-Wallace is one of Canada's most noted scientists. Born in London, England, she did her undergraduate work at Oxford University. In 1966, she moved to Canada and received her PhD from the University of British Columbia. She later accepted a position as professor of chemistry and physics at the University of Toronto. In July, 1990, Kenney-Wallace became president of McMaster University in Hamilton, Ontario.

Kenney-Wallace is recognized for her scientific work on lasers and non-linear optics. She also worked with John Polanyi on molecular and chemical dynamics.

At present, her main concern is to increase the public's awareness and understanding of scientific research. She is also involved in encouraging women to enter the field of science. She believes that scientists should be judged on the merits of their work and not on their gender. Named as chairperson of the Science Council of Canada in 1988, Kenney-Wallace did not expect to bring any special concerns to the Council because she is a woman. She says, "I don't think there is such a thing as a feminist view on science."

Let us consider the reduction of nitrogen monoxide (NO) by hydrogen (H_2), which is an example of a multistep reaction. The overall reaction is

$$2NO(g) + 2H_2(g) \longrightarrow N_2(g) + 2H_2O(g) \qquad [9\text{-}3]$$

Many possible mechanisms have been proposed for this reaction. One mechanism consists of two steps:

Step 1: $\qquad\qquad 2NO + H_2 \longrightarrow N_2 + H_2O_2$
Step 2: $\qquad\qquad H_2 + H_2O_2 \longrightarrow 2H_2O$

Step 1 is a termolecular elementary process involving a three-molecule collision, and Step 2 is a bimolecular elementary process. The sum of the two elementary processes gives the overall reaction mechanism of Equation 9-3.

Another, more probable, series of reactions is as follows:

Step 1: $\qquad\qquad NO + H_2 \longrightarrow NO\text{---}H_2$
Step 2: $\qquad\qquad NO + NO\ \ \ II_2 \quad {}^{,} N_2 + H_2O_2$
Step 3: $\qquad\qquad H_2O_2 + H_2 \longrightarrow 2H_2O$

Rate studies can be used to identify and eliminate an incorrect mechanism, but cannot prove the correctness of a mechanism. Therefore, although a mechanism can be given for a reaction that involves a series of bimolecular steps or one that includes a termolecular step, we cannot prove that one mechanism is more correct than the other. We can only identify one mechanism as statistically more probable.

As a result of rate studies, we can predict that gaseous reactions whose net (overall) equations show more than two or three reactant molecules do not represent elementary processes. This is logical, since we would expect the simultaneous collision of more than two or three gaseous molecules to be a highly improbable event.

9-16
Rate-Determining Step

The rate-determining step in a multistep reaction is the slowest step in the sequence of steps.

When a reaction is the result of a series of elementary processes, *the rate of the overall reaction is determined by the slowest reaction in the sequence*. The situation is analogous to an automobile assembly line. The rate at which completed automobiles roll off the assembly line depends on the rates at which several component parts are produced. If frames are produced at the rate of 100 per hour, bodies at 100 per hour and engines at 95 per hour, the overall rate of production of completed automobiles is 95 per hour, the rate of the slowest step in the assembly line.

In general, overall reactions are rapid if the equations for them show that the simultaneous collision of two simple, oppositely charged ions is all that is needed for a reaction to occur. Consider the following ionic equation for the reaction between silver ions and chloride ions:

$$Ag^+(aq) + Cl^-(aq) \longrightarrow AgCl(s) \qquad [9\text{-}4]$$

This equation shows that a two-particle collision between Ag^+ ions and the Cl^- ions could result in a reaction. Assuming that the reacting particles are uncombined ions, we find that there are no strong bonds to be broken before the reaction can take place. We would predict, therefore, that the rate of reaction would be rapid. As you have no doubt observed, rapid rates are characteristic of precipitation reactions.

For the reaction between NO and H_2 (Equation 9-3), we might assume that the termolecular elementary process (Step 1) is the rate-determining step, since a simultaneous collision of three molecules is less likely and would take longer to occur.

FOLLOW-UP PROBLEM

Consider the following reaction:

$$4HBr(g) + O_2(g) \longrightarrow 2H_2O(g) + 2Br_2(g)$$

a) Does the above equation represent an elementary process? Explain.

b) Experiments show that a change in the concentration of HBr has the same effect on the rate of reaction as an identical change in the concentration of O_2. Propose a reaction mechanism for the overall reaction. Assume that HOOBr and HOBr are intermediates.

c) Identify the rate-determining step.

9-17

Mechanisms of Catalytic Reactions

The mechanisms of many catalytic reactions are not well understood.

Solid catalysts have large surface areas and are capable of adsorbing the reactants on their surfaces. In some cases, one of the reactant molecules may readily react with the atoms of the catalyst to produce an intermediate species. This species readily reacts with the second reagent, forming the desired product and regen-

Any proposed reaction mechanism must yield the net overall reaction for the reaction.

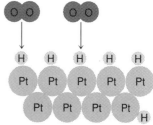

(a) Hydrogen adheres to surface. Bond between hydrogen atoms is greatly extended or broken. Oxygen molecules approach surface containing adsorbed hydrogen atoms.

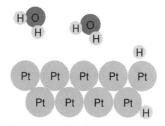

(b) As water molecules are formed, the platinum surface is regenerated.

Figure 9-16
Platinum catalysis of the reaction between H_2 and O_2. Hydrogen is adsorbed on the surface of the platinum, and the covalent bond in the H_2 molecule is extended or broken. The reaction occurs more readily because the activated energy of a single H atom is less than that of H_2.

erating the catalyst. For example, when platinum is used to catalyze the reaction between H_2 and O_2, it is possible that hydrogen molecules are adsorbed on the platinum. Oxygen then reacts with the adsorbed hydrogen, forms water and regenerates metallic platinum (Fig. 9-16).

Many reactions are catalyzed by the presence of an acid. In this reaction, it is possible that hydrogen ions from the acid react with and modify the structure of one of the reactants so that it is more susceptible to reaction with the other reagent. This is believed to be the case in the acid-catalyzed decomposition of methanoic acid (formic acid). The overall equation for the decomposition of methanoic acid is

$$HCOOH \xrightleftharpoons{H^+} CO + H_2O$$

The elementary processes involved in the formation of the intermediate species and the regeneration of the H^+ ion catalyst are

$$HCOOH + H^+ \rightleftharpoons HCOOH_2^+$$
$$HCOOH^+ \rightleftharpoons HCO^+ + H_2O$$
$$HCO^+ \rightleftharpoons H^+ + CO$$

ZEOLITE: A CRYSTAL CATALYST

Intricate, delicate, puzzling—these words describe the colourful structure of zeolites, one of which is depicted on the front cover of this book. Although few people have heard about this class of minerals, zeolites are playing an increasingly important role in such processes as water treatment, petroleum refining and pollution control.

Zeolites were discovered in 1756 by Baron Axel F. Crönstedt, a Swedish mineralogist. Believed to be rare and commercially unimportant, zeolites were of interest only to mineral collectors. In the 1920s, however, chemists noted that dehydrated zeolites could selectively adsorb small organic molecules and thus act as molecular sieves. Since zeolites were considered scarce, chemists developed methods of producing them synthetically. However, in the late 1950s, geologists discovered that zeolites were not only common, but were actually a major component in some sedimentary rock formations. Once the geologists and chemists became aware of each other's discoveries, the mining and use of zeolites increased rapidly. Today, hundreds of millions of tonnes of zeolites are mined around the world and used in a variety of applications.

The name zeolite comes from the Greek words *zein*, meaning to boil, and *lithos*, meaning stone. These terms refer to the fact that, due to their high water content, zeolites swell and boil when heated. The vibrant colours of zeolites come from trace impurities found within their structure. Natural zeolites are green, brown, red, yellow, pink or grey; synthetic zeolites are white or colourless.

Zeolites have an aluminosilicate, tetrahedral framework to which are attached large cations that can be exchanged with other ions. The ratio of aluminum to silicon in the framework determines the number and charge of the cations. These cations typically include Na^+, K^+, Ca^{2+}, Sr^{2+} and Ba^{2+}, and their function is to attract and hold water within the framework. The tetrahedrons consist of four oxygen atoms surrounding an aluminum or silicon atom, linked so that each oxygen is shared between two tetrahedrons. Loops of 4-, 5-, 6-, 8- and 12-membered tetrahedral rings link to form cages and channels. This framework allows water molecules to be held closely by the zeolite and to be easily removed by heating.

The structure of a relatively simple zeolite, analcime, is represented by the formula $Na(AlSi_2O_6) \cdot H_2O$. In addition to water, other polar solutions such as hydrogen sulfide, ammonia and alcohol can be adsorbed by dehydrated zeolites. As well, cavities and channels in the crystal structure of some zeolites allow the passage of certain organic molecules; the pore size ranges between 0.3 and 0.8 nm. Zeolites can thus be used as molecular sieves to purify water and other liquids and gases, and to separate mixtures of chemicals such as gasoline. In the latter case, the zeolite allows the passage of straight-chain molecules only. Synthetic zeolites are useful as molecular sieves because their structure and composition are much more regular. By carefully selecting the type of zeolite used, chemists can achieve highly accurate filtration.

Zeolites are also used as catalysts in the production of petrochemicals. New Zealand, for example, has few oil deposits but an abundance of natural gas (methane). The methane is converted by standard processes into methanol (CH_3OH), which then passes through a synthetic zeolite called ZSM-5. The zeolite acts as a catalyst for a series of reactions that convert the methanol into a mixture of hydrocarbons that can be refined for use as automotive fuel. One-third of New Zealand's gasoline is produced in this way. ZSM-5 is also used to convert toluene, a by-product of petroleum refining, into commercially valuable benzene and para-xylene.

Zeolites have become a standard feature in pollution-control devices. For example, clinoptilolite, a natural zeolite, has been used to remove long-lived radioactive products from nuclear-waste effluent by means of ion exchange. Clinoptilolite resists nuclear degradation and can easily be incorporated into cement and glass mixtures, which are then sealed into steel drums, isolating the radioactive species from the environment.

Clinoptilolite is also used in Japan to reduce nitrogen pollution and farmyard odours. It selectively removes the ammonium ions from lakes, agricultural wastes and sewage. Other natural zeolites can be used to remove sulfur dioxide and other pollutants from the smokestacks of oil- and coal-burning power stations, thereby

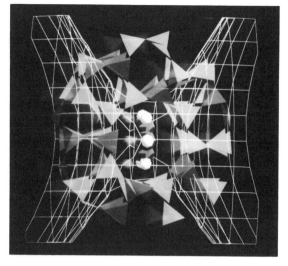

reducing acid rain.

Research is currently underway to find other uses of zeolites. A mixture of zeolites and other materials has been tested as a sorbent for oil spills. Catalysts that were previously unusable because of their high volatility can now be carried within the structure of synthetic zeolites, which trap them where they can be used. Some zeolites, particularly the natural zeolite, mordentite, and the synthetic zeolite, Ca-A, have been used to enrich the oxygen content of air by selectively removing other gases such as nitrogen. Zeolites may also be useful in coal gasification and natural-gas purification because they selectively remove nitrogen oxides, hydrocarbons and carbon dioxide.

The strange and beautiful structures of zeolites are sure to have important effects on our lives in the future, as new and innovative ways of using them are being developed every year.

9-18

Mechanisms of Chain Reactions

A chain reaction is a multistep reaction that involves formation of a reactive intermediate in a continuous series of steps. An example of a simple chain reaction is the formation of hydrogen chloride (HCl) from hydrogen gas (H_2) and chlorine gas (Cl_2) in the presence of ultraviolet light. At room temperature, the reaction between gaseous H_2 and Cl_2 is extremely slow. Because the bond energy of Cl_2 is relatively high, considerable energy is required to rupture the Cl—Cl bond and bring about the formation of the active species needed to initiate the reaction. However, when a mixture of the gases is heated or exposed to ultraviolet

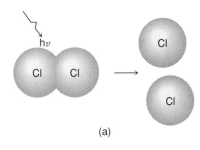

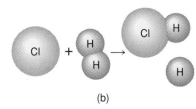

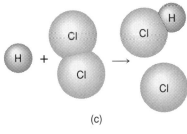

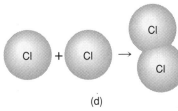

Figure 9-17
Reaction mechanism for the formation of HCl.

light, a violent reaction takes place (Fig. 9-17). The reaction, however, does not occur directly between H_2 and Cl_2 molecules. It has been shown that the first step in the reaction mechanism occurs when Cl_2 molecules absorb a quantum of ultraviolet light:

$$Cl_2 + \text{light energy} \longrightarrow Cl\cdot + Cl\cdot$$

This reaction is called a *chain-initiating step*. The Cl• atoms generated in this step are highly reactive species known as *free radicals*. The Cl• free radical reacts with an H_2 molecule to form a molecule of HCl and an H• atom:

$$H_2 + Cl\cdot \longrightarrow HCl + H\cdot$$

The reactive H• atoms are also free radicals that attack the Cl_2 molecules and produce another molecule of HCl and a Cl• atom:

$$H\cdot + Cl_2 \longrightarrow HCl + Cl\cdot$$

The preceding free-radical reactions are the *chain-propagating steps* of the mechanism. The regenerated chlorine atom continues the process so that HCl is formed continuously until a *chain-breaking reaction* occurs. A chain-breaking reaction removes the reactive free radicals from the system; the free radicals react with each other as follows:

$$Cl\cdot + Cl\cdot \longrightarrow Cl_2$$
$$H\cdot + H\cdot \longrightarrow H_2$$

Because the concentration of Cl• atoms is low, the chain-breaking reaction is very slow. Therefore, the Cl• atom can cause the formation of many molecules of HCl before it is made unreactive.
The following is a summary of the chain reaction of H_2 and Cl_2:

$$Cl_2 \xrightarrow{h\nu} Cl\cdot + Cl\cdot \qquad \text{chain-initiating step}$$
$$\left.\begin{array}{l} Cl\cdot + H_2 \longrightarrow HCl + H\cdot \\ H\cdot + Cl_2 \longrightarrow HCl + Cl\cdot \end{array}\right\} \text{chain-propagating step}$$
$$Cl\cdot + Cl\cdot \longrightarrow Cl_2 \qquad \text{chain-breaking step}$$

The clue to what occurs on the path between reactants and products, as represented by the equation for the overall reaction, is found in the so-called *rate laws*. These laws, which are determined experimentally, relate the rate of a reaction to the concentration of the participants. The rate laws can be used to tell if the equation for an overall reaction represents an elementary process and to deduce a reaction mechanism.

REACTION RATE LAW

9-19

The Rate Law Expression

The rate of a chemical reaction is proportional to the concentrations of the reactant species.

The relationship between the rate of a reaction and the masses (expressed as concentrations) of reactants was recognized in 1863 by two Norwegian chemists, Cato M. Guldberg (1836–1902) and Peter Waage (1833–1900). The relationship is summarized in their *law of mass action*, which states that *the rate of a chemical reaction is dependent on the concentrations of the reactants*. We can use this *rate law expression*, or *equation*, to relate the rate of reaction to the concentrations of the reactants. For example, for the reaction,

$$a\text{A} + b\text{B} \longrightarrow \text{products}$$

the rate law expression is

$$\text{rate} \propto [\text{A}]^m[\text{B}]^n$$

or

$$\text{rate} = k[\text{A}]^m[\text{B}]^n$$

where [A] and [B] represent the concentrations of A and B, m and n are the powers to which the concentrations must be raised and k is a proportionality constant known as the *rate constant*. The only way to determine m and n is to use experimental data. For example, m and n can be derived by determining the effect of changing reactant concentration on the rate of the reaction. The exponents m and n may be zero, a fraction or an integer and may or may not agree with the coefficients (a and b) in the overall equation. Data shows that the rate constant is not affected by concentration changes but does vary with temperature changes.

Each exponent is called an *order* and corresponds to the order of reaction for each reactant. The overall *reaction order* is the sum of the exponents of the concentration terms in the rate law equation. For example, the experimentally derived rate law expression for the reaction

$$\text{H}_2(g) + \text{I}_2(g) \longrightarrow 2\text{HI}(g) \tag{9-5}$$

is

$$\text{rate} = k[\text{H}_2][\text{I}_2] \tag{9-6}$$

The reaction is a second-order reaction overall because the sum of the exponents is 2.

When the exponents, as determined experimentally, do not agree with the coefficients in the net equation, then the net

Guldberg and Waage
Cato Maximilian Guldberg and Peter Waage interpreted the rate of a reaction in terms of the concentrations of the reactants rather than the amounts. In their pamphlet on the law of mass action, published in 1863, they wrote, "Investigations in this field are doubtless more difficult, more tedious and less fruitful than those which now enjoy the attention of most chemists, mostly the discovery of new compounds." However, Guldberg and Waage recognized that work such as theirs was necessary to bring chemistry "into the class of the truly exact sciences."

Free Radicals and the Aging Process
Free radicals may play a major part in the aging process. Exposure to the ultraviolet light in sunlight damages human skin, causing wrinkling. This may occur because free radicals break down protein molecules in collagen, which is a component of flexible tissues, including the skin, muscles, lungs and blood vessels. This protein breakdown may reduce the flexibility of the collagen, making the tissues stiffer.

Free radicals may affect the body's structures in other ways. They may damage the DNA in cells, impeding the cells' ability to function and eventually killing them. Free radicals may also affect lipid metabolism by attacking the enzymes that process lipids—again reducing cell efficiency.

One natural inhibitor of free radicals appears to be vitamin E. A deficiency of this vitamin can produce signs similar to aging.

equation must represent the sum of a series of elementary processes. This does not imply, however, that when they do agree the net equation represents an elementary process. For example, in the above reaction, the exponents in Equation 9-6 happen to agree with the coefficients of the reactants in Equation 9-5. This does not prove, however, that Equation 9-5 represents a bimolecular elementary process or that the collision of one H_2 molecule with one I_2 molecule produces HI molecules directly. Let us see how the exponents can be determined experimentally.

9-20
Experimental Determination of Reaction Order

The overall order of a reaction can be determined only from experimental data.

Let us consider the reaction between NO and H_2, which forms H_2O and N_2:

$$2NO(g) + 2H_2(g) \longrightarrow N_2(g) + 2H_2O(g) \qquad [9\text{-}7]$$

As this reaction proceeds, four moles of reactant gas form three moles of product gas, and the pressure drops. The rate of the reaction can be determined by following the pressure change.

For convenience and clarity, we express the rate in terms of mol/L·s. To determine the relationship between the rate of the reaction and the concentration of NO, it is necessary to keep the concentration of H_2 and the temperature constant and to vary the concentration of NO. The initial rate of reaction may then be determined using various concentrations of NO. The concentration of NO and the temperature are then held constant, and the initial rates of reaction for various concentrations of H_2 are determined. The data in Table 9-1 shows that increasing the concentration of either of the reactants increases the rate of the reaction.

Examination of the data reveals that when the concentration of NO is held constant at 0.004 mol/L and the concentration of hydrogen is doubled, the rate doubles from 8 to 16 units. When the concentration of hydrogen is tripled, the rate triples from 8 to 24 units. Mathematically, the rate of the reaction is directly proportional to the concentration of hydrogen; that is,

$$\text{rate} \propto [H_2]$$

When the concentration of H_2 is held constant and that of NO is varied, the data shows that the rate of the reaction is proportional to the square of the concentration of NO. Specifically, when the concentration of NO is doubled from 0.001 to 0.002 mol/L, the rate is quadrupled from 2 to 8 units. When the concentration of NO

TABLE 9-1
RATES OF REACTION BETWEEN NO and H_2 AT 800°C

Experiment	NO (mol/L)	H_2 (mol/L)	Initial Rate of Reaction (mol/L·s)
1	0.001	0.004	0.002
2	0.002	0.004	0.008
3	0.003	0.004	0.018
4	0.004	0.001	0.008
5	0.004	0.002	0.016
6	0.004	0.003	0.024

is tripled from 0.001 mol/L to 0.003 mol/L, the rate increases by a factor of 9. Mathematically, this rate is proportional to the square of the concentration of NO:

$$\text{rate} \propto [NO]^2$$

Since the rate is proportional to $[H_2]$ and $[NO]^2$, it is also proportional to their product:

$$\text{rate} \propto [H_2][NO]^2$$

Mathematically, a proportionality can be changed to an equality by inserting the constant of proportionality:

$$\text{rate} = k[H_2][NO]^2 \qquad [9\text{-}8]$$

where k is the *specific rate constant* at the temperature of the reaction. Equation 9-8 is the rate law expression for the reaction in Equation 9-7. In Equation 9-8, the values of the exponents are $m = 1$ and $n = 2$. Thus, the reaction represented by Equation 9-8 is a *third-order reaction*.

Note that Equation 9-7 does not represent an elementary process; that is, the sum of the coefficients of the reactants (H_2 and NO) in Equation 9-7 is four, while the sum of the exponents in Equation 9-8 is three. One of many possible mechanisms for this reaction has been discussed in Section 9-15.

In recent years, progress has been made in identifying many reaction mechanisms. The importance of kinetics cannot be overemphasized. It provides a description of what happens on the microparticle level during a reaction. Analyses and interpretation of the data help scientists find solutions to such problems as atmospheric pollution, as well as understand reactions of biological systems and develop more efficient processes for producing desired products.

In this chapter we investigated factors related to the rates of reactions. Because the equilibrium condition can be described on a molecular level in terms of the rates of opposing reactions, it is now logical to make a detailed study of molecular equilibrium. In this study we will look at the principles that will help us predict the extent of a reaction. In a large number of reactions, the reactants are not quantitatively converted into products. We will focus our attention on these "incomplete" reactions in the next chapter.

Chemists are concerned with the efficiency of a reaction and with methods of controlling it in order to obtain a maximum yield of desired product. In the next chapter, we will develop equilibrium principles that will help us determine the amount of product we can expect to obtain from a reaction and how changing various factors will affect the yield of product.

OZONE: THE SUNSCREEN IN SPACE

The sunlight that we enjoy on earth sustains life. However, sunlight also contains ultraviolet radiation that can harm life on earth if it is not absorbed by certain molecules. The most important molecule in this process is ozone (O_3).

If you have ever worked near electric motors or been outside after lightning has struck nearby, you are probably familiar with the smell of ozone. This pale blue, highly reactive gas is the triatomic form of oxygen. Ozone can either be a pollutant or a vital protector, depending on its location in the atmosphere. Ozone found near the surface of the earth is a component of photochemical smog formed when sunlight energizes reactions between nitrogen oxides and hydrocarbons from automobile exhaust. The reactivity of ozone means that it is a relatively short-lived species at low altitudes.

Ozone acts as a protective shield where it occurs naturally in the stratosphere, 10 to 50 km above the earth's surface. Ozone in the stratosphere is constantly being formed and destroyed by the following processes:

$$O_2 \longrightarrow 2O\bullet$$
$$O\bullet + O_2 \longrightarrow O_3$$
$$O_3 \longrightarrow O_2 + O\bullet$$

The relative rates of these reactions determine how much ozone exists at a given time. The concentration of ozone in the atmosphere is very small; the ozone layer is only a few millimetres thick. In spite of its low concentration, however, ozone is critical to the protection of the earth's surface because it absorbs the sun's harmful ultraviolet radiation and releases heat:

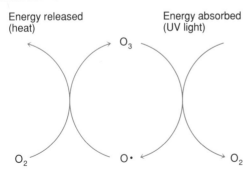

Ozone's absorption of ultraviolet radiation is crucial because such radiation can cause skin cancer and eye damage in humans and can affect other organisms as well.

The presence of ozone in the stratosphere has been monitored since 1956. In October 1979, a temporary area of lowered ozone concentration, or *ozone hole*, was detected over the Antarctic. This finding prompted investigations into the production, distribution and destruction of ozone. Although the ozone hole has reappeared every year and seems to be growing, scientists do not know whether the hole is a regular, annual phenomenon or a new event in the earth's history. In 1988, a smaller hole appeared over the Arctic. As well, minor drops in ozone concentrations have been observed outside of polar regions; it is not known whether this is a long-term trend or a short-term fluctuation.

What causes this hole in the ozone layer and why does it occur only in the polar regions at certain times of the year? Evidence suggests that chlorofluorocarbons (CFCs) are, in large part, responsible for the ozone hole.

Chlorine is thought to destroy ozone. One source of chlorine in the atmosphere is from CFCs, which are used as coolants, aerosol propellants and in plastic foam. Although CFCs are chemically inert at low altitudes, they may break down in the stratosphere to produce chlorine in the form of free radicals:

$$CCl_3F \longrightarrow CCl_2F + Cl\bullet$$

These chlorine free radicals destroy ozone by the following chain reaction:

$$Cl\bullet + O_3 \longrightarrow ClO\bullet + O_2$$
$$ClO\bullet + O\bullet \longrightarrow Cl\bullet + O_2$$

The chlorine free radical is regenerated and can continue to destroy ozone:

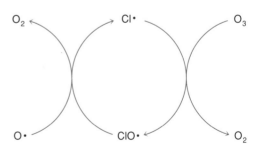

Other substances, however, can counteract the effect of chlorine. Nitrogen monoxide, for example, can regenerate ozone according to the following reactions:

$$ClO• + NO \longrightarrow Cl• + NO_2$$
$$NO_2 \longrightarrow NO + O•$$
$$O• + O_2 \longrightarrow O_3$$

The ozone hole seems to appear regularly over the Antarctic in October. Scientists have various theories to account for this phenomenon. One theory suggests that nitrogen-containing molecules capture chlorine free radicals, tying them up in a reservoir and preventing them from destroying ozone. During the Antarctic winter, these nitrogen-containing molecules can freeze into ice clouds that form in the stratosphere below −80°C. During October, the return of sunlight and relative warmth in the Antarctic causes the release of chlorine from this reservoir, resulting in the formation of a temporary hole in the ozone layer. The formation of ice clouds may have another effect: because the conversion of chlorine gas to chlorine free radicals occurs much more rapidly on solid ice crystals than in the gas phase, the ice clouds may accelerate ozone destruction. This may explain why the ozone hole is seen only in polar regions, where it is cold enough for ice clouds to form.

Another theory that may explain why ozone depletion is severe only in the Antarctic is the unique pattern of air movement in the region. The polar vortex, an isolated mass of air over the Antarctic,

prevents the ozone-rich air of the equatorial regions, where most of it is produced, from moving into the Antarctic, where it is scarce.

Concerns about ozone depletion and its effect on the world's environment have mounted in the last few years. Canada and other countries have agreed to reduce CFC usage to 50% of 1986 levels by the year 2000. Canada has also developed the technology for monitoring ozone-layer depletion, including the Brewer ozone spectrophotometer, which is used around the world.

The ozone hole is another example of human abuse of the environment. It is a concern that requires immediate action if life as we know it on earth is to survive.

QUESTIONS

1. What is the meaning of the term *rate* as applied to a chemical reaction?

2. Write three simple rate expressions for the reaction

$$HgO(s) \longrightarrow Hg(l) + \tfrac{1}{2}O_2(g)$$

3. Explain why the rate of a simple chemical reaction such as

$$NO(g) + \tfrac{1}{2}O_2(g) \longrightarrow NO_2(g)$$

is likely to be most rapid at the beginning of the reaction.

4. (a) List four factors that affect the rate of a homogeneous reaction. (b) What additional factors must be considered for heterogeneous reactions?

5. Which of the following reactions are likely to proceed rapidly? Explain.
   a) $H_2(g) + Cl_2(g) \longrightarrow 2HCl(g)$
   b) $C_6H_{12}O_6(aq) + 6O_2(g) \longrightarrow$
   $$6CO_2(g) + 6H_2O(l)$$
   c) $Cu^{2+}(aq) + S^{2-}(aq) \longrightarrow CuS(s)$
   d) A lump of iron in melted sulfur.
   e) Powdered iron in melted sulfur.
   Answers:
   (a) Probable, because reactants are gaseous. (d) Not likely, since reaction is limited to surface of iron.

6. What property might be measured in order to follow the rate of reaction for each of the following reactions?
   a) $KI(aq) + \tfrac{1}{2}Cl_2(aq) \longrightarrow \tfrac{1}{2}I_2(s) + KCl(aq)$
   b) $PCl_5(g) \longrightarrow PCl_3(g) + Cl_2(g)$
   c) $2NO_2(g) \longrightarrow N_2O_4(g)$

d) $Cu(s) + 2Ag^+(aq) \longrightarrow$
$$Cu^{2+}(aq) + 2Ag(s)$$
e) $Fe(s) + 2HCl(aq) \longrightarrow H_2(g) + FeCl_2(aq)$
Answer: (b) pressure

7. Explain why reaction rates generally increase with temperature.

8. Explain why a mixture of hydrogen and chlorine gas is stable if kept in the dark, yet is likely to explode if exposed to sunlight.

9. If you wish to dissolve a lump of sugar in water, how could you increase the rate at which the sugar dissolves? Explain why each procedure is effective.

10. A mixture of natural gas and air does not react appreciably at room temperature. When a piece of platinum is inserted into the reaction vessel, the mixture explodes. Explain.

11. A fresh starch suspension shows no positive test for sugar. If boiled for a long time, a small quantity of sugar is detected. If boiled with acid, additional sugar is present. If saliva is added to the original mixture, even more sugar is formed in the same time. Explain.

12. What is an elementary process?

13. What is a bimolecular process?

14. What is meant by the expression, *mechanism of a reaction*?

15. (a) Describe the "reaction mechanism" in the "reaction" that gets the dinner dishes cleaned and into the cupboard. (b) Which is the rate-determining step? (c) Can the reaction be catalyzed? (d) How else can the reaction be speeded up?

16. Using collision theory, explain (a) the speed at which gas reactions usually occur, (b) the speed of ionic reactions, (c) the temperature dependence of the rate of chemical reactions.

17. Lavoisier was able to form the oxide of mercury by moderately heating liquid mercury in air. On heating the same oxide more strongly, he was able to decompose the oxide and reform liquid mercury and oxygen. If the rate of reaction is increased by an increase in temperature, why wasn't the oxide of mercury formed more rapidly?

18. Distinguish between reaction rate and reaction rate constant.

19. What is activation energy?

20. Distinguish between activation energy and activated complex.

21. Compound A reacts with compound B and forms the products C and D. This reaction proceeds very slowly at first, then accelerates rapidly until virtually all A and B have been consumed. (a) Suggest a possible reason for this. (b) A highly unstable species ABCD is formed as an intermediate. What is ABCD called?
Answers:
(a) One of the products C or D could be acting as a catalyst for this reaction. Thus, the more C and D produced, the more rapidly the reaction takes place. Such reactions are said to be *autocatalytic*.
(b) An activated complex.

22. (a) Compare the kinetic energies of the reactants, activated complex and products of a reaction when all are at the same temperature. (b) How do the potential energies compare?

23. Draw a representative reaction curve for an exothermic reaction. (a) Label the activation energy for the forward reaction, the activation energy for the reverse reaction and the enthalpy of the forward and reverse reactions. (b) Do the same for a representative endothermic reaction. (c) How do both curves change when a catalyst is added?

24. On the reaction curve (question 23) for an exothermic reaction, indicate the regions where (a) the bond-breaking energies predominate, (b) the bond-forming energies predominate.

25. Why is the activation energy for a reaction usually less than the bond energy of the reactants?

26. What would be the effect of an increase in temperature on the rate constant of (a) the forward reaction? (b) the reverse reaction?

27. How does a catalyst affect the enthalpy change of a reaction?

28. The mechanism of the reaction between nitrogen(II) oxide (NO) and oxygen (O_2) is believed to take place in two steps:

$$NO + O_2 \longrightarrow NO \cdot O_2 (rapid)$$
$$NO \cdot O_2 + NO \longrightarrow 2NO_2 (slow)$$

The exact nature of the bond between the NO and O_2 in $NO \cdot O_2$ is not understood. Which of the steps above is the rate-determining step?

29. Suggest a mechanism for the decomposition of ozone (O_3) into oxygen (O_2). This reaction takes place in two steps.
Answer:
$$O_3 \longrightarrow O_2 + O (rapid)$$
$$O + O_3 \longrightarrow 2O_2 (slow)$$

30. Explain why, once started, an exothermic reaction is self-sustaining.

31. Propose a mechanism for each of the following catalyzed reactions.
a) $SO_2(g) + \frac{1}{2}O_2(g) \xrightarrow{\text{Pt black}} SO_3(g)$
b) $H_2O_2(aq) \xrightarrow{\text{hemoglobin}} H_2O(l) + \frac{1}{2}O_2(g)$

32. Explain why, once started, an endothermic reaction requires a continual supply of energy.

33. (a) What is meant by the expression, *order of a reaction*? (b) Can the order be determined from the equation for the overall reaction? (c) If the sum of the coefficients of the reactants in the equation equals the total order of a reaction, can it be assumed that the equation represents an elementary process?

34. What is the order of the reactions with these rate law expressions?
a) rate = $k[A]^{1/2}[B]$
b) rate = $k[A][B]^2$

35. Use the following data to derive the rate law expression for the reaction

$$A(g) + B(g) \longrightarrow AB$$

Experiment	[A]	[B]	Initial Rate of Reaction (mol/L•s)
1	0.2	0.1	6×10^{-3}
2	0.4	0.1	1.2×10^{-2}
3	0.4	0.2	1.2×10^{-2}
4	0.1	0.1	3×10^{-3}

The constant flow of hockey players onto and off the ice surface maintains the number of players at six for each team during the game. Thus, there is a dynamic equilibrium.

CHEMICAL EQUILIBRIUM

"By...equilibrium, we mean a state in which the properties of a system, as experimentally measured, would suffer no further observable change even after the lapse of an indefinite period of time. It is not intimated that the individual particles are unchanging."
Gilbert N. Lewis and Merle Randall

M any chemical reactions do not go to completion. In such cases, a state of equilibrium, or balance, is reached when the original substances react at the same rate as the products react with each other to reform the original substances. That is, these reactions are reversible and a balance is reached between the forward and the reverse reaction.

Almost all physical and chemical changes that you encounter are reversible processes. Reversing a process converts some of the products back into reactants. Let us cite a few familiar examples. Water changes into ice when the temperature is lowered; increasing the temperature reverses the process. Chemicals that react and produce electricity in an automobile battery are consumed when the battery is furnishing current; when the battery is recharged, the process is reversed and the original chemicals are regenerated. Hemoglobin in blood cells combines with oxygen in the lungs and forms oxyhemoglobin, which then releases oxygen for use in metabolic processes in different parts of the body.

Applying the principles of chemical equilibrium allows scientists to control the direction and extent of a reaction. In this chapter, we will first consider the qualitative aspects of equilibrium. This will help us to identify equilibrium systems. We will then develop the equilibrium law, which can be used to determine the extent of a reaction and to calculate the quantity of reactant and product that are present together at equilibrium.

Finally, we will briefly examine the driving forces that cause a reaction system to spontaneously reach the equilibrium state in which there is no net particle or energy flow.

CHARACTERISTICS OF THE EQUILIBRIUM STATE

10-1
Equilibrium and Physical Systems

Although this chapter will deal with equilibrium of chemical systems, we will first review many of the concepts of equilibrium of physical systems. When water is poured into an open container and a large bell jar is placed over the container, careful measurement shows that the water level drops a small amount at first. This indicates that evaporation has begun (Fig. 10-1). Continued obser-

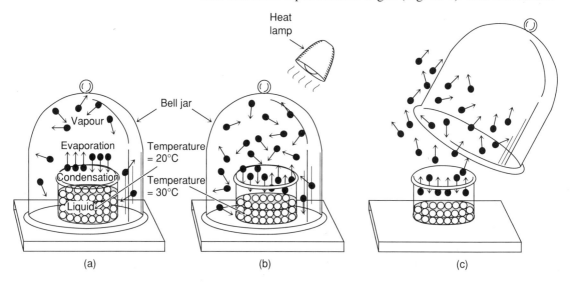

(a)   (b)   (c)

Figure 10-1
In a closed system, a dynamic equilibrium is established when the rate of evaporation is equal to the rate of condensation. When the temperature is increased, as in (b), equilibrium is re-established but there are more molecules in the gaseous phase than in (a). When the bell jar is removed, the system is no longer closed and there is no longer an equilibrium.

vation of this system shows that evaporation appears to stop, and no further change is obvious. This experiment can be explained in terms of the kinetic molecular theory. When the water is first placed in the container, some of the more energetic molecules near the surface of the water in the beaker escape into the gaseous phase. As more vapour molecules form, they start returning to the liquid phase in increasing amounts until the rates of evaporation and condensation equalize. Thus, molecules within the liquid are constantly exchanging places with those in the vapour even though we cannot observe them. This condition is known as *phase equilibrium*; if the rate of evaporation equals the rate of condensation, then the level of the water in the beaker will not change:

$$\text{liquid} \rightleftharpoons \text{vapour}$$

This will happen in a sealed chamber because the evaporated water cannot escape (Fig. 10-1(a)). Such a system is called a *closed system*. When, in a closed system, opposing changes are taking place at equal rates, the system is said to have reached a state of **dynamic equilibrium**. *In a state of dynamic equilibrium, two opposing processes are going on at an equal rate, and the system undergoes no observable changes in properties*. Strictly speaking, equilibrium can exist only in a closed system.

If the bell jar were removed, the gaseous molecules would escape into the air (Fig. 10-1(c)). Equilibrium could never be established under these conditions because only a few of the gaseous molecules would have the opportunity to return to the liquid phase, since they would have diffused far away from the liquid surface:

$$\text{liquid} \rightleftharpoons \text{vapour}$$

We recognize an equilibrium state by the fact that no visible changes are occurring. However, we must remember that there is a great deal of activity at the molecular level, as particles move from one phase to another. Such a system is said to be in dynamic equilibrium, which can only occur in a closed system in which none of the molecules can leave the system.

There are three conditions necessary for a physical equilibrium system:

1. The system must be closed; that is, the amount of matter in the system must remain constant.

2. The system must be at constant temperature (Fig. 10-2).

3. The visible properties of the system must be unchanging.

Experience has shown that a liquid will evaporate faster when heated, and slower when cooled. When the temperature is raised, the average kinetic energy of the molecules and the evaporation rate increase, causing the relative number of vapour molecules to increase. Chemical changes (reactions) are rather similar to phase changes in this respect. Many chemical reactions reach an equilibrium state long before any product is formed, but these reactions can be made to proceed in either direction by changing temperature, pressure and other factors that affect the process. In other

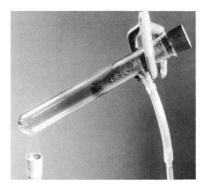

Figure 10-2
As a solid, iodine has a relatively high vapour pressure. When the dark crystals of solid iodine are warmed, a cloud of violet iodine vapour is produced. At a constant temperature, the vapour and solid are in dynamic equilibrium.

words, it is possible to control the direction and extent of reactions. Controlling reversible reactions is useful in the manufacture of drugs, plastics and thousands of other products.

Let us now look at the properties of a chemical reaction at equilibrium.

EQUILIBRIUM ON THE ICE...
BUT NOT IN THE LUNCH LINE-UP

If you ask hockey fans why they watch the game, they will enthusiastically describe the action and dynamics of the game. If you tell these fans that a hockey game is an example of a system in equilibrium and that a constantly moving line-up at a lunch counter has more action, they will listen in disbelief.

There are twenty players on a hockey team, but only six play on the ice at any one time. Although the coach may have players leave the game after their shift is completed, new players will come in to take their place. In this way, the rate at which players leave the bench is always equal to the rate at which players leave the ice. Throughout the game, only those who are part of the original twenty players may enter or leave the game, so the amount of "matter" in this system is constant.

On the other hand, consider a line of students in a school cafeteria. A casual observer might look at the line several times during the lunch hour. While the line would appear to be the same each time, it is actually changing as students are constantly leaving the line and being replaced by different ones. The "matter" in this case is continually changing. We do not have an equilibrium system but, rather, a *steady state*.

Another example of a system in a steady state is the burning of gas in a Bunsen-burner flame. As the fuel is burned, new fuel is fed into the system. The products of combustion—water vapour and carbon dioxide—are constantly leaving the system.

So the next time you watch your favorite hockey team lose, you can put their loss down to the equilibrium system that exists within the game.

10-2
Constancy of Observable Macroscopic Properties

When a chemical system reaches a state of equilibrium, observable properties become constant.

In our discussion of phase equilibria we found that an equilibrium can exist only in closed systems and that when equilibrium is established, observable macroscopic properties of the system are constant. Let us see how these observations apply in the reaction that occurs between hydrogen and iodine at 448°C. The equation for this reaction is

$$H_2(g) + I_2(g) \longrightarrow 2HI(g) \qquad [10\text{-}1]$$

We can follow the progress of the reaction by noting the colour of the system. All components of the system are colourless except violet iodine vapour. Thus, as the reaction proceeds, the intensity of the colour diminishes because the concentration of I_2 decreases.

Suppose that 1.00 mol each of H_2 and I_2 are placed in a one-litre container and allowed to react at 448°C until no further changes in

Macroscopic properties are properties that are visible to the naked eye, such as colour and phase.

A closed chemical system, like a closed physical system, is a constant-mass system; that is, the quantities of materials remain constant. In physical systems involving gases, a closed system involves a sealed container, while in chemical systems the container need not be sealed as long as none of the reactants or products are escaping from the system.

colour or other observable properties are seen (Fig. 10-3). How many moles of HI would be present? Based on the mole relationship in the equation, you might assume that two moles of HI would be present. This answer, however, is incorrect because it does not take into account the fact that the system reaches a state of equilibrium in which the conversion of reactants to products is incomplete. When equilibrium is attained, analysis of the mixture shows that there are 0.220 mol each of the unreacted H_2 and I_2 and 1.56 mol of HI present. Observation shows that this ratio of product to reactants remains constant at constant temperature after the equilibrium has been reached, regardless of how long the mixture is allowed to react. We can summarize this observation as follows: *Observable properties and concentrations of all participants become constant when a chemical system reaches a state of equilibrium.*

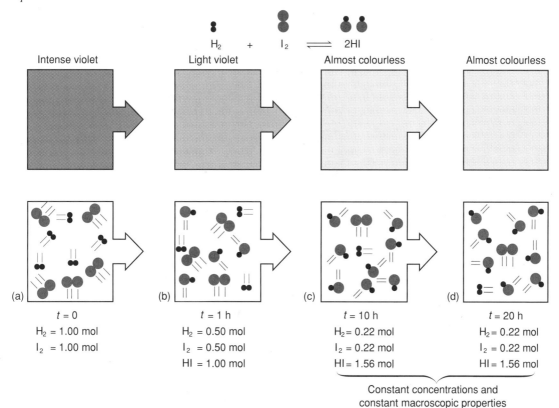

(a)	(b)	(c)	(d)
$t = 0$	$t = 1$ h	$t = 10$ h	$t = 20$ h
$H_2 = 1.00$ mol	$H_2 = 0.50$ mol	$H_2 = 0.22$ mol	$H_2 = 0.22$ mol
$I_2 = 1.00$ mol	$I_2 = 0.50$ mol	$I_2 = 0.22$ mol	$I_2 = 0.22$ mol
	HI $= 1.00$ mol	HI $= 1.56$ mol	HI $= 1.56$ mol

Constant concentrations and constant macroscopic properties

Just because the properties of a closed system appear to be constant does not necessarily mean that the system is at equilibrium. For example, a flask containing a mixture of H_2 and O_2 has constant properties but provides no evidence that it is at equilibrium. The violent explosion that occurs when the mixture is sparked certainly demonstrates that the system was not originally

Figure 10-3
How do the number of moles of hydrogen and iodine and the number of moles of hydrogen iodide in the equilibrium (d) compare with the number of moles in the non-equilibrium system shown in (a)?

Figure 10-4
Which of the systems shown are either at an equilibrium state or will reach an equilibrium state under the conditions noted?
Answer: a, d, f

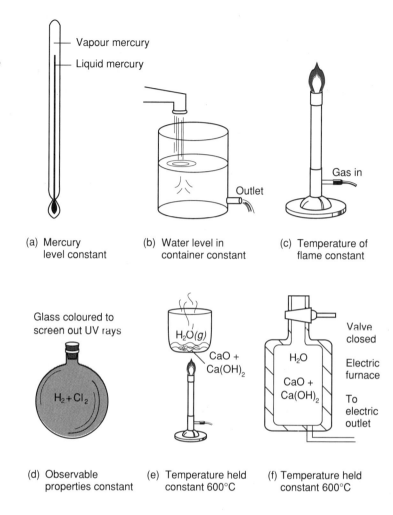

(a) Mercury level constant

(b) Water level in container constant

(c) Temperature of flame constant

(d) Observable properties constant

(e) Temperature held constant 600°C

(f) Temperature held constant 600°C

at equilibrium. It may be helpful, then, to distinguish between systems that have constant properties because two opposing processes are occurring at the same rate and those that have constant properties because the rate of any reaction among the components is too slow to be observable. *The constancy-of-properties criterion for an equilibrium system can be applied only to those systems in which the rate at which possible changes occur is observable.* For example, when the equilibrium described in Equation 10-1 is subjected to a slight increase in temperature, the intensity of the colour changes slightly but rapidly. When the system is returned to the original temperature, the original intensity returns almost immediately. These observations indicate that, under the given conditions, the reaction is quite rapid and *reversible.* Thus, systems at equilibrium can be identified if the following criteria are met:

1. The system is closed.

2. The observable macroscopic properties are constant at a constant and uniform temperature.

3. The amount of each component present in an equilibrium mixture is the same, regardless from which side it is approached experimentally.

10-3
Spontaneous Approach to Equilibrium From Either Direction

A reversible reaction in a closed system tends to equilibrium, and equilibrium can be approached from either direction.
In contrast to the method used in Section 10-2, let us now place two moles of HI(g) in the same container, maintained at 448°C, and then analyse the mixture. The equation for the decomposition of HI is

$$2HI(g) \longrightarrow H_2(g) + I_2(g) \qquad [10\text{-}2]$$

The resulting concentrations at equilibrium are the same as those obtained when we started with one mole of $H_2(g)$ and one mole of $I_2(g)$. The two reactions illustrate two characteristics of all reversible reactions in closed systems: *All reversible reactions spontaneously tend to approach an equilibrium, and equilibrium can be approached from either direction* (Fig. 10-5).

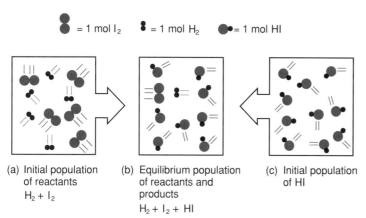

= 1 mol I_2 = 1 mol H_2 = 1 mol HI

(a) Initial population of reactants
$H_2 + I_2$

(b) Equilibrium population of reactants and products
$H_2 + I_2 + HI$

(c) Initial population of HI

Figure 10-5
In a reversible reaction such as

$$H_2(g) + I_2(g) \rightleftharpoons 2HI(g)$$

which takes place in a closed system at a given temperature, equilibrium (b) can be approached from either direction. In (c), 10 mol of HI decompose and yield an equilibrium mixture containing 7.8 mol of HI, 1.1 mol of H_2 and 1.1 mol of I_2. In (a), 5.0 mol of H_2 and 5.0 mol of I_2 react and form the same equilibrium mixture.

Equations 10-1 and 10-2 represent opposing reactions and can be represented by a single equation using double arrows to indicate the forward and reverse reactions. At equilibrium, the reaction is reversible and is represented by

$$H_2(g) + I_2(g) \rightleftharpoons 2HI(g)$$

The graphs in Fig. 10-6 illustrate that equilibrium can be approached from either direction.

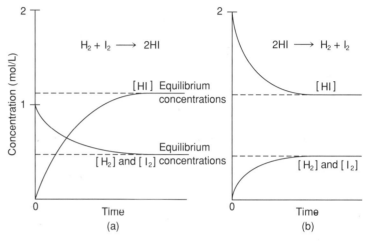

Figure 10-6
The variation in the concentration of H_2, I_2 and HI with time. In (a), 1 mol each of H_2 and I_2 are mixed and allowed to reach equilibrium at a given temperature. In (b), 2 mol of HI are allowed to decompose in the same vessel at the same temperature. In both instances, the same equilibrium concentrations of all species are observed.

10-4

The Dynamic Nature of an Equilibrium System

When a chemical equilibrium is established, the concentrations of the reactants and products remain constant over time because the forward and reverse reactions occur simultaneously. The constancy of observable properties in an equilibrium system does not imply that the reaction on the microscopic level has ceased. In the example of hydrogen iodide, it can be shown by substituting radioactive iodine for non-radioactive iodine that there is a continuous formation of HI after equilibrium has been established. Because radioactive isotopes have the same chemical properties as their non-radioactive counterparts, substitution can be accomplished without disturbing the equilibrium. Subsequent analysis reveals that the HI in the equilibrium mixture contains radioactive iodine. In another equilibrium mixture, the HI containing radioactive iodine can be substituted for some of the non-radioactive HI in the mixture. In this instance, some of the radioactive iodine from the HI becomes free I_2. This illustrates the dynamic nature of chemical equilibria and leads us to conclude that *the properties and concentrations of an equilibrium system are constant because the rates of the forward and reverse reactions are equal* so that it *appears* that no reactions are occurring. Let us investigate the changes that are taking place during the reaction.

As the reaction proceeds, the concentrations of all reactants change less rapidly than they did initially. The decreasing concen-

Addition of a small quantity of radioactive iodine to a system already at equilibrium does not significantly affect the equilibrium position.

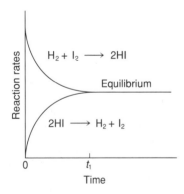

Figure 10-7
Reaction rates expressed as a function of time for the forward and reverse reactions occurring in the system

$$H_2 + I_2 \rightleftharpoons 2HI$$

Equilibrium is established at time t_1.

trations of H_2 and I_2, however, result in a decrease in the rate of the forward reaction, while the increasing concentration of HI results in an increase in the rate of the reverse reaction. Finally, the two rates become equal and equilibrium is established. At this point, the concentrations of all participants remain constant; that is, there is no net reaction. The reactants H_2 and I_2 are forming the product HI at exactly the same rate as HI is decomposing and forming H_2 and I_2. This is an example of *dynamic equilibrium*. The changing rates of the forward and reverse reactions are shown in Fig. 10-7. It can be seen from the graph that neither rate becomes zero at equilibrium. They both reach the same value determined by the nature of the reactants and the conditions of the experiment.

10-5
Reversibility of Reactions at Equilibrium

When a system in equilibrium is disturbed, the system will readjust to a new equilibrium in which the forward and reverse reactions are in balance.

Once a system has reached equilibrium, any factor that causes a change in the rate of either the forward or the reverse reaction disturbs the equilibrium. The participants are then no longer in equilibrium with each other. The system readjusts, however, so that the rates again become equal and a new equilibrium is established. For example, after an equilibrium has been established between H_2, I_2 and HI, let us increase the concentration of H_2:

$$H_2(g) + I_2(g) \rightleftharpoons 2HI(g) \qquad [10\text{-}3]$$

According to the collision theory, increasing the concentration of H_2 means that there is a greater chance of H_2 molecules colliding with I_2 molecules; subsequently, the rate of the forward reaction increases. In Equation 10-3, this temporary increase would result in the formation of HI. As the concentration of HI increases, the rate of the reverse reaction increases until the rate of the reverse reaction and the rate of the forward reaction are equal. At this time, a new equilibrium has been established. In this new equilibrium, the concentration of H_2 is still higher than in the former equilibrium, although some of the newly added H_2 has been consumed in the formation of HI. The resulting concentration of HI is higher, while the concentration of I_2 is less, since some of it has reacted with the H_2.

The principle underlying the behaviour of this system was first stated in 1888 by the French chemist, Henri Le Châtelier. We will discuss Le Châtelier's principle in the next section.

HENRI LOUIS LE CHÂTELIER
1850–1936
Le Châtelier was trained as a mining engineer at the École des Mines in Paris. After working two years in the field of mining engineering, he returned to his old school as professor of chemistry. In 1908 he accepted a position as professor of chemistry at the University of Paris, a position that was previously occupied by Henri Moissan, the discoverer of fluorine.

Le Châtelier was an energetic experimenter who worked on such problems as the calcining and setting of cements, the annealing of ceramics and glassware, the preparation of abrasives and the development of fuels, glasses and explosives.

As a teacher, Le Châtelier stressed precision in measurement as well as scientific reasoning. He was particularly interested in the relationship of science to industry and in how to get the maximum yield from any chemical reaction. His research in this area led to his discovery of the principle for which he is best known, *Le Châtelier's principle*, which deals with chemical equilibrium systems. It states that *if a system at equilibrium is disturbed, changes will occur that tend to restore the original conditions of the equilibrium*. Methods for controlling chemical reactions are based on this principle. The efficiency of many industrial processes has been greatly increased by the application of Le Châtelier's principle.

LE CHÂTELIER'S PRINCIPLE

10-6

Effect of a Change in the Concentration of an Equilibrium System

If a system in equilibrium is disturbed, the system will tend to react so as to establish a new equilibrium.

Le Châtelier's principle states that *when a stress is applied to a system at equilibrium, the system readjusts so as to relieve or offset the stress*. The term *stress* applies to any imposed factor that upsets the balance in rates of the forward and reverse reactions. Such a factor must affect a change in the concentration of one or more of the participants involved in a chemical equilibrium. The three factors that can be varied in order to change the relative rates and disturb a gaseous system at equilibrium are changes in concentration, temperature or total pressure brought about by a volume change.

In the example in Section 10-5, the stress was imposed by adding H_2 to the equilibrium mixture. The effect was offset to some extent when the system reacted and consumed some of the H_2 by forming more product (Fig. 10-8). Thus, the equilibrium position was displaced, or shifted, toward the product side, or to the right. This shift toward the product side would also occur if the concentration of the product were reduced. Increasing the concentration of a reactant or decreasing the concentration of a product causes the rate of the forward reaction to temporarily exceed the rate of the reverse reaction. This has the immediate effect of

Figure 10-8
The effect of adding additional H_2 to a mixture of H_2 and I_2 in equilibrium with the product of HI. Adding another 1 mol of H_2 instantaneously raises the concentration of H_2 to 1.22 mol/L. The stress is offset to some extent by a further reaction between hydrogen and iodine to form more hydrogen iodide. The result is a new equilibrium position with more hydrogen and hydrogen iodide and less iodine than in the original equilibrium mixture.

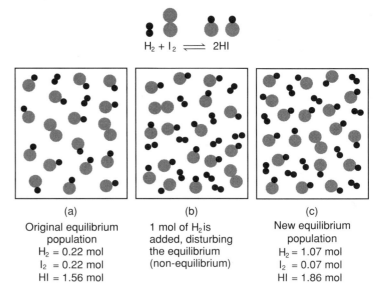

$$H_2 + I_2 \rightleftharpoons 2HI$$

(a)	(b)	(c)
Original equilibrium population	1 mol of H_2 is added, disturbing the equilibrium (non-equilibrium)	New equilibrium population
$H_2 = 0.22$ mol		$H_2 = 1.07$ mol
$I_2 = 0.22$ mol		$I_2 = 0.07$ mol
HI = 1.56 mol		HI = 1.86 mol

increasing the concentration of the product molecules. The subsequent effect of this, of course, is to increase the rate of the reverse reaction because the formation of HI molecules results in more collisions between HI molecules. Additional collisions between HI molecules are thus reflected in an increase in the reverse rate. Ultimately, however, a new balance between the forward reaction and the reverse reaction results.

If, on the other hand, a stress were imposed by adding HI to the equilibrium mixture, the equilibrium would shift to partially compensate. Temporarily, the rate of the reverse reaction would exceed the rate of the forward reaction, and the addition of HI molecules would result in more collisions between HI molecules. The equilibrium position would shift to the left, toward the formation of more H_2 and I_2 and a subsequent reduction in the concentration of HI. A new balance between the rate of the reverse reaction and the rate of the forward reaction would result. Once a new equilibrium is established, there would still be a net increase in HI compared with the original concentration.

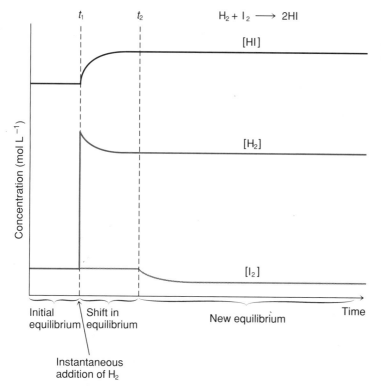

Figure 10-9
A graphical representation of the concentrations of H_2, I_2 and HI after adding H_2 to the equilibrium mixture.

Although our discussion of the effect of concentration on an equilibrium involves gaseous examples, it applies equally well to systems involving non-gases.

In the Haber process, when the volume is decreased (pressure increased), there is a greater increase in the number of collisions between reactant molecules per unit time than between product molecules.

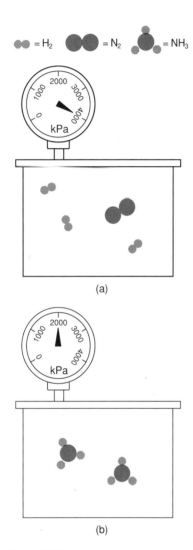

(a)

(b)

Figure 10-10
A decrease in the number of molecules results in a decrease in pressure. When three hydrogen molecules and a single nitrogen molecule combine and form two ammonia molecules, the pressure is reduced to one-half.

10-7

Effect of a Change in the Total Volume (or Related Pressure) of an Equilibrium System

When the volume of a gaseous reaction that has an unequal number of gases on each side of the equation is decreased, the equilibrium will shift so as to reduce the number of gas molecules.

A second stress that can be applied to an equilibrium system involving gases is a change in the volume of the system. To illustrate the effect of this change we will look at the Haber reaction for the formation of ammonia. The thermochemical equation for this reaction is

$$N_2(g) + 3H_2(g) \rightleftharpoons 2NH_3(g) \qquad \Delta H = -92 \text{ kJ} \qquad [10\text{-}4]$$

The stress imposed by a decrease in volume is actually a stress caused by the increase in concentration or in the total number of molecules per unit volume. The stress is relieved when the system reacts and reduces the number of molecules (Fig. 10-10). Equation 10-4 shows that a decrease in the total number of molecules occurs every time four molecules of reactant form two molecules of product. Thus, decreasing the volume results in an increased yield of NH_3 as the equilibrium shifts to the right.

Alternatively, we could interpret the shift caused by a volume decrease in terms of the pressure change that accompanies the decrease in volume. That is, the increase in pressure associated with a decrease in volume causes a shift that reduces the number of molecules and, thus, minimizes the effect of the change. Thus, we can say that *a decrease in the total volume of a gaseous system (or the accompanying increase in pressure) shifts an equilibrium in the direction of the fewer molecules as shown by the equation for the reaction* (Fig. 10-11). In other words, to predict the effect of a volume or related pressure change on a gaseous system, we must look at the number of product and reactant molecules (or moles) separately as shown by the equation for the reaction. If the number of product molecules equals the number of reactant molecules, as in Equation 10-3, then a change in total volume or accompanying pressure does not affect the equilibrium.

In terms of rates, decreased volume or increased pressure means that the molecules are closer together and collide more often. This results in an increase in both the forward and reverse rates of reactions. However, the extent to which these rates are affected depends on the molar ratios of the reactants and products. When the product molecules are fewer than the reactant molecules, as in Equation 10-4, the rate of the forward reaction is found to increase to a larger extent than that of the reverse reaction when the pressure increases. Additional NH_3 molecules then form and bring the reverse rate into balance with the forward rate.

When the same number of molecules of gas occur on both sides of the balanced equation, the rate of the forward reaction and the rate of the reverse reaction increase in the same ratio. Thus, no net change in the molecular population of the reactants or products occurs.

Note that when a noble gas, or any gas that does not react with any of the participants, is added to a gaseous system at equilibrium in a container of fixed volume, the total pressure increases. This, however, has no effect on the equilibrium because the concentrations or partial pressures (the pressure exerted by each component in a mixture) of the reacting gases remain constant.

10-8
Effect of a Change in the Temperature of an Equilibrium System

Increasing the temperature shifts the reaction in the direction that produces an endothermic change, while decreasing the temperature shifts the reaction in a direction that produces an exothermic change.

We can use the Haber reaction to illustrate the effect of a temperature change on a system at equilibrium. According to Le Châtelier's principle, a temperature increase should cause the system to react in a way that would absorb energy. Equation 10-4 indicates that the reaction is exothermic (ΔH is negative), and, thus, the decomposition of ammonia absorbs heat. An increase in temperature, therefore, should cause an increase in the concentrations of H_2 and N_2 and a decrease in the concentration of NH_3. In other words, the stress caused by increasing the temperature is relieved when heat is absorbed during the decomposition of NH_3. Therefore, increasing the temperature of this or any system at equilibrium that is exothermic in the forward direction decreases the quantity of product.

Increasing the temperature increases both the forward and reverse rates. However, as mentioned earlier, because the reverse reaction is endothermic, increasing the temperature increases the rate of the reverse reaction to a greater extent than it does the rate of the forward reaction. During the restoration of the balance in rates, the concentration of the reactants increases to the point where there are enough collisions for the rate of the forward reaction to equal the rate of the reverse reaction.

Consider what would happen if we were to decrease the temperature on the exothermic Haber reaction. The system should react in such a way as to release heat. A decrease in temperature,

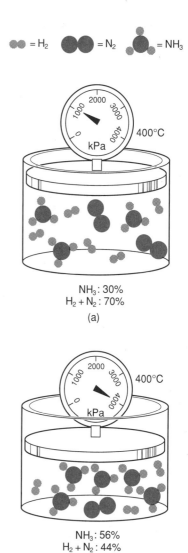

NH_3: 30%
$H_2 + N_2$: 70%
(a)

NH_3: 56%
$H_2 + N_2$: 44%
(b)

Figure 10-11
A decrease in the total volume results in an increase in pressure, which causes a reduction in the total number of molecules but an increase in the number of ammonia molecules. By this action, the system minimizes the stress brought about by the decreased volume.

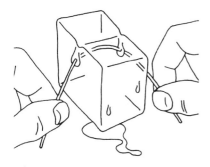

Figure 10-12
If force is applied to a wire placed on an ice cube, the ice under the wire melts and refreezes on top of the wire. Since the system is open, it is not a true equilibrium. Consider Le Châtelier's principle and discuss whether this experiment shows phase equilibrium.

Diamond
Some 40 years ago, the General Electric Company developed the process to convert graphite to industrial diamond. The reaction, which occurs at elevated temperatures approaching 2000°C, is

$$C_{graphite} + 186 \text{ kJ} \rightleftharpoons C_{diamond}$$

Since the density of diamond is greater than graphite, high pressure favours the formation of diamond. As a result, pressures between 5×10^6 kPa and 1×10^7 kPa are used, along with a suitable catalyst.

therefore, should cause a decrease in the concentrations of H_2 and N_2 and an increase in the concentration of NH_3. The stress caused by decreasing the temperature is relieved when heat is released during the formation of NH_3 and both the forward and reverse reactions are decreased. Since the forward reaction is exothermic, decreasing the temperature reduces the rate of the reverse reaction to a greater extent than it does the rate of the forward reaction. During the restoration of the balance in rates, the concentrations of the reactants decrease to the point where there are sufficiently few collisions for the rate of the forward reaction to again equal the rate of the reverse reaction.

10-9

Effect of Catalysts on an Equilibrium System

Catalysts cause reactions to reach equilibrium faster, but they do not alter the amounts of components at equilibrium.
In Chapter 9 we saw that a catalyst generally increases the rate of the forward and reverse reactions equally by providing a new pathway in which the activation energies are lower for both the forward and reverse processes. Since the ratio of the forward to reverse rate remains constant, no net change occurs in the relative amounts of product and reactants present at equilibrium. Addition of a catalyst, therefore, does not affect the position of the equilibrium; *it causes the reaction system to reach equilibrium in a shorter period of time.*

The following example illustrates the use of Le Châtelier's principle as a predictive device for determining the effect of changes in conditions on a system at equilibrium.

EXAMPLE 10-1
Determining the Effects of Changes on Equilibrium Systems
The following equation represents a gaseous system at equilibrium:

$$2SO_2(g) + O_2(g) \rightleftharpoons 2SO_3(g) \qquad \Delta H < 0$$

Indicate the direction in which the equilibrium shifts when the following changes are made.
a) The concentration of SO_2 is increased.
b) The partial pressure of SO_3 is decreased.
c) The temperature of the system is decreased.
d) The volume of the container is increased.
e) A catalyst is added.

SOLUTION

a) The formation of more SO_3 uses up SO_2 and helps to relieve the stress imposed by the increased concentration of SO_2. Thus, the equilibrium shifts to the right.

b) Decreasing the partial pressure is analogous to decreasing the concentration. The formation of additional SO_3 tends to relieve the stress by increasing its concentration (partial pressure). Thus, the equilibrium shifts to the right.

c) The equilibrium shifts to the right to increase the concentration of SO_3 as it produces heat to compensate for the lowering of the temperature.

d) Increasing the volume decreases the partial pressure of each gas. The system adjusts to the stress by forming more gas molecules. For every two SO_3 molecules that decompose, three molecules of reactants form. Thus, the equilibrium shifts to the left.

e) No shift occurs because both the forward and reverse rates are increased by the same ratio. Equilibrium is established sooner, but the equilibrium concentrations remain the same.

Figure 10-13
How is it possible for certain types of sunglasses to automatically adjust to changes in light intensity? Sunglasses that darken automatically in bright sunlight contain small, clear crystals of silver chloride. When ultraviolet light from sunlight strikes the silver chloride, a chemical reaction occurs, and metallic silver atoms and chlorine atoms form:

$$AgCl(s) + light \rightleftharpoons Ag(s) + Cl(s)$$

The presence of solid silver crystals trapped in the glass matrix causes the glass to look dark grey. When a person wearing these glasses enters a darkened room, the chemical system responds to the absence of radiant energy by shifting to a new equilibrium position. Silver recombines with chlorine, and the glass returns to its colourless state. This is an energy-releasing process.

FOLLOW-UP PROBLEM

The following equation represents a gaseous system at equilibrium:

$$heat + 2H_2O(g) \rightleftharpoons 2H_2(g) + O_2(g)$$

Indicate in which direction the equilibrium shifts when the following changes are made. Justify your answer in terms of Le Châtelier's principle.

a) The concentration of H_2 is increased.
b) The partial pressure (concentration) of H_2O is increased.
c) The concentration of O_2 is decreased.
d) The temperature is increased.
e) The volume of the container is decreased.
f) A catalyst is added.

Answers:

(a) to the left, (b) to the right, (c) to the right, (d) to the right, (e) to the left, (f) no shift occurs

10-10

The Haber Process

The Haber process is a practical industrial application of Le Châtelier's principle.

The Haber process for synthesizing ammonia from elemental hydrogen and nitrogen is one of the most important industrial processes in use today (Fig. 10-14). It is the major source of "fixed" nitrogen in compounds, which is an essential plant food applied in the form of chemical fertilizers.

Figure 10-14
Ammonia made by the Haber process is sometimes added directly to the soil as a source of fixed nitrogen.

The Haber process, developed in 1913 by the German chemist, Fritz Haber (1868–1934), was an important factor in World War I. The preparation of explosives used during the war required nitrogen compounds, which, before the war, had been imported from Chile. The blockade by the British early in the war cut off this supply. By converting the NH_3 produced by the Haber process to explosive nitrates, Germany was able to prolong the war. Let us examine the conditions under which this important chemical is produced.

In our discussion of Le Châtelier's principle, we applied it separately to temperature and pressure factors. The principle indicates that, for some reactions, high pressure and low temperature are favourable equilibrium conditions for high yields of product. At low temperatures, reaction rates may be too slow to be practical. In these cases, a compromise between the temperature and

In 1901, Henri Le Châtelier tried an experiment that was similar to the work of Haber, but a violent explosion forced Le Châtelier to stop work on the process we now call the Haber process. Late in life, Le Châtelier wrote, "I let the discovery of ammonia synthesis slip through my hands. It was the greatest blunder of my scientific career."

pressure factors must be made so that a good yield is obtained in a reasonable time. A number of important chemical manufacturing processes depend on such a compromise. One of them is the Haber process (Equation 10-4). Application of Le Châtelier's principle shows that, in theory, the most favourable conditions for a high yield of NH_3 would be low temperature and high pressure. At low temperatures, however, it takes so long for the system to reach equilibrium that the amount of NH_3 produced in a reasonable time would not be economically practical. Even with the best catalyst known, the process is slow. It has been found that temperatures near 500°C must be used. Because increasing the temperature tends to decrease the yield of ammonia, the only solution to the problem is to run the process at a high pressure, which gives a favourable yield in a reasonable period of time. The effect of different temperature and pressure combinations on the percentage of ammonia at equilibrium is shown in Table 10-1. A schematic diagram of the process is shown in Fig. 10-15.

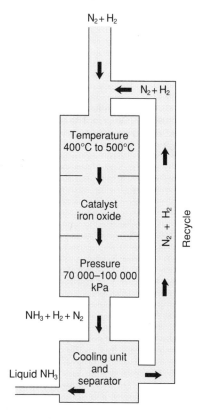

TABLE 10-1
PERCENTAGE OF AMMONIA IN THE EQUILIBRIUM MIXTURE (HABER PROCESS)

Temperature (°C)	Pressure (× 10⁵ kPa)						
	1.00	2.00	3.00	4.00	6.00	8.00	10.0
200	82	90	92	96	97	98	99
300	52	64	71	76	82	88	92
350	38	51	59	65	73	80	88
400	25	39	48	55	65	73	80
500	11	20	27	32	43	51	58
600	5	8	14	16	24	28	32

Figure 10-15
The Haber process makes practical use of Le Châtelier's principle. A satisfactory yield requires the use of high pressure, a relatively low temperature (500°C), a catalyst and the continuous removal of the product. Unreacted hydrogen and nitrogen are recycled through the reaction chamber with any residual ammonia gas. Additional hydrogen and nitrogen are added as required. In the cooling unit, only the NH_3 condenses. This, of course, lowers the concentration of NH_3 and shifts the equilibrium farther to the product side, as predicted by Le Châtelier's principle.

The data in Table 10-1 shows that the conditions that would produce the optimum yield of NH_3 are 200°C and 10.0×10^5 kPa pressure. However, the rate of reaction at 200°C is so slow that the time required for the system to reach equilibrium is prohibitively long. Therefore, a temperature of 400 to 500°C and a catalyst are used to speed up the reaction so that equilibrium is established within a reasonable time interval. Although the increased rate of reaction is achieved at the expense of a reduced yield, the process is still economically feasible.

We have seen that, at a given temperature, different chemical systems reach an equilibrium state at varying degrees of "completeness." Let us now develop an expression that relates the concentrations of reaction participants after equilibrium is established. This expression, called the *equilibrium law expression*, enables us to determine the extent of a reaction and to calculate the quantity of product present at equilibrium. The notion that the equilibrium concentrations of reactants and products are interrelated in a simple way is verified by experimentation.

Figure 10-16
An ammonia manufacturing plant in Courtwright, Ontario. The Haber process is used worldwide as a source of "fixed" nitrogen.

THE EQUILIBRIUM LAW EXPRESSION

10-11
Determining the Equilibrium Law Expression, K_e

At equilibrium, the concentrations of the reactants and products are related in a mathematical and predictable way by the equilibrium law expression.

There is a simple way to relate the concentrations of the reactants of a reaction to those of the products at a given temperature. To show this, we will use the gaseous reaction of nitrogen dioxide in equilibrium with dinitrogen tetroxide. Consider the following system:

$$2NO_2(g) \rightleftharpoons N_2O_4(g)$$

If we analyse the concentrations of the components of this system at four different conditions of pressure, we will obtain data similar to that in Table 10-2.

TABLE 10-2
EQUILIBRIUM CONCENTRATIONS OF $NO_2(g)$ AND $N_2O_4(g)$ AT FOUR DIFFERENT CONDITIONS OF PRESSURE AT 25°C

Pressure Condition Number	Equilibrium Concentrations (mol/L)	
	$NO_2(g)$	$N_2O_4(g)$
1	8.1×10^{-3}	1.2×10^{-2}
2	1.6×10^{-2}	4.5×10^{-2}
3	3.2×10^{-2}	1.8×10^{-1}
4	4.8×10^{-2}	4.0×10^{-1}

If we calculate each of the following expressions for each of the conditions in Table 10-2, we will obtain the following table.

TABLE 10-3
EVALUATION OF THREE EXPRESSIONS INVOLVING $NO_2(g)$ AND $N_2O_4(g)$ AT 25°C

Pressure Condition Number	$[NO_2] \times [N_2O_4]$ $(mol^2 \cdot L^{-2})$	$\dfrac{[N_2O_4]}{[NO_2]}$	$\dfrac{[N_2O_4]}{[NO_2]^2}$ $(L \cdot mol^{-1})$
1	9.7×10^{-5}	1.5	1.8×10^2
2	7.2×10^{-4}	2.7	1.8×10^2
3	5.8×10^{-3}	5.6	1.8×10^2
4	1.9×10^{-2}	8.3	1.7×10^2

The expressions used in Table 10-3 are only three of many possibilities. In the first two expressions, a different value is obtained for each set of calculations. The third expression, however, is of particular significance because it is nearly identical for all four conditions. No matter what mixture is used, the ratio of $[N_2O_4]$ to $[NO_2]^2$ at equilibrium is close to 1.8×10^2 L/mol at 25°C. This is called the *equilibrium constant* (K_e) for the reaction

$$2NO_2(g) \rightleftharpoons N_2O_4(g)$$

By convention, chemists always write the equilibrium constant expression with the product concentration in the numerator. Thus,

$$K_e = \frac{[product]}{[reactants]}$$

Other examples of equilibrium constant expressions are shown in Table 10-4.

TABLE 10-4
**EQUILIBRIUM CONSTANT EXPRESSIONS AND
VALUES OF THREE SELECTED EQUILIBRIA**

Equilibrium Equation	Equilibrium Constant Expression	Numerical Value
$H_2(g) + I_2(g) \rightleftharpoons 2HI(g)$	$K_e = \dfrac{[HI]^2}{[H_2][I_2]}$	56 at 423°C
$N_2(g) + 3H_2(g) \rightleftharpoons 2NH_3(g)$	$K_e = \dfrac{[NH_3]^2}{[N_2][H_2]^3}$	$650 \text{ mol}^{-2} \cdot \text{L}^2$ at 200°C
$2H_2(g) + O_2(g) \rightleftharpoons 2H_2O(g)$	$K_e = \dfrac{[H_2O]^2}{[H_2]^2[O_2]}$	$1 \times 10^{-7} \text{ mol}^{-1} \cdot \text{L}$ at 2000°C

Note that the exponents in each equilibrium constant expression in Table 10-4 can be obtained directly from the coefficients in the balanced equation. The exponent of $[H_2O]$, for example, is 2, just as the coefficient of $[H_2O]$ in the equation is 2. This regularity has stood the test of experimental verification so well that it is called the *equilibrium law expression*.

In general, for the system

$$aA + bB \rightleftharpoons cC + dD$$

the equilibrium constant is

$$K_e = \frac{[C]^c[D]^d}{[A]^a[B]^b}$$

It must be remembered that the concentrations in the equilibrium constant expression are the concentrations at equilibrium. The value of K_e should not be given without also giving the temperature and the balanced equation on which the value is based.

The *equilibrium law expression* can be stated as follows: *In a system at equilibrium, at a fixed temperature, the product of the equilibrium concentrations of the products divided by the product of the equilibrium concentrations of the reactants, each concentration being raised to a power equal to the coefficient of the substance in the equation, must be equal to a constant.* The equation applies only to systems of ideal gases and ideal solutions; however, we will assume that the expression applies to the systems we encounter in this text. For example, the equilibrium law expression for

$$H_2(g) + I_2(g) \rightleftharpoons 2HI(g) \qquad \Delta H < 0 \qquad \text{[10-5]}$$

is

$$K_e = \frac{[HI]^2}{[H_2][I_2]}$$ [10-6]

Experimental data shows that, at a given temperature, the equilibrium concentrations of the participants may vary, but always in such a way as to satisfy Equation 10-6. That is, at constant temperature, K_e is constant, and there are countless values for the concentrations of the participants that satisfy the equation. The concentrations in the equilibrium expression can be stated in moles per litre. In the case of gases, they can be given in terms of partial pressures that are proportional to the concentrations. In either case, units must be used consistently.

10-12
Effect of Temperature on K_e

It is usually necessary to specify the temperature when giving a value for K_e, since K_e varies with changes in temperature. To understand how a chemical reaction at equilibrium responds to a change in temperature, we must know how the energy of the system changes when the reaction occurs. For instance, the reaction to produce NH_3 from N_2 and H_2 is exothermic; heat is evolved when NH_3 molecules are formed:

$$N_2(g) + 3H_2(g) \rightleftharpoons 2NH_3(g) \qquad \Delta H = -ve \qquad [10-7]$$

When we raise the temperature, we do so by adding heat from some external source. The equilibrium in Equation 10-7 can counter the temperature increase by absorbing some of the added heat. It does this by proceeding from right to left, because the decomposition of NH_3 to N_2 and H_2 is endothermic and consumes some of the added heat. Thus, raising the temperature shifts the equilibrium to the left.

When the temperature is changed, the concentrations change, even though the volume stays the same and no chemical substances have been added or removed. The system comes to a new equilibrium, which means that K_e has changed. Note that the equilibrium constant (K_e) can also be symbolized by K_c because we write the mass action expression using concentration in mol/L.

The value of K_e changes when the temperature is changed, and it is not difficult to determine the direction of the change. The equilibrium law expression for Equation 10-7 is

$$K_e = \frac{[NH_3]^2}{[N_2][H_2]^3}$$

When the temperature is raised, the concentration of ammonia decreases, while the concentrations of nitrogen and hydrogen

Symbols for the Equilibrium Constant
For gaseous reactions, the equilibrium law expression can be written using either concentrations in mol/L or partial pressures. The equilibrium constant can be symbolized as K_e or by K_c when concentrations in mol/L are used. When partial pressures are used, the symbol K_p can be used.

The advantage of using different symbols is that, although the partial pressure of a gaseous reactant or product is directly proportional to its concentration in mol/L at a given temperature, the numerical values are not necessarily identical.

increase. Therefore, the resulting value for K_c is smaller. When the temperature of an exothermic reaction is raised, the value of the equilibrium constant becomes smaller. Conversely, if the temperature of an endothermic reaction is raised, the value of the equilibrium constant becomes larger.

Changing the equilibrium concentrations does not affect K_e at constant temperature. *When the concentration of one of the participants is changed, the concentrations of the others vary in such a way as to maintain a constant value for K_e.*

We can obtain an expression for the equilibrium constant, K_e, for any equilibrium system. For example, the equilibrium constant for the reaction

$$2SO_2(g) + O_2(g) \rightleftharpoons 2SO_3(g)$$

is

$$K_e = \frac{[SO_3]^2}{[SO_2]^2[O_2]}$$

In this example, K_e will have the following units:

$$\frac{(mol/L)^2}{(mol/L)^2 \times (mol/L)} = \frac{1}{mol/L} = L/mol$$

FOLLOW-UP PROBLEM

Write the equilibrium law expressions for the following equilibrium reactions:

a) $3H_2(g) + N_2(g) \rightleftharpoons 2NH_3(g)$

b) $2NO(g) + O_2(g) \rightleftharpoons 2NO_2(g)$

10-13
Relationship of K_e to Stoichiometric Coefficients

The form and value of the equilibrium constant depends on the way the equation is written.

For the reaction

$$H_2 + I_2 \rightleftharpoons 2HI$$

at 448°C, the equilibrium constant expression can be written

$$K_{e1} = \frac{[HI]^2}{[H_2][I_2]} = 50.2 \qquad [10\text{-}8]$$

However, this equation could just as easily be written

$$2H_2 + 2I_2 \rightleftharpoons 4HI$$

The equilibrium constant would then be

$$K_{e2} = \frac{[HI]^4}{[H_2]^2[I_2]^2} = (50.2)^2$$

If we compare these two K_e values, we can see that when the coefficients of a given reaction equation are doubled, the K_e for the new reaction equation is the square of the original K_e. In general, when we multiply the terms in an equation by a certain value, the K_e for the equation must be raised to a power equal to that value.

What happens to K_e when the equilibrium expression is reversed? The equilibrium constant expression for the equation

$$H_2 + I_2 \rightleftharpoons 2HI$$

is

$$K_{e1} = \frac{[HI]^2}{[H_2][I_2]} = 50.2$$

while the equilibrium constant expression for the reverse equation

$$2HI \rightleftharpoons H_2 + I_2 \qquad\qquad [10\text{-}9]$$

is

$$K_{e3} = \frac{[H_2][I_2]}{[HI]^2} = \frac{1}{50.2}$$

If we compare the two K_e expressions, we find that $K_{e3} = K_{e1}^{-1}$. Therefore, when a given reaction equation is reversed, the K_e for the reverse reaction is the reciprocal of the K_e for the original reaction.

FOLLOW-UP PROBLEM

Write the equilibrium law expressions for the following equilibrium reactions:

a) $N_2(g) + 3H_2(g) \rightleftharpoons 2NH_3(g)$
b) $2SO_2(g) + O_2(g) \rightleftharpoons 2SO_3(g)$
c) $SO_2(g) + \frac{1}{2}O_2(g) \rightleftharpoons SO_3(g)$
d) $SO_3(g) \rightleftharpoons SO_2(g) + \frac{1}{2}O_2(g)$
e) $4HCl(g) + O_2(g) \rightleftharpoons 2H_2O(g) + 2Cl_2(g)$

10-14

Relationship of K_e to the Extent of a Reaction

The magnitude of K_e is usually a measure of the extent to which a reaction has taken place.

In general, the magnitude of K_e is a measure of the extent to which a given reaction has taken place before equilibrium was established. A large K_e value indicates that, at equilibrium, there is a high concentration of products and a relatively low concentration of reactants. On the other hand, a small K_e value indicates that, at equilibrium, the concentrations of reactants are high compared with those of the products. A K_e value equal to 1 for the general reaction

$$A + B \rightleftharpoons C + D$$

in which the coefficients all have a value of 1 indicates that, at equilibrium, one-half the mass of the reactants is converted to products. That is, the yield is 50%. *Therefore, the larger the value of K_e, the more complete the conversion of reactants to products.* A large value of K_e for a forward reaction indicates a small K_e for a reverse reaction. In general, a reaction with a K_e of about 1×10^{10} is "complete" enough to be considered quantitative. One with a K_e equal to 1×10^{-10} is relatively "incomplete." That is, the equilibrium concentrations of the products are extremely small and probably not measurable by ordinary means. Actually, the constants for reactions have a much greater range than this. For example, some reactions have a K_e as low as 1×10^{-50}. On the other hand, some reactions have a K_e greater than 1×10^{100}, a number so large it is difficult to comprehend. In the reaction represented by Equation 10-8, the K_e value is 50.2 at 448°C. Starting with one mole each of H_2 and I_2, we can show that the equilibrium yield of HI is

$$\frac{1.56 \text{ mol actual yield}}{2.00 \text{ mol theoretical yield}} \times 100\% = 78.0\%$$

For the reverse reaction represented by Equation 10-9, K_e is 1/50.2. If we start with two moles of HI, the equilibrium yield of H_2 and of I_2 is

$$\frac{0.22 \text{ mol actual yield}}{1.00 \text{ mol theoretical yield}} \times 100\% = 22.0\%$$

Thus, the yield for a reaction with a large value for K_e is greater than that for one with a small value of K_e.

10-15
Calculations Involving K_e and Equilibrium Concentrations

Calculations involving equilibrium constants and concentrations can be used to compare different reactions.

We can make qualitative predictions about equilibria using Le

Châtelier's principle. It is useful to know that lowering the temperature in the Haber process will favour the production of ammonia; but by how much will a particular temperature change improve its production? Will the yield change by a factor of 10% or 0.1%? In order to control a chemical reaction and to achieve a maximum yield, we need quantitative information. Such quantitative predictions can be explained in terms of our understanding of the laws that govern equilibrium. We will look at various calculations that provide industries and labs around the world with information essential to achieving their objectives.

In our discussion of equilibrium constants we found that they could be used to help predict how far a reaction will proceed in the direction of the products. Such information, if it were quantitative, could be used to compare different reactions to determine which one would produce the best yield. In Example 10-2 we will determine K_e from the concentrations of the reactants and products of a system at equilibrium.

Here is a general guide to solving equilibrium problems:
– Use balanced equations.
– Remember that mass balance must prevail; that is, matter is neither created nor destroyed in chemical reactions.
– The basic approach is the same for all problems: use logic and common sense.

EXAMPLE 10-2
Calculating K_e from Equilibrium Concentrations
A mixture of H_2 and I_2 is allowed to react at 448°C. When equilibrium is established, the concentrations of the participants are found to be $[H_2] = 0.46$ mol/L, $[I_2] = 0.39$ mol/L and $[HI] = 3.0$ mol/L. Calculate the value of K_e at 448°C from this data.

SOLUTION
1. Write the balanced equation and the equilibrium law expression for the reaction:

$$H_2(g) + I_2(g) \rightleftharpoons 2HI(g)$$
$$K_e = \frac{[HI]^2}{[H_2][I_2]}$$

2. Substitute the equilibrium concentrations in the equilibrium law expression and solve for K_e:

$$K_e = \frac{[3.0]^2}{[0.46][0.39]} = 50$$

In Example 10-3 we will use the K_e calculated in Example 10-2 to determine the amount of product present at equilibrium.

EXAMPLE 10-3
Calculating the Equilibrium Concentration of the Product Using K_e

Assume that in the analysis of an equilibrium mixture of H_2 and I_2 at 448°C, the equilibrium concentrations of I_2 and H_2 are found to be 0.50 mol/L. What is the equilibrium concentration of HI?

SOLUTION

Because the value of K_e does not change at constant temperature, the equilibrium concentration of HI must increase in order to compensate for the increased equilibrium concentrations of H_2 and I_2. The new equilibrium concentration for HI can be determined by substituting the known values of H_2 and I_2 into the equilibrium law expression using the same value of K_e that was determined in Example 10-2.

$$50 = \frac{[HI]^2}{[0.50][0.50]}$$
$$[HI]^2 = (50)(0.25) = 12.5$$
$$[HI] = 3.5 \text{ mol/L}$$

In Example 10-2, the equilibrium constant was calculated from the concentrations of the participants at equilibrium; however, the concentrations of all participants at equilibrium are not always known. Example 10-4 illustrates how the equilibrium concentrations can be determined, based on the initial concentrations of the products and the equilibrium concentration of one of the participants. These values will then be used to calculate the equilibrium constant.

EXAMPLE 10-4
Calculating Equilibrium Concentrations and K_e

When 0.40 mol of PCl_5 is heated in a 1 L container, an equilibrium is established in which 0.25 mol of Cl_2 is present. The equation for the reaction is

$$PCl_5(g) \rightleftharpoons PCl_3(g) + Cl_2(g)$$

a) What are the equilibrium concentrations of all three components?

b) What is the equilibrium constant for the reaction?

SOLUTION

a) The balanced equation shows that for each mole of Cl_2 formed, 1 mol of PCl_3 is formed and 1 mol of PCl_5 is consumed. We are told that, at equilibrium, 0.25 mol of Cl_2 has been produced. This means that 0.25 mol of PCl_3 must also have been produced and that 0.25 mol of PCl_5 was consumed. Therefore, at equilibrium,

$$0.25 \text{ mol } Cl_2 \times \frac{1 \text{ mol } PCl_3}{1 \text{ mol } Cl_2} = 0.25 \text{ mol } PCl_3$$

$$0.40 \text{ mol } PCl_5 - \left[0.25 \text{ mol } Cl_2 \times \frac{1 \text{ mol } PCl_5}{1 \text{ mol } Cl_2} \right]$$
$$= 0.15 \text{ mol } PCl_5$$

and the equilibrium concentrations are:

$$[Cl_2] = \frac{0.25 \text{ mol}}{1 \text{ L}} = 0.25 \text{ mol/L}$$

$$[PCl_3] = \frac{0.25 \text{ mol}}{1 \text{ L}} = 0.25 \text{ mol/L}$$

$$[PCl_5] = \frac{0.15 \text{ mol}}{1 \text{ L}} = 0.15 \text{ mol/L}$$

b) Substitute the equilibrium concentrations in the equilibrium law expression and solve for K_e:

$$K_e = \frac{[PCl_3][Cl_2]}{[PCl_5]}$$

$$= \frac{0.25 \text{ mol/L} \times 0.25 \text{ mol/L}}{0.15 \text{ mol/L}}$$

$$= 0.42 \text{ mol/L}$$

It is possible to calculate the equilibrium concentrations given only K_e and the initial concentrations of the participants. This type of problem is more difficult than the preceding ones but can be made simpler by the use of concentration tables. The equilibrium concentrations can then be used to calculate the percentage yield of the reaction.

EXAMPLE 10-5
Calculating Equilibrium Concentrations Using K_e and Initial Concentrations

The equilibrium constant for the reaction

$$H_2(g) + I_2(g) \rightleftharpoons 2HI(g)$$

is 50 at 448°C.

1. What amount of HI is present at equilibrium when 1.0 mol of H_2 is mixed with 1.0 mol of I_2 in a 0.5 L container and allowed to react at 448°C?

2. What amount of H_2 and I_2 are left unreacted?

3. If the conversion of H_2 and I_2 to HI were essentially complete, what amount of HI would be present?

4. What is the percentage yield of HI in the equilibrium mixture?

SOLUTION

1. a) Write the equilibrium law expression for the reaction:

$$K_e = \frac{[HI]^2}{[H_2][I_2]} = 50$$

b) Since we only know values for the initial concentrations, we will represent the equilibrium concentrations as x mol/L. We will arrange the data in the form of an ICE table, which shows the *I*nitial concentrations, *C*hanges in concentration and *E*quilibrium concentrations. The reactants and products in the balanced equation will make up the headings of the table. The completed ICE table for the reaction is:

	$H_2(g)$	+	$I_2(g)$	$\rightleftharpoons$	$2HI(g)$
Initial concentrations (mol/L)	2.0		2.0		0.0
Changes in concentration (mol/L)	$-x$		$-x$		$+2x$
Equilibrium concentrations (mol/L)	$2.0 - x$		$2.0 - x$		$2x$

Let us now look closely at how this table was set up.

Initial Concentrations: We are told that 1.0 mol each of H_2 and I_2 were originally placed in a 0.5 L container without any HI. As the equilibrium expression relates quantities in concentration units of mol/L only, we must first determine the concentrations in these units.

Therefore,

$$[H_2]_{initial} = \frac{1.0 \ mol}{0.5 \ L} = 2.0 \ mol/L$$

$$[I_2]_{initial} = \frac{1.0 \ mol}{0.5 \ L} = 2.0 \ mol/L$$

Since there was no initial HI, its value is 0.0 mol/L.

Concentration Changes: In order to reach equilibrium, some of the H_2 and I_2 must have reacted to form HI. In order to calculate the equilibrium concentrations, we must assign a variable, x mol/L, to represent the amount of one of the reactants consumed. Let us assign $-x$ to the amount of H_2 consumed to indicate that there was a decrease in the concentration. According to the balanced equation, an equal number of moles per litre of H_2 and I_2 are consumed; therefore, the amount of I_2 consumed is also assigned a value of $-x$. On the other hand, for each mole of H_2 consumed, 2 mol of HI are produced; therefore, we assign a value of $2x$ to the concentration change of HI (this value is positive because the concentration of HI has increased).

Equilibrium Concentrations: The equilibrium concentrations in the table are determined by algebraically adding the initial concentrations and the concentration changes. Thus, the initial concentration of H_2 is changed by $-x$, giving an equilibrium concentration of $2.0 - x$. Since I_2 started with the same initial concentration as H_2 and is changed by the same amount, it also has an equilibrium concentration of $2.0 - x$. HI had no initial concentration but changed by $+2.0x$ mol/L and so has an equilibrium concentration of $2.0x$ mol/L.

c) Substitute the equilibrium concentrations and the value of K_e in the equilibrium law expression:

$$K_e = \frac{[HI]^2}{[H_2][I_2]}$$

$$50 = \frac{(2x)^2}{(2.0 - x)(2.0 - x)} = \frac{(2x)^2}{(2.0 - x)^2}$$

This equation can be solved by taking the square root of both sides and solving for x:

$$\sqrt{50} = \sqrt{\frac{(2x)^2}{(2.0-x)^2}}$$
$$7.1 = 2x/(2.0-x)$$
$$14.2 - 7.1x = 2x$$
$$x = 14.2/9.1 = 1.6 \text{ mol/L}$$

d) Determine the equilibrium concentrations by substituting the value of x in the expressions for equilibrium concentrations:

$$[H_2] = 2.0 - x = 2.0 - 1.6 = 0.40 \text{ mol/L}$$
$$[I_2] = 2.0 - x = 2.0 - 1.6 = 0.40 \text{ mol/L}$$
$$[HI] = 2x = 2(1.6) = 3.2 \text{ mol/L}$$

e) Determine the total number of moles of HI by multiplying the concentration of HI by the volume of the container:

Number of moles = 3.2 mol/L × 0.5 L = 1.6 mol

2. The amount of H_2 and I_2 left unreacted can be found by multiplying their equilibrium concentrations by the volume of the container:

Number of moles = 0.40 mol/L × 0.5 L = 0.20 mol

3. The stoichiometric equation shows that 2 mol of HI form for each mole of H_2 and I_2 that react. Therefore, if the reaction were essentially complete, 1.0 mol of H_2 would react with 1.0 mol of I_2 and form 2.0 mol of HI.

4. The percentage yield of HI at equilibrium would be the actual equilibrium yield divided by the yield if the reaction were complete:

$$\% \text{ yield HI} = \frac{1.6 \text{ mol}}{2.0 \text{ mol}} \times 100\% = 80\%$$

In the preceding problem, when the values of the equilibrium concentrations, given in terms of x, were substituted into the equilibrium law expression, the math required to solve for x was not complicated. If, however, the initial concentrations of the reactants, or their ratios in the chemical equation, are not the same, then we must use the quadratic equation to solve for x. We will demonstrate this in the next example, using a system that has different initial concentrations of the reactants.

EXAMPLE 10-6
Calculating Equilibrium Concentrations Using the Quadratic Equation

What amount of HI is present at equilibrium when 2.0 mol of H_2 is mixed with 1.0 mol of I_2 in a 0.50 L container and allowed to react at 448°C? At this temperature, $K_e = 50$.

SOLUTION
1. Express the initial concentration of all participants in mol/L:

$$[H_2] = 2.0 \text{ mol}/0.50 \text{ L} = 4.0 \text{ mol/L}$$
$$[I_2] = 1.0 \text{ mol}/0.50 \text{ L} = 2.0 \text{ mol/L}$$
$$[HI] = 0 \text{ mol/L}$$

2. Let x mol/L equal the concentration of H_2 consumed in reaching equilibrium, and express the equilibrium concentration of all participants in terms of x:

$$H_2 = 4.0 - x$$
$$I_2 = 2.0 - x$$
$$HI = 2x$$

3. Substitute the equilibrium concentrations and the value of K_e in the equilibrium law expression and solve for x:

$$50 = \frac{(2x)^2}{(4.0 - x)(2.0 - x)}$$

$$50 = \frac{4x^2}{(8.0 - 6.0x + x^2)}$$

$$400 - 300x + 50x^2 = 4x^2$$

$$46x^2 - 300x + 400 = 0$$

This quadratic equation has the form

$$ax^2 + bx + c = 0$$

and can be solved by

$$x = \frac{-b \pm \sqrt{b^2 - 4ac}}{2a}$$

where

$$a = 46$$
$$b = -300$$
$$c = 400$$

Substituting these values in the quadratic formula yields:

$$x = \frac{+300 \pm \sqrt{(-300)^2 - 4(46)(400)}}{92}$$

$$x = \frac{+300 \pm 128}{92}$$

$$x = 4.7 \text{ or } 1.9$$

The value of 4.7 for x has no meaning since it is larger than the original concentration of H_2. Physically meaningless solutions do occur from time to time and need to be recognized as such. If we use a value of 1.9 for x, the equilibrium concentration of HI is $2x$, or 3.8 mol/L, and thus, the number of moles of HI is

Number of moles = 0.50 L $\times$ 3.8 mol/L = 1.9 mol

Equilibrium constants can be used to predict the net direction in which a reaction will proceed from a non-equilibrium condition. If certain amounts of H_2, I_2 and HI are mixed, will there be more or less HI when equilibrium has been reached? To answer this question we calculate a reaction quotient, Q. We obtain this value using the same expression as for the equilibrium constant, except that the concentrations of the reactants and products are the initial concentrations and not the equilibrium concentrations. When the reaction quotient, Q, is compared with K_e, the following conclusions can be made:

– If $Q < K_e$, the reaction will proceed in the direction of the products, thus increasing the concentrations of the products and decreasing the concentrations of the reactants. In this way, Q approaches K_e.

– If $Q > K_e$, the reaction will proceed in the direction of the reactants.

– If $Q = K_e$, the reactants and products are at equilibrium and there will be no change in their respective concentrations.

In Example 10-7 we will use the reaction quotient to determine the net direction of the reaction to reach equilibrium.

EXAMPLE 10-7
Determining the Net Direction of a Reaction
Using the Reaction Quotient, Q
When 3.0 mol of HI, 2.0 mol of H_2 and 1.5 mol of I_2 are placed in a 1 L container at 448°C, will a reaction occur? If so, which reaction takes place? At 448°C, $K_e = 50$.

SOLUTION

Substitute the given concentrations in an expression similar to the equilibrium law expression and use the given experimental concentrations to determine the reaction quotient, Q. If the reaction quotient is exactly equal to K_e, the given concentrations are equilibrium concentrations, and no net reaction occurs. If the reaction quotient is greater than K_e, the numerator in the expression is larger than it would be at equilibrium. Therefore, the concentration of the product, HI, must decrease to reach the equilibrium concentration. On the other hand, if the reaction quotient is too small, the numerator is smaller than it would be at equilibrium. Therefore, the reactants, H_2 and I_2, would form additional product to increase the concentration of HI to an equilibrium value. Substituting given values yields

$$Q = \frac{(3.0)^2}{(2.0)(1.5)} = 9.0/3.0 = 3.0$$

Since the reaction quotient of 3.0 is less than the K_e value of 50, the reaction goes to the right and forms more HI and reduces the concentrations of H_2 and I_2.

FOLLOW-UP PROBLEMS

1. When 0.040 mol of PCl_5 is heated to 250°C in a 1.0 L vessel, an equilibrium is established in which the concentration of Cl_2 is 0.025 mol/L. Find the equilibrium constant, K_e, at 250°C for the reaction

$$PCl_5(g) \rightleftharpoons PCl_3(g) + Cl_2(g)$$

Note that the initial, not the equilibrium, concentration of PCl_5 is given. The amount of PCl_5 reacted is the same as the amount of Cl_2 formed.

2. Assume that the analysis of another equilibrium mixture of the system in problem 1 shows that the equilibrium concentration of PCl_5 is 0.012 mol/L and that of Cl_2 is 0.049 mol/L. What is the equilibrium concentration of PCl_3 at 250°C?

3. How many moles of PCl_5 must be heated in a 1.0 L flask at 250°C in order to produce enough chlorine to give an equilibrium concentration of 0.10 mol/L?

4. Will there be a net reaction when 2.5 mol of PCl_5, 0.60 mol of Cl_2 and 0.60 mol of PCl_3 are placed in a 1 L flask and heated to 250°C? If so, which reaction takes place?

Answers:
1. 4.2×10^{-2}
2. 1.0×10^{-2} mol
3. 0.34 mol
4. Cl_2 and PCl_3 react and form more PCl_5.

10-16
Quantitative Aspects of Le Châtelier's Principle

When a system in equilibrium is disturbed, the equilibrium position will shift.

Let us consider the effect of changing the concentration of a participant in a system already at equilibrium. Consider this system:

$$SO_2(g) + NO_2(g) \rightleftharpoons SO_3(g) + NO(g) \qquad [10\text{-}10]$$

K_e can be expressed as

$$K_e = \frac{[SO_3][NO]}{[SO_2][NO_2]} \qquad [10\text{-}11]$$

Suppose we add SO_2 to an equilibrium mixture of the above components. This addition produces a non-equilibrium condition. Increasing the denominator in Equation 10-11 means that the reaction quotient, Q, is less than K_e. Therefore, to re-establish equilibrium, the value of the products represented in the numerator must increase. In other words, the equilibrium position must shift to the right and increase the yield of products. The quantitative aspects of this change are illustrated in Example 10-8.

EXAMPLE 10-8
Calculating the Concentration of a Product When an Equilibrium Has Been Disturbed and Then Re-established

Analysis of an equilibrium mixture represented by Equation 10-10 shows the following:

$$[SO_2] = 4.0 \text{ mol/L}, [NO_2] = 0.50 \text{ mol/L}$$
$$[SO_3] = 3.0 \text{ mol/L}, [NO] = 2.0 \text{ mol/L}$$

What is the new equilibrium concentration of NO when 1.5 mol of NO_2 is added to a litre of the first mixture?

SOLUTION

1. Use the original equilibrium concentrations to calculate the equilibrium constant:

$$K_e = \frac{[SO_3][NO]}{[SO_2][NO_2]}$$

$$= \frac{(3.0)(2.0)}{(4.0)(0.50)} = 3.0$$

2. Let x mol/L represent the [NO] formed as a result of increasing the concentration of NO_2 from 0.50 mol/L to 2.0 mol/L. Express the second set of equilibrium concentrations in terms of x:

	$SO_2(g)$ +	$NO_2(g)$	$\longrightarrow$	$SO_3(g)$ +	$NO(g)$
First equil. conc.	4.0 mol/L	0.50 mol/L		3.0 mol/L	2.0 mol/L
Second equil. conc.	(4.0 − x)	(0.50 + 1.5 − x)		(3.0 + x)	(2.0 + x)

3. Substitute the new equilibrium concentrations in the expression for K_e and solve the resulting quadratic equation for x:

$$\frac{(3.0 + x)(2.0 + x)}{(4.0 - x)(2.0 - x)} = 3.0$$

$$2.0x^2 - 23x + 18 = 0$$

$$x = 0.85 \text{ mol/L}$$

4. Calculate the new equilibrium concentration of NO:

$$[NO] = 2.0 + x = 2.0 + 0.85 = 2.9 \text{ mol/L}$$

FOLLOW-UP PROBLEM

How many mol/L of NO_2 would have to be added to the original equilibrium mixture in Example 10-8 to increase the equilibrium concentration of SO_3 from 3.0 to 4.0 mol at the same temperature?

Answer: 1.8 mol/L

A GALLING MATTER: MINERAL SALTS IN THE EXCRETORY SYSTEM

A pproximately 1% of all North Americans between the ages of 30 and 60 develop kidney stones in the urinary tract. These stones can cause considerable suffering and, if lodged in the ureter, can develop into an excruciatingly painful condition.

Kidney stones are hard-mass objects that can vary in size from that of a grain of sand to that of a large goose egg; the largest stone on record weighed 6.3 kg. Kidney stones develop when poorly soluble substances in the urine precipitate out of solution and form crystals. The exact composition of the stones varies, but many are found to contain the mineral salt, calcium phosphate.

Although the conditions that cause the formation of kidney stones are not well understood, it is believed that stone development is related to the body's regulation of calcium. About 99% of the body's calcium is found in the bones. Our bodies require appropriate levels of calcium for nerve and muscle function and for bone metabolism. The normal blood-calcium level is 10 mg/100 ml. Calcium levels in the blood are controlled by the parathyroid hormone (PTH), which stimulates the release of calcium from bones or the reabsorption of calcium by the kidney. Kidney stones form when either too much PTH is produced or when too much potential stone-forming material such as calcium is ingested.

Over-production of PTH causes an increase in the amount of calcium released from bone. The kidneys try to decrease the blood levels of calcium by excreting the excess. Calcium ions combine

with phosphate ions to form calcium salts that are only semi-soluble in water:

$$3Ca^{2+} + 2PO_4^{3-} \rightleftharpoons Ca_3(PO_4)_2$$

If the level of calcium in the blood is too high, Le Châtelier's principle operates to make the ions precipitate out of solution. These ions aggregate and eventually form kidney stones.

Most stones are small enough that they pass down the urinary tract with no trouble. Sometimes the stone is not passed and surgery is required to remove it. A recently developed treatment called *extracorporeal shock-wave lithotripsy* involves focusing shock waves, which are generated in water by electric discharges, on the stone to break it into smaller fragments.

EQUILIBRIA IN HETEROGENEOUS SYSTEMS INVOLVING GASES

10-17

Equilibrium Constants for Systems Involving Solids

The K_e for systems involving solids is independent of the quantity of solid present.

As you know, systems in which more than one phase is present are called *heterogeneous reaction systems*. The form of the equilibrium constant for these reactions differs markedly from that for homogeneous reactions involving only gases. Consider the thermal decomposition of calcium carbonate in a closed container. The equation for the reaction is

$$CaCO_3(s) \rightleftharpoons CaCO(s) + CO_2(g)$$

Experiments show that, at a given temperature, an equilibrium is established in which the concentration or pressure of CO_2 is constant. Furthermore, it is noted that the concentration of CO_2 is not affected by the quantity of the solid $CaCO_3$ or solid CaO in the container. As long as both solids are present, the concentration of CO_2 is constant at a given temperature. At 900°C, the concentration of $CO_2(g)$ is 0.011 mol/L. Following our original convention, we would write the equilibrium constant expression for the reaction as

$$K_e = \frac{[CaO][CO_2]}{[CaCO_3]}$$

Since K_e does not vary with the quantities of solid present, we can assume that they have a constant concentration. The concentration of the solid at a given temperature is fixed by its density (particles, grams or moles of solid per unit volume); if the temperature is constant, the density of the solid is constant.

Since the concentrations of the solids are unchanging, they may be incorporated into the equilibrium constant, K_e, to give a new equilibrium constant, K:

$$[CO_2] = K_e \frac{[CaCO_3]}{[CaO]} = K$$

The value of K for this reaction at 900°C is, therefore, equal to the concentration of CO_2, or 1.1×10^{-2}.

It should be stressed that all solids must be present in the system to establish an equilibrium. We can summarize this discussion by saying that the equilibrium constant expression for a heterogeneous reaction involving gases does not include the concentrations of pure solids. For example, the K for the reaction

$$NH_4Cl(s) \rightleftharpoons NH_3(g) + HCl(g)$$

is

$$K = [NH_3][HCl]$$

Let us now look at some of the fundamental reasons why certain reactions have larger equilibrium concentrations of products than others. What are the factors that are related to the magnitude of K_e and the completeness of a reaction?

Increasing the amount of solid present in a heterogeneous equilibrium system increases the total surface area at which both forward and reverse reactions are occurring. The total number of moles of solid reactant being converted into product per unit time increases. However, the total number of moles of product being converted back to solid reactant per unit time increases proportionally. This results in no net change in total amount of reactant or product. It is assumed that the change in total volume of solid is insignificant in relation to the container volume.

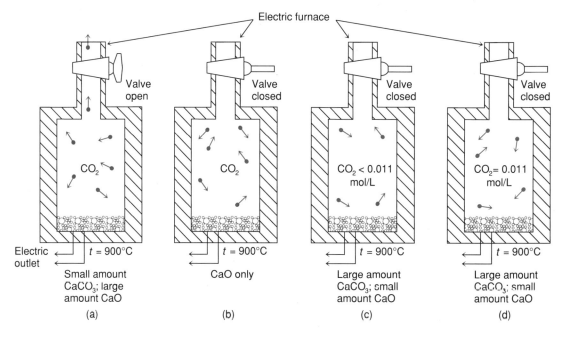

Figure 10-17

1. Which of the systems are in equilibrium?
2. What happens when the pressure (concentration) of CO_2 is increased in (d)?
3. Is it possible to bring the non-equilibrium systems shown above to an equilibrium state? In each case, indicate what can be done, and state the effect on the quantities of CaO and $CaCO_3$.

Answers:
1. c, d
2. Equilibrium shifts to the left.
3. Yes
   a) close valve
   b) add CaO_3
   c) will equilibrate

FACTORS RELATED TO THE MAGNITUDE OF K_e

10-18

The Tendency, or Drive, Toward Minimum Energy (Enthalpy) and Maximum Disorder (Entropy)

Enthalpy and entropy can be used to predict the spontaneity of a reaction.

It is apparent that there is a wide variation in the degree of "completeness" of reactions. For some reactions, equilibrium is achieved when practically all of the reactants have been converted into products. These reactions are referred to as *complete*. For other reactions, the equilibrium state is achieved when only a negligible amount of the reactants have been converted into products. From a stoichiometric viewpoint, these substances do not react appreciably with one another. In between these extremes we find all degrees of "incompleteness" at equilibrium.

Earlier we found that at a given temperature, the H_2–I_2–HI system reached the same equilibrium state when we started with 2 mol of HI as when we started with 1 mol each of H_2 and I_2. We can express this observation by saying *in a closed system, all reactions, unless prevented by exceedingly high activation energy barriers (slow rates), spontaneously approach an equilibrium state.*

It is apparent from our study of the rather inefficient (that is, at standard temperature and pressure), spontaneous, exothermic Haber process,

$$N_2(g) + 3H_2(g) \rightleftharpoons 2NH_3(g) \qquad \Delta H = -ve$$

that equilibrium is established before the system reaches the lowest possible energy state represented by the complete conversion of N_2 and H_2 into NH_3. The "drive" toward the minimum energy is hampered by the opposing drive of the system to achieve a condition of maximum randomness (entropy). This drive favours the decomposition of NH_3 in which two molecules decompose and yield four molecules. Thus, we can say that the equilibrium state and the value of K_e represent a compromise between the drive of atoms and molecules in a reaction to achieve a state of minimum enthalpy and a state of maximum entropy.

We can use the thermal decomposition of $CaCO_3$ to illustrate the point further. The equation for the reaction is

$$CaCO_3(s) \rightleftharpoons CaO(s) + CO_2(g) \qquad \Delta H = +ve$$

The equilibrium law expression for this equation is

$$K = [CO_2] \qquad\qquad [10\text{-}12]$$

Equation 10-12 shows that the value of K is equal to the equilibrium concentration or partial pressure of CO_2. If the system were unhampered by a drive to achieve a minimum enthalpy condition, its drive to attain maximum entropy would result in the complete conversion of $CaCO_3(s)$ into $CaCO(s)$ and gaseous CO_2. This is because the random distribution of gas molecules represents greater entropy than the orderly arrangement of ions in the crystal. However, the decomposition of $CaCO_3$ and the formation of CO_2 involve the absorption of energy and result in an increase in the enthalpy of the system. Thus, both the actual equilibrium concentration of CO_2 and the value of K represent a compromise between the drive of the system to remain in the lower-enthalpy, more ordered, crystalline form and the drive to change into a higher-entropy, less ordered, gaseous form. The relative importance of each drive depends on the temperature. At low temperatures the energy factor predominates. This means that the equilibrium favours the formation of the substances with the lowest enthalpy (heat content). At high temperatures, equilibrium favours the tendency toward maximum disorder (entropy). The higher the temperature, the more "thermal motion" there is and the greater the entropy.

This discussion suggests that the likelihood of a reaction occurring is related to the temperature and the relative enthalpy and entropy changes associated with the reaction. We would predict, therefore, that reactions involving an increase in entropy and a decrease in enthalpy would be highly probable (spontaneous), while those involving a decrease in entropy and an increase in enthalpy would be highly improbable (nonspontaneous).

As we noted earlier, a decrease in the enthalpy of a system is associated with the tendency of the reacting particles to form strong bonds with a negative value for ΔH. Qualitatively, it is often possible to predict the entropy change (ΔS) by inspecting the equation for a reaction. It should be noted that to determine whether S increases or decreases, we have to know the actual values of S and use them to determine if ΔS is positive or negative. Following is a list of conditions in which there is an increase in the entropy of a system.

1. When a gas is formed from a solid, as in

$$CaCO_3(s) + heat \longrightarrow CaO(s) + CO_2(g)$$

2. When a gas is evolved from a solution, as in

$$Zn(s) + 2H^+(aq) \longrightarrow H_2(g) + Zn^{2+}(aq)$$

3. When the number of moles of gaseous product exceeds the moles of gaseous reactant, as in

$$2C_2H_6(g) + 7O_2(g) \longrightarrow 4CO_2(g) + 6H_2O(g)$$

4. When many crystals dissolve in water, as in

$$NaCl(s) \longrightarrow Na^+(aq) + Cl^-(aq)$$

Dissolution of $NaCl(s)$ yields freely moving ions and, as predicted, a greater S. However, the system also has water molecules moving randomly. Some of the water molecules become more ordered because of the process of hydration. This would cause a decrease in S. The increase caused by the dissolution of the crystals usually predominates in the case of soluble salts.

FOLLOW-UP PROBLEM

For each of the following processes, predict whether the entropy increases or decreases.

a) $2H_2(g) + O_2(g) \longrightarrow 2H_2O(g)$
b) $2SO_3(g) \longrightarrow 2SO_2(g) + O_2(g)$
c) $MgCO_3(s) + 2H_3O^+ \longrightarrow Mg^{2+}(aq) + 3H_2O(l) + CO_2(g)$
d) $Ag^+(aq) + Cl^-(aq) \longrightarrow AgCl(s)$
e) $NH_4NO_3(s) \longrightarrow NH_4^+(aq) + NO_3^-(aq)$
f) $H_2O(l) \longrightarrow H_2O(g)$
g) $Mg(s) + 2H_3O^+ \longrightarrow Mg^{2+}(aq) + H_2(g) + 2H_2O$

h) $2C_2H_2(g) + 5O_2(g) \longrightarrow 4CO_2(g) + 2H_2O(g)$

i) $NH_3(g) + HCl(g) \longrightarrow NH_4Cl(s)$

Answers:

(a) decreases, (b) increases, (c) increases, (d) decreases, (e) increases, (f) increases, (g) increases, (h) decreases, (i) decreases

10-19
The Second Law of Thermodynamics

The entropy, or the tendency toward randomness, of the universe increases for spontaneous reactions.

When changes occur in a system, particles are more likely to achieve a disordered condition than an ordered one. A new deck of cards, arranged numerically and by suits, represents an ordered system. Once the cards are put into play, it is highly unlikely that they will spontaneously reach the original ordered arrangement.

The randomness, or disorder, of a system is expressed in terms of a quantity called entropy, which is symbolized by S. A perfectly ordered system has zero entropy. The imaginary, ideal, perfectly ordered system used as a standard for entropy measurement is a perfect crystal at absolute zero. At any temperature other than absolute zero, thermal energy gives rise to some disorder. The more disordered the system, the greater its entropy (Fig. 10-18). On the basis of many experiments, it can be stated that *molecular systems favour the state of maximum entropy, provided that energy factors do not prohibit it*. It is apparent that the tendency to achieve maximum entropy is not the only factor that affects the behaviour of a molecular system. If it were, all substances would spontaneously change into the gaseous state.

The drive of a system toward equilibrium does not necessarily imply that the energy (enthalpy) of the system is decreasing or that the entropy of the system is increasing. There is a competition between the drive toward minimum enthalpy and the drive toward maximum entropy of the same system. We need additional criteria for predicting the spontaneity of reactions in which the enthalpy and entropy factors oppose each other. These criteria must take into account temperature, enthalpy changes, entropy changes, and also relate to the ***second law of thermodynamics***, which states that *the entropy of the universe increases for any spontaneous process*.

Applied to chemical systems, the second law indicates that the entropy of a system may increase or decrease, but if it does decrease, then the entropy of the surroundings must increase to a

It can be shown that during the condensation of water vapour at a temperature below 100°C, the heat released by the process increases the entropy of the surroundings to a greater extent than the decrease in the entropy of the water molecules.

Figure 10-18
As our society becomes more "disposable," refuse is constantly being dumped at landfill sites. These changes increase the entropy at the sites.

greater extent so that the overall entropy change in the universe is positive. That is,

$$\Delta S_{\text{universe}} = \Delta S_{\text{system}} + \Delta S_{\text{surroundings}} > 0$$

where ΔS represents a change in entropy.

10-20
The Change in Free Energy and the Spontaneity of a Reaction

The determination of free energy can be used to predict the probable spontaneity of a reaction.

We can use the total entropy change of the universe as a criterion to predict the spontaneity of a reaction. To do this, however, we have to calculate the entropy change in both the system undergoing the change and in the surroundings. A more specific criterion that we could apply directly to a chemical system without calculating the entropy change of the surroundings would be of more use to us in predicting reaction spontaneity. This criterion, known as the ***change in the free energy of a system***, is symbolized by ΔG and is related to the enthalpy change, entropy change and temperature of a system. The relationship is given by the *Gibbs-Helmholtz equation*,

$$\Delta G = \Delta H - T\Delta S \qquad [10\text{-}13]$$

where T is the temperature in kelvin. Qualitatively, the sign of ΔG can be used to predict the spontaneity of a reaction at constant temperature and pressure as follows:

1. If ΔG is negative, then the reaction is spontaneous (probable) as written. Thus a negative value for ΔG_{system} means that $\Delta S_{universe}$ must be positive.

A *spontaneous reaction* is a reaction that tends to proceed of itself in the direction of the equilibrium state and one that increases the entropy of the universe.

2. If ΔG is positive, the reaction is improbable as written, but the reverse reaction is probable. Reversing the equation reverses the sign of ΔG.

3. If ΔG is zero, the system is at equilibrium and there is no net reaction. This means there is no net flow of particles or energy and no energy is available for work. When $\Delta G = 0$, then $\Delta H = T\Delta S$. Thus, at equilibrium, the entropy factor is balanced by the enthalpy factor.

Let us determine how different values of ΔH and ΔS affect the value of ΔG and the probability that a spontaneous reaction will occur. Inspection of Equation 10-13 shows that when ΔH is negative and ΔS is positive, ΔG is negative. Thus, *exothermic reactions that are accompanied by an increase in entropy of the system are probable*.

When ΔH is positive and ΔS is negative, ΔG is positive. This means that *endothermic reactions accompanied by a decrease in entropy are improbable*.

At very high temperatures, the sign and magnitude of ΔG and the spontaneity of a reaction are determined primarily by the change in entropy. When both ΔH and $T\Delta S$ are positive, ΔG may be either positive or negative. The reaction may or may not be spontaneous. The higher the temperature, the greater are the chances that the reaction will be spontaneous. A high value of T gives the $-T\Delta S$ term a large negative value that eventually overbalances a positive ΔH and gives ΔG a negative value.

At very low temperatures, the sign and magnitude of ΔG and the spontaneity of a reaction are determined primarily by the enthalpy change, ΔH. When T is very low, the $T\Delta S$ term is very small and has little influence on the value of ΔG. In other words, it will be overbalanced by a large negative ΔH. Large negative values of

ΔH are associated with exothermic reactions. Therefore, when T is small, exothermic reactions are very probable and endothermic reactions with a positive ΔH are improbable.

The drive to achieve a state of minimum free energy can be interpreted as the driving force of a chemical reaction. In any reaction, there is a compromise between the tendency of a system to achieve a state of minimum enthalpy and the tendency to achieve a state of maximum entropy. If the entropy change is small, then the primary driving force is to achieve minimum enthalpy (energetically stable products). If the reactants and products are energetically similar, then the primary driving force is to achieve greater entropy.

The effects described above are summarized in Table 10-5.

TABLE 10-5
ENTHALPY, ENTROPY AND SPONTANEITY OF A REACTION

Thermal Effect	ΔH	ΔS	Spontaneity of Reaction as Written	Comment
Exothermic	−	+	probable	no exceptions
Exothermic	−	−	probable	at low temperatures
Endothermic	+	+	probable	at high temperatures
Endothermic	+	−	improbable	no exceptions

In this chapter we have looked at the principles of equilibrium. We have also qualitatively and quantitatively evaluated equilibrium systems by applying the equilibrium law.

In the next chapter we will consider the quantitative aspects of equilibria between ions and molecules in pure water. We will also focus our attention on the equilibria that exist in saturated solutions of slightly soluble salts.

THE GREENHOUSE EFFECT

Of the many environmental problems that currently threaten our planet, perhaps the most subtle is global warming, better known as the *greenhouse effect*. The earth's atmosphere is an envelope of oxygen, nitrogen, carbon dioxide and other gases. These atmospheric constituents are maintained in a delicate balance that, if significantly altered, could seriously disrupt our climate.

The temperature of the earth's surface is determined by the balance between the energy absorbed from the sun and the energy emitted back into space from the earth. Because carbon dioxide

(CO_2) absorbs infrared radiation and acts as an insulating blanket to prevent the earth's heat from escaping, its levels are very important for maintaining a normal climate. At any given time, carbon dioxide is being added to and removed from the atmosphere. Respiration by plants and animals, combustion of fossil fuels and the natural combustion of volcanoes and forest fires all tend to increase the levels of carbon dioxide. Counteracting these increases are photosynthesis reactions in plants, the dissolving of CO_2 in rain and ocean water, and the weathering of rocks.

For thousands of years there has been a balance between the

amount of carbon dioxide being removed from the atmosphere and the amount being added. This balance has been maintained by a process of equilibrium, which has tended to decrease concentrations by dissolving the gas in the oceans or, if need be, by releasing it from the oceans as relative concentrations drop. There are several equilibria involved in this process:

$$CO_2(g) + H_2O(l) \rightleftharpoons H_2CO_3(aq)$$

$$H_2CO_3(aq) \rightleftharpoons H^+(aq) + HCO_3^-(aq)$$

$$H^+(aq) + HCO_3^-(aq) \rightleftharpoons 2H^+(aq) + CO_3^{2-}(aq)$$

Applying Le Châtelier's principle to this series of reactions shows that any increase in CO_2 concentration in the atmosphere would cause the first reaction to shift to the right, decreasing the concentration. Each of the other reactions would similarly shift to the right. On the other hand, a decrease in atmospheric CO_2 would cause the first reaction to shift to the left, releasing CO_2 gas into the atmosphere. The other two reactions would similarly shift to the left.

These changes do not happen instantaneously; instead, they take place over a long period of time. If, for example, the reactants were deep underwater, it would take many years before the reactions could respond to the stresses imposed by changes in atmospheric carbon dioxide levels and shift accordingly.

Environmentalists are concerned that changes in atmospheric carbon dioxide levels have begun to modify the earth's climate in a process known as the greenhouse effect. Carbon dioxide is transparent to the incoming solar radiation but opaque to the earth's reradiation of heat. Scientists believe that a high concentration of carbon dioxide will tend to block the release of the earth's heat at night and, over time, will cause the earth's temperature to increase. This is similar to the way a greenhouse works in that glass allows the infrared rays to enter but prevents heat from leaving after the sun has gone down.

Records kept since the nineteenth century show that the world is, in fact, experiencing a warming trend. Scientists are increas-

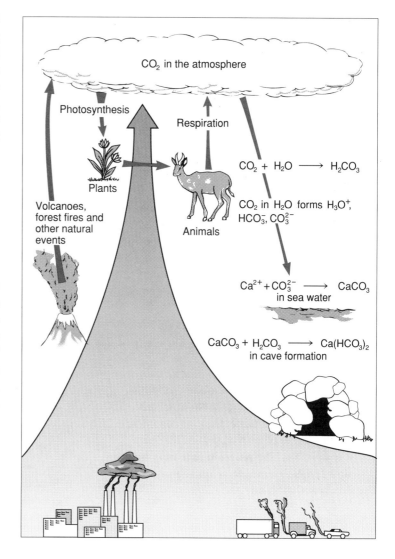

ingly concerned that the burning of fossil fuels may be accelerating a process that could have disastrous consequences. It is believed that a warming effect created by increases in atmospheric carbon dioxide levels would eventually result in the melting of polar ice caps, changes in growing seasons and weather patterns, as well as changes in the epidemiology of many diseases. Scientists estimate the global average temperature may increase by as much as 5°C before the year 2100.

Global warming is a problem of more than theoretical concern. Atmospheric concentrations of carbon dioxide have been growing steadily since the late 1800s, the start of the Industrial Revolution. The pre-industrial concentrations of CO_2 are estimated to have been between 260 and 275 ppm. If something is not done to decrease the amount of CO_2 being produced, levels exceeding 400 ppm can be expected in the near future. In addition, scientists have estimated that the global sea level is rising between 2.0 mm and 2.4 mm per year.

Although greenhouses are beneficial structures that protect tender plants from the heat and cold, the greenhouse effect is anything but beneficial. More research must be undertaken to find ways to reduce our dependence on fossil fuels or to find alternative fuels and thereby decrease the carbon dioxide levels in the atmosphere.

QUESTIONS

1. Two colourless solutions are mixed in a stoppered flask. As the reaction proceeds, the resulting solution turns red, and a colourless gas is formed. After a few minutes, no more gas is evolved but the red colour remains. What evidence is there that equilibrium has been established?
Answer: No further changes in colour or pressure.

2. An open flask contains a mixture of compound A and compound B. No observable reaction is taking place. Can we conclude that this system has reached equilibrium?
Answer: No. The reaction rate may be too slow to be observable or there may not be any reaction at all.

3. Two gases are mixed and allowed to stand for a period of time. Continued observation reveals no change in the macroscopic properties of the system. This apparent constancy of properties might be due either to the presence of an equilibrium condition or to a very slow reaction. How could you decide whether or not an equilibrium has been established?

4. Define *equilibrium state* in terms of
   a) reaction rates
   b) change in observable properties
   c) energy and entropy states

5. For each of the following reactions, indicate the property that might be observed in order to determine when equilibrium has been reached.
   a) $PCl_5(g) \rightleftharpoons PCl_3(g) + Cl_2(g)$
   b) $CaCO_3(s) \rightleftharpoons CaO(s) + CO_2(g)$
   c) $H_2O(l) \rightleftharpoons H_2O(g)$
   d) $Cl_2(g) + 2HI(g) \rightleftharpoons I_2(s) + 2HCl(g)$
   e) $2HBr(g) \rightleftharpoons H_2(g) + Br_2(g)$
   Answers: (a) pressure, (b) pressure, (c) pressure or temperature, (d) pressure or colour, (e) colour

6. What evidence is there to indicate that equilibrium is a dynamic state?

7. Explain why pressure can be considered as a concentration unit for gases.

8. Consider the reaction
   $$N_2O_4(g) \rightleftharpoons 2NO_2(g) \qquad \Delta H = 59 \text{ kJ}$$
   $$K_e = 0.87 \text{ at } 55°C$$

   What is the effect of each of the following changes on the concentration of N_2O_4 at equilibrium?
   a) increasing the temperature
   b) increasing the volume
   c) adding more $NO_2(g)$ to the system without changing pressure or temperature
   d) adding a catalyst
   Answers: (a) decrease, (b) increased volume decreases the concentration of N_2O_4, (c) increase, (d) no change

9. Answer questions a, b and d for $H_2O(g)$ in the following reaction as you did for N_2O_4 in question 8.

$$H_2(g) + \tfrac{1}{2}O_2(g) \rightleftharpoons H_2O(g) \quad \Delta H = -238 \text{ kJ}$$
$$K_e = 1 \times 10^{40} \text{ at } 25°C$$

10. How can you increase the concentration(s) of the product(s) in each of the following reactions by varying the temperature and pressure (caused by volume change)?
   a) $4NH_3(g) + 5O_2(g) \rightleftharpoons$
   $\qquad 4NO(g) + 6H_2O(g) \quad \Delta H = -903 \text{ kJ}$
   b) $Br_2(g) + Cl_2(g) \rightleftharpoons 2BrCl(g)$
   $\qquad\qquad\qquad\qquad \Delta H = 14.6 \text{ kJ}$
   c) $BaSO_4(s) \rightleftharpoons Ba^{2+}(aq) + SO_4^{2-}(aq)$
   $\qquad\qquad\qquad\qquad \Delta H = 24\ 244 \text{ kJ}$
   Answers: (a) cool, reduce pressure; (b) heat, no change; (c) heat, no change

11. Write the equilibrium expressions *(K)* for each of the following reactions:
   a) $H_2(g) + F_2(g) \rightleftharpoons 2HF(g)$
   b) $4NO(g) + 3O_2(g) \rightleftharpoons 2N_2O_5(g)$
   c) $BaCO_3(s) \rightleftharpoons BaO(s) + CO_2(g)$

12. The equilibrium constants for three different reactions are (i) $K_e = 1.5 \times 10^{12}$, (ii) $K_e = 0.15$, (iii) $K_e = 4.3 \times 10^{-15}$. In which reaction is (a) the ratio of product to reactant large? (b) the ratio of product of reactant small?

13. Does the equilibrium constant for the reaction

$$Br_2(l) \rightleftharpoons Br_2(g)$$

increase or decrease as temperature increases? Explain.

14. Suggest four ways in which the equilibrium concentration of NH_3 can be increased in a closed vessel if the only reaction is

$$N_2(g) + 3H_2(g) \rightleftharpoons 2NH_3(g)$$

15. The graph on the next page (Fig. 10-19) shows the concentration of all three species of the system

$$CO(g) + Cl_2(g) \rightleftharpoons COCl_2(g)$$

plotted against time under a given set of conditions.
   a) How much time was required for the system to reach equilibrium?
   b) Approximate the value of K_e using the concentrations at $t = 17$ s.
   c) Explain the changes 20 s after the initiation of the reaction.
   d) What change in conditions might have been imposed on the system 30 s after the initiation of the reaction?
   e) Are any events taking place between the interval of 15 s and 20 s? Explain.
   f) What change may have taken place at 45 s?
   g) What differences would you have noted if a catalyst had been present during the entire course of this reaction?
   h) List the changes you might impose on this system if you wanted to produce a maximum amount of $COCl_2$.
   i) How could you account for the differences in the value of K_e at different points?
   Answers:
   a) 15 s
   b) $K_e = 0.65$
   c) CO was introduced.
   d) An increase in total pressure caused by a decrease in total volume.
   e) In a state of dynamic equilibrium, microscopic changes are occurring, but there is no net change in amount of products or reactants.
   f) A massive amount of $COCl_2$ was added to the system.
   g) Equilibrium would have become established more rapidly.
   h) Force more CO and Cl_2 into the reaction vessel, increase the pressure, remove $COCl_2$ as rapidly as it is formed.
   i) Changes in temperature.

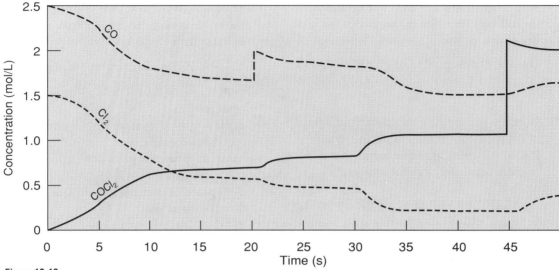

Figure 10-19
Graph for question 15.

PROBLEMS

1. The following system is at equilibrium:

$$N_2(g) + 2O_2(g) \rightleftharpoons 2NO_2(g) \quad \Delta H = +ve$$

What happens to the concentration of oxygen as a result of each of the following changes?
a) injecting oxygen
b) raising pressure by shrinking the container
c) lowering temperature
d) adding a catalyst

2. Consider the following reaction:

$$N_2(g) + 2O_2(g) \rightleftharpoons 2NO_2(g)$$

At a certain temperature, the following are the equilibrium concentrations for the above reaction:
$[N_2] = 8.0$ mol/L
$[O_2] = 2.0$ mol/L
$[NO_2] = 4.0$ mol/L
Determine the equilibrium constant.
Answer: $K_e = 0.5$ L/mol

3. The equilibrium constant for the following reaction has a value of 0.020 at a certain temperature.

$$2HCl(g) \rightleftharpoons H_2(g) + Cl_2(g)$$

If 2.0 mol of HCl are placed in an empty 1.0 L vessel, sealed and brought to this same constant temperature, what will be the equilibrium concentrations of HCl, H_2 and Cl_2?

4. Predict whether reactants or products are favoured in the following equilibrium systems.
a) $CH_3COOH(aq) \rightleftharpoons$
   $H^+(aq) + CH_3COO^-(aq)$
   $\qquad\qquad K_e = 1.8 \times 10^{-5}$
b) $H_2O_2(aq) \rightleftharpoons H^+(aq) + HO_2^-(aq)$
   $\qquad\qquad K_e = 2.6 \times 10^{-12}$ at 25°C
c) $Zn(s) + CuSO_4(aq) \rightleftharpoons$
   $ZnSO_4(aq) + Cu(s)$
   $\qquad\qquad K_e = 10^{37}$ at 25°C
Answers: (a) reactants, (b) reactants, (c) products

5. For each of the following reactions, decide whether the forward or the reverse reaction is favoured by the tendency toward (i) minimum potential energy and (ii) maximum disorder.
a) freon(l) $\rightleftharpoons$ freon(g)
The forward reaction is endothermic.
b) $2Mg(s)CO_2(g) \rightleftharpoons 2MgO(s) + C(s)$
$$\Delta H = -ve$$
c) $S_8(s) \rightleftharpoons S_8(l)$
d) $HCl(g) + NH_3(g) \rightleftharpoons NH_4Cl(s)$
$$\Delta H = -ve$$

6. Without using Le Châtelier's principle, predict the effect of an increase in temperature on each of the following systems.
a) $Ag(s) + Br_2(g) + S^{2-}(aq) \rightleftharpoons$
$$Ag_2S(s) + 2Br^-(aq)$$
Predict the effect on Ag_2S.
b) $2Pb(s) + N_2O_4(g) + 4H^+(aq) \rightleftharpoons$
$$2Pb^{2+}(aq) + 2NO(g) + 2H_2O(l)$$
Predict the effect on the concentration of Pb^{2+} ions.
c) $CaCO_3(s) \rightleftharpoons CaO(s) + CO_2(g)$
Predict the effect on pressure in a closed system.
d) $MnO_2(s) + H_2O(l) \rightleftharpoons$
$$H_3O^+(aq) + Cl^-(aq)$$
Predict the effect on $[MnCl_2]$.
Answers: (a) increases, (b) increases, (c) increases, (d) increases

7. A Canadian company is now making nitrogen compounds directly from nitrogen with oxygen. The essential equation is

$$N_2(g) + O_2(g) + heat \rightleftharpoons 2NO(g)$$

Using Le Châtelier's principle, select conditions that would favour the best yields of $NO(g)$.

8. In the reaction

$$Fe^{2+}(aq) + Ag^+(aq) \rightleftharpoons Fe^{3+}(aq) + Ag(s)$$

the value of K_e is 3.0. If, at equilibrium, the concentration of Fe^{2+} is 0.20 mol/L and the concentration of Ag^+ is 0.30 mol/L, what is the concentration of Fe^{3+} in the system?
Answer: 0.18 mol/L

9. A substance (CD) decomposes into C and D:

$$CD(g) \rightleftharpoons C(g) + D(g)$$

At a given temperature, 15.0% of CD is decomposed when equilibrium is established.
a) If the initial concentration of CD is 0.200 mol/L, what are the equilibrium concentrations of CD, C and D?
b) What is the equilibrium contstant, K_e, for this reaction?

10. A reaction can be represented by

$$A(g) + B(g) \rightleftharpoons AB(g)$$

At a given temperature, 1.0 mol of A and 1.0 mol of B are placed in a 1.0 L reaction vessel and allowed to reach equilibrium. Analysis reveals that the equilibrium concentration of AB is 0.40 mol/L. What percentage of A is converted to products?

11. Gas X_2 reacts with gas Y_2 according to the equation

$$X_2 + Y_2 \rightleftharpoons 2XY$$

0.50 mol each of X_2 and Y_2 are placed in a 1.0 L vessel and allowed to reach equilibrium at a given temperature. The equilibrium concentration of XY is found to be 0.025 mol/L. What is the equilibrium constant for this reaction?

12. Consider the equilibrium reaction

$$A(g) \rightleftharpoons 2B(g) + C(g)$$

When 1.00 mol of A is placed in a 4.00 L container at temperature t, the concentration of C at equilibrium is 0.050 mol/L. What is the equilibrium constant for the reaction at temperature t?

13. The equilibrium constant for

$$2X(g) \rightleftharpoons Y(g) + Z(g)$$

is 3.0. What amount of X is present at equilibrium when 1.00 mol each of Y and Z are placed in a 5.00 L container?
Answer: 0.450 mol

14. Under a given set of conditions, an equilibrium mixture

$$SO_2(g) + NO_2(g) \rightleftharpoons SO_3(g) + NO(g)$$

in a 1.00 L container is analysed and found to contain 0.300 mol of SO_3, 0.200 mol of NO, 0.0500 mol of NO_2 and 0.400 mol of SO_2. Calculate the equilibrium constant for this reaction.
Answer: $K_e = 3.00$

15. At 55°C, the K_e for the reaction

$$2NO_2(g) \rightleftharpoons N_2O_4(g)$$

is 1.15. (a) Write the equilibrium expression. (b) Calculate the concentration of $N_2O_4(g)$ present in equilibrium with 0.50 mol/L of NO_2.
Answer: 0.29 mol/L

16. Calculate the K_e for the following reaction from the data below.

$$CO_2(g) + H_2(g) \rightleftharpoons CO(g) + H_2O(g)$$

$[CO_2] = 1.17 \times 10^{-3}$ mol/L
$[H_2] = 1.17 \times 10^{-3}$ mol/L
$[CO] = 1.33 \times 10^{-3}$ mol/L
$[H_2O] = 1.33 \times 10^{-3}$ mol/L
Answer: 1.29

17. One mole of NH_3 is injected into a 1 L flask at a certain temperature. The equilibrium mixture

$$2NH_3 \rightleftharpoons N_2 + 3H_2$$

is then analysed and found to contain 0.300 mol of H_2.

a) Calculate the concentration of N_2 at equilibrium.
b) Calculate the concentration of NH_3 at equilibrium.
c) Calculate the equilibrium constant for this system.
d) Which way would the equilibrium be shifted if 0.600 mol of $H_2(g)$ were injected into the flask?
e) How would the injection of hydrogen into the flask affect the equilibrium constant?
f) How would the equilibrium constant be affected if the pressure of this system were suddenly increased?
Answers: (a) 0.100 mol of N_2/L, (b) 0.800 mol of NH_3/L, (c) 4.2×10^{-3}, (d) favouring the formation of NH_3, (e) no effect, (f) gets smaller

18. When 0.5 mol of CO_2 and 0.5 mol of H_2 are forced into a 1 L reaction container, the following equilibrium is established:

$$CO_2(g) + H_2(g) \rightleftharpoons H_2O(g) + CO(g)$$

Under the conditions of the experiment, $K_e = 2.00$.
a) Find the equilibrium concentration of each reactant and product.
b) How would the equilibrium concentrations differ if 0.50 mol of H_2O and 0.50 mol of CO had been introduced into the reaction vessel instead of the CO_2 and H_2?

19. An equilibrium mixture,

$$H_2(g) + CO_2(g) \rightleftharpoons H_2O(g) + CO(g)$$

in a 10.00 L container at a certain temperature is analysed and found to contain $H_2 = 1.17$ mol, $CO_2 = 1.17$ mol, $H_2O = 1.33$ mol and CO = 1.33 mol.
a) Calculate the equilibrium constant.
b) How would the equilibrium quantity of H_2O be affected by an increase in the total volume of the system?

c) How would the equilibrium concentration of water be affected by the increase in total volume?

d) How would the equilibrium constant be affected by an increase in total volume?

e) How many moles of water vapour would have to be injected into the original equilibrium mixture to increase the H_2 concentration to 0.150 mol/L?

20. At 462°C, the reaction

$$\text{heat} + 2NOCl(g) \rightleftharpoons 2NO(g) + Cl_2(g)$$

has an equilibrium constant, K_e, of 8.0×10^{-2}.

a) What is K_e at 462°C for the reaction

$$2NO(g) + Cl_2(g) \rightleftharpoons 2NOCl(g)$$

b) What is K_e at 462°C for the reaction

$$NOCl(g) \rightleftharpoons NO(g) + \tfrac{1}{2}Cl_2(g)$$

Answers: (a) 12.5, (b) $\sqrt{8.0 \times 10^{-2}} = 0.28$

21. Consider the following heterogeneous equilibrium:

$$H_2(g) + S(s) \rightleftharpoons H_2S(g) + x \text{ kJ}$$

At a given temperature, K for this reaction is 14.3.

a) What are the equilibrium concentrations of H_2 and H_2S when 0.200 mol of each is allowed to react and reach equilibrium in a 2.00 L container?

b) How is the magnitude of K affected by increasing the temperature of the system?

The precipitation of calcium carbonate causes the formation of stalagmites and stalactites found in beautiful caverns.

APPLICATIONS OF EQUILIBRIUM: SOLUTIONS AND SOLUBILITY

"We must lay it down as an incontestable axiom, that in all the workings of art and nature, nothing is made from nothing; an identical quantity of matter exists both before and after the experiment...upon this principle, the whole art of performing chemical experiments depends."
Antoine Lavoisier (1743–1794)

Water is the most important solvent on earth. In fact, it is often referred to by chemists as a *universal solvent* because of its ability to dissolve a wide array of substances. Water is the solvent that allows life, in all its complex forms, to exist. It is the fluid in which cellular materials are suspended as well as the fluid that allows the transport of materials throughout your body by means of the circulatory system.

The concept of solutions and solubility is of great interest to chemists. Of primary interest are *electrolytic solutions*, which contain mobile ionic solute particles, uniformly dispersed throughout the solvent. Solutes can be classified as strong, weak or non-electrolytes, depending on the extent to which they dissociate in solution. Interesting reactions occur when solutions of two different electrolytes are mixed together. Often, solid precipitates form, which can be identified by means of solubility rules that determine which ionic compounds can dissolve in water.

When a solid precipitates, an equilibrium system is established in solution. Since an equilibrium exists, an equilibrium law expression, called a *solubility product constant*, can be written for the reaction. Once this is done, equilibrium calculations can be performed involving these precipitation reactions.

Much of our economic survival depends on obtaining various chemical compounds and metals found in the earth, usually in the form of insoluble ionic salts. Some of these deposits include magnetite (Fe_3O_4), a source of iron; bauxite ($Al_2O_3 \cdot xH_2O$), a source of aluminum; galena (PbS), a source of lead; gypsum ($CaSO_4 \cdot 2H_2O$), a source of calcium sulfate; and calcite ($CaCO_3$), a source of calcium carbonate and lime (CaO). All of these compounds are insoluble in water. Industrial methods are designed to recover the metals from the salts using solubility principles.

In this chapter we will investigate solubility principles, electrolytes, precipitation reactions and their related equilibrium calculations.

THE PROCESS OF DISSOLUTION

11-1
Solute, Solvent, Solution and Solubility

A solute dissolved in a solvent produces a solution.

As you will recall from your introductory chemistry studies, matter can be classified as either *heterogeneous* or *homogeneous*. Mixtures such as tomato juice or paint are referred to as heterogeneous mixtures. Since these mixtures contain at least two different phases, particles will settle out of the mixture after a period of time. Heterogeneous mixtures in which the undissolved particles are extremely small and do not usually settle out over a period of time are called *colloidal dispersions*. Examples of colloids are whipped cream, mayonnaise, milk, butter, cheese and smog. In homogeneous mixtures, such as seawater, black coffee, automotive oil, gasoline and vinegar, the components are distributed uniformly throughout the mixture and will not settle out. Homogeneous and heterogeneous mixtures are not always liquids. For example, a solid such as granite is a heterogeneous mixture. Our gaseous atmosphere and such solids as brass (copper and zinc) and stainless steel (iron, carbon and nickel) are examples of homogeneous mixtures.

Homogeneous mixtures are ***solutions***. Every solution consists of a ***solute*** (the medium dissolved) and a ***solvent*** (the medium that is present in greater abundance and dissolves the solute). In most aqueous solutions, water is the solvent; however, this is not always the case. For example, in normal 80-proof alcohol (40% alcohol and 60% water), water is the solvent. However, if the alcohol solution is 140-proof (70% alcohol and 30% water), the alcohol is the solvent while water is the solute. Thus, the solvent is the substance present in the greatest abundance.

If you add one teaspoon of sugar to a cup of hot tea, the sugar quickly dissolves. As you are well aware, you could add and dissolve much more sugar into that same cup of tea. By adding one teaspoon of sugar to the tea, you have formed an **unsaturated solution**. The solution is unsaturated because it is capable of dissolving much more sugar. If you were making candy, you would heat water to boiling and add sugar until no more could dissolve. The solution is said to be a **saturated solution** because no more sugar can be dissolved at that specific temperature. Since no more solute dissolves, an excess of the solid solute stays on the bottom of the container. As a result, *a saturated solution is an equilibrium system in which the rate the solute enters the solution equals the rate the solute precipitates out of solution*.

As you learned in Chapter 10, equilibrium constants are temperature dependent. Therefore, it is important to specify the temperature when discussing saturated solutions. For example, Fig. 11-1 shows the solubility of various solutes at different temperatures. You can see that potassium nitrate forms a saturated solution at 20°C when 300 g of KNO_3 has been dissolved in 1 L of water. When heat is added to this equilibrium system at 20°C, the equilibrium shifts to the right and more solute can be added to form a new equilibrium system at a higher temperature. If the temperature of the saturated solution were lowered, the equilibrium would shift to the left and the solute would precipitate out of solution.

Let us look at another example. You can see from Fig. 11-1 that if a solution of KNO_3 is cooled from 60°C to 20°C, 800 g of KNO_3 will precipitate out (1.1 kg − 0.3 kg). The *solubility* of a substance can be expressed in various ways, one of which is the number of kilograms of solute required to form a saturated solution in one kilogram of water.

We will begin our discussion by investigating why solutes tend to dissolve in a solvent.

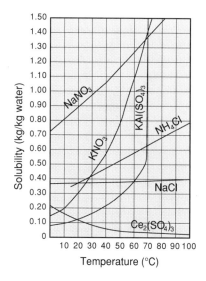

Figure 11-1
Solubility curves. Every point on each curve represents the number of kilograms of solvent that dissolves in 1.00 kg of water at a given temperature. As you can see, as the temperature increases, so does the solubility of the solutes.

11-2

Entropy and Solubility

Since there appears to be a natural drive of substances toward a more random state, many solids will dissolve in a solvent. In Chapter 10 we briefly investigated the second law of thermodynamics, which states that *the entropy of the universe increases for any spontaneous process*. What is a spontaneous process? When a rock is dropped, it loses potential energy as it falls; however, it gains kinetic energy as it speeds up. When it hits the ground, that kinetic energy is transferred as heat to the surroundings. The net result of this spontaneous reaction is a conversion of energy. When

Freezing-Point Depression
The freezing point of a solution is lower than the freezing point of water. As the water is cooled, the kinetic energy of the molecules decreases. Adding a solute to the water causes the solute molecules to interfere with the growth of the ice crystals. To make up for this interference, more kinetic energy (heat) has to be removed from the water to freeze it. Thus, the freezing point of water is reduced. This is the principle behind putting salt on winter roads or antifreeze in car radiators.

The tendency toward maximum entropy favours dissolution (dissolving).

At equilibrium the solubility is fixed when the tendency toward minimum enthalpy is balanced by the tendency toward maximum entropy.

The tendency toward minimum enthalpy favours crystallization.

Figure 11-2
At a given temperature, the solubility of a solid is fixed by enthalpy and entropy factors.

a substance such as a piece of wood burns in the fireplace, there is a spontaneous chemical reaction in which the conversion of the wood to carbon, carbon dioxide and water releases energy. Thus, there appears to be a spontaneous process in which physical and chemical systems attempt to reach a point of minimum energy. However, this is not the only factor that determines spontaneity.

When you place an ice cube on a table at room temperature, it melts spontaneously; yet no heat is given off, since melting is an endothermic process. In other words, there is a net increase in energy. So why does the ice melt? Let us look at another example. When you place table salt (NaCl) in water, the salt dissolves. In the process, the particles leave the ordered state of the solid and begin moving about randomly, gaining in kinetic energy. Why does the salt dissolve? It would appear from these two examples that there is a tendency for some systems to try to increase the randomness of the movement of particles. As discussed in Chapter 10, this randomness, or disorder, is called *entropy* and is given the symbol S; the change in entropy is ΔS. When calculating *enthalpy* (ΔH) we used the following relationship:

$$\Delta H_{reaction} = \Delta H_{products} - \Delta H_{reactants}$$

Similarly, to calculate the change in entropy, we can use the relationship

$$\Delta S_{system} = \Delta S_{product} - \Delta S_{reactants}$$

Values for the entropies of various substances are given in Appendix 3, Table 4.

Even though some substances may seem to undergo a decrease in entropy, the second law of thermodynamics still holds. For example, when a car rusts, iron(III) oxide (Fe_2O_3) is formed from the reaction between iron and oxygen from the air. Oxygen is a gas in a highly disordered state, yet when bonded to iron it is in a highly ordered state. This would appear to be a reverse of the process of entropy (ΔS is negative). However, the reaction is also exothermic ($\Delta H = -821$ kJ/mol), meaning that the reaction itself has achieved a minimum energy. When energy is released from the reaction, the surroundings gain entropy and, thus, there is an overall positive change in the entropy of the universe, as required by the second law of thermodynamics:

$$\Delta S_{universe} = \Delta S_{system} + \Delta S_{surroundings} > 0$$

From the examples discussed, you can see that there is a competition between the drive toward maximum entropy and the drive toward minimum enthalpy of the system (see Fig. 11-2). As discussed in Chapter 10, Gibbs free energy (ΔG) relates the enthalpy change, temperature and entropy change for a system. If

ΔG is negative, the reaction will occur spontaneously.

How does this discussion apply to solubility? Let us consider what happens when $NaCl(s)$ dissolves in water. In the solid form, the atoms are in a highly ordered state. When placed in water, there is an obvious tendency for the NaCl to achieve a random state (ΔS is positive) since the NaCl dissolves. In solution, the $Na^+(aq)$ and $Cl^-(aq)$ ions have a greater freedom of movement and, thus, a greater randomness of state. The motion of these dissolved ions has changed from vibrational in the solid state to vibrational, with some translational and rotational motion, in the liquid state.

Since it appears that many substances have this natural tendency to dissolve, we will now look at how different solids dissolve in water and thus achieve an increase in entropy.

FOLLOW-UP PROBLEMS

1. Predict the direction of entropy change for each of the following reactions:

   a) $N_2(g) + 3H_2(g) \longrightarrow 2NH_3(g)$
   b) $2C(s) + O_2(g) \longrightarrow 2CO(g)$
   c) $H_2O(l) \longrightarrow H_2(g) + \frac{1}{2}O_2(g)$
   d) $CaCO_3(g) \longrightarrow CaO(s) + CO_2(g)$

2. Using the values in Appendix 3, Table 4, calculate ΔS for each of the above reactions. Is the entropy change as you predicted?

Answers:
2. a) **–198.3 J/mol•K**
   b) **179.4 J/mol•K**
   c) **163.2 J/mol•K**
   d) **160.7 J/mol•K**

NON-ELECTROLYTIC SOLUTIONS

You first learned about electrolytes and non-electrolytes in your introductory chemistry studies. You may remember an experiment in which a light bulb was connected to a test circuit with a battery (the source of current) and a pair of electrodes immersed in a solution, as shown in Fig. 11-3. If the solution contained charged ions that could provide a conducting path between the two electrodes, the light bulb lit up. These solutions are termed *electrolytic*. Other solutions made from neutral molecules of a covalent nature could not provide a conducting path, and the light bulb did not light up. These are termed *non-electrolytic* solutions.

In this section, we will investigate the dissolution of non-electrolytes.

11-3

Dissolution of Polar Covalent Molecular Species

Polar substances dissolve due to the interaction between the dipole of the solute and the dipole of the solvent.

A large number of molecular solids and liquids such as sugar and alcohol are composed of polar covalent molecules. These are soluble to varying degrees in polar covalent solvents such as

Figure 11-3
An apparatus used to test the conductivity of solutions. Electrolytic solutions (a) contain ions that carry the charge between electrodes. Non-electrolytic solutions (b), such as water, do not dissociate appreciably into ions and therefore conduct very little current. The ions in a solid ionic crystal are held together by strong ionic bonds, and at room temperature do not possess enough kinetic energy to move freely under the influence of an applied voltage. Hence, when electrodes are placed on solid NaCl and other solid ionic crystals,
no appreciable electric current is conducted.

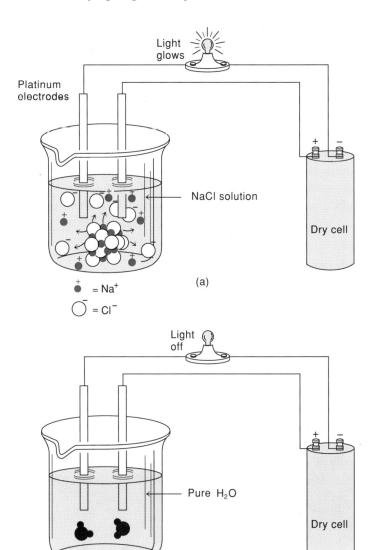

water. Solution of these substances is generally not the result of a chemical reaction but of *dipole-dipole* interaction between solute and solvent. For example, there are attractive forces between the opposite poles of ethanol (ethyl alcohol) and water molecules. The interaction is great enough for the two substances to be completely *miscible* (soluble in all proportions).

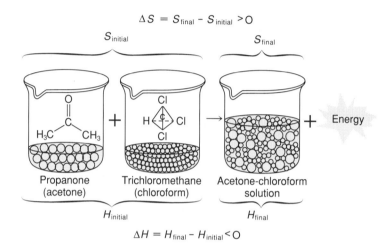

$$\Delta S = S_{final} - S_{initial} > 0$$

$S_{initial}$

S_{final}

Propanone (acetone) + Trichloromethane (chloroform) → Acetone-chloroform solution + Energy

$H_{initial}$

H_{final}

$$\Delta H = H_{final} - H_{initial} < 0$$

Figure 11-4
When propanone (acetone) and tri-chloromethane (chloroform) are mixed, the enthalpy of the system decreases and the entropy increases. As a result, the two liquids dissolve in each other in all proportions.

The degree to which a molecular substance composed of covalent molecules dissolves in a molecular solvent depends on the attraction between the solute and solvent molecules relative to that between the solvent molecules themselves. If the two attractions are of approximately the same magnitude, solution takes place. For example, when liquid trichloromethane (chloroform) is mixed with liquid propanone (acetone), a relatively small quantity of heat is liberated (less than 2 kJ/mol) (Fig. 11-4). This indicates that the energy of the solution is slightly less than that of the two pure substances, and suggests that the solute-solvent attractive forces are slightly greater than the solute-solute forces. That is, more energy is liberated through solute-solvent interaction than is absorbed in separating solute molecules or solvent molecules. Although the energy effect is relatively minor, it favours the mutual solubility of acetone and chloroform. The entropy effect, therefore, is largely responsible for the observed high solubility. The dispersion of chloroform molecules throughout the acetone increases the entropy of the system. Large negative values for $\Delta H^{\circ}_{solution}$ and large positive values for $\Delta S^{\circ}_{solution}$ are associated with high solubilities. This is consistent with the observation that acetone and chloroform are completely miscible.

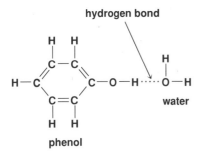

hydrogen bond

water

phenol

Figure 11-5
The solubility of phenol in water can, in large part, be attributed to the hydrogen bonds formed between the oxygen atom of water molecules and the hydrogen atoms of the hydroxyl groups (—OH) of phenol molecules.

hydroxyl group $\overset{..}{\underset{..}{O}}$ H

hydroxide ion $\left[\overset{..}{\underset{..}{O}} H \right]^{-}$

The formation of intermolecular hydrogen bonds between the solute and solvent molecules enhances the solubility of a solute. This explains why some molecules with a low polarity dissolve in water, while ones with higher polarities do not. For example, nitrobenzene ($C_6H_5NO_2$) is more polar than phenol (C_6H_5OH), but phenol is more soluble in water than nitrobenzene. The greater solubility of phenol is caused by the formation of hydrogen bonds between the oxygen atom of water and the hydrogen atom of the hydroxyl group (—OH) in a phenol molecule (Fig. 11-5). Unlike a hydroxide ion (OH⁻), a hydroxyl group does not carry a charge and is not a free species in solution. Since a hydroxyl group has one fewer electron than a hydroxide ion, it shares an electron and forms a covalent bond with the carbon atom in carbon compounds. In general, organic compounds that contain one or more hydroxyl groups (—OH), such as phenol, sugar, alcohol and glycerol, are quite soluble in water.

11-4
Dissolution of Nonpolar Covalent Molecular Species

Nonpolar covalent molecules dissolve in nonpolar solvents but not in polar solvents.

Nonpolar covalent substances such as methane (CH_4) and benzene (C_6H_6) are composed of nonpolar covalent molecules. Their structures do not permit appreciable hydrogen bonding; thus, such compounds do not readily dissolve in polar solvents such as water. The energy required to rupture the hydrogen bonds in water is large and would not be balanced by the energy released through the formation of hydrogen bonds between solute and solvent or by the entropy increase of the system. Therefore, $\Delta H°$ would have a large positive value, and the process would be nonspontaneous (improbable).

Many molecular crystals composed of nonpolar covalent molecules that do not dissolve appreciably in water do dissolve in nonpolar solvents. For example, naphthalene (C_6H_8), a solid composed of nonpolar molecules, dissolves in nonpolar solvents such as benzene. The van der Waals forces between the naphthalene molecules and benzene molecules are about the same as those between benzene molecules. Hence, there are no strong linkages to be disrupted in either the solvent or the solute, and no appreciable energy effects have to be considered. Because the dissolution of the naphthalene increases the entropy of the system, the drive toward maximum entropy predominates, and the crystal dissolves. On the basis of these observations, we can conclude that nonpolar solutes generally dissolve in nonpolar solvents.

In general, nonpolar and polar molecular liquids are *immiscible*.

That is, when mixed, they do not dissolve in one another and produce a one-phase system. When immiscible liquids are mixed and allowed to separate, an equilibrium is established in which both phases are saturated solutions with respect to the other component. These phenomena are illustrated in Fig. 11-6.

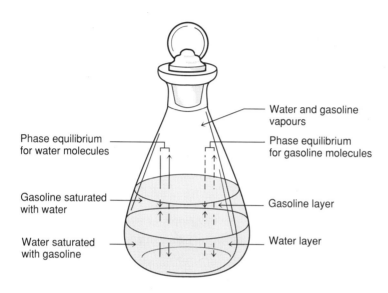

Phase equilibrium for water molecules

Water and gasoline vapours

Phase equilibrium for gasoline molecules

Gasoline saturated with water

Gasoline layer

Water saturated with gasoline

Water layer

Figure 11-6
When water (a polar liquid) and gasoline (a mixture of nonpolar liquids) are mixed, a two-phase (two-layered) system results. Each liquid layer is saturated with the other liquid. The double arrows represent the equilibria that exist between the molecules in the different phases.

11-5
Solubility of Gases in Liquids

Since gases have a lower energy and entropy in solution than in the gaseous phase, the solubility of gases decreases as the temperature increases.

There are many examples of gases that can be dissolved in liquids. Carbonated beverages and the numerous products packaged in spray cans contain gases dissolved in liquids. The small solubility of air in water is great enough to sustain marine life. The small solubility of air in blood is also an example in which gases dissolve in liquids.

The solubility of gases, like that of solids and liquids, is related to enthalpy and entropy changes that occur during the solution process. However, the fact that molecules are more disordered in the gas phase than in solution suggests that *the drive to achieve greater disorder (entropy) inhibits the dissolution of a gas in a liquid* (Fig. 11-7(a)).

In general, there is little attraction between molecules in the gas phase. When gas molecules are brought into contact with a liquid, they usually interact with solvent molecules and lower the energy of the system. *In most cases, therefore, the drive to reduce the*

Figure 11-7
For most gases, both the energy and entropy are lower in solution than in the gas phase. Higher temperatures, therefore, favour the gas phase. This means that most gases become less soluble as the temperature rises.

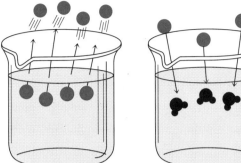
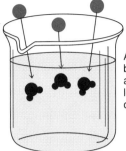

Attractive forces between solute and solvent lower the energy of the system.

(a) The tendency toward maximum entropy opposes the dissolution of a gas and favours its escape.

(b) The tendency toward minimum energy generally favours dissolution of a gas.

energy of a system favours the dissolution of a gas in a liquid (Fig. 11-7(b)). In other words, the dissolution of a gas in a liquid is usually exothermic. If we assume that the entropy of solution for similar gases is about the same, then the gas with the largest negative $\Delta H°$ solution is the most soluble.

Figure 11-8
The partial pressure of O_2 (P_1) in (a) is twice that in (b). Therefore, the concentration (C_1) of dissolved oxygen in (a) is twice that in (b).

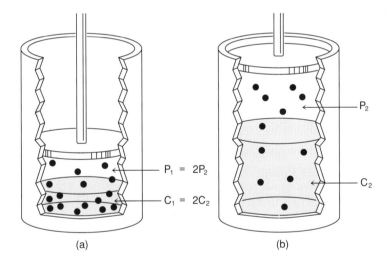

$P_1 = 2P_2$

$C_1 = 2C_2$

P_2

C_2

(a)   (b)

Applying Le Châtelier's principle to the solubility equilibrium represented by

$$Cl_2(g) \rightleftharpoons Cl_2(aq) + 25 \text{ kJ}$$

reveals that increasing the temperature favours the more disordered state and decreases the solubility of chlorine in water. The fine bubbles of dissolved air that rise to the surface when you heat a pan of water also reflect the decreasing solubility of air in hot water.

The effect of changing the pressure on a liquid containing a dissolved gas can be summarized in ***Henry's law:*** *The solubility of a gas in a liquid is proportional to the partial pressure of the gas on the surface of the liquid.* Application of this law indicates that doubling the number of molecules of a given gas above a liquid doubles the number of gas molecules dissolved in the liquid. Since gas pressure is proportional to the number of molecules, doubling the number of specific gas molecules in a closed container doubles its partial pressure (Fig. 11-8).

If you test the electric conductivity of a variety of substances, you find that certain molecular substances composed of polar covalent molecules are, like ionic salts, electrolytes. In the next section we will examine the behaviour of these compounds when they are added to water.

(a)   (b)

Figure 11-9
In going from (a) to (b), does the entropy of the system increase or decrease?

GETTING AROUND THE BENDS

The image is often seen in movies—a deep-sea diver returning to the surface after a long, deep dive suddenly convulses with pain and is unable to move. The diver suffers from decompression sickness, or the *bends*, a condition that results when gas bubbles are formed in the body as a result of the rapid transition from high to low pressure.

Pilots of unpressurized aircraft are also susceptible to decompression sickness because they experience abnormal atmospheric pressures. When an aircraft ascends, the external pressures on the pilot's body decrease and the dissolved gases contained in body tissues come out of solution. If the ascent is slow enough, the gases diffuse into the blood and are transported to the respiratory tract where they are exhaled.

Similarly, underwater divers breathing compressed air experience abnormal atmospheric pressures. Air pressure at sea level is 1 atm, or 101.3 kPa. When divers enter water, the pressure effects increase by 1 atm for every 10 m of depth. For example, at 10 m depth, the pressure is 2 atm and at 30 m it is 4 atm. Thus, the external pressure increases in proportion with the depth. This increase in pressure on the body is compensated for by an increase in the air pressure delivered from the diver's storage tanks.

Most divers breathe a mixture of nitrogen and oxygen. The solubility of oxygen and nitrogen in the blood and tissue fluids

increases with increased pressure, according to Henry's law. The increased oxygen gas solubility is not a concern since the oxygen is rapidly consumed during normal cell respiration. It is only the dissolved nitrogen that causes problems for divers. Since nitrogen is approximately five times more soluble in fat than in water, overweight divers will have more potential difficulties than others.

The dissolved nitrogen causes many problems. The first occurs during the dive itself. Dissolved nitrogen has an intoxicating effect in deep water. At approximately 15 m depth, dissolved nitrogen has the same effect on the diver as one alcoholic beverage. At 30 m, the diver may begin to feel lightheaded or somewhat euphoric. As a result of these effects, divers have been known to lose their mouthpieces or have been unable to determine which direction is up. This has caused serious problems for some divers, especially beginners.

Another effect of dissolved nitrogen occurs when the diver begins to return to the surface. If the pressure is reduced too quickly—that is, if the diver returns to the surface too quickly—the nitrogen will leave the blood and tissue fluids as bubbles of gas. These bubbles cause the bends. The bends is very painful and can be fatal if blood is forced out of capillaries, thus depriving various organs, especially the brain, of oxygen. To avoid the bends, divers must stop several times during the resurfacing process to expire the excess nitrogen. If the bends do occur, the diver should be repressurized at once to force the bubbles of gas back into solution. One way of accomplishing this is to return to the original diving depth. The pressure can then be slowly decreased as the diver comes back up, allowing the excess nitrogen to be released.

Many deep-sea divers and pilots are beginning to use mixtures of helium and oxygen rather than nitrogen and oxygen. While the helium does not dissolve in body fluids as much as nitrogen, it can do strange things to the vocal cords, making one's voice sound like Donald Duck. Although this may not bother deep-sea divers, aircraft pilots who use helium mixtures may have problems communicating seriously with air-traffic controllers.

ELECTROLYTIC SOLUTIONS

11-6

Classification of Electrolytes

Electrolytes are classified by their ability to dissolve and form ions in solution.

Solutes can be classified according to the extent to which they dissociate into ions in aqueous solution. Solutes that dissolve completely to form ions are called *strong electrolytes*. When less than 50% of a dissolved solute exists as ions, the solute is called a *weak electrolyte*. When less than 0.01% of a dissolved solute exists as ions, the solute is called a *non-electrolyte*. Knowing whether a substance is a strong or weak electrolyte or a non-electrolyte is valuable for predicting reactions and writing equations.

It can be demonstrated that *almost all salts are strong electrolytes*. This means that most dissolved salts exist largely in the form of ions. An ionic salt may not dissolve to an appreciable extent, but the quantity that does dissolve exists as hydrated ions in solution. For example, the solubility of silver chloride (AgCl) is approximately 1×10^{-4} mol/L. Yet the small percentage that does dissolve exists in the form of ions. Let us now examine in some detail the dissolution of an ionic crystal and some of the factors related to its solubility.

11-7
Hydration Energy

Hydration energy is the energy released when ion-dipole interactions occur between water molecules and charged ions during the dissolving process.

If an ionic crystal is to dissolve, the oppositely charged ions must be separated. This means that work must be done and energy must be supplied. Part of this energy comes from the interaction (attractive forces) between the polar water molecules and the ions of the solute. That is, energy is released as the polar water molecules interact with the electric field surrounding the charged ions.

Water molecules are extremely polar, and therefore attract and hold ions by relatively strong electrostatic forces. The positive pole (hydrogen end) of a water molecule attracts negative ions, and the negative pole (oxygen end) attracts positive ions (Fig. 11-10). The *ion-dipole interaction* is called **solvation**, or **hydration**. The energy released as a result of the process is known as the **hydration energy**. Hydration energies for the hydration of various ions are listed in Table 11-1. The hydration energy of a given ion depends on the strength of the electric field surrounding it. In turn, the magnitude of the field depends on the charge and radius of the ion. The ratio

ionic charge/ionic radius

is known as the **charge density**. The data in Table 11-1 can be used to show that *charge density, field strength and hydration energy increase as the charge of an ion increases and as its radius decreases*. High hydration energies, which represent a greater degree of interaction between the ions of a crystal and water molecules, enhance the solubility of an ionic substance.

The tendency of an ionic salt to dissolve in water is associated

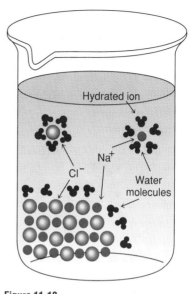

Figure 11-10
When an ionic crystal such as NaCl is added to water, the Na⁺ ions attract the negative ends of water molecules and the Cl⁻ ions attract the positive ends, resulting in the dissociation of the ionic crystal.

TABLE 11-1
HYDRATION ENERGIES

Ion	Radius (pm)	Hydration Energy (kJ/mol)	Ion	Radius (pm)	Hydration Energy (kJ/mol)
Li^+	65	523	Na^+	96	418
Na^+	96	418	Mg^{2+}	65	1940
Ca^{2+}	168	293	Al^{3+}	55	4690

Hydration energy decreases as radius increases.

Hydration energy increases with increasing charge and decreasing radius.

SVANTE AUGUST ARRHENIUS
1859–1927
When Svante Arrhenius presented his doctoral dissertation at the University of Upsala, Sweden, it contained some unorthodox ideas. In his thesis, Arrhenius pointed out that neither pure water nor dry salt would conduct an electric current but that salt dissolved in water produced a solution that would conduct electricity. He explained this observation by suggesting that "molecules" of salt broke up into charged particles, or "ions," which were able to transport an electric charge.

Although the chemists of Upsala grudgingly granted him a doctor of philosophy degree, they refused to accept the idea of ions. They argued that sodium chloride dissolved in water gives no visible evidence of the greenish chlorine gas that should accompany the decomposition of sodium chloride. Arrhenius replied that the chlorine ion had different properties from the chlorine atom.

Arrhenius claimed that ions were already present in a salt solution prior to the passage of current through the solution and that these ions were responsible for conducting the current. He even ventured to say that chemical reactions involving these salts were merely combinations of these ions. He also defined acids and bases in terms of ions.

Since Arrhenius could not get support for his theories in Sweden, he

with the relative magnitudes of the hydration energy and the crystal-lattice energy. As you recall from Chapter 4, crystal-lattice energy is the energy required to separate ions in a crystal into gaseous ions. A high crystal-lattice energy reflects high crystal stability and indicates that much energy is required to separate the crystal into ions. Other factors being equal, *high crystal-lattice energies inhibit solubility; however, high hydration energies lower the energy of the system and enhance solubilities.*

11-8
Dielectric Effect

Oppositely charged ions in solution do not recombine, due to the insulating effect of the water molecules.

As an ionic crystal dissociates, a number of water molecules surround each ion and form a protective, or insulating, mantle that partially neutralizes the charge on the ions and prevents them from recombining (Fig. 11-11). The capsule of water molecules acts as an insulator and reduces the force of attraction between ions. The insulating effect is called the **dielectric effect**. It is described in terms of a *dielectric constant (D)*, which is a measure of the ability of a substance to reduce the force of attraction between charged particles. The force of attraction is expressed by **Coulomb's law**,

$$F = k\frac{q_1 q_2}{r^2}$$

where k is a constant of proportionality. The dielectric constant D can be considered a part of the constant of proportionality (k). It has been found that F varies *inversely* with D. We can therefore insert D in the above equation to show this relationship. The equation then becomes

$$F = k'\frac{q_1 q_2}{D r^2}$$

where k' is a new constant of proportionality whose value depends on the units used for the other factors in the equation.

The dielectric constant for water is approximately 80, which means that the force of attraction between charged particles in water is approximately $\frac{1}{80}$ of that in a vacuum or in air. In general, *ionic substances dissolve more rapidly in a solvent with a high dielectric constant than in one with a low constant.* The dielectric constants for various solvents are listed in Table 11-2.

The low dielectric constant of benzene is consistent with the fact that NaCl, an ionic solute, does not dissolve in benzene, a nonpolar solvent. Benzene molecules cannot effectively reduce the force of attraction between the ions in the crystal. Since there is little attraction (interaction) between the solute and solvent particles, dissolution does not occur.

TABLE 11-2
DIELECTRIC CONSTANTS

Solvent	Formula	Constant
Hydrogen peroxide (0°C)	H_2O_2	84
Hydrogen fluoride (0°C)	HF	84
Water	H_2O	80
1,2,3-Propanetriol (glycerol)	$C_3H_5(OH)_3$	42
1,2-Ethanediol (ethylene glycol)	$C_2H_4(OH)_2$	37
Methanol (methyl alcohol)	CH_3OH	33.6
Benzene	C_6H_6	2.3
Ammonia	NH_3	2.2
Hexane	C_6H_{14}	1.9

sent his dissertation to several German chemists. Wilhelm Ostwald read the dissertation and, with Arrhenius, championed the cause of ions for several years against strong opposition.

In 1903, Arrhenius was awarded the Nobel Prize in chemistry for his work and was later appointed director of the newly founded Nobel Institute for Physical Research at Stockholm.

(a)

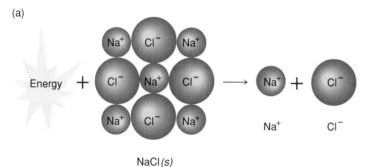

NaCl(s)

(b)

H_2O Na^+ $Na^+(aq)$

H_2O Cl^- $Cl^-(aq)$

Figure 11-11
(a) The dissociation of ions in an ionic crystal raises the energy of the system. This energy factor opposes dissolution of the crystal. (b) The hydration of ions liberates energy to the surroundings and lowers the energy of the system. The relative magnitude of the two energy factors determines the net energy change for the overall process.

SOLUBILITY PRODUCT CALCULATIONS

11-9

Solubility of Ionic Compounds

Not all ionic compounds are completely soluble in water. There are many that dissolve only to a small extent, while others do not dissolve at all.

In chemistry, the terms *soluble* and *insoluble* are not absolutes. In other words, they have no exact quantitative meaning. The most reliable way to gain information about the solubilities of ionic compounds in water is to rely on experimental data from observations. These observations are called the ***general solubility rules*** (Table 11-3) and are of value in predicting reactions and writing equations.

TABLE 11-3
GENERAL SOLUBILITY RULES

1. Most salts of Group IA cations and ammonium ions are soluble.

2. Most nitrates and acetates are soluble. $AgC_2H_3O_2$ is moderately soluble.

3. Chlorides, bromides and iodides are soluble except the silver, mercury(I) and lead compounds. $PbCl_2$ is moderately soluble in hot water.

4. Most sulfates are soluble except $BaSO_4$, $SrSO_4$ and $PbSO_4$. $CaSO_4$ and Hg_2SO_4 are moderately soluble.

5. Most carbonates and phosphates are slightly soluble except those listed in rule 1.

6. Most hydroxides are slightly soluble except those listed in rule 1 and $Ba(OH)_2$. $Ca(OH)_2$ is moderately soluble.

7. Most sulfides are only slightly soluble except those listed in rule 1. Magnesium, calcium, barium and aluminum sulfides decompose in water.

8. Most silver salts are slightly soluble except $AgNO_3$ and $AgNO_2$. $AgClO_4$ and Ag_2SO_4 are moderately soluble.

Why Seashells Do Not Dissolve in Water
The ocean is a solution full of ions. One of these ions is the calcium (Ca^{2+}) ion. Many sea creatures, especially crustaceans, have the ability to remove calcium ions from seawater. The Ca^{2+} ions react with carbonate ions, also present in the ocean, to form $CaCO_3$ (calcium carbonate), which makes up the crustacean's outer shell. In seawater, calcium carbonate has a solubility of about 0.01 mol/L (or 0.006 g/L). Because of this low solubility, the outer shells do not dissolve once they are formed.

Let us apply the solubility rules to $Pb(NO_3)_2$ and $PbCO_3$. According to rule 2, we see that $Pb(NO_3)_2$ is soluble as it contains nitrate ions, while, according to rule 5, $PbCO_3$ is only slightly soluble as it contains carbonate ions. Note that a compound is at least slightly soluble as long as it contains one of the ions listed as soluble in Table 11-3.

FOLLOW-UP PROBLEM

Which of the following pairs of compounds is more soluble? Explain your choice.

a) $ZnCl_2$ or $Zn(OH)_2$?

b) AgCl or LiCl?

c) $(NH_4)_2SO_4$ or $BaSO_4$?

d) K_2S or Ag_2S?

Answers:

(a) **$ZnCl_2$**, (b) **LiCl**, (c) **$(NH_4)_2SO_4$**, (d) **K_2S**

11-10
The Solubility Product Constant

Since a saturated solution of a slightly soluble salt is an equilibrium system, an equilibrium law expression can be written for this reaction.

Application of the equilibrium law to the equilibrium that exists between a slightly soluble solid and its ions in a saturated solution yields an equilibrium expression that chemists can put to practical use. This expression can be used for calculating ionic concentrations, approximating solubilities, determining whether precipitates will form when two solutions are mixed (Fig. 11-12) and devising methods of separating mixtures of ions in solution.

Consider a solution of silver chloride. The equilibrium can be expressed as

$$AgCl(s) \rightleftharpoons Ag^+(aq) + Cl^-(aq) \qquad [11\text{-}1]$$

The extent to which the solid AgCl dissolves can be expressed in terms of an equilibrium constant for this dissociation:

$$K = [Ag^+][Cl^-] \qquad [11\text{-}2]$$

Notice that the solid AgCl is not included in the equilibrium since, as you learned in Chapter 10, solids are not included in heterogeneous equilibrium law expressions.

From Equation 11-1 you will notice that for every mole of AgCl that dissolves, one mole of Ag^+ and one mole of Cl^- ions are produced. Thus, Equation 11-2 indicates that the value of K is determined by the *product* of the concentrations of the ions in the saturated solution. The concentrations of these ions are determined by the *solubility* of the salt. For this reason, Equation 11-2 is the equation for the *solubility product constant* and is desig-

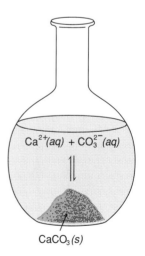

$Ca^{2+}(aq) + CO_3^{2-}(aq)$

$CaCO_3(s)$

Figure 11-12
In a saturated calcium carbonate solution, solid $CaCO_3$ is at equilibrium with the $Ca^{2+}(aq)$ and the $CO_3^{2-}(aq)$ ions. Addition of solid $CaCO_3$ does not change the concentration of the ions.

nated K_{sp}. Thus, Equation 11-2 should be written as

$$K_{sp} = [Ag^+][Cl^-]$$

For another reaction such as

$$Fe(OH)_3(s) \rightleftharpoons Fe^{3+}(aq) + 3OH^-(aq)$$

the K_{sp} equation is

$$K_{sp} = [Fe^{3+}][OH^-]^3$$

The solubility product constants of various slightly soluble salts are given in Table 11-4.

TABLE 11-4
SOLUBILITY PRODUCT CONSTANTS (25°C)

Salt	K_{sp}	Salt	K_{sp}
$AgCH_3COO$	1.9×10^{-3}	$FeCO_3$	2.1×10^{-11}
$AgBr$	5.4×10^{-13}	$Fe(OH)_2$	4.9×10^{-17}
Ag_2CO_3	8.4×10^{-12}	$Fe(OH)_3$	2.6×10^{-39}
$AgCl$	1.8×10^{-10}	FeS	1.6×10^{-19}
Ag_2CrO_4	1.1×10^{-12}	HgS	3.0×10^{-53}
$AgCN$	2.2×10^{-16}	Hg_2Br_2	1.3×10^{-22}
AgI	8.5×10^{-17}	Hg_2CO_3	8.9×10^{-17}
Ag_2SO_4	1.2×10^{-5}	Hg_2SO_4	8.0×10^{-7}
Ag_2S	1.1×10^{-49}	$MgCO_3$	6.8×10^{-6}
$Al(OH)_3$	1.9×10^{-33}	$Mg(OH)_2$	5.6×10^{-12}
$AlPO_4$	9.8×10^{-21}	$MnCO_3$	2.2×10^{-11}
$BaCO_3$	2.6×10^{-9}	$Mn(OH)_2$	2.1×10^{-13}
$BaCrO_4$	1.2×10^{-10}	MnS	4.6×10^{-14}
$Ba(OH)_2$	5.0×10^{-3}	$NiCO_3$	6.6×10^{-9}
BaF_2	1.7×10^{-6}	$Ni(OH)_2$	5.5×10^{-16}
$BaSO_4$	1.1×10^{-10}	$PbCO_3$	1.5×10^{-13}
Bi_2S_3	1.8×10^{-99}	$PbCl_2$	1.7×10^{-5}
$CaCO_3$	5.0×10^{-9}	$PbCrO_4$	1.8×10^{-14}
CaF_2	3.9×10^{-11}	PbI_2	8.5×10^{-9}
$Ca(OH)_2$	4.7×10^{-6}	$PbSO_4$	1.8×10^{-8}
$Ca_3(PO_4)_2$	2.1×10^{-33}	PbS	9.0×10^{-29}
$CaSO_4$	2.4×10^{-5}	$Sn(OH)_2$	2.0×10^{-26}
$Cd(OH)_2$	1.2×10^{-14}	SnS	1.0×10^{-4}
CdS	3.6×10^{-29}	$SrCO_3$	9.3×10^{-10}
$CoCO_3$	8.0×10^{-13}	$SrCrO_4$	3.6×10^{-5}
$CuCO_3$	2.5×10^{-10}	SrF_2	4.3×10^{-9}
$Cu(OH)_2$	1.6×10^{-19}	$SrSO_4$	3.4×10^{-7}
$CuBr$	5.3×10^{-9}	$ZnCO_3$	1.2×10^{-10}
$CuCl$	1.7×10^{-7}	$Zn(OH)_2$	4.3×10^{-17}
CuS	1.3×10^{-36}	$Zn_3(PO_4)_2$	9.1×10^{-33}
Cu_2S	2.3×10^{-48}	ZnS	2.9×10^{-25}

FOLLOW-UP PROBLEM

Write K_{sp} expressions for each of the following insoluble salts.

a) Ag_2CrO_4
b) $Al(OH)_3$
c) $Pb(IO_3)_2$
d) $AuCl_3$

Answers:

(a) $[Ag^+]^2[CrO_4^{2-}]$ (c) $[Pb^{2+}][IO_3^-]^2$
(b) $[Al^{3+}][OH^-]^3$ (d) $[Au^{3+}][Cl^-]^3$

In solving problems using solubility product constants and other equilibrium constants, we will assume that the solutions involved resemble *ideal solutions*. That is, we will not take into account the deviations that result from interionic attractions caused by the presence of other ions in the solution. The attraction between ions in a solution hinders their movements so that they are less "active." This causes their *effective concentrations* (called their *activity*) to be lower than the measured, or calculated, concentrations might indicate. In precise measurements, activities rather than concentrations are used. The activity of a species is equal to the product of its concentration and an experimentally determined correction factor known as an *activity coefficient*. For example, the activity of Ag^+ ions in a saturated solution of AgCl is

$$a_{Ag^+} = f_{Ag^+}[Ag^+]$$

where a_{Ag^+} is the *activity* of Ag^+ ions, and f_{Ag^+} is the *activity coefficient* whose value can be determined indirectly by experimental methods. In our calculations involving slightly soluble salts, we will use concentrations and, unless specifically noted, we will also assume that the dissolved species do not undergo reactions with the solvent. It is important to be aware of the assumptions and limitations of our calculations, but it is not important at this point to apply the above refinements.

11-11
Determining K_{sp}

If the solubility of a slightly soluble ionic compound can be determined, it is possible to calculate the numerical value for the K_{sp} of the compound.

The solubility product constants listed in Table 11-4 were determined by very careful laboratory measurements. One method of determining K_{sp} values involves adding a measured amount of solute to 1 L of water, stirring until no further change is observed and then filtering out the remaining solute. This solute is then weighed and the difference between the original and final mass is calculated. This quantitative value is then used to calculate the K_{sp} of the solute. More precise measurements for solubility product constants can be obtained through spectroscopic studies. Example 11-1 illustrates how the K_{sp} of a compound can be determined from information about its solubility.

EXAMPLE 11-1
Calculating K_{sp} From Solubility Information
The molar solubility of copper(II) hydroxide ($Cu(OH)_2$) is 3.42×10^{-7} mol/L. What is the K_{sp} for $Cu(OH)_2$?

SOLUTION
1. Write the dissociation reaction and the K_{sp} expression for the equilibrium reaction. Thus,

$$Cu(OH)_2(s) \rightleftharpoons Cu^{2+}(aq) + 2OH^-(aq)$$
$$K_{sp} = [Cu^{2+}][OH^-]^2$$

2. Calculate the concentrations of the ions at equilibrium from the stoichiometric information provided in the equilibrium equation. The equation shows that 1 mol of $Cu(OH)_2$ produces 1 mol of Cu^{2+} and 2 mol of OH^- at equilibrium. Therefore,

$$[Cu^{2+}] = 3.42 \times 10^{-7} \text{ mol/L}$$
$$[OH^-] = 2(3.42 \times 10^{-7} \text{ mol/L})$$
$$= 6.84 \times 10^{-7} \text{ mol/L}$$

3. Substitute the concentrations into the K_{sp} expression:

$$K_{sp} = (3.42 \times 10^{-7})(6.84 \times 10^{-7})^2$$
$$= 1.6 \times 10^{-19}$$

FOLLOW-UP PROBLEMS
1. The molar solubility of $Fe(OH)_3(s)$ in water is 9.9×10^{-11} mol/L. Calculate the value of the K_{sp}.
2. The molar solubility of Ag_2CrO_4 in water is 6.5×10^{-5} mol/L. Calculate the value of the K_{sp}.

Answers: (1) 2.6×10^{-39}, (2) 1.1×10^{-12}

11-12
Calculating Solubility From K_{sp}

Given the K_{sp} of a salt and the stoichiometric relationships from the equilibrium equation, we can calculate the concentration of the ions in solution.

The K_{sp} for AgCl is 1.8×10^{-10} from Table 11-4. This small constant shows that the concentrations of the Ag^+ ions and the Cl^- ions are very small in a saturated solution of AgCl. In other words, the equilibrium represented by Equation 11-1 is displaced to the left. This means that equilibrium is established before a significant amount of AgCl dissolves. Another way of expressing this is that Ag^+ ions and Cl^- ions can exist together at equilibrium in the same solution only when their concentrations are low enough so that the product of their concentrations does not exceed the K_{sp} value. When the original concentrations exceed the equilibrium value indicated by the K_{sp}, they are then reduced by the crystallization of solid AgCl. The concentrations of the Ag^+ ions and the Cl^- ions in a saturated solution of AgCl can be calculated easily if we use the solubility product constant. Example 11-2 illustrates how the approximate solubility of a solid can be determined.

EXAMPLE 11-2
Calculating Ion Concentration from K_{sp}

Calculate the concentrations of Ag^+ ions and Cl^- ions in a saturated solution of the salt at 25°C. What is the approximate solubility of AgCl in mol/L at this temperature?

SOLUTION

1. Write the equation and the K_{sp} expression for the reaction:

$$AgCl(s) \rightleftharpoons Ag^+(aq) + Cl^-(aq)$$
$$K_{sp} = [Ag^+][Cl^-]$$

2. Let x equal the number of moles of AgCl that must dissolve in 1 L of solution to attain equilibrium (this represents the solubility of AgCl in mol/L). The equation shows that for each mole of silver chloride that dissolves, 1 mol of Ag^+ ions and 1 mol of Cl^- ions go into solution. Therefore, the equilibrium concentrations of Ag^+ ions and Cl^- ions are also equal to x.

3. Substitute the equilibrium concentrations of the ions and the value of K_{sp} into the equilibrium law expression and solve for x:

$$1.8 \times 10^{-10} = (x)(x)$$
$$x^2 = 1.8 \times 10^{-10}$$
$$x = 1.3 \times 10^{-5}$$

Therefore, 1.3×10^{-5} mol of AgCl dissolves in 1 L of solution, and the equilibrium concentrations of the Ag^+ ions and the Cl^- ions are each 1.3×10^{-5} mol/L.

FOLLOW-UP PROBLEMS
1. Determine the solubility of AgI in (a) mol/L and (b) g/L at 25°C.
2. What is the concentration of the cation, in mg/mL, in a solution of Ag_2CO_3 at 25°C?

Answers:
1. (a) 9.1×10^{-9} mol/L, (b) 2.1×10^{-6} g/L
2. 2.76×10^{-2} mg/mL

As you have noticed from these problems, the K_{sp} value gives information that allows us to compare the solubilities of various salts. If the salt has the general formula MX, the smaller the K_{sp} value, the smaller the solubility of the salt. For example, from Table 11-4, the K_{sp} of AgCl is 1.8×10^{-10} and CuS is 1.3×10^{-36}. The CuS has a much smaller K_{sp} and a much smaller molar solubility (1.1×10^{-18} mol/L) than AgCl (1.34×10^{-5} mol/L). This relationship holds true for salts of the general formula MX_2, MX_3, M_2X and M_3X.

We cannot use K_{sp} to compare salts of different general formulas. For example, if we compare the solubility of AgCl (an MX salt with a K_{sp} of 1.8×10^{-10}) to Ag_2CO_3 (an M_2X salt with a K_{sp} of 8.4×10^{-12}), we might assume that the Ag_2CO_3 is less soluble because it has a smaller K_{sp}. However, because of the stoichiometric relationships among its ions, the molar solubility of Ag_2CO_3 is 1.28×10^{-4} mol/L. Thus, the Ag_2CO_3 is more soluble than the AgCl. When using K_{sp} to compare solubilities, be sure to compare salts of the same general formula.

STALACTITES, STALAGMITES AND SPELUNKERS

In the summer of 1901, a New Mexican cowboy named Jim White noticed a black cloud rising out of the ground. The cloud was a swarm of bats coming out of what is now known as the Carlsbad Caverns, a national park in New Mexico. Caverns such as the Carlsbad Caverns and the Bonnechere Caves in Ontario are well-known caves that have been richly decorated with calcium carbonate deposits.

At the beginning of this chapter is a photograph of a cavern full of imposing and beautiful structures called *stalactites* and *stalagmites*. Stalactites and stalagmites are formed by the dissolution and precipitation of calcium carbonate ($CaCO_3$), achieved by the shifting back and forth of the solubility equilibrium of calcium carbonate:

$$CaCO_3(s) \rightleftharpoons Ca^{2+}(aq) + CO_3^{2-}(aq)$$

Limestone rock is composed mainly of calcium carbonate and will dissolve in the presence of excess carbon dioxide (CO_2). The reason for this is that CO_2 dissolves in water according to

$$CO_2(g) + H_2O \rightleftharpoons HCO^-(aq) + OH^-(aq)$$

In addition, the carbonate ion produced by the $CaCO_3$ will hydrolyze according to

$$CO_3^{2-}(aq) + H_2O \rightleftharpoons HCO_3^-(aq) + OH^-(aq)$$

As the CO_2 concentration increases, so does that of the H^+ ions. These H^+ ions neutralize the OH^- ions produced by the hydrolysis of the carbonate ion:

$$H^+(aq) + OH^- \rightleftharpoons H_2O(l)$$

This neutralization causes a shift in the equilibrium to the product side, causing more CO_3^{2-} to be used up. As the concentration of CO_3^{2-} decreases, the equilibrium of calcium carbonate shifts to the right to compensate for this stress, and the limestone dissolves.

Ultimately, these reactions result in the formation of stalactites and stalagmites. Water droplets, containing dissolved calcium carbonate, enter cave chambers through ceiling cracks and deposit the calcium carbonate at the opening of the crack. Eventually, these droplets accumulate to form a column of calcium carbonate, called a *stalactite*, which hangs down from the ceiling. Falling drops of water pass through this column and splatter as they hit the floor. This splatter forms the foundation for a column of calcium carbonate, or a *stalagmite*, to be built up from the floor. To remember which is which, note that stalactites contain the letter "c" for *ceiling* and that stalagmites contain the letter "g" for *ground*.

Finally, what are *spelunkers*? These are people who enjoy visiting and exploring every corner of these beautiful natural wonders. Some people have even elevated this love of cave exploration into a sport.

11-13

The Common-Ion Effect

When a slightly soluble salt is dissolved in a solvent containing one of the same ions found in the solute, the dissociation equilibrium is affected.

Le Châtelier's principle indicates that it should be possible to vary the solubility of a solid by varying the concentrations of the ions at equilibrium with the solid. For example, to decrease the concentration of Ag^+ ions in a saturated solution of AgBr, we can add excess Br^- ions in the form of a soluble salt such as NaBr. This excess produces a stress, which the equilibrium system,

$$AgBr(s) \rightleftharpoons Ag^+(aq) + Br^-(aq)$$

adjusts by shifting to the left as it consumes Br⁻ ions and forms additional solid AgBr. Each Br⁻ ion that reacts ties up an Ag⁺ ion, thus reducing the concentration of Ag⁺ until the product of the ion concentrations satisfies the relationship

$$K_{sp} = [Ag^+][Br^-] = 5.4 \times 10^{-13}$$

The action decreases the solubility of AgBr. In other words, AgBr is less soluble in NaBr than in pure water. The same results could be accomplished by adding excess Ag⁺ in the form of soluble AgNO₃. The phenomenon is known as the ***common-ion effect*** because both NaBr and AgNO₃ have an ion in common with AgBr.

Figure 11-13
The common-ion effect. Addition of a soluble silver salt (AgNO₃) to a saturated solution of AgBr increases the Ag⁺ ion concentration to a value that exceeds the equilibrium value. To restore equilibrium, additional AgBr precipitates. At the new equilibrium position, the concentration of Ag⁺ is greater, and the Br⁻ concentration is less than in the original saturated solution. However, the product of the [Ag⁺] and [Br⁻] in solution is constant.

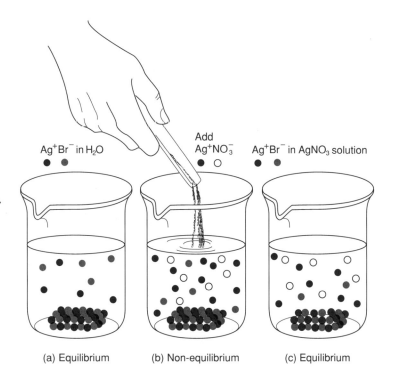

(a) Equilibrium   (b) Non-equilibrium   (c) Equilibrium

EXAMPLE 11-3
Calculating Solubility Using the Common-Ion Effect
Calculate the solubility of Ag₂CO₃ at 25°C in (a) pure water and (b) a 0.1 mol/L Na₂CO₃ solution.

SOLUTION
1. Write the balanced equation for the silver carbonate equilibrium:

$$Ag_2CO_3(s) \rightleftharpoons 2Ag^+(aq) + CO_3^{2-}(aq)$$

2. Write the K_{sp} expression:

$$K_{sp} = [Ag^+]^2[CO_3^{2-}] = 8.4 \times 10^{-12} \text{ (from Table 11-4)}$$

Solubility in pure water:

3. Let x = the number of mol/L of Ag_2CO_3 that dissolves to form a saturated solution. Thus, at equilibrium,

$$[Ag^+] = 2x$$
$$[CO_3^{2-}] = x$$

4. Substitute for the ion concentrations in the K_{sp} expression and solve for x:

$$8.4 \times 10^{-12} = (2x)^2(x)$$
$$x = \sqrt[3]{\frac{8.4 \times 10^{-12}}{4}}$$
$$= 1.28 \times 10^{-4}$$

Thus, the solubility of Ag_2CO_3 in pure water is 1.28×10^{-4} mol/L.

Solubility in 0.1 mol/L Na_2CO_3 solution:

5. Write a balanced equation for the dissolution of the Na_2CO_3:

$$Na_2CO_3(s) \longrightarrow 2Na^+(aq) + CO_3^{2-}(aq)$$

Note that Na_2CO_3 is completely soluble in water (solubility rule 1). By the stoichiometry of the equation, the $[CO_3^{2-}] = 0.1$ mol/L.

6. Calculate the equilibrium concentrations of the ions:

$$[Ag^+] = 2x$$
$$[CO_3^{2-}] = x + 0.1$$

7. Substitute into the K_{sp} expression:

$$8.4 \times 10^{-12} = (2x)^2(x + 0.1)$$

Notice that the value of x is very small (see step 4 above) with respect to the 0.1 provided by the Na_2CO_3; thus, the x can be ignored for the purposes of this calculation.

$$8.4 \times 10^{-12} = (2x)^2(0.1)$$
$$4x^2 = \frac{8.4 \times 10^{-12}}{0.1}$$
$$x = \sqrt{\frac{8.4 \times 10^{-11}}{4}}$$
$$= 4.58 \times 10^{-6}$$

Thus, the solubility of Ag_2CO_3 in 0.1 mol/L Na_2CO_3 is 4.58×10^{-6} mol/L.

Note that because of the common ion CO_3^{2-}, the solubility of the Ag_2CO_3 decreased as expected. The additional CO_3^{2-} produced a stress on the Ag_2CO_3 equilibrium, causing a shift in the equilibrium to the left and decreasing the amount of Ag^+ in solution.

FOLLOW-UP PROBLEMS
1. Compare the molar solubility of PbI_2 in (a) pure water and (b) 0.10 mol/L NaI. See Table 11-4 for K_{sp}.
2. How many grams of $SrCO_3$ will dissolve in 250 mL of 0.08 mol/L $SrNO_3$?

Answers:
1. (a) 1.3×10^{-3} mol/L; (b) 8.5×10^{-7} mol/L. Solubility in water = 1.5×10^3 times as great.
2. 4.3×10^{-7} g

PRECIPITATION REACTIONS

When two different electrolytes are mixed together, we occasionally observe that an insoluble solid comes out of solution. As you know from your introductory chemistry studies, this solid is called a *precipitate* and the observed reaction is a *precipitation reaction*.

We can apply the solubility rules to determine the formula of a precipitate. For example, if a solution of $AgNO_3$ is mixed with an NaCl solution, a white precipitate settles out on the bottom of the container (Fig. 11-14). The $AgNO_3$ dissociates into

$$AgNO_3(s) \longrightarrow Ag^+(aq) + NO_3^-(aq)$$

and the NaCl dissociates into

$$NaCl(s) \longrightarrow Na^+(aq) + Cl^-(aq)$$

When the two solutions are mixed, there exist two cations (Ag^+ and Na^+) and two anions (NO_3^- and Cl^-). The only two possible formulas for the white precipitate are $NaNO_3$ or $AgCl$. From Table 11-3, rule 2 states that all nitrates are soluble; therefore, the white precipitate in our example must be $AgCl$. The precipitation reaction is

$$Ag^+(aq) + Cl^-(aq) \rightleftharpoons AgCl(s)$$

Water Softeners
Water is said to be hard if it contains a lot of Ca^{2+} or Mg^{2+} ions. It is important to remove these ions from the water, otherwise the following reaction may occur:

$$Ca^{2+}(aq) + CO_3^{2-}(aq) \rightleftharpoons CaCO_3(s)$$

The calcium carbonate precipitate is deposited on the inside of pipes, slowly clogging them and causing expensive damage. In addition, the calcium reacts with soaps and detergents to form insoluble salts that cover clothes with a slimy coating.

Water softeners work by exchanging the calcium for sodium ions, which are soluble. A salt such as sodium carbonate is added to the water entering the home. Calcium is precipitated out as calcium carbonate, which is then flushed out on a regular basis as the softener regenerates.

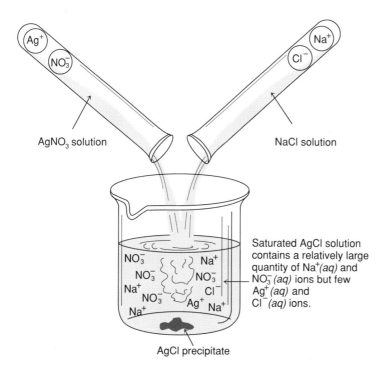

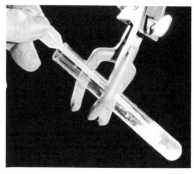

Figure 11-14
When $AgNO_3$ and $NaCl$ solutions are mixed, a precipitate of $AgCl$ forms until the Ag^+ and Cl^- ion concentrations are reduced to the equilibrium values; that is, until their product does not exceed the K_{sp} value at a given temperature.

$AgNO_3$ solution

$NaCl$ solution

Saturated AgCl solution contains a relatively large quantity of $Na^+(aq)$ and NO_3^- (aq) ions but few $Ag^+(aq)$ and $Cl^-(aq)$ ions.

AgCl precipitate

In the following sections we will examine whether precipitates form when different concentrations of two ions in solution are mixed together. We will also investigate how precipitates might be dissolved by putting a stress on the solubility equilibrium of the precipitate.

11-14
Predicting Precipitate Formation

Knowing the value of K_{sp} and the concentrations of two different solutions, we can predict if a precipitate will form when the two solutions are mixed.

Let us see how the K_{sp} expression can be used to determine whether or not a precipitate forms when two solutions are mixed. The K_{sp} puts an upper limit on the product of the concentrations of the two ions. When the product of the concentrations of two ions exceeds the value of K_{sp}, the ions do not exist in equilibrium. They form a precipitate and reduce their concentrations to an equilibrium value (Fig. 11-15).

To determine whether the K_{sp} is exceeded, we substitute the ion concentrations in an expression similar to the K_{sp} expression and determine the *experimental ion product (Q)*. If the experimental ion product exceeds the given K_{sp}, then a precipitate forms. If the experimental ion product is less than the K_{sp}, no precipitate forms.

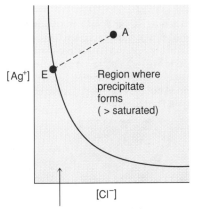

Figure 11-15
Graphical representation showing the inverse relationship between [Ag⁺] and [Cl⁻]. Any combination of concentrations, other than those on the curve, are not at equilibrium. If we assume the original concentrations are at point A and precipitation occurs, eventually the equilibrium point (E) is attained.

Note:
If $Q > K_{sp}$, a precipitate forms.
If $Q < K_{sp}$, no precipitate forms.

The following example uses the experimental ion product to predict whether a precipitate will form when two solutions are mixed together.

EXAMPLE 11-4
Predicting Precipitate Formation

If 1 mL of 0.1 mol/L $AgNO_3$ is added to 1.0 L of 1.0×10^{-5} mol/L KCl, will a precipitate form?

SOLUTION

1. Determine the formula of the possible precipitate that might form, and write the K_{sp} expression of this insoluble salt. If the precipitate forms, it will be AgCl, since KNO_3 is soluble (see Table 11-3).

$$AgCl(s) \rightleftharpoons Ag^+(aq) + Cl^-(aq)$$

$$K_{sp} = [Ag^+][Cl^-] = 1.8 \times 10^{-10} \text{ (from Table 11-4)}$$

2. Calculate the concentration of each of the Ag^+ and Cl^- ions available in solution:

$$[Ag^+] = \frac{\text{number of mol of } Ag^+}{\text{total volume of solution}}$$

$$= \frac{0.1 \text{ mol/L } (1 \times 10^{-3} \text{ L})}{1 \text{ L} + 1 \times 10^{-3} \text{ L}}$$

$$= 1.0 \times 10^{-4} \text{ mol/L}$$

$$[Cl^-] = \frac{1.0 \times 10^{-5} \text{ mol/L } (1 \text{ L})}{1 \text{ L} + 1 \times 10^{-3} \text{ L}}$$

$$= 1.0 \times 10^{-5} \text{ mol/L}$$

3. Substitute the ion concentrations into an experimental ion product (Q) equation that is identical to the K_{sp} expression. This will allow us to compare two solubility product values and determine whether a precipitate will form.

$$\text{Experimental ion product } (Q) = [Ag^+][Cl^-]$$
$$= (1.0 \times 10^{-4})(1.0 \times 10^{-5})$$
$$= 1.0 \times 10^{-9}$$

Since Q is greater than K_{sp}, a precipitate will form.

FOLLOW-UP PROBLEMS

1. Does a precipitate form if 10 mL of 0.1 mol/L $AgNO_3$ is added to 90 mL of a 1×10^{-10} mol/L KI solution?

2. Will a precipitate form if 15 mL of 1.2×10^{-3} mol/L K_2CrO_4 is added to 20 mL of 2.5×10^{-2} mol/L $Sr(NO_3)_2$?

Answers: (1) yes, (2) no

Example 11-5 is an interesting variation on the problem just discussed. Once you have decided which precipitate you want produced, you can calculate exactly what concentration or mass of an ion must be added to a solution to cause a precipitation reaction to start.

EXAMPLE 11-5
Calculating the Ion Concentration Required to Begin a Precipitation Reaction
You have just made up a solution that contains 5×10^{-5} mol/L of Ag^+ ions (from $AgNO_3$). What mass of KI would you have to add to the solution to begin the precipitation of AgI from the solution?

SOLUTION
1. Write the equilibrium reaction and the K_{sp} expression for the precipitate:

$$AgI(s) \rightleftharpoons Ag^+(aq) + I^-(aq)$$
$$K_{sp} = [Ag^+][I^-] = 8.5 \times 10^{-17} \text{ (from Table 11-4)}$$

2. Substitute the value given for the $[Ag^+]$ into the K_{sp} expression and solve for $[I^-]$:

$$8.5 \times 10^{-17} = (5 \times 10^{-5})[I^-]$$
$$[I^-] = \frac{8.5 \times 10^{-17}}{5 \times 10^{-5}} = 1.7 \times 10^{-12}$$

This tells us that the $[I^-]$, in equilibrium with the Ag^+, is 1.7×10^{-12} mol/L. To cause a precipitate of AgI, the $[I^-]$ must be greater than 1.7×10^{-12} mol/L.

3. Calculate the mass of KI needed to start the precipitation reaction:

$$\text{Molar mass of KI} = (39.1 + 126.9) \text{ g/mol}$$
$$= 166 \text{ g/mol}$$
$$\text{Mass of KI required} = (1.7 \times 10^{-12} \text{ mol/L})(166 \text{ g/mol})$$
$$= 2.8 \times 10^{-10} \text{ g/L}$$

Therefore, a mass of KI in excess of 2.8×10^{-10} g will begin the precipitation of AgI from the solution.

FOLLOW-UP PROBLEMS

1. What is the highest concentration of I⁻ ions that can exist in equilibrium with 0.001 mol/L Tl⁺ ions at 25°C? (K_{sp} for TlI = 8.9×10^{-8}.)

2. Calculate the [Cl⁻] required to begin precipitation of the following metal ions from solutions containing 1 g of metal ions per litre of solution: (a) Ag^+, (b) Cu^+, (c) Pb^{2+}.

Answers:

1. 8.9×10^{-5} **mol/L**
2. (a) 1.9×10^{-8} **mol/L**
   (b) 1.08×10^{-5} **mol/L**
   (c) 5.9×10^{-2} **mol/L**

11-15
Dissolving Precipitates

When various reagents are added to a precipitate, it is possible to shift the precipitate equilibrium to the right, causing the precipitate to dissolve.

Consider a saturated ZnS solution:

$$ZnS(s) \rightleftharpoons Zn^{2+}(aq) + S^{2-}(aq) \qquad [11\text{-}3]$$

In this example, the slightly soluble solid, zinc sulfide, is in equilibrium with its anion and cation in solution. According to Le Châtelier's principle, the equilibrium illustrated in Equation 11-3 can be shifted to the right if the concentration of one or both of the ions in solution is decreased. If the equilibrium is shifted far enough to the right, the ZnS will dissolve.

In this section we will investigate various ways in which the cation or anion concentrations can be reduced. The simplest method of accomplishing this is simply to add excess water to dilute the solution. Consider the following equilibrium:

$$AgCH_3COO(s) \rightleftharpoons Ag^+(aq) + CH_3COO^-(aq)$$

The K_{sp} of this equilibrium, 1.9×10^{-3}, is quite large compared with the other values given in Table 11-4. When water is added, the concentrations of the Ag^+ ions and CH_3COO^- ions will be reduced. If enough water is added, the equilibrium will shift to the right and the silver acetate precipitate will dissolve. However, precipitates with very small K_{sp} values cannot be dissolved in this manner. Other methods must be used to decrease the anion and cation concentrations.

Refining Nickel

Nickel is one of the most useful metals. Its chief value is its resistance to corrosion. When nickel is added to iron, it makes steel more resistant to impact, producing excellent armour plate. When nickel and chromium are added to iron, stainless steel is produced.

The refining of nickel is an example of the application of the solubility rules. Nickel oxide is usually found in rock in small concentrations. It can be extracted from the rock when it is dissolved in sulfuric acid:

$NiO(s) + H_2S(aq) \longrightarrow NiSO_4(aq) + H_2O$

Since the nickel(II) sulfate is soluble in water, the nickel is free to leave the ore and enter solution. To remove the nickel from the solution, hydrosulfuric acid is added to the solution:

$NiSO_4(aq) + H_2S(aq) \longrightarrow$
$\qquad NiS(s) + H_2SO_4(aq)$

The nickel(II) sulfide that forms is insoluble in water and precipitates out of solution. The pure nickel is then separated from the precipitate by an industrial process such as smelting or electrolysis.

A second method involves the formation of a *weakly dissociated species*. Consider the equilibrium

$$CaCO_3(s) \rightleftharpoons Ca^{2+}(aq) + CO_3^{2-}(aq) \qquad [11\text{-}4]$$

Experiments show that a $CaCO_3$ precipitate will dissolve in a strong acid (Fig. 11-16). A strong acid, such as HCl, produces hydronium (H_3O^+) ions in solution. The stronger the acid, the greater the amount of hydronium ions produced. The H_3O^+ ions react with the CO_3^{2-} ions to form H_2CO_3, a very weak acid. The attractive force bonding the hydrogen to the anion in the weak carbonic acid is much stronger than that of a strong acid. Therefore, carbonic acid has less tendency to dissociate and is considered a weakly dissociated species. The H_2CO_3 then decomposes to form carbon dioxide gas and water. The formation of the carbonic acid and CO_2 reduces the concentration of the CO_3^{2-} in the equilibrium in Equation 11-4, and the equilibrium shifts to the right by Le Châtelier's principle. The net reaction is

$$CaCO_3(s) + 2H_3O^+(aq) \longrightarrow Ca^{2+}(aq) + CO_2(g) + 3H_2O(l)$$

Notice that in this example, not only is a weakly dissociated species formed, but a *volatile substance*—carbon dioxide gas—is formed as well. This gas escapes, causing more $CaCO_3$ to dissolve in order to re-establish equilibrium conditions (Fig. 11-16).

A large number of slightly soluble salts do not dissolve readily in acids. Unlike the slightly soluble carbonates and hydroxides, the silver halides (AgCl, AgBr and AgI) cannot be dissolved to an appreciable extent by the addition of a strong acid. A third method of dissolving precipitates involves the formation of complex ions. Consider the equilibrium

$$AgCl(s) \rightleftharpoons Ag^+(aq) + Cl^-(aq) \qquad [11\text{-}5]$$

This equilibrium can be shifted to the right by the addition of either ammonia (NH_3) or CN^- (from NaCN). For example, when NH_3 is added,

$$Ag^+(aq) + 2NH_3(aq) \rightleftharpoons Ag(NH_3)_2^+(aq) \qquad [11\text{-}6]$$

When CN^- is added,

$$Ag^+(aq) + 2CN^-(aq) \rightleftharpoons Ag(CN)_2^-(aq) \qquad [11\text{-}7]$$

Equations 11-6 and 11-7 illustrate the formation of complex ions. These complex ions are fairly stable and, thus, are weakly dissociated. The net result of the formation of these complex ions is that the concentration of the Ag^+ ions in Equation 11-5 is reduced and the equilibrium shifts to the right, dissolving the AgCl (Fig. 11-17).

A final method of dissolving a precipitate is to form a new precipitate that is less soluble than the original one. For example,

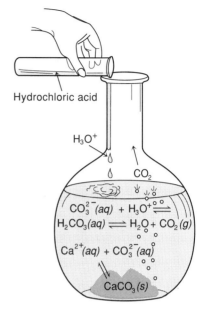

Hydrochloric acid

H_3O^+

CO_2

$$CO_3^{2-}(aq) + H_3O^+ \rightleftharpoons$$
$$H_2CO_3(aq) \rightleftharpoons H_2O + CO_2(g)$$

$$Ca^{2+}(aq) + CO_3^{2-}(aq)$$

$CaCO_3(s)$

Figure 11-16
When hydrochloric acid is added to a saturated $CaCO_3$ solution, the H_3O^+ ions react with the CO_3^{2-} ions and form CO_2 gas, which escapes from the solution. Additional solid $CaCO_3$ then dissolves and re-establishes equilibrium conditions.

Photography and K_{sp}

Film in a camera is covered with silver ions in the form of silver salts such as silver bromide. When light strikes the film, the silver ions are reduced to silver atoms. The more light admitted, the more silver deposited and the darker the negative. During the developing of the film, the silver salts that are not reduced must be removed from the film. This is done by washing the film with *hypo*, a sodium thiosulfate solution:

AgBr*(s)* + S$_2$O$_3^{2-}$ *(aq)* $\rightleftharpoons$
Ag(S$_2$O$_3$)$_2^{3-}$ *(aq)* + Br$^-$*(aq)*

In this manner, a stable complex ion (Ag(S$_2$O$_3$)$_2^{3-}$) is formed and the AgBr is dissolved away from the film.

the solubility equilibrium illustrated in Equation 11-5 has a K_{sp} of 1.8×10^{-10}. If a reagent such as S^{2-} (from Na_2S) is added to this equilibrium, the following reaction will occur:

$$2Ag^+(aq) + S^{2-}(aq) \rightleftharpoons Ag_2S(s)$$

The K_{sp} of Ag_2S is 1.1×10^{-49}, a much lower value than that of AgCl. As a result of the formation of Ag_2S, the Ag^+ concentration in Equation 11-5 is reduced, causing the equilibrium to shift to the right and the AgCl to dissolve.

In summary, precipitates can be dissolved by dilution, formation of a weakly dissociated species, formation of a volatile substance, formation of a complex ion or by the formation of a precipitate that is less soluble than the original. Some of these methods, especially the last one, have applications in qualitative analysis.

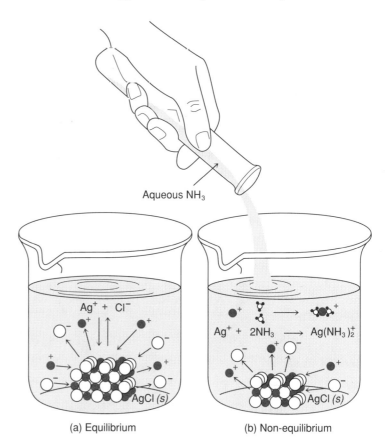

Aqueous NH$_3$

(a) Equilibrium   (b) Non-equilibrium

Figure 11-17
When ammonia is added to a saturated AgCl solution, the NH$_3$ reacts with the Ag$^+$ and forms diamminesilver(I) ions (Ag(NH$_3$)$_2^+$). Reducing the number of Ag$^+$ ions creates a non-equilibrium condition. Additional solid AgCl dissolves to re-establish equilibrium conditions.

11-16

Qualitative Analysis

Since different salts have different K_{sp} values, this information can be used to selectively precipitate ions out of solution.

The separation and identification of ions in a solution provides an interesting illustration and application of acid-base, solubility and complex-ion equilibria. It also provides us with an opportunity to learn a great deal about the descriptive chemistry of the elements. There are a number of rather extensive schemes designed for laboratory work in qualitative analysis. All of them involve the systems and principles we have studied up to this point.

One method of separating and identifying ions in solution is based on the differences in the solubilities of their compounds. The wide range of K_{sp} values shown in Table 11-4 is evidence of wide differences in the solubilities of salts. For example, when a precipitating agent is slowly added to a solution that contains more than one ion that precipitates, then the compound whose solubility product is exceeded first precipitates first. For example, if an I^- ion solution is slowly added to a solution containing 0.01 mol/L Ag^+ and 0.01 mol/L Pb^{2+}, AgI precipitates as soon as the $[I^-]$ exceeds

$$\frac{K_{sp}}{[Ag^+]} = \frac{8.5 \times 10^{-17}}{1 \times 10^{-2}} = 8.5 \times 10^{-15} \text{ mol/L}$$

The lead ions do not precipitate until $[I^-]$ exceeds

$$\sqrt{\frac{K_{sp}}{[Pb^{2+}]}} = \sqrt{\frac{8.5 \times 10^{-9}}{1 \times 10^{-2}}} = 9.2 \times 10^{-4} \text{ mol/L}$$

At this point, when PbI_2 starts to precipitate, the amount of Ag^+ left in solution is very small. When $[I^-]$ reaches 9.2×10^{-4} mol/L, which is needed to precipitate Pb^{2+}, then

$$[Ag^+] = \frac{K_{sp}}{[I^-]} = \frac{8.5 \times 10^{-17}}{9.2 \times 10^{-4}} = 9.2 \times 10^{-14} \text{ mol/L}$$

As you can see from this example, by controlling the concentrations of various ionic reagents, we can add a reagent that precipitates specific ions out of solution and leaves others behind.

Let us look at another example. The data in Table 11-4 shows that $BaSO_4$ is only slightly soluble ($K_{sp} = 1.1 \times 10^{-10}$). Table 11-4 does not list K_{sp} values for aluminum, zinc or magnesium sulfate; therefore, we can infer that these compounds are relatively soluble. Thus, it should be possible to separate Ba^{2+} ions from a solution containing Al^{3+}, Zn^{2+} and Mg^{2+} ions by adding a solution of some soluble sulfate such as Na_2SO_4. A small amount of added SO_4^{2-} ions causes the K_{sp} for $BaSO_4$ to be exceeded. The $BaSO_4$ precipitates and can be filtered from the solution. Similarly, we could precipitate out the Al^{3+} as $AlPO_4$ ($K_{sp} = 9.8 \times 10^{-21}$) by adding a very small amount of Na_3PO_4. Next, we could precipitate out Zn^{2+} as ZnS ($K_{sp} = 2.9 \times 10^{-25}$) by adding some Na_2S to the remaining solution. Finally, the Mg^{2+} that remains can be precipitated out as $Mg(OH)_2$ ($K_{sp} = 5.6 \times 10^{-12}$) by adding NaOH.

FOLLOW-UP PROBLEM

A solution contains 0.010 mol/L Ag^+ ions and 0.010 mol/L Sr^{2+} ions.

a) Which ion precipitates first when dilute K_2CrO_4 is slowly added to the mixture?

b) What percentage of the ion that is precipitated first remains unprecipitated when the second ion begins to precipitate?

Answers: (a) Ag^+, (b) 0.17%

In this chapter we have studied the solubility equilibria that exist in saturated solutions of slightly soluble substances. We have also used the equilibrium principles to help us predict whether a precipitate forms when ionic solutions are mixed and the conditions in which a precipitate dissolves.

In the next chapter we will examine the qualitative and quantitative aspects of equilibria in acid-base systems. We will apply the equilibrium law to systems involving weak acids and bases to obtain a dissociation constant that we can use to calculate the hydronium ion (H_3O^+) concentrations and, hence, the pH of the solution, the percentage dissociation of the solute and the extent of acid-base reactions. Applications of these concepts and calculations will be made in our discussion of volumetric analysis.

QUESTIONS

1. Distinguish between electrolytic and non-electrolytic solutions.

2. What characteristics of water molecules make them a good solvent for ionic substances?

3. What properties of ammonia molecules indicate that liquid ammonia might be a good solvent for ionic substances?

4. What property of water is responsible for preventing the oppositely charged ions in a solution from recombining?

5. How can you distinguish between solutions of polar molecular substances in water that form ions and those that do not?

6. The following reactions might be considered as hypothetical steps for the dissolution of $NaCl(s)$ in water:
   i) $765 \text{ kJ} + NaCl(s) \longrightarrow Na^+(g) + Cl^-(g)$
   ii) $Na^+(g) + H_2O(l) \longrightarrow Na^+(aq) + 397 \text{ kJ}$
   iii) $Cl^-(g) + H_2O(l) \longrightarrow Cl^-(aq) + 364 \text{ kJ}$
   a) Which reaction represents the crystal-lattice energy of sodium chloride?
   b) Which reaction(s) represent(s) the hydration energy?
   c) Which reactions are exothermic?

d) Which reactions are endothermic?

e) Does a large or small temperature change occur when $NaCl(s)$ is dissolved in water?

7. Which of the following ions have the greatest hydration energy?

	Ionic Charge	Ionic Radius (pm)
a) A^+		95
b) B^+		135
c) C^{2+}		65
d) D^{3+}		55
e) E^-		181

8. The dielectric constants for some substances are: water, 80; liquid ammonia, 18; ethanol, 25; and carbon tetrachloride, 2. Which of these substances are good solvents for (a) ionic solutes? (b) nonpolar solutes?

9. Name and identify each of the following salts as soluble or slightly soluble (insoluble) in water. Write equations showing the equilibrium that exists in saturated solutions of slightly soluble salts. (a) NaBr, (b) $MgCO_3$, (c) NH_4Cl, (d) AgI, (e) K_2CrO_4, (f) KOH, (g) $Fe(OH)_3$, (h) CuS, (i) $Cd(NO_3)_2$, (j) $Ba_3(PO_4)_2$, (k) $CoCl_2$, (l) $NiSO_4$, (m) NH_4NO_3

10. Which compound in each of the following pairs is the more soluble? (a) K_2CO_3 and $MnCO_3$, (b) $CuSO_4$ and $SrSO_4$, (c) NH_4I and AgI, (d) $FePO_4$ and $FeCl_3$, (e) $Cu(OH)_2$ and KOH, (f) CdS and Na_2S

11. Refer to the solubility curves in Fig. 11-1 and answer the following questions:

a) How many grams of sodium chloride can dissolve in 0.500 kg of water at 0°C?

b) How many grams of KNO_3 can dissolve in a litre of water at 25°C?

c) Which of the substances shown in the graph is the most soluble at 50°C?

d) Which is the least soluble at 50°C?

e) Which shows the least change in solubility between 0° and 100°C?

f) What mass of water at 30°C is needed to dissolve 50 g of NaCl?

g) What is the concentration of a saturated solution of KNO_3 at 20°C?

12. Using equations, show the dissociation of each of the following ionic substances in water: (a) KCl, (b) $Ca(C_2H_3O_2)_2$, (c) NH_4Br, (d) $NaNO_3$, (e) Li_2CO_3, (f) $MgSO_4$.

13. When solid anhydrous sodium sulfate is placed in water, heat is evolved.
(a) Does the system have higher or lower enthalpy than in its original state? Explain.
(b) Is it possible to predict accurately the direction of the entropy change? Explain.

14. Cesium iodide and lithium fluoride are both ionic compounds with general formulas M^+X^-. On the basis of the different charge densities of the ions, what are some of the differences in properties of these two compounds?

15. Fluoride ions and iodide ions both have a charge of I^-. Which ions have the greater charge density? Explain.

16. (a) Explain why a compound such as 1,2,3-propanetriol (glycerol, $C_3H_5(OH)_3$) is miscible with water. (b) Give several reasons why sugar is relatively soluble in water.

17. a) What two factors help explain the solution of polar solutes in polar solvents?
b) Give an example of each factor.

18. The following substances are all water soluble to varying degrees. Which ones dissolve and form ions? Which dissolve in molecular form? (a) CsI, (b) CH_3OH, (c) KNO_3, (d) HCl, (e) $C_3H_5(OH)_3$, (f) NH_4NO_3, (g) $C_6H_{12}O_6$ (glucose)

19. Which aqueous solutions in question 18 would be classed as electrolytes?

20. Ethanol (CH_3CH_2OH) is soluble in both water and carbon tetrachloride, although water and carbon tetrachloride are immiscible. (a) What features of ethanol molecules are responsible for their miscibility in both H_2O and CCl_4? (b) Which exhibits the greater entropy, a mixture of 5 mL of CCl_4 and 5 mL of H_2O, or a mixture of 5 mL of C_2H_5OH and 5 mL of H_2O?

21. When trichloromethane (chloroform, $CHCl_3$) is dissolved in propanone (acetone,

$$CH_3\overset{\displaystyle O}{\overset{\displaystyle \|}{C}}CH_3),$$ energy is evolved. As more acetone is added, more energy is released. This energy is sometimes referred to as enthalpy of dilution. (a) Considering the bonding and molecular geometry of these species, why should there be any energy change during this process? (b) Explain, in terms of energy, why the miscibility of these liquids is favoured.

22. When iodine is dissolved in carbon tetrachloride (CCl_4), 23.4 kJ/mol is absorbed. When iodine is dissolved in alcohol, 6.3 kJ/mol is absorbed. In which of the two solvents is iodine more soluble? Assume that dissolution in both solvents results in relatively the same increase in entropy. **Answer: I_2 is more soluble in alcohol.**

23. (a) Does the dissolution of a gas in a liquid increase or decrease the entropy of the system? Explain. (b) Does the tendency of a system to achieve maximum entropy favour or oppose the dissolution of a gas? Explain. (c) When most gases are dissolved in a liquid, energy is liberated. Give two reasons why the solubility of most gases in a liquid decreases when the temperature is increased.

24. Explain why butane ($CH_3CH_2CH_2CH_3$) is not water soluble, while butanol ($CH_3CH_2CH_2CH_2OH$) is water soluble.

25. The spontaneous dissolution of sodium chloride is represented by the equation

$$NaCl(s) \rightleftharpoons Na^+(aq) + Cl^-(aq)$$

The heat of solution is

$$\Delta H = +3.89 \text{ kJ/mol}$$

(a) Is the decrease in disorder of the water molecules when they interact with the ions more or less than the increase in disorder resulting from the dissociation of the crystal? Explain. (b) Is more or less heat absorbed in separating ions than is liberated in hydrating them? Explain. (c) Would increasing the temperature increase or decrease the solubility of NaCl? Explain. (d) Which factor is responsible for the spontaneous dissolution of NaCl: the change in enthalpy or the change in entropy?

26. (i) Write net ionic equations for any of the following reactions that result in the formation of a precipitate. If no reaction occurs, write N.R. Assume equal volumes of 0.1 mol/L solutions are mixed. (ii) Write the K_{sp} expressions for each precipitate.
a) silver nitrate and sodium cyanide
b) potassium chloride and ammonium sulfate
c) mercury(I) nitrate and potassium bromide
d) iron(III) chloride and aqueous ammonia
e) calcium nitrate and sodium oxalate
f) bismuth nitrate and aqueous hydrogen sulfide
g) lead(II) nitrate and ammonium iodide

27. Write net ionic equations for any of the following acid-base reactions that result in the formation of a weakly dissociated species.
a) $NaOH(aq) + HNO_3(aq)$
b) $NaCN(s) + H_2SO_4(l)$

c) $K_3BO_3(s) + HClO_4(aq)$

d) $CaSO_3(s) + HCl(aq)$

e) $(NH_4)_2CO_3(s) + HBr(aq)$

f) $FeS(s) + HI(aq)$

g) $NH_4Cl(s) + KOH(s)$

h) $CuO(s) + HCl(aq)$

i) $Cl_2O_7(l) + H_2O(l)$

j) $MgCO_3(s) + HI(aq)$

k) $Mg_2N_3(s) + H_2O(l) \longrightarrow$
$$Mg(OH)_2(s) + NH_3(g)$$

l) $NH_4OH(aq) + H_2SO_4(l)$

m) $Cd(OH)_2(s) + HNO_3(aq)$

28. Which of the following substances dissolve to a significant extent in dilute (1 mol/L) HNO_3? Justify your answers. (a) $BaCO_3$, (b) $BaSO_4$, (c) $AgOH$, (d) AgI, (e) $PbCrO_4$, (f) BaF_2

29. Is $CaCO_3$ more or less soluble in a 6 mol/L Na_2CO_3 solution than in pure water? Explain in terms of Le Châtelier's principle.

30. Explain in terms of Le Châtelier's principle why $AgCH_3COO$ ($K_{sp} = 1.9 \times 10^{-3}$) can be dissolved in an excess of each of the following reagents: (a) H_2O, (b) $HNO_3(aq)$, (c) $NH_3(aq)$.

31. (a) Is AgCN more or less soluble in a 6.0 mol/L NaCN solution than in pure water? Explain. (b) Is $Mg(OH)_2$ more or less soluble in excess NH_4Cl solution than in pure water? Explain.

32. Why are all slightly soluble carbonates appreciably soluble in dilute strong acids?

33. AgCl is appreciably soluble in 6 mol/L aqueous NH_3, but AgI is not. Explain.

34. When 1 mol/L Na_2CO_3 is added to a solution of $Fe(NO_3)_3$, a precipitate of $Fe(OH)_3$ is observed. Explain.

35. A solution may contain Ba^{2+} and/or Al^{3+}. Explain how you would prove the presence or absence of these ions.

PROBLEMS

1. Calculate the K_{sp} for each of the salts whose solubility is listed below.
   a) $CaSO_4 = 3.3 \times 10^{-3}$ mol/L
   b) $MgF_2 = 2.7 \times 10^{-3}$ mol/L
   c) $AgCH_3COO = 1.02$ g/100 mL
   d) $SrF_2 = 12.2$ mg/100 mL
   Answer: (b) 7.9×10^{-8}

2. Calculate (a) the solubility in mol/L of each of the salts and (b) the concentration of the cations in mg/mL in each of the following saturated solutions.
   a) $AgCN$, $K_{sp} = 2.2 \times 10^{-16}$
   b) $BaSO_4$, $K_{sp} = 1.1 \times 10^{-10}$
   c) FeS, $K_{sp} = 1.6 \times 10^{-19}$
   d) $Mg(OH)_2$, $K_{sp} = 5.6 \times 10^{-12}$
   e) Ag_2S, $K_{sp} = 1.1 \times 10^{-49}$

f) CaF_2, $K_{sp} = 3.9 \times 10^{-11}$
Answer: (c) 4×10^{-10} mol/L, 2.2×10^{-8} mg/mL

3. Consider these slightly soluble salts:
   i) PbS, $K_{sp} = 9.0 \times 10^{-29}$
   ii) $PbSO_4$, $K_{sp} = 1.8 \times 10^{-8}$

   (a) Which is the most soluble? (b) Calculate the solubility in mol/L of $PbSO_4$. (c) How many grams of $PbSO_4$ dissolve in one litre of solution? (d) How can you decrease the concentration of Pb^{+2} (aq) in a saturated $PbSO_4$ solution? (e) What is the concentration in mol/L of Pb^{2+} in a saturated solution of the salt?
   Answers: (c) 4.06×10^{-2} g/L, (e) 9.5×10^{-15} mol/L

4. For each of the following substances, calculate the milligrams of metallic ion that can remain at equilibrium in a solution having a $[OH^-] = 1.0 \times 10^{-4}$ mol/L.
   a) $Zn(OH)_2$, $K_{sp} = 4.3 \times 10^{-17}$
   b) $Fe(OH)_3$, $K_{sp} = 2.6 \times 10^{-39}$
   c) $Mg(OH)_2$, $K_{sp} = 5.6 \times 10^{-12}$
   Answer: (b) 1.45×10^{-25} mg/mL

5. Calculate the $[Ag^+]$ needed to begin precipitation of each of the following anions from solutions containing 1 mg of anion per mL of solution: (a) Br^-, (b) S^{2-}, (c) BrO_3^-, (d) CrO_4^{2-}, (e) IO_3^-.
   K_{sp} for $AgBrO_3 = 5.3 \times 10^{-5}$
   K_{sp} for $AgIO_3 = 3.2 \times 10^{-8}$
   Answer: (a) 4.3×10^{-11} mol/L

6. How many mg of TlI can dissolve in 500 mL of (a) water? (b) 0.1 mol/L $TlNO_3$? (c) 0.02 mol/L KI? (K_{sp} for TlI $= 8.9 \times 10^{-8}$.)
   Answer: (a) 49.4 mg

7. What is the solubility in mol/L AgBr in a solution resulting from the addition of 50.0 mL of 0.01 mol/L $CaBr_2$ to 50.0 mL of 0.008 mol/L $AgNO_3$?

8. Fifty mL of 0.10 mol/L $AgNO_3$ is added to 150 mL of 0.10 mol/L $CaCl_2$. What is the concentration of each ion in the resulting solution?

9. In which of the following reactions does a precipitate form?
   a) 10.0 mL of 0.01 mol/L $AgNO_3$ + 10.0 mL of 0.10 mol/L Na_2SO_4. K_{sp} for $Ag_2SO_4 = 1.2 \times 10^{-5}$.
   b) 1 mg of $MgCl_2$ + 1 L of 0.01 mol/L $Na_2C_2O_4$. K_{sp} for $MgC_2O_4 = 8.6 \times 10^{-5}$
   c) 1 mL of 0.1 mol/L $Ca(NO_3)_2$ + 1 L of 0.01 mol/L HF

d) 1 mL of 0.1 mol/L $Ca(NO_3)_2$ + 1 L of 0.01 mol/L NaF
   e) 5 mL of 0.004 mol/L $AgNO_3$ + 15 mL of a solution containing 1.5 mg Br^- ions
   Answers: c, d, e

10. How many mg of Pb^{2+} must be present in 10.0 mL of a 0.135 mol/L NaCl solution for $PbCl_2$ to precipitate?

11. A solution contains 0.01 mol/L $TlNO_3$ and 0.01 mol/L $AgNO_3$. (a) Which compound precipitates first when NaI is slowly added to 100 mL of this solution? (b) How many mg of this ion remain unprecipitated when the second compound begins to precipitate?
    Answer: (b) 1.0×10^{-7} mg

12. A litre of solution contains 100 mg of Ba^{2+} and 10.0 g of Sr^{2+}. Within what range must the concentration of CrO_4^{2-} be to precipitate Ba^{2+} without precipitating any Sr^{2+}?

13. Does a precipitate of $Mg(OH)_2$ form when 10.0 mL of a 0.10 mol/L NH_3 solution containing 3.0 g of NH_4Cl is mixed with 10.0 mL of 0.10 mol/L $MgCl_2$ solution?

14. Does a precipitate of $Mg(OH)_2$ form when 10.0 mL of 0.050 mol/L NH_3 solution is mixed with 10.0 mL of 0.15 mol/L $MgCl_2$?
    Answer: yes

15. Barium nitrate reacts with potassium sulfate solution and forms insoluble $BaSO_4$. What volume of 0.40 mol/L $Ba(NO_3)_2$ solution is required to precipitate effectively the sulfate ions in 25 mL of 0.80 mol/L K_2SO_4 solution?

16. What volume of 0.25 mol/L KCl solution is required to effectively precipitate the silver ions from a 160.0 mL sample of 0.60 mol/L $AgNO_3$ solution?

17. What mass of silver chloride can be precipitated from a silver nitrate solution by
200 mL of a solution of 0.50 mol/L $CaCl_2$?
Answer: 57.4 g

18. A sample of an unknown chloride (mass
0.210 g) is treated with 30.00 mL of
0.100 mol/L $AgNO_3$. The precipitate is filtered and the excess silver in the filtrate is
titrated with 5.65 mL of 0.0900 mol/L
KSCN. What is the percentage of Cl^- in the
sample?

Sulfur dioxide is one of the major contributing gases responsible for acid rain. Emissions of sulfur dioxide and other gases from the Inco plant in Sudbury, Ontario will be cut by more than 50% by 1995 to reduce the threat of acid rain.

ACID-BASE SYSTEMS AND IONIC EQUILIBRIA

The acid-base reaction has occupied the attention of chemists since medieval times. The concept of acids and bases has evolved from a very limited definition to a highly generalized one that includes a large number of substances.

In your introductory chemistry studies, acids were operationally defined as substances whose water solutions have a sharp taste, conduct an electric current, turn blue litmus red, corrode metals and neutralize bases. The sour taste of vinegar, lemon juice and grapefruit juice is associated with the presence of weak acids. Bases were defined as substances whose water solutions turn red litmus blue, conduct an electric current, feel slippery and neutralize acids. Common examples of bases are sodium hydroxide, antacids and soaps.

These qualitative observations provided the first definitions of acids and bases. Later, the Swedish chemist, Svante Arrhenius, defined acids as substances that ionized in aqueous solution to produce hydrogen ions, and bases as substances that reacted to produce hydroxide ions. More recently, general definitions of acids and bases have been developed by Brønsted, Lowry and Lewis.

In this chapter we will see that acids and bases are electrolytes that can be classified as either weak or strong, depending on whether they are weakly or highly dissociated in solution. The concepts of K_w, pH and pOH will be discussed to help us designate the relative acidity of a solution and relate it to the hydronium or hydroxide ion concentration.

After looking at the Arrhenius and Brønsted-Lowry definitions of acids and bases, we will consider the quantitative aspects of acid-base equilibria. Because solutions of weak acids and bases are equilibrium systems, we can apply the concepts developed in Chapter 10 to calculate the concentrations of various species at equilibrium. We will then look at some important lab techniques, including volumetric analysis and titration. This section will give us the opportunity to apply both stoichiometric principles and equilibrium concepts.

After discussing the theory of chemical indicators, we will end with a brief, generalized discussion of the concept of acids and bases known as the *Lewis theory*.

DEFINITIONS OF ACIDS AND BASES

12-1
Arrhenius Acids and Bases

Arrhenius defined acids and bases in terms of their ability to produce hydrogen ions (H^+) and hydroxide ions (OH^-) in water.

In 1884, Swedish chemist Svante Arrhenius (1859–1927) submitted his doctoral dissertation, which proposed that certain compounds could dissociate in solution to produce atoms bearing positive and negative charges. Today, we know these are electrolytic solutions, but at that time the electron had not yet been discovered, and chemists had difficulty in understanding how atoms could be charged. The theory was not readily accepted at first but in 1903, the same thesis that barely earned him a passing grade won Arrhenius the Nobel Prize in chemistry.

With the development of this theory came the realization that acids were substances that gave rise to hydrogen ions (H^+) in aqueous solution, while bases were associated with the formation of hydroxide ions (OH^-). By this definition, HCl was classified as an acid according to the equation

$$HCl(aq) \longrightarrow H^+(aq) + Cl^-(aq)$$

and NaOH was classified as a base:

$$NaOH(aq) \longrightarrow Na^+(aq) + OH^-(aq)$$

While earlier definitions had relied on the common properties of acids and bases, the concentrations of hydrogen and hydroxide ions in solution could now be determined by measuring the electric conductivity of the solution. This provided a quantitative measure of acidity, which is related to the concentration of hydrogen ions, and of alkalinity, which is related to the concentration of hydroxide ions.

Despite the theory's success, it did present some problems. First, the Arrhenius definition did not apply to non-aqueous solutions, which, instead of hydroxide ions, produce anions (negatively charged ions) that vary from solvent to solvent. Second, the hydrogen ion is not the ion responsible for acid characteristics. A hydrogen ion is a single proton with a diameter of approximately 0.2 pm. Because of its small size and its unit charge, the proton is surrounded by a strong electric field. Thus, it is highly reactive and strongly attracted to the polar water molecule. A stable co-ordinate bond forms when the proton (H^+) shares a pair of electrons from the oxygen atom of the water molecule. This hydrated proton is called a *hydronium ion* (H_3O^+) (Fig. 12-1). Scientists now have spectroscopic evidence that the hydrated protons, or hydronium ions, are also present as $H_5O_2^+$, $H_7O_3^+$ and $H_9O_4^+$.

Finally, the Arrhenius model could not explain certain types of acid-base reactions. For example, because Arrhenius considered a base to be a substance that released OH^- ions into solution, he was unable to explain the reaction of ammonia in water:

$$NH_3(g) + H_2O(l) \rightleftharpoons NH_4^+(aq) + OH^-(aq) \qquad [12\text{-}1]$$

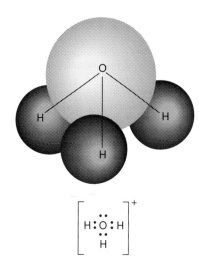

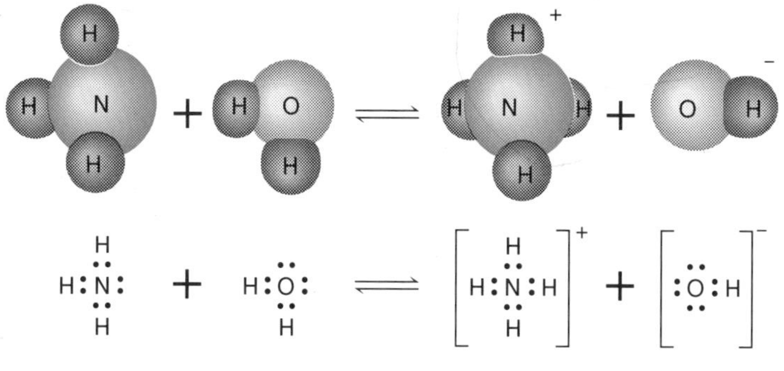

Figure 12-1
A hydronium ion. The hydronium ion can be represented as H_3O^+ or abbreviated to $H^+(aq)$.

Figure 12-2
When ammonia is dissolved in water, a proton is donated by the water molecule to the unshared pair of electrons of the nitrogen atom.

Consequently, more general definitions were developed to explain all acid-base systems.

12-2

Brønsted-Lowry Acids and Bases

Brønsted and Lowry defined acids and bases in terms of their ability to donate and accept protons.

In 1923, J. N. Brønsted (1879–1947) of Denmark and T. M.

Lowry (1874–1936) of England independently recognized that the loss and gain of hydrogen ions (protons) might furnish a basis for classifying substances as acids or bases, irrespective of the solvent used. A neutral hydrogen atom (H) has a nucleus with one proton and a single electron moving about the nucleus. When covalently bonded with highly electronegative atoms, a hydrogen atom behaves as if it had a partial positive charge because the bonding electrons are drawn toward the more electronegative atom. This often permits another polar molecule or negative ion to remove the hydrogen nucleus (proton). In this context, therefore, we refer to a hydrogen ion as a proton. Accordingly, Brønsted and Lowry defined an ***acid*** as *any substance capable of giving up a hydrogen ion or proton*, or as a *proton donor*. A ***base*** was defined as *any substance capable of combining with and thus removing a proton*, or as a *proton acceptor*.

The Brønsted-Lowry theory can explain the formation of NH_4^+ and OH^- ions (Equation 12-1) by assuming that a hydrogen ion (proton) is transferred from a water molecule to an ammonia molecule. The gain of a positive hydrogen ion by a neutral ammonia molecule converts it into a positive ammonium ion. The simultaneous loss of a proton by a neutral water molecule converts it into a negative hydroxide ion. Thus, we can classify NH_3 as a base and water as an acid.

The Brønsted-Lowry definition of an acid as a proton donor and a base as a proton acceptor implies that, in general, we should not classify a given compound as an acid or base unless we specify the reaction in which it participates. Consider the role of water in its reaction with HCl gas:

$$HCl(g) + H_2O(l) \rightleftharpoons H_3O^+(aq) + Cl^-(aq) \qquad [12\text{-}2]$$

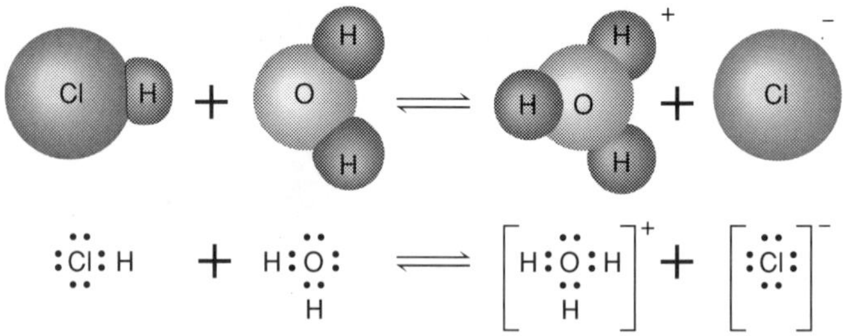

Figure 12-3
When hydrogen chloride dissolves in water, protons are transferred from the HCl molecules to the water molecules.

In Fig. 12-3, H_2O accepts a proton from HCl and behaves as a Brønsted base (or a Brønsted-Lowry base), while in Fig. 12-2, H_2O donates a proton and behaves as a Brønsted acid (or a Brønsted-Lowry acid). It is apparent that *the role played by water depends on the reaction in which it is involved*.

Classifying a chemical species as a Brønsted acid or base is like classifying the behaviour of a person. Someone who is isolated and inactive is difficult to classify. He or she may be classified as a criminal or philanthropist only through their interactions with other people. Like a person's actions, the behaviour of a chemical species varies with the environment. Thus, in one equilibrium system, water gives up protons and behaves as an acid, while in another system, it accepts protons and acts as a base. Substances capable of acting as an acid in one situation and a base in another are said to be **amphiprotic**, or **amphoteric**. An amphiprotic substance can both donate and accept a proton. An amphoteric substance can behave as both an acid or a base. "Amphoteric" is a more general term than "amphiprotic." Ammonia (NH_3) is an amphiprotic species. In Equation 12-1, NH_3 accepts a proton and behaves as a base. In some reactions, NH_3 acts as a Brønsted acid when it donates a proton and is converted into an amide ion (NH_2^-).

FOLLOW-UP PROBLEM

Identify the Brønsted acid and the Brønsted base in each of the following reactions:

a) $HNO_3 + H_2O \rightleftharpoons H_3O^+ + NO_3^-$

b) $H_2CO_3 + H_2O \rightleftharpoons H_3O^+ + HCO_3^-$

c) $HX + H_2O \longrightarrow H_3O^+ + X^-$

A little reflection will reveal that the formulas of all Brønsted acids contain hydrogen, and that the structures of all Brønsted bases include an available, unshared electron pair. For example, the electron-dot formula for methane (CH_4), shown in the margin, reveals that this substance could act as a Brønsted acid but not as a Brønsted base.

Brønsted acids are classified according to the number of protons that can be donated per molecule in an acid-base reaction. Any acid that can donate only one proton per molecule to a base is called a **monoprotic acid**. An acid that can donate more than one proton per molecule is called a **polyprotic acid**. For example, hydrochloric acid (HCl) is a monoprotic acid, and hydrogen sulfide (H_2S) is a polyprotic acid. Hydrochloric acid and hydrogen sulfide are also known as **binary acids** because they contain only hydrogen and one other nonmetal element. The hydrogen atom in a molecule that donates a proton is said to be an *acidic hydrogen* and is often shown first in the formula; thus, ethanoic acid (acetic acid), a monoprotic acid, can be written as $HC_2H_3O_2$, and phthalic acid, a polyprotic acid, as $H_2C_8H_4O_4$. Acids that contain oxygen, such as phthalic acid, are called **oxyacids**. The acidic hydrogen in oxyacids is always bonded to an oxygen atom, as shown in the diagram for sulfuric acid (H_2SO_4) in the margin.

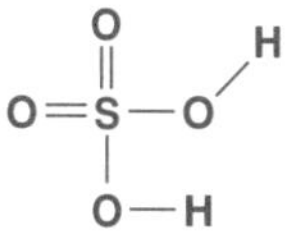

In the Brønsted concept, *ions as well as molecules can behave*

H
H : C : H
H

methane

sulfuric acid
(hydrogen sulfate)

Spectator ions such as Na⁺ ions, which are a part of the system but do not participate in the reaction, are not shown in net ionic equations.

as acids or bases. For example, when an ionic salt such as Na_2CO_3 is added to water, the solution is found to contain small concentrations of HCO_3^- ions and OH^- ions. The presence of these ions can only be explained if we assume that the CO_3^{2-} ions accept protons from water, according to the equation

$$CO_3^{2-} + H_2O(l) \rightleftharpoons HCO_3^-(aq) + OH^-(aq) \qquad [12\text{-}3]$$

Figure 12-4
Reaction between water and carbonate ions.

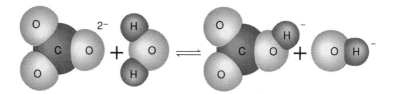

In this reaction, the CO_3^{2-} ions are acting as a Brønsted base. A solution of Na_2CO_3 is quite basic, as shown by its ability to turn red litmus blue; thus, it must contain a significant concentration of OH^- ions.

12-3

Conjugate Acid-Base Pairs

Any reactant that acts as a Brønsted acid and donates protons forms a conjugate Brønsted base on the product side. Similarly, a reactant that acts as a Brønsted base becomes a conjugate Brønsted acid on the product side.

Examination of Equations 12-1, 12-2 and 12-3 reveals that in a reaction in which molecules or ions act as a Brønsted base, there must be some molecules or ions that act as an acid by losing protons. Furthermore, it can be seen that the base that accepts protons becomes a Brønsted acid on the product side of the equation. The species acting as a Brønsted acid on the reactant side loses protons and becomes a Brønsted base on the product side. Consider the reaction between cyanide ions (CN⁻) and water, represented by the equation

The cyanide ions (CN⁻) are obtained from a soluble ionic salt such as NaCN or KCN.

$$\underset{\substack{\text{Brønsted} \\ \text{base}}}{CN^-} + \underset{\substack{\text{Brønsted} \\ \text{acid}}}{H_2O} \rightleftharpoons \underset{\substack{\text{Brønsted} \\ \text{acid}}}{HCN} + \underset{\substack{\text{Brønsted} \\ \text{base}}}{OH^-}$$

In this reaction, the CN⁻ ions, acting as a Brønsted base, accept one proton each and become HCN, a Brønsted acid on the product side of the equation. Water, acting as a Brønsted acid, donates one proton per molecule and becomes OH⁻ ions, a Brønsted base on the product side of the equation.

In general, *Brønsted acid-base reactions are equilibrium systems involving two acid-base pairs*. The equations below show

how the members of an acid-base pair are formed from each other by the transfer of a proton. Each pair is known as a ***conjugate acid-base pair***. Proton transfer reactions are sometimes called ***protolysis***, or ***protolytic***, ***reactions***. The protolytic reactions between two conjugate acid-base pairs are shown in Equations 12-4 and 12-5. The general relationship between two conjugate acid-base pairs is shown in Equation 12-6.

Pair 1 $\qquad$ $acid_1 \rightleftharpoons H^+ + base_1$ $\qquad$ [12-4]

Pair 2 $\qquad$ $\underline{base_2 + H^+ \rightleftharpoons acid_2}$ $\qquad$ [12-5]

conjugate pair 2

Overall
reaction $\qquad$ $acid_1 + base_2 \rightleftharpoons acid_2 + base_1$ $\qquad$ [12-6]

conjugate pair 1

The species participating in the following Brønsted acid-base reactions are labelled to show the relationship between the conjugate acid-base pairs:

$$NH_4^+(aq) + H_2O(l) \rightleftharpoons H_3O^+(aq) + NH_3(aq)$$

conjugate	conjugate	conjugate	conjugate
acid of the	base of the	acid of the	base of the
base NH_3	acid H_3O^+	base H_2O	acid NH_4^+

Ammonium ions (NH_4^+) are obtained from a soluble ionic salt such as NH_4NO_3. The nitrate ions (NO_3^-), which are part of the system but do not participate in the reaction, are not shown in an ionic equation.

$$CH_3COO^-(aq) + H_2O(l) \rightleftharpoons CH_3COOH(l) + OH^-(aq)$$

conjugate base	conjugate	conjugate	conjugate
of the acid	acid of the	acid of the	base of the
CH_3COOH	base OH^-	base CH_3COO^-	acid H_2O

Can you suggest a source of acetate ions (CH_3COO^-)?

Note that the conjugate acid-base pairs never have the same charge. The conjugate acid-base concept indicates that all four species are present at equilibrium (the original acid and base and their respective conjugates). The relative concentration of each in the system depends on the nature of the reacting species, which we will discuss in the next two sections.

FOLLOW-UP PROBLEMS

1. Identify clearly the Brønsted acids and bases in the following reaction:

   $$HSO_3^-(aq) + CH_3COO^-(aq) \rightleftharpoons$$
   $$SO_3^{2-}(aq) + CH_3COOH(aq)$$

2. What is the conjugate acid of CH_3^-?

3. What is the conjugate base of $N_2H_5^+$?

Answers:

1.

$$HSO_3^- \rightleftharpoons SO_3^{2-} + H^+$$
$$CH_3COO^- + H^+ \rightleftharpoons CH_3COOH$$

$$\overline{HSO_3^- \; + \; CH_3COO^- \rightleftharpoons \; SO_3^{2-} \; + \; CH_3COOH}$$

| conjugate acid of the base SO_3^{2-} | conjugate base of the acid CH_3COOH | conjugate base of the acid HSO_3^- | conjugate acid of the base CH_3COO^- |

2. CH_4

3. N_2H_4

12-4
Strong and Weak Acids

A strong acid completely dissociates in water to produce hydronium ions and is thus a good proton donor. A weak acid incompletely dissociates in water to produce hydronium ions and is thus a poor proton donor.

The Arrhenius definition of acids and bases applies only to aqueous solutions.

We can classify acids that dissolve in water as strong or weak, using the Arrhenius or the Brønsted-Lowry definition of acids. According to the Brønsted-Lowry theory, a strong acid is a substance that readily donates protons to a base; thus, the proton transfer reaction is complete. For example, hydrochloric acid is a strong acid and reacts with water to produce hydronium ions:

$$HCl(aq) + H_2O(l) \longrightarrow H_3O^+(aq) + Cl^-(aq)$$

Because a strong acid (in this case, HCl) reacts completely with water, we do not write the reaction as an equilibrium. In this example, HCl is a good proton donor, so water must, at the same time, be an equally good proton acceptor (strong base). Strong acids are usually strong electrolytes because they dissociate completely in water to form ions.

Weak acids incompletely dissociate in water to produce hydronium ions. For example, in the reaction of acetic acid and water,

$$CH_3COOH(aq) + H_2O(l) \rightleftharpoons H_3O^+(aq) + CH_3COO^-(aq)$$

only a small percentage of acid dissociates to form acetate and hydronium ions. Therefore, water solutions of weak acids are equilibrium mixtures consisting of a higher concentration of reactant molecules than product ions. The implication is that the hydrogen atoms in the molecules of weak acids are more firmly bonded to the other atoms than in strong acids.

From the Brønsted-Lowry definition of acids, we can conclude that weak acids are poor proton donors. Thus, in reactions with weak acids, proton transfers occur to a small extent.

It is often convenient to know the names and formulas of the most common strong acids, and these are listed in Table 12-1. All other acids may be considered weak, unless specifically noted.

TABLE 12-1
STRONG ACIDS

Formula	Name		Ions Formed in Aqueous Solution	
$HClO_4$	perchloric acid	H_3O^+ (or H^+)	ClO_4^-	
HCl	hydrochloric acid	H_3O^+	Cl^-	
HBr	hydrobromic acid	H_3O^+	Br^-	
HI	hydriodic acid	H_3O^+	I^-	
HNO_3	nitric acid	H_3O^+	NO_3^-	
H_2SO_4	sulfuric acid	H_3O^+	$\begin{cases} HSO_4^- \text{ (high concentration)} \\ SO_4^{2-} \text{ (low concentration)} \end{cases}$	

12-5
Strong and Weak Bases

According to the Arrhenius definition, a strong base completely dissociates in water to produce hydroxide ions and, conversely, a weak base incompletely dissociates in water. The Brønsted-Lowry theory relates the strength of bases to their ability to accept protons.

Using the Arrhenius definition, we can classify bases according to the degree to which they dissociate in water to form hydroxide ions. Strong bases highly dissociate in water and include the hydroxides of the Group IA metals plus calcium hydroxide ($Ca(OH)_2$) and barium hydroxide ($Ba(OH)_2$). The conductivity of strong bases indicates that the solutes are completely dissociated into ions. Using the Arrhenius definition, we can conclude that weak bases incompletely dissociate to give hydroxide ions in water solutions. However, we know that not all bases are hydroxides. By the Brønsted-Lowry definition, we can define strong bases as substances that readily accept protons and weak bases as substances that are poor proton acceptors. For example, in the reaction between ammonia and water,

Note that the four strong bases are NaOH, KOH, LiOH and $Ba(OH)_2$. Most other bases are considered to be weak.

$$NH_3(aq) + H_2O(l) \rightleftharpoons NH_4^+(aq) + OH^-(aq)$$

not all ammonia molecules readily accept a proton from water molecules, and therefore a dynamic equilibrium is set up between the species of the product and reactant sides of the equation.

Equilibria in Brønsted Acid-Base Systems

In acid-base reactions, equilibrium favours the production of the weaker acid and base.

In terms of the Brønsted concept, a *strong acid* readily releases protons, and a *strong base* readily accepts protons. *The stronger the reacting acid and base, the more complete is the reaction*. For example, a perchloric acid solution is an excellent conductor of an electric current. This indicates that it is highly dissociated and readily gives up protons to water molecules. The equilibrium may be represented as

$$\underset{\text{acid}}{HClO_4(aq)} + \underset{\text{base}}{H_2O(l)} \rightleftharpoons \underset{\text{acid}}{H_3O^+(aq)} + \underset{\text{base}}{ClO_4^-(aq)} \qquad \text{[12-7]}$$

However, because perchloric acid is a strong acid, dissociation is essentially complete, and the equilibrium is displaced almost completely to the right. That is, at equilibrium, the ratio of products to reactants is very large. In general, in aqueous solutions, strong acids are not assigned equilibrium constants, and equations for their reactions are usually written with a single arrow. For example, Equation 12-7 should be written as

$$HClO_4(aq) + H_2O(l) \longrightarrow H_3O^+(aq) + ClO_4^-(aq)$$

We can think of a Brønsted acid-base reaction as a competition for protons between the two bases in the system. The stronger base "wins" the competition and forces the equilibrium in the direction of the weaker acid and base. In Equation 12-7, two bases, H_2O and ClO_4^- ions, are competing for protons. Water, the stronger base, "wins" and the equilibrium is shifted to the right in the direction of the weaker base, ClO_4^- ions. The stronger acid, $HClO_4$, has a greater tendency to give its protons to H_2O than the H_3O^+ ions have to give their protons to ClO_4^- ions. The equilibrium is displaced so far to the right that we can consider the reaction represented by Equation 12-7 as complete.

In contrast to $HClO_4$, HCN is a weak acid and is only partially dissociated:

$$HCN(aq) + H_2O(l) \rightleftharpoons H_3O^+(aq) + CN^-(aq) \qquad \text{[12-8]}$$

This indicates that the equilibrium represented by Equation 12-8 is reached with the majority of the HCN molecules unreacted. The H_3O^+ ions are a much stronger acid than HCN, and the CN^- ions are a much stronger base than H_2O. This means that the CN^- ions "win" the competition for protons and force the equilibrium to the left in the direction of the weaker acid and base. Thus, the H_3O^+ ion concentration of a 0.1 mol/L HCN solution is much less than that of a 0.1 mol/L $HClO_4$ solution. The displacement of the equilibrium position toward the reactant side is indicated by the relative length of the two arrows.

A list of acids in order of decreasing acid strength is given in Table 12-2. The conjugate bases of each acid are also shown.

TABLE 12-2
RELATIVE STRENGTHS OF ACIDS AND BASES

	Conjugate Acid	Formula	Conjugate Base	Formula	
	Perchloric acid	$HClO_4$	perchlorate ion	ClO_4^-	
	Hydriodic acid	HI	iodide ion	I^-	
	Hydrochloric acid	HCl	chloride ion	Cl^-	
	Nitric acid	HNO_3	nitrate ion	NO_3^-	
	Sulfuric acid	H_2SO_4	hydrogen sulfate ion	HSO_4^-	
	Hydronium ion	H_3O^+	water	H_2O	
Decreasing acid strength	Sulfurous acid	$H_2SO_3 (H_2O + SO_2(g))$	hydrogen sulfite ion	HSO_3^-	Decreasing base strength
	Hydrogen sulfate ion	HSO_4^-	sulfate ion	SO_4^{2-}	
	Phosphoric acid	H_3PO_4	dihydrogen phosphate ion	$H_2PO_4^-$	
	Hydrofluoric acid	HF	fluoride ion	F^-	
	Nitrous acid	HNO_2	nitrite ion	NO_2^-	
	Acetic acid	CH_3COOH	acetate ion	CH_3COO^-	
	Carbonic acid	$H_2CO_3 (H_2O + CO_2(g))$	hydrogen carbonate ion	HCO_3^-	
	Hydrogen sulfide	H_2S	hydrogen sulfide ion	HS^-	
	Hydrogen sulfite ion	HSO_3^-	sulfite ion	SO_3^{2-}	
	Ammonium ion	NH_4^+	ammonia	NH_3	
	Hydrogen carbonate ion	HCO_3^-	carbonate ion	CO_3^{2-}	
	Hydrogen sulfide ion	HS^-	sulfide ion	S^{2-}	
	Water	H_2O	hydroxide ion	OH^-	
	Hydroxide ion	OH^-	oxide ion	O^{2-}	
	Ammonia	NH_3	amide ion	NH_2^-	
	Hydrogen	H_2	hydride ion	H^-	

Equations 12-7 and 12-8 show that in a Brønsted acid-base reaction, *the stronger acids and bases react to form their weaker conjugates*. In Equation 12-7, the ClO_4^- ions are the weak conjugate base of the strong acid, $HClO_4$. Since the base, H_2O, "won" the competition for the protons, it is a stronger base than the ClO_4^- ions. Thus, we can conclude that *the conjugate base of a strong acid is a weak base*. Note that the perchlorate ions (ClO_4^-) are such a weak base that any base below it in Table 12-2 will accept protons more readily than the ClO_4^- ions. In Equation 12-7, water completely removes the protons from the $HClO_4$ molecule and forms H_3O^+ ions.

On the other hand, Equation 12-8 shows that *the conjugate base of a weak acid is a strong base*. The CN^- ions "won" the competition for the protons and are therefore a stronger base than water. Accordingly, HCN, the weak conjugate acid of CN^- ions, is weaker than the H_3O^+ ions. On the basis of these observations, we can conclude that *the stronger the Brønsted acid, the weaker is its conjugate base*.

You can use Table 12-2 to qualitatively determine the extent to which a given acid and base react. In general, the strong acids in the upper part of the left-hand column have the greatest tendency to react with the strong bases in the lower part of the right-hand column. The products are a weaker acid and a weaker base. For example, H_3O^+ ions, a strong acid, have a relatively great tendency to react with NH_3, a strong base, to form NH_4^+ and H_2O. However, H_3O^+ has a still greater tendency to react with OH^- ions to form H_2O because OH^- is a stronger base than NH_3.

We can now use the concept of equilibrium in acid-base systems to determine the concentration of hydronium and hydroxide ions in water solution. We will also study the equilibrium between weak acids and their dissociation products and weak bases and their dissociation products.

ION CONCENTRATION AND pH

12-7

The Dissociation Constant for Water

Water undergoes a process of self-ionization in which it is in equilibrium with its hydronium and hydroxide ions.

Water is amphiprotic and can therefore act as a Brønsted acid (proton donor) and as a Brønsted base (proton acceptor). Collisions between water molecules can result in a proton transfer from one molecule to the other. This reaction represents the self-dissociation, or self-ionization, of water and is written

$$H_2O(l) + H_2O(l) \rightleftharpoons H_3O^+(aq) + OH^-(aq)$$

This equation, illustrated in Fig. 12-5, indicates that in pure water there is an equilibrium between the H_3O^+ and OH^- ions and the water molecules. As in all other equilibrium systems, the product of the concentrations of H_3O^+ and OH^- ions divided by the concentration of H_2O molecules, raised to the power of the coefficient of H_2O in the balanced equation, is a constant at a given temperature. This equilibrium constant, K_w, is known as the ***dissociation constant***, or ionic product, of water:

$$K_w = [H_3O^+][OH^-] \qquad [12-9]$$

The square brackets denote the concentration in mol/L.

Because the concentration of water is essentially constant, [H_2O] is not included in the expression for K_w. Measurements show that at 25°C, the concentrations of each of H_3O^+ and OH^- ions in pure water is 1.0×10^{-7} mol/L. Substituting this value for both H_3O^+ and OH^- ions into Equation 12-9 shows that $K_w = 1.0 \times 10^{-14}$. Therefore, in any aqueous solution at 25°C, the product of the [H_3O^+] and the [OH^-] must equal 1.0×10^{-14}. Note that K_w, like all equilibrium constants, is temperature dependent; therefore, the value of 1.0×10^{-14} only applies at 25°C. The values of K_w range from 1.5×10^{-15} at 0°C to 1.0×10^{-12} at 100°C.

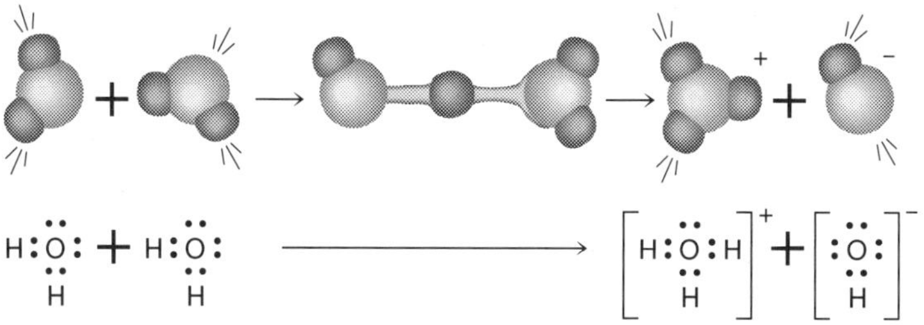

Figure 12-5
Proton transfer between water molecules.

The extent of the dissociation of water is very slight, and only a small percentage of pure water exists as H_3O^+ and OH^- ions. We can apply the principle of self-dissociation of water to any reaction in an aqueous solution. However, in an aqueous solution of a strong acid, we can assume that the [H_3O^+] from the self-ionization of water is generally negligible if the [H_3O^+] contributed from the acid is far greater than 10^{-7} mol/L.

Equation 12-9 can be used to calculate the H_3O^+ and the OH^- ion concentrations of a solution if one of the quantities is known. For example, the OH^- ion concentration of a solution having an H_3O^+ concentration of 1.0×10^{-3} mol/L is calculated as follows:

$$K_w = 1.0 \times 10^{-14} = [H_3O^+][OH^-]$$
$$1.0 \times 10^{-14} = 1.0 \times 10^{-3} \, [OH^-]$$
$$[OH^-] = \frac{1.0 \times 10^{-14}}{1.0 \times 10^{-3}}$$
$$= 1.0 \times 10^{-11} \text{ mol/L}$$

Example 12-1 illustrates this type of calculation in more detail.

EXAMPLE 12-1
Calculating [H_3O^+] and [OH^-] Using K_w
A student in a laboratory prepares a solution by adding 1 mL of 1 mol/L HCl to 9 mL of water. Assuming that the HCl dissociates completely, what are the [H_3O^+] and [OH^-] in this solution?

SOLUTION

1. Write the dissociation reaction for HCl in water. Note that HCl is a strong acid; it reacts completely with water and dissociates to form H_3O^+ and Cl^- ions:

$$HCl(aq) + H_2O(l) \longrightarrow H_3O^+(aq) + Cl^-(aq)$$

2. Calculate the concentration of H_3O^+ in the solution. The total $[H_3O^+]$ comes from the dissociation of HCl and the self-ionization of water, which is a minuscule amount, since the reaction is driven to the left.

$$\text{Volume of HCl added} = 1 \text{ mL} = 1 \times 10^{-3} \text{ L}$$
$$\text{Total volume of solution} = 1 \text{ mL} + 9 \text{ mL} = 10 \text{ mL}$$
$$= 1.0 \times 10^{-2} \text{ L}$$

The dissociation equation shows that for every mole of HCl that dissociates, one mole of H_3O^+ is produced. Therefore,

$$[HCl] = [H_3O^+] = \frac{[HCl_{initial}] \times volume_{HCl}}{volume_{final}}$$
$$= \frac{(1.0 \text{ mol/L})(1 \times 10^{-3} \text{ L})}{1.0 \times 10^{-2} \text{ L}}$$
$$= 1.0 \times 10^{-1} \text{ mol/L}$$

3. Calculate the $[OH^-]$ in solution using Equation 12-9 for K_w:

$$K_w = 1.0 \times 10^{-14} = [H_3O^+][OH^-]$$
$$[OH^-] = \frac{1.0 \times 10^{-14}}{[H_3O^+]}$$
$$= \frac{1.0 \times 10^{-14}}{1.0 \times 10^{-1}}$$
$$= 1.0 \times 10^{-13} \text{ mol/L}$$

Thus, $[H_3O^+]$ is 1.0×10^{-1} mol/L and $[OH^-]$ is 1.0×10^{-13} mol/L.

FOLLOW-UP PROBLEMS

1. What are the $[H_3O^+]$ and $[OH^-]$ of a solution made by adding 1 mL of 0.1 mol/L NaOH to 9 mL of water?

2. Calculate the $[H_3O^+]$ and $[OH^-]$ of the following solutions:
   a) 0.01 mol/L nitric acid (HNO_3) (a strong acid)
   b) 4.0×10^{-1} mol/L HCl
   c) 0.5 mol/L KOH (a strong base)

Answers:
1. $[H_3O^+] = 1 \times 10^{-12}$ mol/L; $[OH^-] = 1 \times 10^{-2}$ mol/L
2. a) $[H_3O^+] = 1 \times 10^{-2}$ mol/L; $[OH^-] = 1 \times 10^{-12}$ mol/L
   b) $[H_3O^+] = 4.0 \times 10^{-1}$ mol/L; $[OH^-] = 2.5 \times 10^{-14}$ mol/L
   c) $[H_3O^+] = 2 \times 10^{-14}$ mol/L; $[OH^-] = 5 \times 10^{-1}$ mol/L

The previous examples show that the concentrations of H_3O^+ and OH^- are expressed as exponential numbers. In the next section, we will see that the use of the pH scale standardizes the expressions for $[H_3O^+]$.

12-8

The pH Scale

The pH scale is used to express and compare the concentrations of hydronium ions for different aqueous solutions.

Every aqueous solution is either acidic, basic or neutral. The qualitative relationship between the concentrations of hydronium ions and hydroxide ions in each of these solutions is as follows:

neutral solution $[H_3O^+] = [OH^-]$

acid solution $\quad [H_3O^+] > [OH^-]$

basic solution $\quad [H_3O^+] < [OH^-]$

The acidity of a solution is a vital factor in determining the outcome of many reactions (Fig. 12-6). The success or failure of many analytical and synthetic processes depends on the hydronium ion concentration. For example, you would not expect to remove carbonate ions from a solution by trying to precipitate it out in an acidic medium. People who have swimming pools carefully control the acidity so as to avoid undesirable reactions with the plumbing and plaster and to expedite reactions with other chemicals. Most chemical industries continually monitor the acidity of the solutions being used in the preparation of their products.

A large number of reactions involve extremely small concentrations of hydronium ions. For example, most swimming-pool owners try to maintain a $[H_3O^+]$ of approximately 4×10^{-8} mol/L. As you can see, this is an awkward number. Solutions of acids and bases in water may have concentrations of H_3O^+ and OH^- ions that vary from relatively large numbers (>1.0 mol/L) to exponential numbers (10^{-14} mol/L). In 1909, Søren P. Sørenson (1868–1939), a Danish chemist, proposed a more concise method for expressing the acidity of a solution. Sørenson's proposal was to express the acidity of a solution in terms of a quantity known as *pH (potency of hydrogen)*. The concentration of H_3O^+ over a narrow range of

Figure 12-6
A lab technician processes a black-and-white print. Exposure of the photographic paper to light causes silver-halide crystals in the paper to form minute clumps of metallic silver that correspond to the dark and light contrasts of the image.

The next step involves placing the paper in a chemical reducing solution (developer), which contains organic reducing compounds, and an alkali—usually sodium carbonate or sodium hydroxide—which activates the developer.

After the image has been developed to the desired extent, a rapid decrease in pH is required to stop the development process. This is achieved by transferring the print from the alkaline developer solution to an acidic stop bath composed of a dilute solution of a weak acid (0.5% acetic acid).

Finally, the print is transferred to a fix bath where the undeveloped silver halide crystals are converted to water-soluble complexes that are washed away in solution.

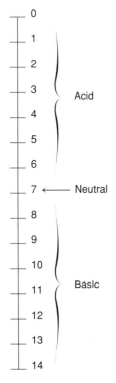

Figure 12-7
The pH scale. Most solutions that we will deal with have pH values that fall between 0 and 14. Some very acidic solutions, however, have negative pH values, and some very basic solutions have pH values greater than 14.

values has been expressed using the *pH scale* (Fig. 12-7).

The pH scale is a numerical scale that, for most applications, extends from 0 through 14. The numbers on the scale represent the relative acidity of solutions and can be converted to actual hydronium ion concentrations. The midpoint of the scale is taken as 7.0. At 25°C, a solution with a pH of 7.0 contains equal concentrations of H_3O^+ and OH^- ions and is neutral. A solution with a pH less than 7.0 has a greater H_3O^+ than OH^- ion concentration and is acidic. Solutions with a pH above 7.0 have greater OH^- than H_3O^+ ion concentrations and are basic. The pH values of some common liquids are given in Table 12-3.

The pH of a solution can be determined by the use of an electronic instrument known as a *pH meter* or by the use of *chemical indicators*. Acid-base indicators are dyes that undergo slight changes in molecular structure and colour when the pH of a solution changes. Specific colours correspond to certain pH values. Litmus and phenolphthalein are two chemical indicators. Litmus is red in a solution whose pH is less than 5.5, and blue in one whose pH is greater than 8. Between pH values of 5.5 and 8, litmus remains an intermediate colour (reddish purple or bluish purple). Phenolphthalein is pink in a solution whose pH is above 8.2 and colourless when the pH is below 8.2. Chemical indicators are discussed in more detail in Section 12-18.

The actual relationship between the pH and the H_3O^+ ion concentration is given by

$$[H_3O^-] = 10^{-pH} \text{ mol/L} \qquad [12\text{-}10]$$

This equation shows that the pH of a solution is defined as the negative power to which 10 must be raised to obtain the concentration of H_3O^+ ions. For example, if the pH of a solution is 5, then

$$[H_3O^+] = 10^{-5} \text{ mol/L} = 1.0 \times 10^{-5} \text{ mol/L}$$

If the pH of the solution is 7, then

$$[H_3O^+] = 10^{-7} \text{ mol/L} = 1.0 \times 10^{-7} \text{ mol/L}$$

As long as concentrations can be converted to whole-number powers of 10, it is relatively simple to convert H_3O^+ ion concentrations to their pH values, and vice versa. In practice, however, solutions are not so accommodating, and actual concentrations usually yield pH values that are not whole numbers. In order to work with fractional pH values, it is easier to use the general definition of pH given by Sørenson:

$$pH = -\log [H_3O^+] \qquad [12\text{-}11]$$

If you examine Equations 12-10 and 12-11 as well as the examples given, you will notice that there is a reciprocal relationship between pH and $[H_3O^+]$. That is, the lower the value of pH, the higher is the H_3O^+ ion concentration and the more acidic is the solution; the higher the value of pH, the lower is the H_3O^+ ion concentration and the more basic is the solution. Be sure to remember this relationship whenever you are using pH values.

In order to express the OH^- ion concentrations in solutions, we can define pOH in the same way we defined pH. Therefore, the relationship between the pOH and the concentration of OH^- ions is given by

$$[OH^-] = 10^{-pOH} \text{ mol/L} \qquad [12\text{-}12]$$

For example, a solution in which the $[OH^-]$ is 1×10^{-4} mol/L has a pOH value of 4. If the solution has a pOH of 5, then the $[OH^-]$ is 1×10^{-5} mol/L.

As we discussed, the pH of a solution is generally calculated by taking the negative logarithm of the concentration of H_3O^+ ions in mol/L. Similarly, pOH is defined as

$$pOH = -\log [OH^-] \qquad [12\text{-}13]$$

In Section 12-7 we defined the dissociation constant of water as

$$K_w = [H_3O^+][OH^-] \qquad [12\text{-}9]$$

having a value of 1.0×10^{-14} at 25°C. If we substitute Equations 12-10 and 12-12 into Equation 12-9 and take the negative logarithm of both sides, we obtain the following relationship between pH and pOH in any aqueous solution at 25°C:

$$pH + pOH = 14 \qquad [12\text{-}14]$$

Thus, a solution with a pH of 7 also has a pOH of 7. The relationship between $[H_3O^+]$, pH, pOH and $[OH^-]$ is shown in Table 12-4.

TABLE 12-3
APPROXIMATE pH OF SOME COMMON LIQUIDS

Liquid	pH
1.0 mol/L HCl	0
0.1 mol/L HCl	1.0
Gastric juice	2.0
Lemon juice	2.3
Vinegar	2.8
0.1 mol/L CH$_3$COOH	2.9
Soft drinks	3.0
Apple juice	3.1
Grapefruit juice	3.1
Orange juice	3.5
Tomato juice	4.2
Banana (fluid)	4.6
Rain water	5.6
Milk	6.5
Pure water	7.0
Egg	7.8
0.1 mol/L NaHCO$_3$ (baking soda)	8.4
Sea water	8.5
Milk of magnesia (Mg(OH)$_2$)	10.5
0.1 mol/L NH$_3$(*aq*)	11.1
0.1 mol/L NaOH	13.0
1.0 mol/L NaOH	14.0

TABLE 12-4
RELATIONSHIP BETWEEN [H$_3$O$^+$], pH, pOH and [OH$^-$]

[H$_3$O$^+$]	pH	pOH	[OH$^-$]	Solution
10^{-3} mol/L	3	11	10^{-11} mol/L	acidic
10^{-7} mol/L	7	7	10^{-7} mol/L	neutral
10^{-9} mol/L	9	5	10^{-5} mol/L	basic

EXAMPLE 12-2
Calculating the pH, pOH and [OH$^-$] of an Acid
Find the pH, pOH and $[OH^-]$ of a 0.000 10 mol/L HCl solution. HCl is 100% dissociated.

Swimming-Pool Maintenance
Hypochlorous acid (HClO) is added to swimming-pool water to kill bacteria. The hypochlorite ion (OCl^-) kills bacteria by reacting with and oxidizing specific chemicals within the bacteria. The amount of hypochlorite ion in the water depends on the pH of the water. The hypochlorous acid equilibrium is

$$HOCl(aq) + H_2O(l) \rightleftharpoons$$
$$H_3O^+(aq) + OCl^-(aq)$$

If the pH of the pool drops, this means that the H_3O^+ ion concentration has increased. As a result, the equilibrium shifts left, decreasing the amount of OCl^- available to kill bacteria. Adding a reagent that increases the pool pH causes the equilibrium to shift to the right, increasing the amount of OCl^- and allowing more bacteria to be destroyed.

SOLUTION

1. Express the concentration of HCl in exponential form:
$$[HCl] = 0.000\ 10\ mol/L = 1.0 \times 10^{-4}\ mol/L$$

Since HCl dissociates to give one mole of H_3O^+ ions for each mole of HCl, the concentration of H_3O^+ ions equals the original concentration of HCl:
$$[H_3O^+] = 1.0 \times 10^{-4}\ mol/L$$

2. Substitute the $[H_3O^+]$ in Equation 12-11 and solve for pH:
$$pH = -\log (1.0 \times 10^{-4}) = -(-4.00) = 4.00$$

3. Substitute the pH value obtained in step 2 into Equation 12-14 and solve for pOH:
$$pOH = 14.00 - 4.00 = 10.00$$

4. Substitute the pOH into Equation 12-12 to obtain the $[OH^-]$:
$$[OH^-] = 10^{-pOH}\ mol/L = 1.0 \times 10^{-10}\ mol/L$$

Calculating the pH of a Base Using K_w
Rather than use pOH as an intermediate step in determining pH, we can use K_w instead. In Example 12-3, $[OH^-] = 0.003\ 25\ mol/L$. Using K_w, we can find $[H_3O^+]$:

$$[H_3O^+][OH^-] = 1.0 \times 10^{-14}$$
$$[H_3O^+] = \frac{1.0 \times 10^{-14}}{[OH^-]}$$
$$= \frac{1.0 \times 10^{-14}}{0.003\ 25}$$
$$= 3.08 \times 10^{-12}\ mol/L$$

$$pH = -\log [H_3O^+]$$
$$= -\log (3.08 \times 10^{-12})$$
$$= 11.511$$

EXAMPLE 12-3
Calculating the pH of a Base
Find the pH of a 0.003 25 mol/L NaOH solution. NaOH is 100% dissociated.

SOLUTION

1. Because NaOH is a strong base that completely dissociates, the $[OH^-]$ is equal to the [NaOH]. Express the $[OH^-]$ in exponential form:
$$[OH^-] = 0.003\ 25\ mol/L = 3.25 \times 10^{-3}\ mol/L$$

2. Calculate the pOH using Equation 12-13:
$$pOH = -\log (3.25 \times 10^{-3}) = -(-2.488) = 2.488$$

3. Calculate the pH by substituting the pOH into Equation 12-14:
$$pOH = 14.000 - 2.488 = 11.512$$

EXAMPLE 12-4
Calculating the Hydronium Ion Concentration
What is the H_3O^+ ion concentration of a solution that has a pH of 3.62?

SOLUTION

Substitute the pH value into Equation 12-10 and solve for $[H_3O^+]$:

$$[H_3O^+] = 10^{-3.62} \text{ mol/L}$$

Calculate the expression $10^{-3.62}$ using the 10^x function of your calculator, where x is replaced by -3.62. If your calculator does not have this function, you can use the *INV log* function instead.

The $[H_3O^+]$ of a solution with a pH of 3.62 is 2.4×10^{-4} mol/L.

FOLLOW-UP PROBLEMS

1. Determine the $[OH^-]$, $[H_3O^+]$, pOH and pH of a 0.001 mol/L KOH solution. KOH is 100% dissociated.
2. What is the $[H_3O^+]$, $[OH^-]$, pH and pOH of a 0.045 mol/L HCl solution?
3. What is the $[H_3O^+]$ of a solution having a pH of 3.4?

Answers:

1. $[OH^-] = 1 \times 10^{-3}$ mol/L; $[H_3O^+] = 1 \times 10^{-11}$ mol/L; pOH = 3; pH = 11
2. $[H_3O^+] = 4.5 \times 10^{-2}$ mol/L; $[OH^-] = 2.2 \times 10^{-13}$ mol/L; pH = 1.35; pOH = 12.65
3. 4×10^{-4} mol/L

We are now able to investigate the quantitative aspects of strong acids and strong bases in solution to calculate the $[H_3O^+]$ and, hence, the pH of the solution. In Section 12-10 we will apply the equilibrium law to solutions of weak acids and bases to obtain a dissociation constant that we can use to calculate the $[H_3O^+]$, the pH and the percentage dissociation of the solute.

COSMETICS AND pH VALUES

Many cosmetic products are advertised as "pH balanced." The question that arises from such a claim is whether these products actually benefit the consumer or whether they are merely a successful marketing ploy designed to benefit the manufacturer.

Adult skin has a pH range between 5 and 6. This acid pH results from the excretion of lactic acid from the sweat glands in the skin.

The pH level of the skin is important, since the thin layer of acid on the skin offers protection against bacterial infection. The bacteria *Propionibacterium acnes*, however, has the ability to somewhat modify the acid medium on the skin and can readily propagate, leading to the condition *acne vulgaris*.

If you get ill, the pH of your skin changes and becomes more alkaline (pH increases). As a result, your skin may dry out, and the

Propionibacterium populations increase. When your health returns, your skin regains its normal, healthy, acidic glow.

Excessive use of certain types of soaps may also change the skin's pH. Cosmetics, including soaps, shaving lotions and shampoos, can alter the structure and function of the skin. Alkaline soaps, made from the saponification of animal or vegetable fats, have been used for thousands of years. In the 1940s, syndet bars, which contain synthetic detergent cleansers, appeared on the market. At that time, pH levels in soaps had been linked to skin irritation. Because the pH of the syndet bars could be adjusted much closer to that of the skin (7–9), while the older alkaline soaps had higher pH levels (9.0–10.5), the manufacturers of the syndet bars claimed that their soaps were milder and caused less skin irritation. These claims, however, were misleading: normal skin pH is rapidly restored after regular washing with an alkaline soap, since the skin has a natural buffering capacity. Although cleansing with a high-pH soap puts stress on this buffering system, the skin is not subject to long-lasting alterations of pH levels and will return to normal pH after a period of time (minutes to hours). In addition, buffered, acidic cleansing creams can help the skin return to its normal pH level more rapidly. Recent studies have found that, in fact, skin irritations caused by either alkaline soaps

or syndet bars are more related to the specific composition of the soap rather than its pH.

Shaving can leave the skin quite alkaline, and the skin recovers its normal acidity more slowly. As a result, small amounts of weak acids, such as benzoic acid or boric acid, are often added to aftershave lotions to neutralize this alkalinity and to help restore the normal pH more quickly.

Shampoos contain water, detergents, thickeners and fragrances and, in some cases, additives such as allantoin, calcium pantothenate and collagen. Hair is made of long strands of protein. The sebaceous gland, located at the base of the hair, secretes a waxy substance that coats the hair to prevent water loss. The primary aim of shampoo is to remove dirt and excess sebaceous gland secretions, while still maintaining the oils that make the hair look shiny and full of life. Hair conditioners replace some of the oils removed by shampoos.

Hair can be damaged chemically, with hair dyes and bleaches, or mechanically, with hair dryers and curling irons. Although very acidic (low-pH) shampoos containing hydrolyzed animal proteins can repair split ends, most commercial shampoos (pH range between 5.5 and 7.0) do not. Conditioners containing protein repair split ends by literally gluing the ends together.

Alkaline (high-pH) shampoos may crack the surface of the hair, making the hair look dull and causing split ends. Dermatologists usually recommend neutral or slightly acidic shampoos for badly damaged hair. Studies have shown that shampoos with a pH range of 5.5 to 7.0 will not damage the hair and may even counteract mild damage caused by hair dyes and bleaches.

Healthy human skin has certain protective mechanisms that control its pH value. Therefore, it would seem that products that are pH balanced probably do not benefit the skin to any appreciable extent. This reasoning, however, is not likely to dissuade manufacturers from claiming that their pH-balanced products are better than unbalanced products. Consumers should therefore give credence to the Latin expression, *caveat emptor*, or "buyer beware!"

12-9

Solutions of Strong Acids and Bases

Strong acids and bases are strong electrolytes with a high degree of dissociation.

If we use the symbol A^- to represent the anion of a strong acid, then the general equation for the dissociation in aqueous solution can be written as

$$HA(aq) + H_2O(l) \longrightarrow H_3O^+(aq) + A^-(aq)$$

In this strong-acid system, we assume that the equilibrium is completely displaced to the right; that is, the dissociation is complete. In other words, all strong acids are assumed to be completely converted to H_3O^+ ions. This means that H_3O^+ ions represent the strongest acid that can exist in significant concentration in aqueous solution.

The strongest base found in water solution is OH^- ions. The oxide ions (O^{2-}), amide ions (NH_2^-) and other bases stronger than OH^- ions react completely with water and produce OH^- ions:

$$O^{2-} + H_2O \longrightarrow 2OH^-$$

and

$$NH_2^- + H_2O \longrightarrow OH^- + NH_3(g)$$

It is relatively easy to calculate the hydronium ion concentration and pH of a solution of a strong acid or base. Since a strong monoprotic acid is completely dissociated in dilute solution, the H_3O^+ ion concentration equals the original concentration of the acid. For example, in a 1.0×10^{-3} mol/L HCl solution, the concentrations of the different species are

$$[Cl^-] = 1.0 \times 10^{-3} \text{ mol/L}$$
$$[H_3O^+] = 1.0 \times 10^{-3} \text{ mol/L}$$
$$[OH^-] = 1.0 \times 10^{-11}$$

The pH of the solution is 3.00 and the pOH is 11.00. In this solution, we assumed that the H_3O^+ ions that resulted from the dissociation of water did not significantly affect the pH of the solution. For this reason, we did not consider the dissociation of water in our calculations. Actually, the $[H_3O^+]$ from the HCl shifts the water equilibrium,

$$H_2O + H_2O \rightleftharpoons H_3O^+ + OH^-$$

to the left and decreases the dissociation of water. Because the $[H_3O^+]$ contributed by the HCl (10^{-3} mol/L) is far greater than that from water, which is only 10^{-7} mol/L by self-dissociation, we can assume that the $[H_3O^+]$ from the dissociation of water is negligible.

12-10
Solutions of Weak Monoprotic Acids

Weak acids do not completely dissociate in solution. The acid dissociation constant, K_a, is used to quantitatively determine the relative strength of a weak acid.

A weak acid reacts incompletely with water to form an equilibrium system between the undissociated molecules of the acid and the

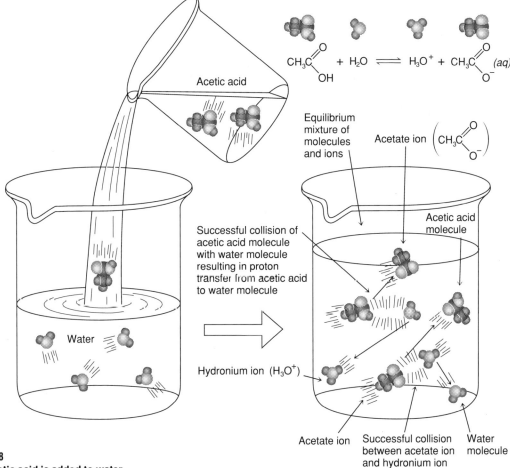

Figure 12-8
When acetic acid is added to water, collisions between the CH₃COOH and H₂O molecules occur. When the molecules are oriented properly and have enough kinetic energy, a proton transfer occurs, resulting in the formation of acetate ions (CH₃COO⁻) and hydronium ions (H₃O⁺). In a weak acid, the acid proton is rather tightly bound, so few collisions are energetic enough to result in proton transfer. Collisions between acetate ions and hydronium ions can also result in a proton transfer. This results in the formation of acetic acid and water molecules (lower right). An equilibrium is established when the rates of the two proton-transfer reactions are equal. When equilibrium is reached at a fixed temperature, there is a constant number of all species (CH₃COOH, CH₃COO⁻, H₃O⁺, H₂O).

ions produced from the reaction with water (Fig. 12-8). Applying the law of chemical equilibrium to this equilibrium system yields a dissociation constant that quantitatively expresses the strength of the acid. A general equation for the dissociation of a weak monoprotic acid is

$$HX(aq) + H_2O(l) \rightleftharpoons H_3O^+(aq) + X^-(aq) \qquad [12\text{-}15]$$

where X^- represents the anion of the weak acid. The equilibrium constant expression for Equation 12-15 is

$$K = \frac{[H_3O^+][X^-]}{[HX][H_2O]}$$

In dilute solutions of acids and bases, the concentration of water is essentially constant (approximately 55.6 mol/L) and can be combined with K to give what is called the *dissociation constant*, K_d. The *acid dissociation constant* (K_a) for a reaction between a weak acid and water is also called the *acid ionization constant* and is expressed as

$$K_a = \frac{[H_3O^+][X^-]}{[HX]} \qquad [12\text{-}16]$$

The dissociation constants for a number of acids are listed in Table 12-5. Note that there are no K_a values listed for the acids stronger than H_3O^+; because of their very high degree of dissociation, their denominators in Equation 12-16 would approach zero and result in an infinitely large K_a. The magnitude of the constants reflects the relative tendencies of the species on the left to give up protons to water. Note that K_a can be used as the dissociation constant only if the weak acid donates a proton to water; that is, K_a only applies to solutions of weak acids in water.

The larger the K_a value, the stronger the acid.

TABLE 12-5
DISSOCIATION CONSTANTS FOR SELECTED ACIDS (25°C)

Acid	Reaction	Conjugate Base	K_a
Perchloric acid	$HClO_4 + H_2O \longrightarrow H_3O^+ + ClO_4^-$	perchlorate ion	large
Hydriodic acid	$HI + H_2O \longrightarrow H_3O^+ + I^-$	iodide ion	large
Hydrobromic acid	$HBr + H_2O \longrightarrow H_3O^+ + Br^-$	bromide ion	large
Hydrochloric acid	$HCl + H_2O \longrightarrow H_3O^+ + Cl^-$	chloride ion	large
Nitric acid	$HNO_3 + H_2O \longrightarrow H_3O^+ + NO_3^-$	nitrate ion	large
Sulfuric acid	$H_2SO_4 + H_2O \longrightarrow H_3O^+ + HSO_4^-$	hydrogen sulfate ion	large
Iodic acid	$HIO_3 + H_2O \rightleftharpoons H_3O^+ + IO_3^-$	iodate ion	1.7×10^{-1}
Nitrous acid	$HNO_2 + H_2O \rightleftharpoons H_3O^+ + NO_2^-$	nitrite ion	4.6×10^{-4}
Hydrofluoric acid	$HF + H_2O \rightleftharpoons H_3O^+ + F^-$	fluoride ion	3.5×10^{-4}
Formic acid	$HCOOH + H_2O \rightleftharpoons H_3O^+ + HCOO^-$	formate ion	1.8×10^{-4}
Benzoic acid	$C_6H_5COOH + H_2O \rightleftharpoons H_3O^+ + C_6H_5COO^-$	benzoate ion	6.5×10^{-5}
Acetic acid	$CH_3COOH + H_2O \rightleftharpoons H_3O^+ + CH_3COO^-$	acetate ion	1.8×10^{-5}
Hypochlorous acid	$HClO + H_2O \rightleftharpoons H_3O^+ + ClO^-$	hypochlorite ion	3.0×10^{-8}
Boric acid	$H_3BO_3 + H_2O \rightleftharpoons H_3O^+ + H_2BO_3^-$	dihydrogen borate ion	7.3×10^{-10}
Ammonium ion	$NH_4^+ + H_2O \rightleftharpoons H_3O^+ + NH_3$	ammonia	5.6×10^{-10}
Hydrocyanic acid	$HCN + H_2O \rightleftharpoons H_3O^+ + CN^-$	cyanide ion	4.9×10^{-10}
Water	$H_2O + H_2O \rightleftharpoons H_3O^+ + OH^-$	hydroxide ion	1.0×10^{-14}

We can use K_a to determine the equilibrium concentrations of the species present in the solution of a weak acid. Knowledge of the H_3O^+ ion concentration enables us to calculate the pH and pOH of the solution. These calculations, as well as calculations of the percentage dissociation of the solutes, are illustrated in the following examples.

EXAMPLE 12-5
Calculating K_a from the pH

At 25°C, a 0.10 mol/L solution of acetic acid is prepared and found to have a pH of 2.87. Calculate the K_a of acetic acid.

SOLUTION

1. Write the dissociation reaction for acetic acid and the expression for K_a:

$$CH_3COOH + H_2O \rightleftharpoons H_3O^+ + CH_3COO^-$$

$$K_a = \frac{[H_3O^+][CH_3COO^-]}{[CH_3COOH]}$$

2. Calculate the $[H_3O^+]$ and $[CH_3COO^-]$. From Equation 12-10 we know that $[H_3O^+] = 10^{-pH}$ mol/L. Therefore,

$$[H_3O^+] = 10^{-2.87} \text{ mol/L} = 1.4 \times 10^{-3} \text{ mol/L}$$

From the dissociation reaction we can see that the number of moles of H_3O^+ produced is equal to the number of moles of CH_3COO^- produced. Therefore,

$$[H_3O^+] = [CH_3COO^-] = 1.4 \times 10^{-3} \text{ mol/L}$$

3. Calculate the K_a value using Equation 12-16. A concentration table, shown below, can be used to simplify the calculations.

	CH$_3$COOH + H$_2$O $\rightleftharpoons$ H$_3$O$^+$ + CH$_3$COO$^-$		
Initial concentration (mol/L)	0.10	0	0
Change in concentration due to dissociation reaction (mol/L)	−0.0014	+0.0014	+0.0014
Equilibrium concentration (mol/L)	(0.10 − 0.0014) = 0.099	0.0014	0.0014

Substitute the equilibrium concentration values into Equation 12-16:

$$K_a = \frac{(0.0014)(0.0014)}{(0.099)} = 2.0 \times 10^{-5}$$

Thus, the acid dissociation constant for acetic acid is 2.0×10^{-5}.

FOLLOW-UP PROBLEM

Butanoic acid is responsible for the smell of rancid butter. At 25°C, the pH of a 0.45 mol/L butanoic acid (C_3H_7COOH) solution is 2.90. Calculate the K_a for butanoic acid.

Answer: 3.8×10^{-6}

EXAMPLE 12-6
Calculating [H_3O^+] and pH From K_a

Calculate the hydronium ion concentration and the pH of 0.25 mol/L hydrocyanic acid at 25°C. K_a for HCN is 4.9×10^{-10} from Table 12-5.

SOLUTION

1. Write the dissociation reaction for hydrocyanic acid and the expression for K_a:

$$HCN + H_2O \rightleftharpoons H_3O^+ + CN^-$$

$$K_a = \frac{[H_3O^+][CN^-]}{[HCN]} = 4.9 \times 10^{-10}$$

2. Calculate the [H_3O^+] and [CN^-]. Let x mol/L represent the [H_3O^+]. Since one mole of CN^- is formed as each mole of H_3O^+ is produced, x mol/L also represents the [CN^-]. The concentration of undissociated HCN that remains at equilibrium is $(0.25 - x)$. Therefore,

$$[H_3O^+] = x$$
$$[CN^-] = x$$
$$[HCN] = (0.25 - x)$$

Although we could substitute these concentration values into Equation 12-16 and solve for x using the solution methods for a quadratic equation, there is a simpler method for calculating x. By substituting the concentration values into the expression for K_a, we see that

$$4.9 \times 10^{-10} = \frac{x^2}{0.25 - x}$$

We can see that the order of x will be about 10^{-5}, which is very small compared with the initial concentration of HCN. We can, therefore, assume that x is much smaller than 0.25 mol/L and can be ignored with respect to the concentration of HCN at equilibrium. Thus, the [HCN] is 0.25 mol/L at equilibrium.

For most purposes, except when accuracy is essential, we can omit the x value relative to the acid concentration when x is much less than the initial acid concentration. For more accurate values of x, the equation must be solved as a quadratic equation.

In general, a 5% error is permitted in our calculation. If x is 5% of the initial acid concentration, [HX], and is being ignored,

$$K_a = \frac{(5 \times 10^{-2})^2 [HX]^2}{[HX]}$$

$$\frac{[HX]}{K_a} = 400$$

Therefore, for x to be negligible with respect to the initial acid concentration, the ratio of initial acid concentration to K_a has to be greater than 400.

3. Substitute the concentration values into the K_a expression and solve for x:

$$4.9 \times 10^{-10} = \frac{(x)(x)}{(0.25)}$$
$$x^2 = (4.9 \times 10^{-10})(0.25)$$
$$x = 1.1 \times 10^{-5}$$

Thus, the [H_3O^+] is 1.1×10^{-5} mol/L

4. Substitute [H_3O^+] into Equation 12-11 to calculate pH:

$$pH = -\log [H_3O^+]$$
$$= -\log (1.1 \times 10^{-5})$$
$$= -(-4.96)$$
$$= 4.96$$

FOLLOW-UP PROBLEM

Calculate (a) the $[H_3O^+]$ and (b) the pH of 0.50 mol/L hydrocyanic acid at 25°C.

Answers: (a) 1.6×10^{-5} mol/L, (b) 4.79

EXAMPLE 12-7
Calculating the Percentage Dissociation of a Weak Acid

What is the percentage dissociation of 0.035 mol/L benzoic acid at 25°C? K_a for benzoic acid is 6.5×10^{-5} from Table 12-5.

SOLUTION

1. Write the dissociation reaction for benzoic acid and the expression for K_a:

$$C_6H_5COOH + H_2O \rightleftharpoons H_3O^+ + C_6H_5COO^-$$

$$K_a = \frac{[H_3O^+][C_6H_5COO^-]}{[C_6H_5COOH]} = 6.5 \times 10^{-5}$$

2. To simplify the calculation shown in Example 12-6, we will use a concentration table as we did in Example 12-5. Let x mol/L represent the $[H_3O^+]$.

	$C_6H_5COOH + H_2O \rightleftharpoons H_3O^+ + C_6H_5COO^-$		
Initial concentration (mol/L)	0.035	0	0
Change in concentration due to dissociation (mol/L)	$-x$	$+x$	$+x$
Equilibrium concentration (mol/L)	$(0.035 - x)$	x	x

In this example, the ratio of the initial acid concentration to K_a is about 540. Because the ratio is greater than 400, we can ignore x when calculating the equilibrium acid concentration. Thus, the equilibrium concentration of C_6H_5COOH is assumed to be 0.035 mol/L.

3. Substitute the concentration values into the K_a expression and solve for x:

$$6.5 \times 10^{-5} = \frac{(x)(x)}{0.035}$$
$$x^2 = (6.5 \times 10^{-5})(0.035)$$
$$x = 1.5 \times 10^{-3}$$

Thus, the $[H_3O^+]$ equals 1.5×10^{-3} mol/L.

4. Calculate the percentage dissociation. Since the $[C_6H_5COOH]$ that is dissociated is equal to the $[H_3O^+]$ that is formed, the percentage dissociation can be calculated by the following relationship:

$$\% \text{ dissociation} = \frac{\text{amount of acid dissociated}}{\text{initial concentration of acid}} \times 100\%$$
$$= \frac{1.5 \times 10^{-3} \text{ mol/L}}{0.035 \text{ mol/L}} \times 100\%$$
$$= 4.3\%$$

Thus, only 4.3% of the C_6H_5COOH dissociates.

From the preceding examples, we can see that there are certain assumptions and simplifications that can be made in calculations involving weak acids:

- The $[H_3O^+]$ contributed from the dissociation of water is negligible.
- The $[H_3O^+]$ formed from the dissociation of the weak acid is negligible relative to the initial acid concentration and, thus, the concentration of the weak acid at equilibrium is equal to the initial concentration of the weak acid.

FOLLOW-UP PROBLEM
Calculate the percentage dissociation, at 25°C, of
a) 0.50 mol/L formic acid (HCOOH)
b) 0.025 mol/L hypochlorous acid (HClO)

Answers: (a) **1.9%** (b) **0.11%**

THE BREWING INDUSTRY AND pH

The brewing of beer and ale uses the same chemical procedures found in such industries as bread making and cheese production as well as in many pharmaceutical processes. Although the chemistry of beer making has been in use for thousands of years, it has only been understood in detail for the past few decades.

Beer is made by the fermentation of yeast and barley. Since barley is mostly starch and because yeasts cannot ferment starch, the barley is allowed to sprout in a process called *malting*. In this process, the starch molecule is split into smaller sugar units, which are more easily fermented by the yeast. A simple equation for the malting process is

$$C_{12}H_{22}O_{11} + H_2O \longrightarrow 2C_6H_{12}O_6$$
$$\text{starch} \qquad\qquad\quad \text{maltose}$$

During the soaking stages leading to the germination of the barley grain, limewater is added to maintain the correct alkalinity. Next, the malt is ground and mixed with water to form a thick mash whose pH is closely held to 5.6. This mash is subjected to various heating cycles, and many unconverted (or unmalted) grains are added to improve such qualities as clarity, flavour and foaming. At this stage, the brewery also adds its secret ingredients that will distinguish its brand from others on the market.

The *wort*, or liquid, that is finally drawn off the mash is what the yeast needs to make alcohol. At this stage, the wort is boiled with hops to give the brew a slightly bitter taste. Special yeasts are added to the wort, which has been deliberately aerated. In this enriched oxygen medium, the yeast grows rapidly, obtaining energy from some of the sugar in the wort and producing H_2O and

CO$_2$, but no alcohol. Eventually, all the oxygen in the wort is consumed, and the yeast, through anaerobic conversion, produces ethanol and carbon dioxide from the sugars:

$$C_6H_{12}O_6 \xrightarrow[\text{enzymes}]{\text{yeast}} 2C_2H_5OH + 2CO_2$$
$$\text{maltose} \qquad\qquad \text{ethanol} \qquad \text{carbon}$$
$$\text{(ethyl alcohol)} \quad \text{dioxide}$$

During this conversion period, pH meters constantly monitor and control the solution to maintain a pH between 5.1 and 5.3. This will ensure efficient and complete fermentation over a period of a few days. As with the making of bread, temperature plays an important role in the fermentation stage and must be closely controlled.

Techniques at this stage lead to the production of ale, stout, beer or lager. The ales and stouts use a higher fermentation temperature (15° to 20° C). Beers need temperatures of 10° to 15° C, while lagers require 0° to 10° C. At these lower temperatures fermentation may take up to several months.

The final step in the brewing process is the addition of special enzymes that act on the dissolved protein and control the amount of foam. The pH is corrected to an optimum of 4.1.

The brewing process involves enzymes and fermentation products that are still not completely known to the biochemist, but seem to be adequately controlled through the skills of the brewmaster at each stage of the brewing. The role of the chemist in the brewing cycle is to ensure correct pH levels, since clarity, smoothness and taste are directly influenced by the pH at the various stages.

Solutions of Weak Bases

Weak bases do not react completely with water to form hydroxide ions. The base dissociation constant, K_b, is used to quantitatively determine the relative strength of a weak base. A weak base, like a weak acid, reacts incompletely in water to form an equilibrium system between the undissociated molecules of the base and the ions produced during the reaction with water. The *base dissociation constant* (K_b) quantitatively determines the relative ability of a weak base to accept a proton from water. This constant can be determined experimentally or derived by combining the water dissociation constant (K_w) with the dissociation constant of the conjugate acid, K_a. Consider a solution made by adding ammonia to water:

$$NH_3(g) + H_2O(l) \rightleftharpoons NH_4^+(aq) + OH^-(aq) \qquad [12\text{-}17]$$

The equilibrium law expression for this reaction is

$$K_b = \frac{[NH_4^+][OH^-]}{[NH_3]}$$

At 25°C, K_b is found to be 1.8×10^{-5}. Let us see how we could calculate the value of K_b by combining the water constant, K_w, with the K_a for NH_4^+ ions, the conjugate acid of NH_3. The fact that we can obtain K_b for Equation 12-17 by combining K_w and K_a implies that we can obtain Equation 12-17 by combining the equations for the ammonium ion and water from Table 12-5:

$$NH_4^+ + H_2O \rightleftharpoons H_3O^+ + NH_3 \qquad K_a = 5.6 \times 10^{-10}$$
$$H_2O + H_2O \rightleftharpoons H_3O^+ + OH^- \qquad K_w = 1.0 \times 10^{-14}$$

We must first reverse the top equation to get NH_3 on the left-hand side so that when we add the equations, it appears as a reactant. The constant for the reverse reaction is the reciprocal of that for the forward reaction. Therefore, if we add

$$NH_3 + H_3O^+ \rightleftharpoons NH_4^+ + H_2O \qquad K = \frac{1}{K_a} = \frac{1}{5.6 \times 10^{-10}}$$

to

$$H_2O + H_2O \rightleftharpoons H_3O^+ + OH^- \qquad K_w = 1.0 \times 10^{-14}$$

we obtain

$$NH_3 + H_2O \rightleftharpoons NH_4^+ + OH^-$$

The net equation is the same as Equation 12-17. It can be shown that the dissociation constant for the net equation is the product of the constants for the equations that were added. Thus, the dissociation constant for any of the conjugate bases listed in Table 12-5 can be obtained by applying the expression

$$K_b = \frac{1}{K_a} \times K_w = \frac{K_w}{K_a}$$

In the case of NH_3, the value of the constant is

$$K_b = \frac{1.0 \times 10^{-14}}{5.6 \times 10^{-10}} = 1.8 \times 10^{-5}$$

The magnitude of this constant shows that NH_3 is a *relatively weak base*. That is, it does not have a great tendency to accept protons from water. In solution it exists largely in molecular form. This is consistent with our observation that NH_3 solutions are relatively poor conductors of an electric current. The base dissociation constant can be used to determine the concentration of the OH^- ions in an NH_3 solution of given concentration.

The class of organic compounds known as *amines* contain nitrogen and behave much like NH_3 in aqueous solution. These compounds are often referred to as *organic bases*. One of the simplest is aminomethane (methyl amine, CH_3NH_2). When methyl amine is added to water, the reaction is

$$CH_3NH_2(g) + H_2O(l) \rightleftharpoons CH_3NH_3^+(aq) + OH^-(aq)$$

Application of the equilibrium law yields

$$K_b = \frac{[CH_3NH_3^+][OH^-]}{[CH_3NH_2]}$$

It can be seen that the equation for the dissociation constant for an organic base is the same as that for the inorganic base, NH_3. The constants for a number of weak bases are listed in Table 12-6.

Amines

Amines are Brønsted bases that contain one or more N—H bonds. Like ammonia, amines are proton acceptors.

Amines of high molecular weights make up such drugs as amphetamine, caffeine, quinine and codeine.

amphetamine

Amines of low molecular weights are responsible for the odours that emanate from decaying plant and animal matter. One of these amines has been given the name *cadaverine* ($H_2N(CH_2)_5NH_2$), presumably because it is found in decaying flesh.

TABLE 12-6
DISSOCIATION CONSTANTS FOR SELECTED WEAK BASES (25°C)

Name	Formula	Reaction	K_b
Trimethylamine	$(CH_3)_3N$	$(CH_3)_3N + H_2O \rightleftharpoons (CH_3)_3NH^+ + OH^-$	7.4×10^{-5}
Ethanolamine	$HOC_2H_4NH_2$	$HOC_2H_4NH_2 + H_2O \rightleftharpoons HOC_2H_4NH_3^+ + OH^-$	3.2×10^{-5}
Ammonia	NH_3	$NH_3 + H_2O \rightleftharpoons NH_4^+ + OH^-$	1.8×10^{-5}
Hydrazine	N_2H_4	$N_2H_4 + H_2O \rightleftharpoons N_2H_5^+ + OH^-$	9.6×10^{-7}
Hydroxylamine	$HONH_2$	$HONH_2 + H_2O \rightleftharpoons HONH_3^+ + OH^-$	6.6×10^{-9}
Pyridine	C_5H_5N	$C_5H_5N + H_2O \rightleftharpoons C_5H_5NH^+ + OH^-$	1.5×10^{-9}
Aniline	$C_6H_5NH_2$	$C_6H_5NH_2 + H_2O \rightleftharpoons C_6H_5NH_3^+ + OH^-$	4.1×10^{-10}

12-12
Solutions of Polyprotic Acids

A polyprotic acid contains more than one ionizable hydrogen and dissociates one step at a time. It is possible to calculate separate equilibrium constants for the ionization of each hydrogen.

Acids with more than one proton (hydrogen ion) per molecule that

sulfuric acid
(hydrogen sulfate, H_2SO_4)

phosphoric acid
(hydrogen phosphate, H_3PO_4)

can be transferred to solvent molecules are called *polyprotic acids*. Examples of some polyprotic acids are shown in the margin. The protons that can be donated are usually shown first in the formula.

When a solution of a weak polyprotic acid such as phosphoric acid (H_3PO_4) is analysed, it is found to be an equilibrium mixture of H_2O, $H_2PO_4^-$, HPO_4^{2-}, PO_4^{3-} and H_3O^+. The observed concentrations of each species can be explained by assuming that H_3PO_4 dissociates in a series of steps and that there is an equilibrium between the species involved in each step. The steps are:

1. $H_3PO_4 + H_2O \rightleftharpoons H_3O^+ + H_2PO_4^-$

2. $H_2PO_4^- + H_2O \rightleftharpoons H_3O^+ + HPO_4^{2-}$

3. $HPO_4^{2-} + H_2O \rightleftharpoons H_3O^+ + PO_4^{3-}$

The first step of dissociation always proceeds to a greater extent than subsequent steps. Thus, polyprotic acids dissociate to a lesser extent in each step because it is harder for an ion such as HPO_4^{2-}, which is already negatively charged, to release a proton than it is for a neutral ion such as H_3PO_4. This means that in phosphoric acid, most of the hydrogen ions in the solution are derived from the primary dissociation of H_3PO_4. The concentration of PO_4^{3-} ions from the third dissociation step is observed to be extremely low.

For each dissociation step, we can calculate a dissociation constant by using Equation 12-16. Table 12-7 lists the successive dissociation constants for some polyprotic acids. These dissociation constants can be used to derive pH and [H_3O^+], as is shown in Example 12-8.

TABLE 12-7
DISSOCIATION CONSTANTS FOR SELECTED POLYPROTIC ACIDS (25°C)

Name of Acid	Reaction for K_1	K_1	K_2	K_3
Sulfuric acid	$H_2SO_4 + H_2O \rightleftharpoons H_3O^+ + HSO_4^-$	very large	1.0×10^{-2}	
Oxalic acid	$H_2C_2O_4 + H_2O \rightleftharpoons H_3O^+ + HC_2O_4^-$	5.6×10^{-2}	5.4×10^{-5}	
Sulfurous acid	$H_2SO_3 + H_2O \rightleftharpoons H_3O^+ + HSO_3^-$	1.2×10^{-2}	6.6×10^{-8}	
Phosphoric acid	$H_3PO_4 + H_2O \rightleftharpoons H_3O^+ + H_2PO_4^-$	7.1×10^{-3}	6.3×10^{-8}	4.5×10^{-13}
Carbonic acid	$H_2CO_3 + H_2O \rightleftharpoons H_3O^+ + HCO_3^-$	4.5×10^{-7}	4.7×10^{-11}	
Hydrosulfuric acid	$H_2S + H_2O \rightleftharpoons H_3O^+ + HS^-$	1.0×10^{-7}	1.3×10^{-13}	
Arsenic acid	$H_3AsO_4 + H_2O \rightleftharpoons H_3O^+ + H_2AsO_4^-$	5.6×10^{-3}	1.7×10^{-7}	4.0×10^{-12}
Malonic acid	$H_2C_3H_2O_4 + H_2O \rightleftharpoons H_3O^+ + HC_3H_2O_4^-$	1.4×10^{-3}	2.0×10^{-6}	
Phthalic acid	$H_2C_8H_4O_4 + H_2O \rightleftharpoons H_3O^+ + HC_8H_4O_4^-$	1.1×10^{-3}	3.9×10^{-6}	
Maleic acid	$H_2C_4H_2O_4 + H_2O \rightleftharpoons H_3O^+ + HC_4H_2O_4^-$	1.4×10^{-2}	8.6×10^{-7}	

FOLLOW-UP PROBLEM

Write equations representing the dissociation of each of the following acids or bases in aqueous solution. Use a single arrow in the case of a strong acid or base, and a double arrow to represent the equilibrium condition that exists in the solution of a weak acid or base. Show each step of dissociation for polyprotic acids.

a) KOH

b) H_3AsO_4

c) $HClO_4$

d) HCN

e) $C_6H_5NH_2$ (a weak base)

EXAMPLE 12-8
Calculating the pH and Equilibrium Ion Concentrations of Polyprotic Acids

Carbonic acid (H_2CO_3) is a major component of soda. What is the pH of 0.1 mol/L H_2CO_3? What are the equilibrium concentrations of H_2CO_3, HCO_3^- and CO_3^{2-}? K_1 of carbonic acid is 4.5×10^{-7} and K_2 is 4.7×10^{-11} from Table 12-7.

SOLUTION

1. Write the two dissociation reactions and their K expressions:

$$H_2CO_3 + H_2O \rightleftharpoons H_3O^+(aq) + HCO_3^-(aq)$$

$$K_1 = \frac{[H_3O^+][HCO_3^-]}{[H_2CO_3]} = 4.5 \times 10^{-7}$$

$$HCO_3^-(aq) + H_2O \rightleftharpoons H_3O^+(aq) + CO_3^{2-}(aq)$$

$$K_2 = \frac{[H_3O^+][CO_3^{2-}]}{[HCO_3^-]} = 4.7 \times 10^{-11}$$

Note that the K_1 value is approximately 10^4 times greater than K_2. Because each successive acid dissociation constant is approximately 10^{-4} times the value of the preceding constant, the $[H_3O^+]$ and pH will be largely determined by the first dissociation reaction.

2. Use a concentration table to calculate the ion concentrations and pH for the first reaction. Let x mol/L represent the $[H_3O^+]$.

	$H_2CO_3 + H_2O \rightleftharpoons H_3O^+ + HCO_3^-$		
Initial concentration (mol/L)	0.1	0	0
Change in concentration due to dissociation (mol/L)	$-x$	$+x$	$+x$
Equilibrium concentration (mol/L)	$(0.1 - x)$	x	x

Because the $[H_2CO_3]$ is not very small and the constants K_1 and K_2 differ by a sufficient amount (a factor of 100 or more), we can simplify the calculations and assume that the value of x will have no effect on the concentration of the acid. Therefore, we can assume the equilibrium concentration of H_2CO_3 to be 0.1 mol/L.

Substitute the equilibrium concentrations into the K_1 expression and solve for x:

$$4.5 \times 10^{-7} = \frac{(x)(x)}{(0.1)}$$
$$x^2 = (4.5 \times 10^{-7})(0.1)$$
$$x = 2.1 \times 10^{-4}$$

Thus,

$$[H_3O^+] = [HCO_3^-] = 2.1 \times 10^{-4} \text{ mol/L}$$

Substitute this value into Equation 12-11 and solve for pH:

$$pH = -\log (2.1 \times 10^{-4})$$
$$= 3.7$$

3. Substitute the concentration of HCO_3^- and H_3O^+ calculated in step 2 into a concentration table, and calculate the concentration of CO_3^{2-} formed during the second dissociation reaction. Let y mol/L represent the additional $[H_3O^+]$ that is formed.

	$HCO_3^- + H_2O \rightleftharpoons H_3O^+$	$+$	CO_3^{2-}
Initial concentration (mol/L)	2.1×10^{-4}	2.1×10^{-4}	0
Change in concentration due to dissociation (mol/L)	$-y$	$2.1 \times 10^{-4} + y$	$+y$
Equilibrium concentration (mol/L)	$2.1 \times 10^{-4} - y$	$2.1 \times 10^{-4} + y$	y

As we previously noted, the second reaction occurs to a much smaller extent; thus, the amount of H_3O^+ and CO_3^{2-} produced is very small. As well, since K_2 is much smaller than K_1, we can omit y with respect to the calculations of $[HCO_3^-]$ and $[H_3O^+]$ at equilibrium.

4. Substitute the equilibrium concentrations into the K_2 expression:

$$4.7 \times 10^{-11} = \frac{(2.1 \times 10^{-4})(y)}{2.1 \times 10^{-4}}$$
$$y = 4.7 \times 10^{-11}$$

Thus,

$$[H_3O^+] = 4.7 \times 10^{-11} \text{ mol/L}$$

In summary, the equilibrium concentrations are:

$$[CH_2CO_3] = 0.1 \text{ mol/L}$$
$$[HCO_3^-] = 2.1 \times 10^{-4} \text{ mol/L}$$
$$[H_3O^+] = 2.1 \times 10^{-4} \text{ mol/L}$$
$$[CO_3^{2-}] = 4.7 \times 10^{-11} \text{ mol/L}$$

From the preceding example, we can make some general conclusions about the dissociation of a polyprotic acid (H_2A) when K_1 is at least 100 times greater than K_2:
- The $[H_3O^+]$ contributed from the second ionization step is negligible.
- The $[A^-]$ at equilibrium is equal to the value of K_2.

FOLLOW-UP PROBLEM

Calculate the $[HSO_3^-]$, $[SO_3^{2-}]$ and pH for 0.25 mol/L H_2SO_3.

Answer: $[HSO_3^-] = 5.5 \times 10^{-2}$ mol/L; pH = 1.26

Now that we have considered the equilibria of acid-base reactions, we can examine the cations and anions of salts that behave as acids and bases.

12-13
Solutions of Anions That Behave as Brønsted Bases

Anions of salts that are derived from weak acids hydrolyze to form weak, basic equilibrium systems.

An **anion** is a negatively charged ion or molecule formed when a neutral atom acquires an electron. We have already seen examples of anions (from the salts of weak acids) reacting as weak bases in aqueous solutions. For example, the cyanide ion (CN^-) is an anion derived from the reaction of the weak acid, hydrocyanic acid (HCN), with water:

$$HCN(aq) + H_2O(l) \rightleftharpoons CN^-(aq) + H_3O^+(aq)$$

This anion will hydrolyze in water and produce a measurable concentration of hydroxide ion:

$$CN^-(aq) + H_2O(l) \rightleftharpoons HCN(aq) + OH^-(aq)$$

Therefore, the CN^- ion acts as a base and accepts protons from water. The dissociation constant for this reaction is

$$K_{CN^-} = K_b = \frac{[HCN][OH^-]}{[CN^-]}$$

As was the case for NH_3 in Section 12-11, K_b can be calculated by combining the K_a constant for the acid (from Table 12-5) with the K_w constant for water:

$$K_b = \frac{K_w}{K_a} = \frac{1.0 \times 10^{-14}}{4.9 \times 10^{-10}} = 2.0 \times 10^{-5}$$

The reaction of ions with water is sometimes referred to as **hydrolysis**. This means the ions disturb the water equilibrium by reacting with either hydronium ions or hydroxide ions that are in equilibrium with water molecules. Decreasing the concentration of either the hydronium or hydroxide ions results in a solution that will be either basic or acidic. The constants for these reactions are often called *hydrolysis constants* and are symbolized as K_h rather than K_b. We will, however, use K_b to be consistent with the discussion above.

The constants for a number of ions that behave as Brønsted bases are listed in Table 12-8. The magnitude of the constant reflects the relative tendency of the species on the left to accept a proton from water.

The anions related to very strong acids (those with infinitely large K_a), such as HCl, HNO_3, HBr, HI and $HClO_4$, have very little tendency to accept protons and thus do not hydrolyze to any extent. Therefore, the anions do not disturb the water equilibrium. We may thus classify the anions Cl^-, NO_3^-, Br^-, I^- and ClO_4^- as very weak bases ($K_b = 0$) and assume that they do not appreciably affect the acidity of an aqueous solution.

TABLE 12-8
SELECTED ANIONS THAT BEHAVE AS BRØNSTED BASES

| Name | Formula | Reaction | | $K_b = \dfrac{K_w}{K_a}$ |
		Base	Conjugate Acid	
Oxide	O^{2-}	$O^{2-} + H_2O \rightleftharpoons OH^- + OH^-$		very large
Amide	NH_2^-	$NH_2^- + H_2O \rightleftharpoons NH_3 + OH^-$		very large
Sulfide	S^{2-}	$S^{2-} + H_2O \rightleftharpoons HS^- + OH^-$		7.7×10^{-2}
Phosphate	PO_4^{3-}	$PO_4^{3-} + H_2O \rightleftharpoons HPO_4^{2-} + OH^-$		2.2×10^{-2}
Arsenate	AsO_4^{3-}	$AsO_4^{3-} + H_2O \rightleftharpoons HAsO_4^{2-} + OH^-$		2.5×10^{-3}
Hypoiodite	IO^-	$IO^- + H_2O \rightleftharpoons HIO + OH^-$		4.3×10^{-4}
Carbonate	CO_3^{2-}	$CO_3^{2-} + H_2O \rightleftharpoons HCO_3^- + OH^-$		2.1×10^{-4}
Cyanide	CN^-	$CN^- + H_2O \rightleftharpoons HCN + OH^-$		2.0×10^{-5}
Hypobromite	BrO^-	$BrO^- + H_2O \rightleftharpoons HBrO + OH^-$		4.8×10^{-6}
Hypochlorite	ClO^-	$ClO^- + H_2O \rightleftharpoons HClO + OH^-$		3.3×10^{-7}
Sulfite	SO_3^{2-}	$SO_3^{2-} + H_2O \rightleftharpoons HSO_3^- + OH^-$		1.5×10^{-7}
Acetate	CH_3COO^-	$CH_3COO^- + H_2O \rightleftharpoons CH_3COOH + OH^-$		5.6×10^{-10}
Benzoate	$C_6H_5COO^-$	$C_6H_5COO^- + H_2O \rightleftharpoons C_6H_5COOH + OH^-$		1.6×10^{-10}
Formate	$HCOO^-$	$HCOO^- + H_2O \rightleftharpoons HCOOH + OH^-$		5.6×10^{-11}
Cyanate	CNO^-	$CNO^- + H_2O \rightleftharpoons HCNO + OH^-$		2.8×10^{-11}
Fluoride	F^-	$F^- + H_2O \rightleftharpoons HF + OH^-$		2.8×10^{-11}
Nitrite	NO_2^-	$NO_2^- + H_2O \rightleftharpoons HNO_2 + OH^-$		2.2×10^{-11}

EXAMPLE 12-9
Calculating the pH of an Anion That Undergoes Hydrolysis

What is the pH of a 0.1 mol/L NaCN solution?
K_b for CN^- is 2.0×10^{-5} from Table 12-8.

SOLUTION

1. Write the dissociation reaction for the salt:

$$NaCN \longrightarrow Na^+(aq) + CN^-(aq)$$

2. Write the dissociation reaction for the anion that undergoes hydrolysis and the K_b expression:

$$CN^-(aq) + H_2O \rightleftharpoons HCN(aq) + OH^-(aq)$$
$$K_b = \frac{[HCN][OH^-]}{[CN^-]} = 2.0 \times 10^{-5}$$

3. Use a concentration table to calculate the equilibrium concentrations of the species involved. Let x mol/L represent the $[OH^-]$ formed.

	CN⁻ + H₂O ⇌ HCN + OH⁻		
Initial concentration (mol/L)	0.1	0	0
Change in concentration caused by hydrolysis (mol/L)	$-x$	$+x$	$+x$
Equilibrium concentration (mol/L)	$(0.1 - x)$	x	x

Applying the assumption outlined in Example 12-6, step 2, we can simplify the equilibrium concentration of CN⁻ to 0.1 mol/L.

4. Substitute the concentration values into the K_b expression and solve for x:

$$2.0 \times 10^{-5} = \frac{(x)(x)}{0.1}$$
$$x^2 = (0.1)(2.0 \times 10^{-5})$$
$$x = 1.4 \times 10^{-3}$$

Therefore, $[OH^-] = 1.4 \times 10^{-3}$ mol/L.

5. Calculate the pOH and pH using Equations 12-13 and 12-14:

$$\begin{aligned} pOH &= -\log [OH^-] \\ &= -\log (1.4 \times 10^{-3}) \\ &= -(-2.85) \\ &= 2.85 \\ pH &= 14 - pOH \\ &= 14 - 2.85 \\ &= 11.15 \end{aligned}$$

FOLLOW-UP PROBLEM
Calculate the pH of a 0.10 mol/L $NaCH_3COO$ solution.

Answer: 8.9

The answers to the preceding example and problem indicate that a 0.10 mol/L NaCN solution is more basic than a 0.10 mol/L $NaCH_3COO$ solution. This is consistent with the general principle that *the stronger a Brønsted acid, the weaker is its conjugate base*. Specifically, CH_3COOH, with a K_a of 1.8×10^{-5}, is a stronger acid than HCN, which has a K_a of 4.9×10^{-10}. Therefore, CH_3COO^- ions ($K_b = 5.6 \times 10^{-10}$) are a weaker base than CN^- ions ($K_b = 2.0 \times 10^{-5}$). In terms of hydrolysis, we can say that an ion related to a weaker acid hydrolyzes to a greater extent (forms a more basic solution) than one related to a stronger acid. In general, *the weaker the acid, the greater is the strength of its conjugate base*.

12-14
Solutions of Cations That Behave as Brønsted Acids

Some metal cations and cations of salts that are derived from weak bases can react in water to form weak, acidic equilibrium systems.

A *cation* is a positively charged ion of a molecule formed when a neutral atom loses an electron. It has been experimentally observed that when metal salts such as $Fe(NO_3)_3$, $Al(NO_3)_3$ and $SnCl_4$ are added to water, they produce acidic solutions. The metal ions or cations of these salts have a small radius and a large positive charge, which results in a high charge density. Hydrated metal cations act as Brønsted acids and give up protons to water to a significant extent. When a metal ion becomes hydrated, it is bonded to water molecules. For example, Al^{3+} bonds to six water molecules (Fig. 12-9) to form hexaaquoaluminum(III) ions ($Al(H_2O)_6^{3+}$). The $Al(H_2O)_6^{3+}$ acts as an acid in a reaction with water:

$$Al(H_2O)_6^{3+} + H_2O \rightleftharpoons H_3O^+ + Al(H_2O)_5(OH)^{2+} \quad [12\text{-}18]$$

Protons from the $Al(H_2O)_6^{3+}$ ion are transferred easily to water because one of the partially charged protons on one of the six H_2O molecules bonded to Al^{3+} appears to be repelled by the high charge of the metal cation. This transfer of protons produces a measurable concentration of H_3O^+, which can be used to calculate a K_a value for cations:

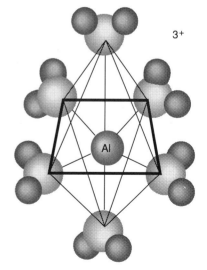

Figure 12-9
An $Al(H_2O)_6^{3+}$ ion. The six water molecules are located at the apices of an inscribed octahedron.

$$K_a = \frac{[H_3O^+][Al(H_2O)_5(OH)^{2+}]}{[Al(H_2O)_6^{3+}]}$$

A list of K_a values for some metal cations is provided in Table 12-9. Note that the K_a for Equation 12-18 is approximately 10^{-5}. This indicates that $Al(H_2O)_6^{3+}$ has an acid strength approximately equal to that of acetic acid.

TABLE 12-9
SELECTED CATIONS THAT BEHAVE AS BRØNSTED ACIDS

Acid	Conjugate Base	K_a
$Bi(H_2O)_6^{3+} + H_2O \rightleftharpoons H_3O^+ + Bi(H_2O)_5(OH)^{2+}$		1×10^{-2}
$Fe(H_2O)_6^{3+} + H_2O \rightleftharpoons H_3O^+ + Fe(H_2O)_5(OH)^{2+}$		6.0×10^{-3}
$Hg(H_2O)_4^{2+} + H_2O \rightleftharpoons H_3O^+ + Hg(H_2O)_3(OH)^+$		2×10^{-3}
$Cr(H_2O)_6^{3+} + H_2O \rightleftharpoons H_3O^+ + Cr(H_2O)_5(OH)^{2+}$		1×10^{-4}
$Al(H_2O)_6^{3+} + H_2O \rightleftharpoons H_3O^+ + Al(H_2O)_5(OH)^{2+}$		1.4×10^{-5}
$Cu(H_2O)_4^{2+} + H_2O \rightleftharpoons H_3O^+ + Cu(H_2O)_3(OH)^+$		1×10^{-8}
$NH_4^+ + H_2O \rightleftharpoons H_3O^+ + NH_3$		5.6×10^{-10}
$Zn(H_2O)_4^{2+} + H_2O \rightleftharpoons H_3O^+ + Zn(H_2O)_3(OH)^+$		2.5×10^{-10}

Most hydrated metal ions (cations) behave as weak Brønsted acids in water, particularly if the metal ion has a charge of two or more. In general, the metal ions of the transition elements have relatively high charge densities and, thus, can behave as Brønsted acids. Note that common ions such as Na^+, K^+, Mg^{2+} and Ca^{2+} are not included in Table 12-9 because little hydrolysis of these ions occurs in water and, therefore, the acidity of the solution is not affected.

Cations of weak bases are weak conjugate acids. The most common cation is the ammonium ion,

$$NH_4^- + H_2O \rightleftharpoons H_3O^+ + NH_3$$

Other cations that are derived from the ammonium ion include methylammonium ($CH_3NH_3^+$) and anilinium ($C_6H_5NH_3^+$).

12-15
Solutions Containing Amphiprotic Anions

Anions derived from the dissociation of polyprotic acids may act as acids or bases in aqueous solutions.

Any species that can either donate or accept a proton is amphiprotic and, thus, can act as a Brønsted acid or a Brønsted base. Certain anions associated with polyprotic acids are amphiprotic. Consider sodium bicarbonate ($NaHCO_3$), a so-called acid salt containing HCO_3^- ions. These ions can react with water in two ways:

As a base,

$$HCO_3^- + H_2O \rightleftharpoons H_2CO_3 + OH^-$$

$$K_b = \frac{[H_2CO_3][OH^-]}{[HCO_3^-]}$$

As an acid,

$$HCO_3^- + H_2O \rightleftharpoons H_3O^+ + CO_3^{2-}$$

$$K_a = \frac{[H_3O^+][CO_3^{2-}]}{[HCO_3^-]}$$

The acidity of a solution of $NaHCO_3$ depends on which of the two reactions occurs to the greater extent. If $K_b > K_a$, the solution is basic; if $K_a > K_b$, the solution is acidic. Note that the K_a for HCO_3^- is equal to the second dissociation constant (K_2) in the stepwise dissociation of H_2CO_3:

$$H_2CO_3 + H_2O \rightleftharpoons H_3O^+ + HCO_3^- \qquad K_1 = 4.5 \times 10^{-7}$$
$$HCO_3^- + H_2O \rightleftharpoons H_3O + CO_3^{2-} \qquad K_2 = 4.7 \times 10^{-11}$$

Note that for HCO_3^-,

$$K_b = \frac{K_w}{K_a \text{ (for conjugate acid)}}$$

Since the conjugate acid of the HCO_3^- ion is H_2CO_3, then

$$K_b = \frac{K_w}{K_1 \text{ for } H_2CO_3} = \frac{1.0 \times 10^{-14}}{4.5 \times 10^{-7}} = 2.2 \times 10^{-8}$$

$$K_a = K_2 \text{ for } H_2CO_3 = 4.7 \times 10^{-11}$$

Since $K_b > K_a$, we would predict that an aqueous solution of $NaHCO_3$ is basic. This prediction is confirmed by tests with indicators.

The H_3O^+ ion concentration of a solution of an amphiprotic anion can be calculated if we simultaneously solve a number of equations that describe the equilibrium system. These equations and their solutions can be found in almost any quantitative-analysis textbook. Here we are interested only in the qualitative aspects of the reactions and the nature of the solution formed when certain commonly encountered salts are added to water. The acidic or basic characteristics of aqueous solutions of sodium salts containing an amphiprotic anion are noted in Table 12-10.

As we saw in Section 12-2, the terms *amphiprotic* and *amphoteric* both describe ions or molecules that can act as either acids or bases. In addition to amphiprotic anions, there is a group of

TABLE 12-10

AMPHIPROTIC ANIONS AND THE CHARACTERISTICS OF THEIR AQUEOUS SOLUTIONS

Name of Ion	Formula	Nature of Solution
Bisulfate	HSO_4^-	acidic
Bicarbonate	HCO_3^-	basic
Dihydrogen phosphate	$H_2PO_4^-$	acidic
Monohydrogen phosphate	HPO_4^{2-}	basic
Bioxalate	$HC_2O_4^-$	acidic
Biphthalate	$HC_8H_4O_4^-$	acidic
Bisulfide	HS^-	basic
Bisulfite	HSO_3^-	acidic
Monohydrogen arsenate	$HAsO_4^{2-}$	basic
Dihydrogen arsenate	$H_2AsO_4^-$	acidic

slightly soluble metallic hydroxides, called ***amphoteric hydroxides***, that dissolve in either an acid or a base. Aluminum hydroxide ($Al(OH)_3$) is an example of this type of compound. When an aluminum salt such as $Al(NO_3)_3$ is added to water, it reacts and forms hexaaquoaluminum(III) ions ($Al(H_2O)_6^{3+}$). Addition of three moles of OH^- ions to one mole of the hexahydrated aluminum ions causes a precipitate of slightly soluble aluminum hydroxide to form. The reaction is represented as

$$Al(H_2O)_6^{3+}(aq) + 3OH^-(aq) \longrightarrow Al(H_2O)_3(OH)_3(s) + 3H_2O(l)$$

which can be written without showing the hydrated species:

$$Al^{3+}(aq) + 3OH^-(aq) \longrightarrow Al(OH)_3(s)$$

When excess sodium hydroxide is added to solid $Al(OH)_3$, it dissolves and forms soluble tetrahydroxoaluminate(III) ions ($Al(OH)_4^-$). The reaction can be represented as

$$Al(OH)_3(s) + OH^-(aq) \longrightarrow Al(OH)_4^-(aq)$$

When hydrochloric acid is added to solid $Al(OH)_3$, it dissolves and forms soluble dihydroxoaluminum(III) ions ($Al(OH)_2^+$) or $Al(OH)^{2+}$ ions, depending on the concentration of the acid:

$$Al(OH)_3(s) + H_3O^+(aq) \longrightarrow Al(OH)_2^+(aq) + 2H_2O(l)$$

Therefore, when a strong base is added to an amphoteric hydroxide, the hydroxide behaves as an acid. Zinc, chromium and tin are three other common metallic ions that form amphoteric hydroxides.

12-16
Hydrolysis of Anions and Cations

When an anion and cation hydrolyze, the degree to which the resulting solution is acidic, basic or neutral depends on the degree of dissociation of the two ions.

When the anion and cation of a salt hydrolyze, the solution can be acidic, basic or neutral. A neutral solution occurs if the interaction between the H_3O^+ ions and the OH^- ions results in a solution with no acidic or basic characteristics. This type of reaction is referred to as a ***neutralization reaction***. The pH of a solution depends on whether the cation can produce more H_3O^+ ions than the anion can produce OH^- ions. Therefore, if the K_a value is greater than the K_b value, the cation is producing more H_3O^+ ions than the anion is producing OH^- ions, and the solution will be acidic. If the K_b value is greater than the K_a value, the solution will be basic. The solution is neutral if the K_a and K_b values are the same and the pH is equal to 7. For example, the salt NH_4CN contains a cation and an anion, both of which hydrolyze. Since the condition of the solution depends on the extent to which each ion hydrolyzes, the reactions and values for the dissociation constants are

If $K_a > K_b$, solution is acidic.
If $K_a < K_b$, solution is basic.
If $K_a = K_b$, solution is neutral.

$$NH_4^+(aq) + H_2O \rightleftharpoons H_3O^+(aq) + NH_3(aq) \qquad K_a = 5.6 \times 10^{-10}$$
$$[12\text{-}19]$$

$$CN^-(aq) + H_2O \rightleftharpoons HCN(aq) + OH^-(aq) \qquad K_b = 2.0 \times 10^{-5}$$
$$[12\text{-}20]$$

The equilibrium constants reveal that the K_b of CN^- is much greater than the K_a of NH_4^+. Therefore, the H_3O^+ ions produced in Equation 12-19 will be neutralized by the OH^- ions produced in Equation 12-20. Since a large quantity of OH^- ions are not neutralized, the solution will be basic.

So far we have discussed the aqueous solutions of three types of salts:

1. Those in which the anion accepts a proton from water (Table 12-8). Solutions of these salts are basic.

2. Those in which there is cation hydrolysis (Table 12-9). Solutions of these salts are acidic.

3. Those in which there is both anion and cation hydrolysis. Solutions of these salts may be neutral, acidic or basic, depending on the relative extent of anion and cation hydrolysis.

We are now ready to consider solutions that contain more than one solute.

12-17
Buffer Solutions

Buffer solutions contain a weak acid and its salt (conjugate base) or a weak base and its salt (conjugate acid). Buffers are defined as solutions that resist changes in pH when acids or bases are added to them.

Every living thing is sensitive to internal changes in pH. For example, the pH of your blood is 7.4. If you consume a small quantity of acid or base, the pH of your blood will not change. If you consume large quantities of acid—for example, in soft drinks or vinegar—the pH of your blood will only change slightly. Since blood has the ability to resist changes in pH when acids and bases are added, it is said to be *buffered*. If your blood were not buffered and its pH dropped to 7 or rose to about 8, you would die.

A buffer solution is a solution that resists slight changes in pH when H_3O^+ or OH^- ions are added. Buffers are prepared by mixing a weak acid with its salt (conjugate base) or a weak base with its salt (conjugate acid). For example, an acetic acid–acetate buffer is made by adding acetate ions from a salt such as sodium acetate to a specified concentration of acetic acid. If we measure the pH of the solution, we find that it increases as we add the acetate. The principal equilibrium of the acetic acid–acetate buffer solution is

$$CH_3COOH(l) + H_2O(l) \rightleftharpoons H_3O^+(aq) + CH_3COO^-(aq)$$

According to Le Châtelier's principle, increasing the concentration of CH_3COO^-, a product species, shifts the equilibrium to the left, causing an increase in the CH_3COOH concentration and a corresponding decrease in the H_3O^+ ion concentration. This means that as the salt is added, the solution becomes more basic and has a higher pH. In general, *the addition of a salt of a weak acid to a solution of the weak acid decreases the* $[H_3O^+]$ *and increases the pH of the solution.*

When NH_4Cl, a salt and conjugate acid of the weak base, NH_3, is added to a solution of NH_3, the solution is observed to become more acidic. The addition of NH_4^+ causes the equilibrium

$$NH_3(g) + H_2O(l) \rightleftharpoons NH_4^+(aq) + OH^-(aq)$$

to shift to the left. This reduces the OH^- concentration so that the pH of the solution decreases. In general, *the addition of a salt of a weak base to a solution of the weak base decreases the* $[OH^-]$ *and decreases the pH of the solution.*

If we assume that the $[H_3O^+]$ is small compared with the concentration of the acid and salt, then we can express the $[H_3O^+]$ of a buffer solution composed of a weak acid and its salt (conjugate base) as

$$[H_3O^+] = K_a \frac{[\text{acid}]}{[\text{salt (conjugate base)}]} \qquad [12\text{-}21]$$

A parallel formula for buffer solutions composed of a weak base and its salt (conjugate acid) is

$$[OH^-] = K_b \frac{[\text{base}]}{[\text{salt (conjugate acid)}]} \qquad [12\text{-}22]$$

Interpretation of Equations 12-21 and 12-22 reveals that the $[H_3O^+]$ of a buffer solution containing a weak acid and its salt or a weak base and its salt depends on the ratio of the acid or base concentration to the salt concentration. Furthermore, *dilution of a buffer solution does not change the pH*. Now that we understand the chemistry of a buffer solution, let us look at the action of buffers.

A buffer solution is an equilibrium system that, because it contains a weak acid and a weak base, can react with both added acids and bases to maintain a constant pH level. For example, if a strong acid is added to the acetic acid–acetate buffer solution, the H_3O^+ concentration will increase. According to Le Châtelier's principle, the equilibrium will shift to the left to adjust to the stress. In other words, the added H_3O^+ reacts with the CH_3COO^- according to the equation

$$H_3O^+(aq) + CH_3COO^-(aq) \rightleftharpoons CH_3COOH(aq) + H_2O$$

Because the added H_3O^+ is consumed by the acetate, there is very little change in the pH.

If a strong base such as NaOH is added to the buffer, the OH^- is neutralized by the acetic acid:

$$OH^-(aq) + CH_3COOH(aq) \rightleftharpoons CH_3COO^-(aq) + H_2O$$

Once again, there is very little change in the pH.

A buffer maintains the pH when small amounts of either an acid or a base are added. This is true whether the buffer is made of a weak acid and its salt (conjugate base), as in the acetic acid–acetate buffer solution, or a weak base and its salt (conjugate acid), such as an ammonia-ammonium buffer solution.

Now that we have seen how a buffer can remove small amounts of excess acid or base without a substantial change in the pH, let us quantitatively determine the pH of a buffer solution. We have already seen that pH is calculated by taking the negative logarithm of the H_3O^+ concentration. To calculate the pH of any weak acid–conjugate base solution, we can use the K_a expression for the weak acid:

$$K_a = \frac{[H_3O^+][\text{conjugate base}]}{[\text{weak acid}]}$$

If we rearrange this equation to solve for $[H_3O^+]$, we obtain

$$-\log [H_3O^+] = \left(-\log \frac{[\text{weak acid}]}{[\text{conjugate base}]}\right)(-\log K_a) \quad [12\text{-}23]$$

Since we know that

$$pH = -\log [H_3O^+]$$

then

$$pK_a = -\log K_a \quad\quad\quad [12\text{-}24]$$

The pK_a of an acid allows us to compare the relative strengths of

In general, a buffer solution contains two species: one species can react with added hydroxide ions and the other can react with added hydronium ions.

weak acids. Similarly, the pK_b of a base can be determined to compare the strengths of bases.

The expression

$$-\log \frac{[\text{weak acid}]}{[\text{conjugate base}]}$$

in Equation 12-23 can be rewritten as

$$+\log \frac{[\text{conjugate base}]}{[\text{weak acid}]}$$

and substituted into the equation,

$$pH = pK_a + \log \frac{[\text{conjugate base}]}{[\text{weak acid}]} \qquad [12\text{-}25]$$

or

$$pH = pK_a + \log \frac{[\text{anion}]}{[\text{acid}]}$$

This equation is called the *Henderson-Hasselbalch equation* and can be used to determine the pH of a buffer if the initial concentrations of the acid and the anion used to make the buffer are known. For example, the equilibrium expression for the acetic acid–acetate buffer system is

$$CH_3COOH(aq) + H_2O \rightleftharpoons H_3O^+(aq) + CH_3COO^-(aq)$$

The Henderson-Hasselbalch equation for this system is

$$pH = pK_a + \log \frac{[CH_3COO^-]}{[CH_3COOH]}$$

The pOH of a weak base–conjugate acid buffer can also be determined by the Henderson-Hasselbalch equation,

$$pOH = pK_b + \log \frac{[\text{conjugate acid}]}{[\text{weak base}]}$$

or

$$pOH = pK_b + \log \frac{[\text{cation}]}{[\text{base}]}$$

The following example illustrates how to calculate the pH of a buffer using the K_a expression and the Henderson-Hasselbalch equation.

EXAMPLE 12-10

Calculating the pH of a Buffer Solution

A chemist wishes to prepare an acetic acid–acetate buffer to test its effects in a cosmetic preparation. If 1 L of a

0.1 mol/L CH_3COOH is prepared and 5 g of sodium acetate ($NaCH_3COO$) is added to the acid, what will be the pH of the buffer system? K_a for CH_3COOH is 1.8×10^{-5} from Table 12-5.

SOLUTION

1. Write the dissociation reaction for acetic acid and the K_a expression:

$$CH_3COOH(aq) + H_2O \rightleftharpoons H_3O^+(aq) + CH_3COO^-(aq)$$

$$K_a = \frac{[H_3O^+][CH_3COO^-]}{[CH_3COOH]} = 1.8 \times 10^{-5}$$

Convert units of $NaCH_3COO$ to mol/L:

$$Molar\ mass = 82\ g/mol$$
$$Number\ of\ moles = \frac{5\ g}{82\ g/mol}$$
$$= 6.1 \times 10^{-2}\ mol$$

Therefore, in 1 L of buffer solution,

$$[NaCH_3COO] = 6.1 \times 10^{-2}\ mol/L$$

2. Calculate the $[H_3O^+]$. Let x mol/L represent the $[H_3O^+]$. Thus, at equilibrium, the concentrations are

$$[H_3O^+] = x$$
$$[CH_3COOH] = 0.1 - x$$

Note that the $[H_3O^+]$ is not equal to the $[CH_3COO^-]$. Since $NaCH_3COO$ is a strong base, it dissociates completely in water. For each mole of $NaCH_3COO$ that dissociates, one mole of CH_3COO^- forms. Therefore,

$$[CH_3COO^-] = [NaCH_3COO] + x = 6.1 \times 10^{-2} + x$$

However, the acetate ion from the sodium acetate represses the dissociation of acetic acid so that the $[H_3O^+]$ is very small relative to the $[CH_3COO^-]$. Thus, we can omit x relative to the $[CH_3COOH]$ and $[CH_3COO^-]$. Therefore,

$$[CH_3COOH] = 0.1\ mol/L$$
$$[CH_3COO^-] = 6.1 \times 10^{-2}\ mol/L$$

3. Substitute the concentration values into Equation 12-16 and solve for x:

$$1.8 \times 10^{-5} = \frac{(x)(6.1 \times 10^{-2})}{0.1}$$
$$x = 2.95 \times 10^{-5}$$

Thus,

$$[H_3O^+] = 2.95 \times 10^{-5} \text{ mol/L}$$

4. Using Equation 12-11, substitute $[H_3O^+]$ to solve for pH:

$$\begin{aligned} \text{pH} &= -\log (2.95 \times 10^{-5}) \\ &= -(-4.53) \\ &= 4.53 \end{aligned}$$

We can also solve this problem by using the Henderson-Hasselbalch equation (Equation 12-25).

5. Determine the pK_a for acetic acid using Equation 12-24:

$$pK_a = -\log K_a = -\log (1.8 \times 10^{-5}) = -(-4.74) = 4.74$$

6. Calculate the pH of the buffer using Equation 12-25:

$$\begin{aligned} \text{pH} &= pK_a + \log \frac{[\text{anion}]}{[\text{acid}]} \\ &= 4.74 + \log \frac{(6.1 \times 10^{-2})}{(0.1)} \\ &= 4.74 + \log (0.61) \\ &= 4.74 + (-0.22) \\ &= 4.52 \end{aligned}$$

FOLLOW-UP PROBLEM

A buffer is prepared by adding 5.0 g of NH_4NO_3 to 1 L of a 0.1 mol/L NH_3 solution. What is the pH of the buffer?

Answer: 9.46

ACIDOSIS AND ALKALOSIS

Children often hold their breath until their faces turn blue in order to get what they want. However, what they may get is a mild case of acidosis—a condition in which the blood pH drops below the normal level.

The pH of blood in the human body is between 7.35 and 7.45. The body works hard at maintaining a normal constant blood pH by means of a carbonic acid–bicarbonate buffer. The simple act of breathing also helps maintain blood pH.

Carbon dioxide is absorbed by the blood where it reacts with water to form the bicarbonate ion, $HCO_3^-(aq)$, which can dissociate into $H^+(aq)$ and $CO_3^-(aq)$ ions. Whether the reaction favours reactants or products in the blood depends on the concentration of the $CO_2(g)$. In our cells, where the CO_2 is produced, the blood system adjusts to reduce the concentration of CO_2 by increasing the rate of the forward reaction and forming more $HCO_3^-(aq)$. In our lungs, where the CO_2 concentration is lower, the blood system adjusts to raise the concentration of CO_2 by increasing the rate of the reverse reaction and forming more CO_2 and less $H^+(aq)$. This CO_2 is exhaled away from the lungs as we breathe. Thus, a shift in the position of the chemical equilibrium is responsible for absorbing and releasing the CO_2 produced in our bodies and maintaining a constant blood pH.

A change in the blood pH, which can be detected through analysis (as shown in the photo), can lead to the development of abnormal blood conditions. If the blood pH drops below 7.35, the condition is called *acidosis*. When the blood pH is above 7.45, *alkalosis* occurs. Acidosis causes depression of the nervous system and can result in fainting, weakness and, in severe cases, coma. Alkalosis causes overstimulation of the nervous system, muscle spasms and convulsions. Either condition can be fatal if allowed to persist over time.

Anything that increases the amount of acids in the blood can cause acidosis. Problems in breathing due to asthma or emphysema can increase the amount of CO_2 in the lungs. The pH of the blood then decreases because the excess amount of CO_2 decreases the concentration of the carbonic acid–bicarbonate buffer. When the body is not supplied enough food, it breaks down fat and produces acidic compounds that enter the bloodstream. Heavy

exercise causes the muscles to produce lactic acid, which also enters the bloodstream. Uncontrolled diabetes causes the overproduction of metabolic acids. Excessive consumption of soft drinks and beer can also cause acidosis.

Alkalosis can result from hyperventilation or vomiting. Hyperventilation causes the excessive loss of CO_2, which raises the $[HCO_3^-]$ to $[H_2CO_3]$ ratio and the pH. Excessive vomiting can substantially reduce the amount of stomach acids and thereby raise the pH of the blood. Alkalosis can also result from the overconsumption of alkali-based drugs.

The maintenance of the constant pH value of human blood is obviously very important to the molecular mechanisms within cells. A small change in blood pH can have serious effects on certain aspects of metabolism and cellular activities within our bodies.

VOLUMETRIC ANALYSIS

In many acid-base reactions, the equilibrium is displaced almost completely toward the product side. That is, the dissociation constant for the reaction is exceedingly large. These reactions can be considered quantitative and can be used to analyse the amount of acid or base in a given sample. The process is called *volumetric analysis*. Any reaction considered for volumetric analysis must meet certain requirements:

1. Only a single, specific reaction must take place between the

unknown substance and the known substance used for the analysis.

2. The unknown substance must react completely and rapidly with the added standard reagent. In other words, the reaction must be quantitative.

3. An indicator or method must be available to signal when all of the unknown substance has reacted with the added standard reagent.

In a volumetric analysis, the usual objective is to determine the mass or percentage of a qualitatively identified component (the desired substance) in a sample whose quantitative composition is unknown. If the sample is a solution, the objective may be to determine its concentration.

Chemical indicators play an important role in volumetric analysis. The choice of an indicator that yields a recognizable colour change at the proper pH is essential if significant endpoint errors are to be avoided. Let us briefly consider the behaviour and characteristics of acid-base indicators.

12-18
Chemical Indicators

A chemical indicator is a weak acid or base that changes colour, depending on the pH of the solution.

Acid-base indicators are weak acids or bases that establish an equilibrium between their molecular and ionic forms. The molecular form has a different colour from that of the ionic form. Changes in acidity cause a shift in the equilibrium, which favours one species over another. For example, phenolphthalein is a weak acid whose formula and equilibrium equation can be represented as

$$HPh + B^- \rightleftharpoons HB + Ph^-$$
colourless   magenta

The molecular form (HPh) is colourless, and the ionic form (Ph$^-$) is magenta. If an acid is added, it donates protons to the ionic form of the indicator and shifts the equilibrium to the left. Phenolphthalein is colourless in acid solution. When a base is added, it reacts with the HPh and produces coloured Ph$^-$ ions. As a result, in basic solution phenolphthalein is magenta, or a reddish colour. Note that the acid must be stronger than HPh to shift the equilibrium to the left, and the base must be stronger than Ph$^-$ to shift it to the right.

When a few drops of phenolphthalein indicator are added to an

Test your understanding of indicator behaviour. The acid colour of a certain indicator, HIn, is yellow and the base colour is blue. When this indicator is added to a certain acid, HB, the solution turns blue. The equation for the reaction can be written

$$HB + In^- \rightleftharpoons HIn + B^-$$

Which is the stronger acid, HB or HIn?

unknown acid sample that is stronger than HPh, and OH⁻ ions are then added, the solution remains colourless until the added OH⁻ ions have reacted with all of the stronger acid. The weaker acid, HPh, then donates protons to OH⁻.

Phenolphthalein has a K_a value equal to 1×10^{-9}. This small value indicates that HPh is a very weak acid; therefore, the indicator does not react appreciably with the OH⁻ ions being added until the concentration of H_3O^+ ions from the unknown acid is very small, comparable to the concentration of H_3O^+ ions in a solution of HPh in water. Phenolphthalein is a satisfactory indicator for the titration of a weak acid such as HOAc with OH⁻ because HOAc is much stronger than the acid, HPh.

For any given titration, an indicator should be picked whose K_a is equal to $[H_3O^+]$ at the equivalence point of the titration; at this point the indicator is at its colour transition point such that $[HIn] = [In^-]$. Thus, in this case,

$$[H_3O^+] = K_a \frac{[HIn]}{[In^-]} = K$$

A number of common indicators with their colour changes and pH ranges are listed in Table 12-11. The colour changes and pH range for some indicators are shown in Colour Plate III. Note that some indicators (thymol blue) undergo two colour transitions; these are called *diprotic* because they have two acidic hydrogens. Thus, as is the case with any diprotic acid, they give up their first and second proton at different points of the pH scale because H_2In is a stronger Brønsted acid than HIn^-.

Household Indicators

Have you ever wondered why tea changes colour when you add lemon? This is because tea is an acid-base indicator; it will turn yellow in the presence of an acid and orange-red in the presence of a base.

If you boil the leaves of a red cabbage, the juice makes an excellent acid-base indicator. It will turn a variety of colours as the pH changes from 0 to 14. The cabbage juice will progressively change from yellow to orange to red and finally to purple.

TABLE 12-11
CHEMICAL INDICATORS

	Transition Range, pH	Colour Change	
		Acid	Base
Methyl violet	0.0–1.6	yellow	blue
Thymol blue	1.2–2.8	red	yellow
Methyl orange	3.2–4.4	red	yellow
Bromcresol green	3.8–5.4	yellow	blue
Methyl red	4.8–6.0	red	yellow
Chlorophenol red	5.2–6.8	yellow	red
Bromthymol blue	6.0–7.6	yellow	blue
Phenol red	6.6–8.0	yellow	red
Neutral red	6.8–8.0	red	yellow-orange
Thymol blue	8.0–9.6	yellow	blue
Phenolphthalein	8.2–10.0	colourless	pink
Thymolphthalein	9.4–10.6	colourless	blue
Alizarin yellow	10.1–12.0	yellow	red

Table 12-11 shows that methyl orange is red in a solution having a pH of 3.2 or less and yellow in a solution having a pH of 4.4 or greater. The transition of the intermediate colour of orange is observed when the pH falls between these extremes. At an intermediate pH, $[HIn] = [In^-]$. That is, the concentration of the red species is equal to that of the yellow species, and the solution appears orange. Thus, methyl orange can be used for a titration reaction in which the pH of the solution at the equivalence point is between 3.2 and 4.4. The K_a for methyl orange at 25°C is 4×10^{-4}. Thus, ideally, the solution at the equivalence point should have a $[H_3O^+] = 4 \times 10^{-4}$ mol/L and a pH of 3.4.

Buret

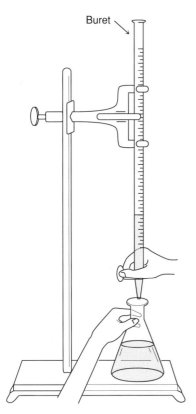

Figure 12-10
Titration involving the use of a buret.

12-19

Acid-Base Titrations

A titration involves the addition of controlled amounts of a standard solution of acid to an unknown concentration of base, or vice versa, until a specific endpoint is reached.

A *titration* is a process in which the volume of a known concentration of acid or base solution is determined by measuring the precise volume of solution of base or acid needed to completely react with a specific volume of unknown solution. The solution of known concentration is called a *standard solution*. Thus, a titration is a process in which a standard solution is added from a graduated tube, or a *buret*, in controlled amounts (Fig. 12-10). For example, the concentration of an acid solution can be determined by measuring the volume of a base needed to completely react with a specific volume of acid.

In theory, the standard solution is added until the amount of the standard solution is chemically equivalent to the amount of unknown solution. In the case of a strong acid–strong base titration, this is the point at which the number of hydronium ions (H_3O^+) from the acid solution is equal to the number of hydroxide ions (OH^-) from the added base solution. In practice, the *equivalence point*, or *stoichiometric point*, is the point at which the number of moles of OH^- added is equal to the number of moles of H_3O^+ originally present. Chemical indicators are used to estimate the equivalence point. The indicators change colour at or very near the pH at the equivalence point. However, the colour change of the indicator often takes place at the *endpoint* of the titration. Although the equivalence point and the endpoint are not necessarily the same, the difference between the two is negligible. In a given acid-base titration, the equivalence point occurs at a specific pH. Choosing an indicator that yields a recognizable colour change at the proper pH is essential if the colour change is to represent the correct equivalence point.

At the endpoint of an acid-base titration, the number of moles of a standard solution required to react with an unknown solution can be calculated from the concentration and volume of the standard solution used. The mole relationship between the unknown solution and the standard reagent is shown by the equation for the reaction. The number of moles can be divided by the volume of the reagent to calculate the concentration of the unknown solution.

Standard solutions play an important role in volumetric analysis. There are two common methods for preparing a standard solution:

1. Direct preparation by dissolving an accurately measured pure

Equivalence Points and Endpoints
The equivalence points and end-points of a titration are not the same. Endpoints are determined by the change in colour of the indicator used. If you change the indicator, you change the endpoint. The equivalence point is the point at which the total number of moles of acid is stoichiometrically equal to the number of moles of base. This point is experimentally determined by means of a graph. Indicators are used only to approximate equivalence points.

dry substance in pure water and diluting to a known volume in a volumetric flask.

2. Reaction of an unstandardized solution with an accurately measured quantity of a primary standard. *Primary standards* are stable, non-hygroscopic (do not absorb water) substances of known composition and high purity that react rapidly and quantitatively with the solution to be standardized. The number of moles in a measured quantity of a solid primary standard can be calculated by the following equation:

$$\text{Amount of substance} = \frac{\text{grams of solid}}{\text{molar mass of solid}} = \text{moles}$$

The primary standard is dissolved in a convenient amount of water that need not be measured precisely. An indicator is added, and the solution of the primary standard is titrated with the solution to be standardized. The coefficients in the balanced equation for the reaction are used to determine the amount of reagent in the solution being standardized.

Examples 12-11 and 12-12 illustrate different types of titration calculations.

Figure 12-11
Although typical laboratory titrations involve the use of a titrant solution, commercial titration meters are used to indicate endpoints. An ampero-metric titration meter, pictured above, is used to determine the change in electric current passed during the titration. The liquid sample reacts with a reagent; if water is consumed during the reaction, the resulting redox system depolarizes the elec-trode and causes an increase in cur-rent. The voltage is reduced to main-tain a standard current, and this change in voltage indicates the end-point of the reaction.

EXAMPLE 12-11
Calculating the Concentration of an Unknown Acid
A student in a laboratory adds 36 mL of a standardized 0.66 mol/L NaOH solution to a 20 mL sample of H_2SO_4 to a green endpoint, using bromthymol blue indicator. The acid is completely neutralized. What is the concentration of the sulfuric acid?

SOLUTION
1. Write a balanced equation for the neutralization reaction:

$$2NaOH(aq) + H_2SO_4(aq) \longrightarrow Na_2SO_4(aq) + 2H_2O(l)$$

2. Calculate the number of moles of NaOH added during the titration:

$$\begin{aligned}\text{Number of moles} &= (0.66 \text{ mol/L})(36 \text{ mL}) \\ &= (0.66 \text{ mol/L})(0.036 \text{ L}) \\ &= 2.38 \times 10^{-2} \text{ mol}\end{aligned}$$

3. Calculate the number of moles of H_2SO_4 in the sample. From the balanced equation, the stoichiometric relation-

ship shows that two moles of NaOH are required to neutralize one mole of H_2SO_4. Derive a conversion factor that will relate mol acid/mol base. Thus,

$$\frac{1 \text{ mol acid}}{2 \text{ mol base}} \times 2.38 \times 10^{-2} \text{ mol base} = 1.19 \times 10^{-2} \text{ mol acid}$$

4. Calculate the concentration of the H_2SO_4:

$$[H_2SO_4] = \frac{\text{mol } H_2SO_4}{\text{volume(L)}}$$
$$= \frac{1.19 \times 10^{-2} \text{ mol}}{20 \text{ mL}}$$
$$= \frac{1.19 \times 10^{-2} \text{ mol}}{0.020 \text{ L}}$$
$$= 0.60 \text{ mol/L}$$

FOLLOW-UP PROBLEMS

1. What is the concentration of a hydrochloric acid solution, 30.0 mL of which is neutralized by 48.0 mL of 0.10 mol/L NaOH?

2. What volume of 1.10 mol/L HCl is required to neutralize 25.0 mL of 0.01 mol/L $Ba(OH)_2$?

Answers: (1) 0.160 mol/L, (2) 4.55 mL

EXAMPLE 12-12
Standardization of a Solution Using a Primary Standard

A chemistry student wishes to standardize a hydrochloric acid solution using pure Na_2CO_3 as a primary standard. What is the concentration of this acid if 30.0 mL of the acid is required to react completely with a 0.500 g sample of sodium carbonate?

SOLUTION

1. Write a balanced equation for the neutralization reaction:

$$Na_2CO_3(s) + 2HCl(aq) \longrightarrow$$
$$2NaCl(aq) + H_2O(l) + CO_2(g)$$

2. Calculate the number of moles of sodium carbonate in the 0.500 g sample:

$$\text{Molar mass} = 106.0 \text{ g/mol}$$

$$\text{Number of moles} = \frac{0.500 \text{ g}}{106.0 \text{ g/mol}}$$

$$= 4.72 \times 10^{-3} \text{ mol}$$

3. Calculate the number of moles of HCl required to react with 4.72×10^{-3} moles of Na_2CO_3. From the stoichiometry of the equation, we know that one mole of Na_2CO_3 reacts with two moles of HCl. Derive a conversion factor that will relate mol acid/mol base. Thus,

$$\frac{2 \text{ mol HCl}}{1 \text{ mol Na}_2\text{CO}_3} \times 4.72 \times 10^{-3} \text{ mol Na}_2\text{CO}_3 =$$

$$9.44 \times 10^{-3} \text{ mol HCL}$$

4. Calculate the concentration of the HCl:

$$[\text{HCl}] = \frac{\text{mol HCl}}{\text{volume}}$$

$$= \frac{9.44 \times 10^{-3} \text{ mol}}{30 \text{ mL}}$$

$$= \frac{9.44 \times 10^{-3} \text{ mol}}{0.030 \text{ L}}$$

$$= 0.32 \text{ mol/L}$$

FOLLOW-UP PROBLEM

A sodium hydroxide solution is standardized by reaction with benzoic acid (C_6H_5COOH). A 2.00 g sample of benzoic acid requires 35.00 mL of NaOH to reach the endpoint. What is the concentration of the base? Benzoic acid is a monoprotic acid.

Answer: 0.468 mol/L

TITRATION CURVES

We have now acquired the principles and tools needed to determine (a) the completeness of a reaction, (b) the composition of a solution at various stages during a titration and (c) the pH of a solution at various stages during a titration. We can apply these

Winemaking
Winemaking is a well documented industry that goes as far back as ancient Egyptian times—2500 BC or earlier.

Wine is produced by the fermentation of grapes and other fruits. It consists mostly of water, about 9 to 11% ethanol, as well as organic acids such as malic and tartaric acids. These acids give wines their characteristic tart flavour.

Because acid levels can affect the quality of the wine, winemakers use titration to make accurate measurements of total acids. Using an alkaline solution of sodium hydroxide, the winemaker measures the amount of solution needed to turn a mixture of wine and 1% phenolphthalein pink, in the case of white wine, and grey in the case of red wine. If the wine is too acidic, water or a calcium carbonate solution is added to neutralize the acid.

Spoilage can occur if the ethanol is oxidized,

$$C_2H_5OH + O_2 \longrightarrow CH_3COOH + H_2O$$

turning the entire batch of wine into vinegar.

principles by constructing a titration curve in which the pH of the solution during the titration is plotted against the volume of standard solution added. The resulting curve shows how rapidly the pH changes with the volume of standard solution and provides a clue to the feasibility of the titration. To define such a curve we need to calculate the pH of a solution at ten to twelve different stages during the titration. In general, there are four significant stages requiring four types of calculations:

1. The pH of the solution before the addition of the standard solution.

2. The pH at the equivalence point.

3. The pH of the solution between the start and equivalence point.

4. The pH of the solution after the equivalence point.

Titration curves depend on whether a strong base is being titrated with a strong acid or with a weak acid. The two different types of titrations are discussed in the following sections.

12-20
Titration of a Strong Acid With a Strong Base

During the titration of a strong acid with a strong base, there is a rapid change in pH very near the equivalence point.

When a strong acid is titrated with a strong base, no dissociation constants are involved. Stoichiometric principles can be used to calculate the $[H_3O^+]$ at any point during the titration by dividing the moles of remaining unreacted H_3O^+ ions by the total volume of solution at that time. We can then calculate the pH of the solution at various points and use these points to plot a titration curve. Example 12-13 illustrates this type of calculation.

> **EXAMPLE 12-13**
> **Calculating pH During the Titration of a Strong Acid With a Strong Base**
> In a laboratory, a student titrates a 25 mL sample of 0.1 mol/L HCl with a standardized 0.1 mol/L NaOH solution. Calculate the pH of the solution at four points during the titration and plot a titration curve.
>
> **SOLUTION**
> 1. Write a balanced equation for the neutralization reaction:
>
> $$HCl(aq) + NaOH(aq) \longrightarrow H_2O(l) + NaCl(aq)$$

2. Calculate the pH of the acid sample before the titration begins, using Equation 12-11. Since HCl is a strong acid and completely dissociates,

$$[HCl] = [H_3O^+] = 0.1 \text{ mol/L}$$
$$pH = -\log [H_3O^+]$$
$$= -\log (0.1)$$
$$= 1$$

3. Calculate the pH after 24.9 mL of NaOH has been added to the HCl. To do this, we must first calculate the number of moles in the original HCl solution and the number of moles of NaOH that were added:

$$\text{Number of moles of HCl} = (0.1 \text{ mol/L})(25 \text{ mL})$$
$$= (0.1 \text{ mol/L})(2.5 \times 10^{-2} \text{ L})$$
$$= 2.5 \times 10^{-3} \text{ mol}$$
$$\text{Number of moles of NaOH} = (0.1 \text{ mol/L})(24.9 \text{ mL})$$
$$= (0.1 \text{ mol/L})(2.49 \times 10^{-2} \text{ L})$$
$$= 2.49 \times 10^{-3} \text{ mol}$$

The coefficients of the neutralization reaction tell us that 1 mol of HCl reacts with 1 mol of NaOH. Therefore, the addition of 2.49×10^{-3} mol of NaOH neutralizes 2.49×10^{-3} mol of HCl, leaving $2.5 \times 10^{-3} - 2.49 \times 10^{-3} = 1.0 \times 10^{-5}$ mol of HCl unneutralized. We can now calculate the concentration of HCl remaining unneutralized.

$$\text{Volume of solution} = 2.5 \times 10^{-2} \text{ L} + 2.49 \times 10^{-2} \text{ L}$$
$$= 4.99 \times 10^{-2} \text{ L}$$
$$[HCl] = \frac{1.0 \times 10^{-5} \text{ mol}}{4.99 \times 10^{-2} \text{ L}}$$
$$= 2.0 \times 10^{-4} \text{ mol/L}$$

Since HCl dissociates completely,

$$[HCl] = [H_3O^+] = 2.0 \times 10^{-4} \text{ mol/L}$$
$$pH = -\log (2.0 \times 10^{-4})$$
$$= -(-3.7)$$
$$= 3.7$$

4. Calculate the pH at the endpoint of the titration when 25 mL of NaOH has been added. At this point, the number of moles of NaOH equals the number of moles of HCl. Thus,

$$[H_3O^+] = [OH^-]$$

and

$$pH = 7$$

5. Calculate the pH when an additional 0.1 mL (for a total of 25.1 mL) of NaOH is added to the HCl past the end-point. First calculate the number of moles of NaOH that have been added:

$$\text{Number of moles} = (0.1 \text{ mol/L})(25.1 \text{ mL})$$
$$= (0.1 \text{ mol/L})(2.51 \times 10^{-2} \text{ L})$$
$$= 2.51 \times 10^{-3} \text{ mol}$$

Therefore, the excess amount of NaOH is

$$2.51 \times 10^{-3} \text{ mol} - 2.5 \times 10^{-3} \text{ mol} = 1.0 \times 10^{-5} \text{ mol}$$

We can now calculate the concentration of NaOH:

$$[\text{NaOH}] = \frac{1.0 \times 10^{-5} \text{ mol}}{(25 \text{ mL} + 25.1 \text{ mL})}$$
$$= \frac{1.0 \times 10^{-5} \text{ mol}}{5.01 \times 10^{-2} \text{ L}}$$
$$= 2.0 \times 10^{-4} \text{ mol/L}$$

Since NaOH dissociates completely,

$$[\text{NaOH}] = [\text{OH}^-]$$
$$\text{pOH} = -\log [\text{OH}^-]$$
$$= -\log (2.0 \times 10^{-4})$$
$$= 3.7$$

Therefore,

$$\text{pH} = 14 - \text{pOH}$$
$$= 14 - 3.7$$
$$= 10.3$$

The titration curve for the neutralization reaction in the preceding example is illustrated in Fig. 12-12. It can be seen from the data and the graph that the addition of 0.01 mL of base (one small drop) near the equivalence point causes a pH change of 4 units. This means that the $[\text{H}_3\text{O}^+]$ changes by a factor of 10^4. A rapid change in pH with a small change in volume of standard solution is desirable if the indicator is to give a pronounced colour change at the endpoint. The graph reveals that any indicator with a detectable colour change occurring in the pH range of 3.0 to 10.0 would be suitable for the titration of a strong acid with a strong base. Three indicators commonly used for this type of titration are:

1. Methyl orange: range = 3.2– 4.4
2. Bromthymol blue: range = 6.0– 7.6
3. Phenolphthalein: range = 8.2–10.0

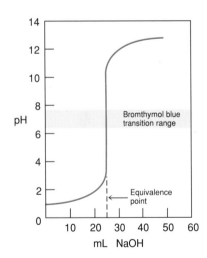

Figure 12-12
Changes in pH during the titration of 25.0 mL of 0.1 mol/L HCl with 0.1 mol/L NaOH.

FOLLOW-UP PROBLEM

Plot a titration curve for the titration of 30 mL of 0.25 mol/L HCl with standardized 0.25 mol/L NaOH.

Answer:

The following four points can be used:

mL of Base Added	pH
0	0.6
29.9	3.3
30	7.0
31	11.6

12-21
Titration of a Weak Acid With a Strong Base

In the titration of a weak acid with a strong base there is a rapid change in the pH around the equivalence point. However, the change in pH is modified by the buffering action of the solution.

In the case of the titration of a weak acid with a strong base, we must use the dissociation constant, K_a, for the dissociation of the weak acid. As with the titration of a strong acid with a strong base, we can calculate the pH of the solution at various points and use these points to plot a titration curve. Example 12-14 illustrates this type of calculation.

EXAMPLE 12-14
Calculating pH During the Titration of a Weak Acid With a Strong Base

A chemistry student titrates a 50 mL sample of 0.1 mol/L acetic acid (CH_3COOH) with standardized 0.1 mol/L NaOH. Calculate the pH of the solution at four points during the titration and plot a titration curve. K_a is 1.8×10^{-5} from Table 12-5.

SOLUTION

1. Write a balanced equation for the neutralization reaction:

$$CH_3COOH(aq) + OH^-(aq) \rightleftharpoons H_2O(l) + CH_3COO^-(aq)$$

2. Using Equation 12-11, calculate the pH of the acid sample before the titration begins. From the stoichiometry of

the equation, we know that

$$[H_3O^+] = [CH_3COO^-]$$
$$[CH_3COOH] = 0.1 \text{ mol/L} - [H_3O^+]$$

However, if we assume that the $[H_3O^+]$ is much smaller than $[CH_3COOH]$, we can assume that its effect on the concentration of the acid is negligible. We can therefore assume that

$$[CH_3COOH] = 0.1 \text{ mol/L}$$

Thus,

$$K_a = \frac{[H_3O^+][CH_3COO^-]}{[CH_3COOH]}$$
$$[H_3O^+]^2 = (1.8 \times 10^{-5})(0.1)$$
$$[H_3O^+] = 1.3 \times 10^{-3} \text{ mol/L}$$
$$pH = -\log (1.3 \times 10^{-3})$$
$$= 2.87$$

3. Calculate the pH after 25.0 mL of NaOH has been added to the acid. At this point, one-half of the acetic acid has been consumed and an equal amount of acetate (CH_3COO^-) has been produced. Thus,

$$[CH_3COOH] = [CH_3COO^-]$$

Since

$$[H_3O^+] = \frac{[CH_3COOH]}{[CH_3COO^-]} \cdot K_a$$

then

$$[H_3O^+] = K_a = 1.8 \times 10^{-5} \text{ mol/L}$$

and

$$pH = -\log (1.8 \times 10^{-5})$$
$$= 4.74$$

Note that at one-half the equivalence point, the pH = pK_a. This point is in the middle of the buffer region.

4. Calculate the pH at the equivalence point when 50 mL of NaOH has been added. First calculate the number of moles of CH_3COO^-. At this point all of the acetic acid is consumed. The moles of acetate that have formed at the equivalence point equal the number of moles of acid initially present.

$$\text{Number of moles} = (0.1 \text{ mol/L})(50 \text{ mL})$$
$$= (0.1 \text{ mol/L})(5.0 \times 10^{-2} \text{ L})$$
$$= 5.0 \times 10^{-3} \text{ mol}$$
$$[CH_3COO^-] = \frac{5.0 \times 10^{-3} \text{ mol}}{(50 \text{ mL} + 50 \text{ mL})}$$
$$= 5.0 \times 10^{-2} \text{ mol/L}$$

However, we must take into account the fact that the acetate acts as a Brønsted base according to the reaction,

$$CH_3COO^-(aq) + H_2O(l) \rightleftharpoons CH_3COOH(aq) + OH^-(aq)$$

At equilibrium,

$$[CH_3COOH] = [OH^-]$$

We can calculate pOH using Equations 12-16, 12-13 and 12-14. $K_b = 5.6 \times 10^{-10}$ from Table 12-8.

$$K_b = \frac{[CH_3COOH][OH^-]}{[CH_3COO^-]}$$
$$[OH^-]^2 = (5.6 \times 10^{-10})(5.0 \times 10^{-2})$$
$$[OH^-] = 5.29 \times 10^{-6} \text{ mol/L}$$
$$pOH = -\log (5.29 \times 10^{-6})$$
$$= 5.28$$
$$pH = 14 - pOH$$
$$= 14 - 5.28$$
$$= 8.72$$

5. Calculate the pH when an additional 0.1 mL (for a total of 50.1 mL) of NaOH is added past the endpoint. First calculate the number of moles of NaOH that have been added:

$$\text{Number of moles} = (0.1 \text{ mol/L})(0.1 \text{ mL})$$
$$= (0.1 \text{ mol/L})(1.0 \times 10^{-4} \text{ L})$$
$$= 1.0 \times 10^{-5} \text{ mol}$$

Since the NaOH completely dissociates,

$$[NaOH] = [OH^-] = \frac{1.0 \times 10^{-5} \text{ mol}}{(50 \text{ mL} + 50.1 \text{ mL})}$$
$$= \frac{1.0 \times 10^{-5} \text{ mol}}{1.01 \times 10^{-1} \text{ L}}$$
$$= 9.9 \times 10^{-5} \text{ mol/L}$$
$$pOH = -\log (9.9 \times 10^{-4})$$
$$= 4.0$$

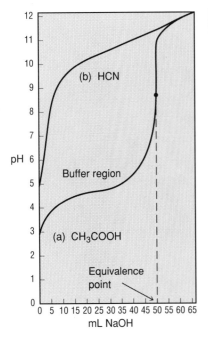

Figure 12-13
(a) Calculated curve for the titration of 50 mL of 0.1 mol/L CH₃COOH (weak acid) with 0.1 mol/L NaOH (strong base). (b) Calculated curve for the titration of 50 mL of 0.1 mol/L HCN with 0.1 mol/L NaOH.

Titration Curves and pH Meters
Rather than laboriously calculate pH values using the methods shown in the text, scientists use pH meters to obtain data for plotting titration curves. A pH meter is attached to an electrode containing a selective membrane that allows it to measure the amount of H_3O^+ in a solution. In this manner, a chemist can measure pH directly after each addition of standardized solution during the titration. Near the equivalence point, pH can be measured after the addition of each 0.1 mL of standard solution. In this way, many points are obtained for a titration curve plot, giving a much more accurate value for the equivalence point.

Therefore,

$$pH = 14 - pOH$$
$$= 14 - 4.0$$
$$= 10$$

The curve for the titration reaction in the preceding problem is shown in Fig. 12-13(a). Note that the vertical section of the curve is not nearly as long as that of the strong acid–strong base curve. This means that near the equivalence point, the change in pH for a given amount of added base is less for strong base–weak acid titration than for a strong acid–strong base titration. Thus, indicator endpoints are not as sharp for the former titration as for the latter. The reaction between OH^- and CH_3COOH produces CH_3COO^-, which, in the presence of CH_3COOH, constitutes a buffer solution. The gradual rather than sudden increase in pH can be attributed to the action of the buffer solution. This drastically reduces the choice of indicator. The pH at the equivalence point suggests that phenolphthalein could be used for this titration.

FOLLOW-UP PROBLEM
Plot a titration curve for the titration of 30 mL of 0.2 mol/L acetic acid with standardized 0.2 mol/L NaOH.

Answer:
The following four points can be used:

mL of Base Added	pH
0	2.7
15	4.74
30	8.9
31	11.5

THE LEWIS THEORY OF ACIDS AND BASES

12-22

Definition of Lewis Acids and Bases

Lewis defined acids and bases in terms of their ability to accept or donate electron pairs. This is the least restrictive definition, since acids do not need to contain hydrogen.

Both the Arrhenius and Brønsted-Lowry theories limit the classification of acids to substances that contain hydrogen. This restriction does not allow a number of substances that behave similarly to acids to be designated as acids. In 1923, Gilbert N. Lewis, an American chemist, proposed a more general theory of acids and bases. The Lewis definitions are:

– An acid is an electron-pair acceptor.
– A base is an electron-pair donor.
– An acid-base reaction involves the formation of a co-ordinate covalent bond between the electron-pair donor (base) and the electron-pair acceptor (acid).

These definitions indicate that any substance with an *unshared pair of electrons* in the outer energy level can act as a ***Lewis base*** and any substance with an *available empty orbital* can act as a ***Lewis acid***.

Lewis acids need not contain hydrogen. A substance that qualifies as a Brønsted base will also be a Lewis base; that is, in order to accept a proton, a substance must donate a pair of electrons. Thus, NH_3 is acting as both a Brønsted and a Lewis base when it reacts with water and forms NH_4^+. Note that when we apply the Lewis theory to a Brønsted acid-base reaction, the *proton itself* is the Lewis acid rather than the species that donates it.

The most familiar Lewis acids can be grouped into the categories listed below.

1. *Molecules having a central atom with an incomplete octet or containing multiple bonds (except between carbon atoms).* Examples of Lewis acid-base reactions are

$$BF_3 + NH_3 \longrightarrow H_3NBF_3$$

Lewis acid	Lewis base	co-ordination compound containing co-ordinate bond

$$SO_3 + \left[:\ddot{O}: \right]^{2-} \longrightarrow \left[\begin{array}{c} O \\ O:\ddot{S}:O \\ O \end{array} \right]^{2-}$$

Lewis acid	Lewis base	ion containing co-ordinate bond

2. *Molecules with a central atom capable of expanding its outer octet by using empty d orbitals.* An example is

$$SnCl_4 + 2Cl^- \rightleftharpoons SnCl_6^{2-}$$

Lewis acid	Lewis base	complex ion containing co-ordinate bond

Because a tin atom has a complete outer octet in $SnCl_4$

GILBERT NEWTON LEWIS
1875–1946
G. N. Lewis received a PhD in chemistry from Harvard University in 1899, and in 1905 joined the Research Laboratory of Physical Chemistry at the Massachusetts Institute of Technology. He remained there until 1912, when he became professor of chemistry at the University of California. During his 30-year career at this university, he helped build one of the finest chemistry departments of any university. Although Lewis never received a Nobel Prize himself, a number of his students did receive this honour.

Lewis received many honours for his work on the electron theory of the covalent bond and the electron theory of acids and bases. For many years, chemists believed that one particular element or group of elements was responsible for the observed properties of acids and bases. Lewis recognized the limitations of this belief and stated, "To restrict the group of acids to those substances which contain hydrogen interferes as seriously with the systematic understanding of chemistry as would the restriction of the term 'oxidizing agent' to substances containing oxygen."

As a result of his search for a more fundamental property common to all acids or bases, Lewis developed his generalized electronic theory. This theory permits the inclusion of a vast number of reactions within the scope of acid-base phenomena and has, therefore, helped chemists to systematize the study of chemical reactions.

molecules, it must use empty d orbitals in its fifth energy level to accept electron pairs from chloride ions.

3. *Simple cations.* All simple cations have an empty orbital in their outer energy level and can, in theory, act as Lewis acids. For example, Zn^{2+} ions have ten electrons in the $3d$ energy level but none in the 4th level. The empty orbitals in the 4th level are available for co-ordinate bond formation. In aqueous solution, Zn^{2+} ions react with four water molecules and form $Zn(H_2O)_4^{2+}$ ions. The four water molecules each share a pair of their electrons with a Zn^{2+} ion. Thus, the water molecules act as Lewis bases and the Zn^{2+} ions act as Lewis acids. The hydrated ion $Zn(H_2O)_4^{2+}$ has a tetrahedral configuration (sp^3 hybrid orbitals). The reaction can be represented by the equation

$$Zn^{2+}(aq) + 4H_2O(l) \rightleftharpoons Zn(H_2O)_4^{2+}(aq)$$

The strength of cations as acids increases with increasing charge density. Thus, zinc ions with a large charge and a small radius have a high charge density and are a much stronger Lewis acid than K^+ ions. In Chapter 11 you learned that charge density depends on the charge and radius of an ion. The charge density of an ion with a given radius increases as the charge increases. The charge density also increases as the radius of an ion with a given charge decreases. The ionic radius decreases as you go from left to right and increases from top to bottom in the periodic table. This means that the acid strength of cations with the same charge generally increases as you go from left to right and decreases as you go from top to bottom in the periodic table.

12-23

Comparison of the Lewis Theory With the Arrhenius and Brønsted-Lowry Theories

Covalent bonds can be classified according to the mechanism of formation as either simple covalent or co-ordinate covalent, depending on whether each atom contributed an electron to the pair or one atom contributed both electrons. In a given molecule, the bonds are identical.

When a covalent bond is broken in a chemical reaction, the shared pair of electrons must either stay with one of the atoms or be divided between the two atoms. Likewise, when a covalent bond is formed in a reaction, each atom must either contribute one electron to the shared pair, or one atom must contribute both. Thus, all reactions that involve the breaking or forming of covalent bonds can be grouped in one of two categories: those in which *the bonding electrons remain intact* and those in which *the bonding electrons are divided between two atoms*. The breadth and unifying characteristic of the Lewis theory enable us to classify all reactions in which the bonding pair of electrons remains intact as *acid-base reactions*. Reactions in which the electron pair is divided so that each atom temporarily has an unpaired electron are known as *free-radical reactions*. Many oxidations occurring in the gaseous phase are of this type.

In going from the Arrhenius to the Brønsted-Lowry and finally to the Lewis theory, we have gone from a very restrictive, limited definition to a very general theory. The Arrhenius theory has only one kind of acid (H^+) and one kind of base (OH^-) and is restricted to aqueous solutions. The Brønsted-Lowry theory has only one kind of acid (must contain a proton) but many bases (any proton acceptor) and can be applied to aqueous or non-aqueous systems. The Lewis theory has many acids (any electron-pair acceptor) and many bases (any electron-pair donor). This information is summarized in Table 12-12. It should be emphasized that each of the theories has certain advantages and useful applications. They all help us to systematize the study of chemical reactions.

TABLE 12-12
SUMMARY OF ACID-BASE THEORIES

Theory	Acid	Base
Arrhenius (in water only)	Specific: substances that furnish hydrogen ions (protons) in water solution	Specific: substances that furnish hydroxide ions in water solution
Brønsted (in any solvent)	Specific: substances that donate protons (H^+)	General: substances that accept protons
Lewis (in any solvent)	General: electron-pair acceptors (may or may not contain hydrogen)	General: electron-pair donors

We have now considered the qualitative and quantitative aspects of molecular equilibria and acid-base equilibria. However, up to this point we have been primarily concerned with reactions that do not involve the transfer of electrons from one reactant to another. We can classify most reactions into the following categories:

1. *Formation of a precipitate (precipitation reactions)*. These are reactions between ions that occur in response to the strong electrostatic forces of attraction between oppositely charged

ions, and generally result in the formation of a slightly soluble ionic solid. An example is

$$Ag^+(aq) + I^-(aq) \rightleftharpoons AgI(s)$$

2. *Formation of a weakly dissociated species or gas.* These reactions occur when strong covalent bonds are formed between reactant ions. Examples are

$$S^{2-}(aq) + 2H_3O^+(aq) \rightleftharpoons H_2S(g) + 2H_2O(l)$$
$$NH_4^+(aq) + OH^-(aq) \rightleftharpoons NH_3(g) + H_2O(l)$$

3. *Formation of a complex ion.* These reactions occur when stable co-ordinate bonds are formed between positive ions and electron-donor species, called *ligands*. Examples are

$$Cu^{2+}(aq) + 4NH_3(aq) \rightleftharpoons Cu(NH_3)_4^{2+}(aq)$$
$$Cu(OH)_2 + 3CN^-(aq) \rightleftharpoons Cu(CN)_3^-(aq) + 2OH^-(aq)$$

There is one more important type of chemical reaction that we must consider before we conclude our study of reactions and reaction principles. This is the *oxidation-reduction reaction*. Oxidation-reduction reactions take place because one reactant has a greater attraction for electrons than another. This suggests that oxidation-reduction reactions involve an electron transfer between reacting species. Thus, in a way, oxidation-reduction reactions involving electron transfer are similar to acid-base reactions involving proton transfer.

We will devote the next chapter to a detailed investigation of oxidation-reduction reactions. You will find that many familiar phenomena can be explained in terms of oxidation-reduction principles. All combustion processes, battery reactions, electroplating operations and corrosion processes involve oxidation-reduction reactions.

ACID RAIN

Since the early 1960s, scientists have been cautioning us about the cumulative effects of acid rain. They even warn us that if it is not stopped, the damage it is doing to our environment may prove irreversible, with long-term consequences for many life forms, including our own.

Simply defined, acid rain is precipitation (rain or snow) whose pH value is lower than 5.6, the average pH of normal rain. This slightly acidic value is the result of atmospheric carbon dioxide, which dissolves in precipitation to produce dilute carbonic acid:

$$CO_2(g) + H_2O \rightleftharpoons H_2CO_3(aq)$$
$$\text{carbon} \quad \text{water} \quad \text{carbonic acid}$$
$$\text{dioxide}$$

Rains with pH values below 5.6 have occurred throughout time—the result of natural sources of air pollution such as volcanic activity and forest fires. Nature produces such rains infrequently, however, and they are not normally of concern.

The two major pollutants that cause acid rain—sulfur oxides and nitrogen oxides—are the unwanted by-products of many of our industrial and energy-consuming processes, such as the smelting of ores and the burning of fossil fuels. Between one-third and one-half of atmospheric sulfur dioxide (SO_2) is produced by human activity, mostly from the burning of coal in power plants. The remainder comes from natural sources such as volcanoes. When nickel(II) sulfide is smelted, for example, the products are nickel and sulfur dioxide:

$$NiS(s) + O_2(g) \xrightarrow{\text{heat}} Ni(s) + SO_2(g)$$

nickel oxygen   nickel   sulfur
sulfide   dioxide

Less than 5% of the nitrogen oxides (NO, NO_2) in the atmosphere are produced by human activity; most are produced by lightning, volcanoes and bacterial action. The nitrogen oxides that we do produce are concentrated in our cities where there are large numbers of cars. Nitrogen oxide results from the high-temperature combustion of such fuels as oil and gas in car, truck and power-plant engines. Under these conditions, atmospheric nitrogen and oxygen react as follows:

$$N_2(g) + O_2(g) \xrightarrow{\text{heat}} 2NO(g)$$

nitrogen   oxygen   nitrogen
monoxide

  Both sulfur dioxide and nitrogen monoxide escape into the atmosphere where they may be carried tens, hundreds or even thousands of kilometres. When exposed to sunlight, a portion of each gas reacts with atmospheric nitrogen to produce sulfur trioxide and nitrogen dioxide, respectively:

$$2SO_2(g) + O_2(g) \xrightarrow{\text{sunlight}} 2SO_3(g)$$

sulfur   oxygen   sulfur
dioxide   trioxide

$$2NO(g) + O_2(g) \xrightarrow{\text{sunlight}} 2NO_2(g)$$

nitrogen   oxygen   nitrogen
monoxide   dioxide

When it rains or snows, sulfur dioxide, sulfur trioxide and nitrogen dioxide all dissolve in water vapour to form acids:

$$SO_2(g) + H_2O(l) \longrightarrow H_2SO_3(aq)$$
sulfurous acid

$$SO_3(g) + H_2O(l) \longrightarrow H_2SO_4(aq)$$
sulfuric acid

$$2NO_2(g) + H_2O(l) \longrightarrow HNO_2(aq) + HNO_3(aq)$$
nitrous acid   nitric acid

These four acids may then fall to earth in snow or rain (*wet deposition*) or as part of the matter adhering to precipitating dust particles (*dry deposition*). Areas located downwind of major sulfur oxide and nitrogen oxide producers are especially at risk.

  How acid is acid rain? Typical measurements from areas downwind of polluting sources show frequent, regular precipitation between pH 4 and 4.5—considerably more acidic than unpolluted rain. Even more acidic rainfalls occasionally happen. A 1974 storm in Scotland, for example, brought a rain with pH values lower than vinegar, while a 1978 storm soaked the inhabitants of Wheeling, West Virginia, with rain more acidic than lime juice. Shocking as these acutely acidic rainfalls are, they are uncommon and typically occur near their polluting sources, seldom accounting for more than a negligible amount of the overall damage caused by acid rain. Far more serious are the chronic, constantly acidic precipitations such as those experienced at Dorset, Ontario, and other points in eastern Canada. During one week of rain at Dorset in 1981, for example, the pH ranged between 3.37 and 4.29. Although exceptional, these values are only slightly more acidic than those to which Dorset and other points in eastern North America are steadily exposed.

  What damage is caused by chronic exposure to acidic deposition? The first damage usually observed is that to property. Exposed metal, glass, paint, stone and concrete can all be pitted or dulled by acid rain. At greatest risk are buildings, monuments and statues made of limestone and marble, whose composition is largely calcium carbonate. For example, calcium carbonate reacts with sulfuric acid as follows:

$$CaCO_3 + H_2SO_4(aq) \longrightarrow CaSO_4(s) + CO_2(g) + H_2O$$
calcium   sulfuric   calcium   carbon   water
carbonate   acid   sulfate   dioxide

Calcium sulfate is soluble and, therefore, is gradually washed away. Thousands of priceless historic buildings and statues are being seriously damaged in this way. The Acropolis in Athens is one such victim. The Sphinx may be another.

  More subtle, but ultimately more serious, is the damage acid deposition does to our environment and the effects these changes are having on species survival and human health. Regions downwind of acidic precipitation whose underlying soils and bedrock contain limestone or other alkaline substances can normally neutralize much of the acid they receive. Regions whose soils are already acidic and/or whose bedrock offers little or no alkaline buffering, like much of the vast terrain of the Canadian Shield and parts of the Appalachian zone of eastern Canada, aren't so lucky. During the winter, acidic precipitation in these regions accumulates as snow. In spring, the melting snow sends a sudden acid shock, sometimes as low as pH 4.0, into rivers and lakeshores just when many species such as trout, suckers, darters, frogs and salamanders are spawning. Their eggs and young typically have little capacity to tolerate this shock and may not survive. Those that do must still face the gradual increase of water acidity steadily brought by each new melting snow or rain.

As a body of water acidifies, its inhabitants begin to disappear, species by species. Among the first to go are freshwater mussels (a favourite food of raccoons and skunks) as the pH drops below 6.5. Below pH 6.0, small-mouth bass die out. At about pH 5.7, opossum shrimp become extinct, depriving young lake trout of a staple food. Other staple fish foods—crayfish and amphipods—begin to succumb below this level. Snails, eaten by birds that wade the shallows, disappear when the pH goes below 5.5, followed by the common shiner, sunfish and blue-gill at pH 5.3. When the pH drops below 5.0, only yellow perch and chubs are able to survive. Important insects such as mayflies, stoneflies and dragonflies are unable to breed successfully. Most of the underwater plant life, including the yellow water lilies on which moose feed, are replaced by disagreeable, foul-smelling algal blooms. Finally, below pH 4.7, the perch and chubs succumb, rendering the lake "dead" except for the undesirable, acid-tolerant algae.

Thousands of lakes in Canada and the northeastern United States and thousands more around the world are already dead from acid rain, while hundreds of thousands are threatened. The damage, however, does not stop here. Acid rain causes direct damage to plant foliage, bark and roots. Additionally, it leaches toxic metal cations from soils and bedrock, particularly aluminum, lead, cadmium and mercury. The reaction of hydrogen ions with insoluble aluminum hydroxide is typical:

$$Al(OH)_3(s) + 3H^+(aq) \longrightarrow Al^{3+}(aq) + 3H_2O$$

| aluminum | hydrogen | aluminum | water |
| hydroxide | ions | ion | |

The aluminum ions are taken up by plant roots, particularly those of trees, with lethal effects. Thousands of hectares of economically valuable maple forests are dying in eastern Canada, the northeastern U.S., Europe and elsewhere. Ions not taken up by plant roots are transported into groundwater wells and reservoirs or into lakes and rivers where they can accumulate in the tissues of aquatic species, making them unsafe to eat. Communities that take their drinking water from these resources may find it similarly contaminated.

The cost of acid rain is staggering. Decaying buildings, statues and monuments tax the public purse at the same time that industries such as forestry, maple-sugar products, tourism, fishing and agriculture are seriously harmed. Numerous species with which we share the planet, along with our water supplies and our health, are threatened. The photo shows a severely deformed smallmouthed bass that experts believe may be the result of acid rain. Scientists warn that the problems of acid rain, coupled with those of the greenhouse effect and the depletion of the ozone layer, may be leading toward the mass extinction of species.

What can be done to lessen the effects of acid rain? Experiments in Sweden and Canada indicate that the pH of endangered lakes can be raised by adding pulverized limestone (calcium carbonate). The calcium carbonate reacts with hydronium ions as follows:

$$CaCO_3(s) + 2H_3O^+(aq) \longrightarrow Ca^{2+}(aq) + CO_2(g) + H_2O$$

| calcium | hydrogen | calcium | carbon | water |
| carbonate | ions | ion | dioxide | |

Although this procedure will neutralize the acid, it cannot bring back species that have died out. It is also cumbersome and expensive, and must be repeated each year. At best, therefore, this method is only an interim solution for selected waters.

The only real solution is to drastically curtail the emissions that cause acid rain, particularly sulfur dioxide. The technology to do this exists—by either removing the sulfur content from fuels before or during the combustion process or by using other fuels. These options can be expensive, however, and the roadblocks to their implementation are often political in nature. Because gases and rains do not respect international boundaries, unilateral agreements and commitments are necessary for success. To date, however, we have lacked the political will to deal with acid rain as a global problem.

Happily, that may be changing. The majority of Canada's provinces have embarked on a program to cut their acidic emissions in half by 1994. The United States has stated that it will bring in new legislation to enforce significant cuts in emissions by specified dates. Many European states have already committed themselves to serious reductions. Also encouraging is the admission by the Soviet Union that they have serious pollution problems that must be quickly addressed. Their involvement in a program to reduce acidic emissions would mean a commitment by most of the major industrial nations across the northern hemisphere. Perhaps then we could all breathe a little easier.

QUESTIONS

1. Name and identify each of the following as strong or weak, acid or base, in aqueous solution: (a) HCl, (b) NH_4OH, (c) $H_2C_2O_4$, (d) KOH, (e) NaOH, (f) H_2S, (g) HBr, (h) HCN, (i) $Ca(OH)_2$, (j) H_3BO_3, (k) H_2CO_3, (l) HF, (m) $HClO_4$, (n) $Ba(OH)_2$, (o) H_2SO_3.

2. Write formulas for the conjugate bases for each of these acids: (a) HCl, (b) CH_4, (c) HSO_3^-, (d) H_2SO_4, (e) NH_3, (f) $HClO_4$.

3. Write equations that represent the dissociation of each of the following acids or bases in aqueous solution. Use a single arrow to show the dissociation of strong acids and bases, and a double arrow to represent the equilibrium condition that exists in the solution of a weak acid or base. Show each step of dissociation for polyprotic acids.
(a) $Ba(OH)_2$, (b) HNO_3, (c) $HC_2H_3O_2$, (d) H_2CO_3, (e) $H_2C_2O_4$

4. Draw the electron-dot structures for the following species and show that each has an unshared pair of electrons: (a) NH_3, (b) CH_3^-, (c) H_2O, (d) CH_3OH, (e) Cl^-, (f) SO_4^{2-}, (g) S^{2-}, (h) NH_2^-, (i) HSO_3^-.

5. Write the equation for the reaction of each of the following ions with water. Experiments show that b, c, and d form acid solutions.
(a) HCO_3^-, (b) $H_2PO_4^-$, (c) HSO_4^-, (d) NH_4^+
(e) HS^-, (f) HPO_4^{2-}, (g) S^{2-}, (h) CO_3^{2-}

6. Show how each of the following acids reacts with water and forms a conjugate acid-base pair: (a) HCl, (b) HNO_3, (c) H_2SO_4, (d) $HClO_4$, (e) H_2S, (f) H_3PO_4.

7. (a) Write the reaction of water with each of the species listed in question 2. (b) Label the acid-base pairs formed.

8. Use Table 12-2 to predict whether a reaction between the following pairs occurs to any appreciable extent. Identify the reacting Brønsted acids and bases. (a) $HCl + H_2O$, (b) $H_2O + H_2SO_4$, (c) $HSO_4^- + H_3O^+$, (d) $HS^- + H_3O^+$, (e) $CH_3COOH + H_2SO_4$, (f) $HClO_4 + OH^-$, (g) $HCO_3^- + OH^-$, (h) $NH_3 + HSO_3^-$

9. The formation of products is strongly favoured in this acid-base system:

$$HX + B^- \rightleftharpoons HB + X^-$$

a) Identify the bases competing for protons.
b) Which base is stronger?
c) Which is the weaker acid, HX or HB?
d) Does the K for this system have a large or small value?
e) How is the equilibrium affected by the addition of the soluble salt NaB?

10. Separate solutions of two acids, HX and HY, have the same pH. Does this mean that the molar concentration of the acids is identical? Explain.

11. Identify the following 1.0 mol/L solutions as basic or acidic. Explain. (a) Na_2CO_3, (b) Na_2S, (c) $FeCl_3$, (d) $(NH_4)_2SO_4$, (e) $Al_2(SO_4)_3$, (f) $MgSO_4$, (g) $KHCO_3$, (h) $AgNO_3$, (i) NH_4I, (j) $NaHSO_4$

12. (a) What are buffer solutions? (b) Why are they useful?

13. Write the equilibrium expression for the indicator HIn. When [In$^-$] and [HIn] are equal, how do the values for K_a and [H$^+$] compare?

14. Boric acid is a much weaker acid than acetic acid. Is a solution of sodium borate more or less basic than a solution of sodium acetate? Explain.

15. A solution of sodium cyanide has a much higher pH than a solution of sodium fluoride. On the basis of this observation, is the value of K_a for HCN larger or smaller than the K_a for HF? Explain.

16. Suggest a reason why the concentration of an NaOH solution changes when it is exposed to air for an extended period of time.

17. Use Le Châtelier's principle to explain the change in pH observed when NH_4Cl is added to an NH_3 solution.

18. What are the general requirements for a volumetric analysis?

19. What is the difference between the terms *equivalence point* and *endpoint*?

20. Use the concept of charge density to explain that HI is a stronger acid than HF.

21. Explain the increasing acid strength of the hydrogen halides as one goes from fluoride to iodide.

22. Does the neutralization of an acid with a standard base always provide a measure of the hydronium ion concentration of the original acid solution? Explain.

23. Explain the differences in acid strength of the oxyacids that contain chlorine.

24. On the basis of the different oxidation states of the central atom, which of the following oxyacids is the stronger: (a) HXO_3 or (b) HXO_4? Explain.

25. Which is the stronger acid, an aqueous solution of H_2Se or one of H_2S? Explain.

26. Explain why H_2SO_4 is a stronger acid than H_2TeO_4.

27. Which is the stronger acid, H_3AsO_4 or H_3SbO_4? Explain.

28. KOH, H_3AsO_4 and $HClO_4$ all contain one or more OH groups. Explain, in terms of bonding principles, why KOH is a base, whereas H_3AsO_4 and $HClO_4$ are acids in water.

29. (a) With the aid of electron-dot structures, show how phosphine (PH_3) and ammonia both act as Brønsted bases when added to water. (b) Name the ions formed.

30. Draw the Lewis structures for each of these compounds: (a) BF_3, (b) NH_3, (c) NCl_3.

31. Which of the following could act as Lewis acids but not as Brønsted acids? (a) HCl, (b) H_2SO_4, (c) SO_3, (d) HSO_3^-, (e) BF_3, (f) CH_3COOH, (g) $SnCl_4$, (h) SeF_4

32. In the following reactions, identify the Lewis acid and the Lewis base:
    a) $Fe^{3+} + 6H_2O \rightleftharpoons Fe(H_2O)_6^{3+}$
    b) $BF_3 + NH_3 \rightleftharpoons F_3BNH_3$
    c) $BF_3 + F^- \rightleftharpoons BF_4^-$
    d) $H^+ + Cl^- \rightleftharpoons HCl$

PROBLEMS

1. Calculate the pH of a solution in which the $[H_3O^+]$ equals (a) 1.0 mol/L, (b) 0.1 mol/L, (c) 0.01 mol/L, (d) 1.0×10^{-7} mol/L, (e) 3.0×10^{-7} mol/L, (f) 4.0×10^{-10} mol/L.

2. What is the pOH of each of the solutions in problem 1?
   Answers: (b) 13, (d) 7, (f) 4.6

3. Calculate the $[H_3O^+]$ and the pH of HCl solutions that are (a) 1.0 mol/L, (b) 6.0 mol/L, (c) 12 mol/L. Assume 100% dissociation.

4. A solution of hydrofluoric acid contains 2.0 g of HF per litre and has a pH of 2.2. What is the dissociation constant for HF?

5. What is the H_3O^+ ion concentration of solutions whose pH and pOH values are (a) pH = 5.0, (b) pOH = 3.0, (c) pH = 3.7, (d) pOH = 9.5?
   Answer: (d) 3.2×10^{-5} mol/L

6. Calculate the $[H_3O^+]$, pH and percentage dissociation of the following solutions: (a) 1.0 mol/L HCN, (b) 0.001 mol/L HCN, (c) 1.0 mol/L HF, (d) 0.50 mol/L HNO_2, (e) 0.5 mol/L $HCHO_2$, (f) 0.50 mol/L H_3BO_3.
   Answer: (d) $[H_3O^+] = 1.5 \times 10^{-2}$ mol/L, pH = 1.8, dissociation = 3.0%

7. A 0.100 mol/L solution of a weak monoprotic acid is 6.0% dissociated. What is the dissociation constant?
   Answer: 3.8×10^{-4}

8. A 1.0×10^{-3} mol/L solution of a weak acid, HX, is 20.0% dissociated. (a) What is the pH of the solution? (b) What is the concentration of X^-? (c) What is the dissociation constant for the acid?
   Answer: (a) pH = 3.7

9. Calculate the $[H_3O^+]$, $[OH^-]$, pH and pOH of the following solutions:
   a) 1.0 mol/L HCl
   b) 0.50 mol/L HNO_3
   c) 0.0020 mol/L $HClO_4$
   d) 1.5×10^{-4} mol/L KOH
   e) a solution prepared by dissolving 0.040 g NaOH in 2.0 L of solution
   f) a solution prepared by diluting 1.0 mL of 0.20 mol/L HCl to a total volume of 5.0 L
   g) a solution made by dissolving 0.10 mol Na_2O in 1.0 L of solution
   Answers: (d) $[H_3O^+] = 6.7 \times 10^{-11}$ mol/L, $[OH^-] = 1.5 \times 10^{-4}$ mol/L, pH = 10.2, pOH = 3.8; (g) $[H_3O^+] = 5.0 \times 10^{-14}$, $[OH^-] = 0.20$ mol/L, pH = 13.30

10. Hypobromous acid (HBrO) has a dissociation constant of 2.0×10^{-9}. A solution of HBrO has a pH of 4.8. What is the concentration of the solution?

11. Calculate the $[OH^-]$, pOH and pH of the following solutions: (a) 1.0 mol/L NH_3, (b) 0.10 mol/L aniline ($C_6H_5NH_2$), (c) 5.0×10^{-2} mol/L hydrazine (N_2H_4), (d) 0.20 mol/L hydroxylamine (NH_2OH), (e) 1.5 mol/L trimethylamine $[(CH_3)_3N]$.
    Answers: (b) $[OH^-] = 6.4 \times 10^{-6}$ mol/L, pOH = 5.2, pH = 8.8; (d) $[OH^-] = 3.6 \times 10^{-5}$ mol/L, pOH = 4.4, pH = 9.6

12. (a) What is the pH of a solution made by combining 0.60 mol of acetic acid with 0.40 mol of sodium acetate in enough water to make one litre of solution? (b) What is the pH of this solution if four additional litres of water are added to it?

13. What concentration of sodium acetate is required to prepare a solution in which the pH is 5.0 and the acetic acid is 0.10 mol/L?
    Answer: 0.18 mol/L

14. Calculate the [OH⁻], pOH and pH of the following solutions: (a) 0.10 mol/L Na_2SO_3, (b) 0.50 mol/L KCN, (c) 1.0 mol/L Na_2CO_3, (d) 0.05 mol/L $NaC_7H_5O_2$, (e) 0.2 mol/L NaClO.
Answer: (c) [OH⁻] = 1.4 × 10⁻² mol/L, pOH = 1.8, pH = 12.2

15. What mass of NH_4Cl must be added to 0.500 L of 1.0 mol/L NH_3 solution to yield a solution with a pH of 9.0? Assume no change in volume occurs.
Answer: 48 g

16. A buffer solution is prepared by adding 1.0 mol of NH_4Cl to 1 L of a solution containing 1.0 mol NH_3.
a) What is the pH of the solution?
b) What is the pH of the solution resulting from the addition of 1.0 mmol of HCl to 10.0 mL of the buffer? Assume no volume change occurs.
c) What is the pH of the solution resulting from the addition of 1.0 mmol NaOH to 10.00 mL of the buffer? Assume no volume change.
d) How many mL of 6 mol/L HCl would be required to change the pH of one litre of buffer by 1 pH unit?
Answers: (b) 9.17, (d) 137 mL

17. How many millilitres of 0.200 mol/L NaOH are required to neutralize 50.0 mL of 0.100 mol/L HCl?
Answer: 25 mL

18. Calculate the value of K for the following reactions. Use the value of K to predict whether the reaction is quantitative and suitable as a basis for a quantitative analysis. Only one proton is removed from H_3BO_3.
(a) HF + OH⁻, (b) H_3BO_3 + OH⁻

19. How many mL of 0.100 mol/L NaOH are required to react completely with 0.400 g of oxalic acid dihydrate ($H_2C_2O_4\cdot2H_2O$)?

20. A solution is prepared by dissolving 0.0370 g of $Ba(OH)_2$ and 0.855 g of KOH in 50.0 mL of solution. How many mL of 0.500 mol/L HCl are required to react with a 25.0 mL sample of this solution?

21. What is the concentration of an NaOH solution if 32.20 mL is needed to titrate a 1.10 g sample of potassium biphthalate ($KHC_8H_4O_4$)?
Answer: 0.168 mol/L

22. What is the percentage of $KHC_8H_4O_4$ in an impure sample, 1.00 g of which requires 25.0 mL of 0.100 mol/L NaOH for neutralization?

23. A 15.20 mL sample of vinegar has a specific gravity of 1.060 and requires 42.40 mL of 0.3460 mol/L NaOH for titration to the endpoint. What is the percentage by mass of acetic acid ($HC_2H_3O_2$) in the vinegar?

24. An impure sample of $Ba(OH)_2$ with a mass of 0.500 g was added to 50.00 mL of 0.100 mol/L HCl. The excess HCl was titrated with 7.50 mL of 0.200 mol/L NaOH. What was the percentage of $Ba(OH)_2$ in the sample?
Answer: 59.8%

25. For each of the following titrations, specify the indicator(s) from column II that should be used. State your reason, but do not make any quantitative calculations.

I Titration	II Indicator pH range
a) NaOH + $KHC_8H_4O_4$	a) neutral red (6.8–8.0)
b) NaOH + HCl	b) bromcresol green (3.8–5.4)
c) $NaHCO_3$ + HCl	c) *o*-cresolphthalein (8.2–9.8)

26. Refer to Table 12-11 and choose a suitable indicator for each of these titrations: (a) H_2SO_4 and NaOH, (b) $Ca(OH)_2$ and CH_3COOH, (c) HCl and $NH_3(aq)$.

27. Fifty mL of 0.200 mol/L NH_3 solution is titrated with 0.200 mol/L HCl solution. K_b for NH_3 is 1.8×10^{-5}. (a) Calculate the pH value of the solution at the start of the titration. (b) Calculate the pH of the solution when the base is one-half neutralized (one-half way to the equivalence point). (c) Calculate the pH at the equivalence point. (d) Calculate the pH after 75.0 mL of the acid has been added.
    Answers: (a) 11.28, (b) 9.26

28. Calculate the pH of the solution resulting from the following reactions:
    a) 30.0 mL of 0.200 mol/L NaOH and 30.00 mL of 0.200 mol/L HCl
    b) 30.0 mL of 0.200 mol/L NaOH and 40.0 mL of 0.200 mol/L HCl
    c) 50.0 mL of 0.10 mol/L HCl and 50 mL of 0.10 mol/L $NaC_2H_3O_2$
    d) 25.0 mL of 0.10 mol/L HCl and 50.0 mL of 0.10 mol/L $NaC_2H_3O_2$
    e) 50.0 mL of 0.10 mol/L NH_4Cl and 50.0 mL of 0.10 mol/L NaOH
    Answer: (b) 1.48

29. Thirty mL of 0.150 mol/L HCOOH is titrated with 0.150 mol/L NaOH.
    a) Calculate the pH of the solution after 15.0 mL of base has been added.
    b) Calculate the pH of the solution after 30.0 mL of base has been added.
    c) Calculate the pH after 40.0 mL of base has been added.

30. A 20.0 mL sample of a weak acid, HX, requires 50.0 mL of 0.050 mol/L NaOH to reach the endpoint. After the addition of 30.0 mL of the base, the pH of the solution is 5.00. What is the dissociation constant for HX?
    Answer: $K_a = 1.5 \times 10^{-5}$

The copper-covered roofs of Canada's Parliament Buildings in Ottawa have undergone oxidation reactions over the years. The copper metal has been oxidized to produce blue-green copper carbonate and copper hydroxide.

OXIDATION-REDUCTION REACTIONS AND ELECTROCHEMISTRY

"The world little knows how many of the thoughts and theories which have passed through the mind of a scientific investigator have been crushed in silence and secrecy by his own severe criticism and adverse examinations; that in the most successful instances not a tenth of the suggestions, the hopes, the wishes, the preliminary conclusions have been realized."

Michael Faraday (1791–1867)

Every time you listen to a portable cassette player, turn on a flashlight or start an automobile, you are using electric energy released by the chemical reactions taking place in a battery. Spontaneous reactions, which liberate electric energy, and nonspontaneous reactions, which consume electric energy, are all part of a large and important class of reactions known as *oxidation-reduction reactions*. These are frequently referred to as *redox reactions*.

Oxidation-reduction reactions also play an important part in industrial processes. Large quantities of pure metals, such as aluminum, magnesium and copper, are only available because of the electrolytic processes used to refine them. This process, known as *electrolysis*, is also used for electroplating.

Not all oxidation-reduction reactions, however, are beneficial. Corrosion, for example, is a redox reaction responsible for the deterioration of metals. The salt (NaCl) spread on winter roads reduces the number of accidents but also increases the rate of corrosion on automobiles and steel bridges. Consequently, a great deal of industrial research is directed to developing ways of inhibiting corrosion.

In this chapter, we will first examine and learn to balance

equations for general, spontaneous oxidation-reduction reactions in which the reactants are in the same vessel. In many of these exothermic reactions, electrons are apparently transferred directly from one species to another. The decrease in potential energy (*enthalpy*) of these redox systems appears as heat given off to the surroundings.

In other systems, the reactants are in separate compartments, linked together by an electric conductor. The decrease in potential energy of these systems (called *voltaic*, *galvanic* or *electrochemical cells*) appears in large part as usable electrochemical energy. You will learn how to calculate the voltage for different electrochemical cells and how to relate this voltage to the spontaneity of a reaction and to the equilibrium constant for a reaction.

After examining a number of applications of electrochemical cells, we will consider redox reactions that take place in electrolytic cells. You will find that these reactions are the reverse of those that take place in electrochemical cells. That is, the reactions are nonspontaneous, so electric energy must be externally supplied in order for the reaction to take place. The electrolysis of water and the charging of an automobile battery are examples of reactions that take place in an electrolytic cell. Unlike the potential energy of the chemical system in a voltaic cell, that of the reaction system in electrolytic cells increases. This means that the products of electrolytic reactions have a higher enthalpy than the reactants.

After discussing applications of electrolytic cells, we will use the laws proposed by the great English chemist, Michael Faraday, to calculate the quantity of product yielded by a given current flowing through an electrolytic cell.

The study of redox reactions taking place in electrochemical or electrolytic cells is known as **electrochemistry**. The study of electrochemistry provides an opportunity to use and relate many of the major chemical concepts you have already encountered.

Redox Reactions in Biology
Essential to life, redox reactions occur in both plants and animals. For example, photosynthesis in plants involves a series of redox reactions in the breakdown of water and the formation of glucose. Respiration in animals involves redox reactions in which glucose is broken down to produce energy. Co-enzymes utilize redox reactions to work with enzymes to catalyze a variety of biological reactions.

OXIDATION-REDUCTION REACTIONS AND EQUATIONS

13-1
Oxidation-Reduction Reactions

Chemical reactions that involve the exchange of electrons are referred to as oxidation-reduction, or redox, reactions.
Like acid-base concepts, oxidation has evolved from a limited concept to a general one. Originally, this term was applied only to reactions in which a metal or a nonmetal combined with oxygen. It

soon became apparent, however, that there was a factor in the reactions of metals with oxygen that was common to many other reactions. This factor is the loss of electrons by metallic atoms, forming metallic ions. For example, in the oxidation reaction,

$$2Mg(s) + O_2(g) \longrightarrow 2MgO(s)$$

each magnesium atom loses two electrons and becomes a magnesium ion (Mg^{2+}), while each oxygen atom gains two electrons and becomes an oxide ion (O^{2-}). Experiments reveal that when magnesium atoms react with any acid or any nonmetal, they always lose two electrons per atom and become Mg^{2+} ions. These observations show that reactions involving oxygen constitute only a small percentage of the total number of reactions in which a substance loses electrons.

To help systematize the study of chemistry, chemists classify all reactions in which a substance loses electrons as ***oxidation reactions***; the process in which an atom or ion loses electrons is called ***oxidation***. Because electrons are not transferred to the surroundings in ordinary chemical reactions, this means that *the electrons lost by one species must be gained by another*. The process in which an atom or ion gains an electron is known as ***reduction***. The loss of electrons by one species and the simultaneous gain by another constitutes an ***oxidation-reduction***, or ***redox***, ***reaction***. Consider a reaction between magnesium and oxygen:

$$Mg(s) + \tfrac{1}{2}O_2(g) \longrightarrow MgO(s)$$

Essentially, the magnesium loses two electrons and the oxygen gains two electrons. Thus, magnesium is oxidized and oxygen is reduced. These changes can be shown by the equations that deal with each element separately:

$$Mg - 2e^- \longrightarrow Mg^{2+}$$
$$\tfrac{1}{2}O_2 + 2e^- \longrightarrow O^{2-}$$

Since oxygen is responsible for the oxidation of magnesium, it is called the *oxidizing agent*. Magnesium brings about the reduction of oxygen and is called the *reducing agent*.

$$Mg + \tfrac{1}{2}O_2 \longrightarrow MgO$$

reducing oxidizing
agent agent

Note that *oxidizing agents accept electrons and*, consequently, *become reduced*, while *reducing agents give up electrons and*

Ionization Energy Versus Oxidation
In Chapter 2, you studied the process of electron removal in the discussion of ionization energy. Ionization is the process involving the complete removal of an electron from a gaseous atom. Oxidation also involves the loss of electrons from atoms; however, the atoms exist in the solid or liquid state.

To keep oxidation and reduction reactions straight, remember the words OIL RIG:

> *Oxidation Is Loss*
> *Reduction Is Gain*

As you go left to right across the periodic table, the ease with which metals can be oxidized generally decreases. For example, sodium and magnesium are much more easily oxidized than iron or zinc. This also parallels the trends in the ionization energies for these elements, since the sodium is much more easily ionized than either the iron or the zinc.

become oxidized. As a result, the oxidation number of an oxidizing agent decreases, while that of a reducing agent increases.

13-2
Oxidation Numbers

An oxidation number is the charge that an atom in a compound would have if the electron pairs in the bond belonged solely to the more electronegative atom.

Oxidation-reduction reactions involve the transfer of electrons. In order to keep track of the electrons being transferred, we can assign oxidation numbers to each atom in a compound according to a set of rules.

In terms of oxidation numbers, *oxidation* can be defined as an *increase in oxidation number* and *reduction* as a *decrease in oxidation number*. In the reaction between magnesium and oxygen, the oxidation number of Mg increases from 0 to +2, while the oxidation number of each oxygen atom in O_2 decreases from 0 to −2. This means that if we are to recognize oxidation-reduction equations, we must be able to determine the oxidation numbers of atoms. For example, we identify the reaction

$$2H_2 + O_2 \longrightarrow 2H_2O$$

as an oxidation-reduction reaction because the oxidation numbers change, not because there is a complete transfer of electrons from hydrogen to oxygen. It is true that the oxygen atoms in H_2O have a greater share in the bonding electrons than hydrogen, but this does not mean that the hydrogen in a water molecule has a 1+ charge. Rather, it has an arbitrarily assigned oxidation number of +1. Thus, the concept of oxidation numbers enables us to readily identify the apparent electron transfer that occurs in oxidation-reduction reactions. Note that the sign of an oxidation number precedes the number, while the sign of an electric charge follows the number. Thus +2 is an oxidation number and 2+ is an electric charge.

Oxidation numbers for atoms in covalent molecules are based on arbitrarily chosen standards. In covalent bonds the electrons are arbitrarily assigned to the more electronegative atom. The rules for assigning and determining oxidation numbers are summarized below. You will need these rules to help you balance oxidation-reduction equations.

RULES FOR DETERMINING OXIDATION NUMBERS

1. The oxidation number of an atom in its pure form, such as Na or

Fe, or in a molecule of that element only, such as O_2 or P_4, is zero.

2. The oxidation number of a monatomic ion is the charge on the ion. For example, the oxidation number of a calcium ion is +2.

3. Oxidation numbers conventionally assigned to atoms combined in common chemical compounds are as follows:
a) Oxygen = −2 (except in peroxides, where it is −1). For example, the oxidation state of oxygen in SO_2, $KClO_3$ and $KMnO_4$ is −2, but in Na_2O_2 and H_2O_2, it is −1.
b) Hydrogen = +1 (except in metallic hydrides, where it is −1). For example, the single oxidation number of hydrogen in H_2O, H_2O_2, NH_3 and $HC_2H_3O_2$ is +1. In LiH, it is −1.
c) Group IA elements = +1.
d) Group IIA elements = +2.
e) Ions of the halogen atoms in binary ionic compounds (halides) = −1. For example, the halogen ions in NaF, KBr and CsI all have an oxidation number of −1.

4. When necessary, use the charges on the polyatomic ions given in Appendix 3, Table 3. Some of the more common polyatomic ions and their charges are SO_4^{2-}, OH^-, NO_3^-, CO_3^{2-}, $C_2H_3O_2^-$.

5. The sum of the positive and negative oxidation numbers in a compound is zero. The single oxidation number of a specified atom in a compound is determined as follows:
a) Assign a common oxidation number by following rules 1, 2 and 3 to all but the specified atom. To illustrate, let us determine the oxidation number of chromium (Cr) in potassium dichromate ($K_2Cr_2O_7$). First, we assign oxygen an oxidation number of −2 and potassium an oxidation number of +1.
b) Algebraically add the *total oxidation numbers* of all but the unknown atom. The total oxidation number of an atom in a formula is the assigned single oxidation number multiplied by the subscript of the atom. For example, the total oxidation number of hydrogen in H_2O is 2(H) = 2(+1). In the case of $K_2Cr_2O_7$, the total oxidation number of oxygen is 7(−2) = −14 and that of potassium is 2(+1) = +2. The algebraic sum is (+2) + (−14) = −12.
c) The total oxidation number of the atom in question is the number that must be assigned such that the sum of the positive and negative oxidation numbers is zero. If the designated atom has a subscript in the formula, the total oxidation number must be divided by the subscript to yield the single oxidation number. In the case of $K_2Cr_2O_7$, the total oxidation number contributed by two chromium atoms must be +12 in order to balance the −12 oxidation number contributed by the other two atoms. There-

fore, the oxidation number of chromium in $K_2Cr_2O_7$ is $+12/2$, or $+6$.

6. The algebraic sum of the positive and negative oxidation numbers of the atoms in a polyatomic ion is equal to the charge on the ion. For example, in a hydroxide ion (OH^-), the oxidation number of oxygen is -2 and that of hydrogen is $+1$. These numbers add and give an overall charge of $1-$. You can also use this principle to determine the single oxidation number of an atom in a polyatomic ion such as a dichromate ion ($Cr_2O_7^{2-}$). You should obtain a value of $+6$ for the single oxidation number of Cr in $Cr_2O_7^{2-}$.

Since the assignment of oxidation numbers is somewhat arbitrary, a certain amount of ambiguity is inherent in the rules given above. That is, it is possible for two people to obtain two different values for the oxidation number of a given atom in a given compound. This, however, is a minor flaw and relatively unimportant. The use of this set of rules is illustrated in Example 13-1.

EXAMPLE 13-1
Determining Oxidation Numbers
What is the single oxidation number of manganese (Mn) in (a) manganese dioxide (MnO_2), (b) manganese heptoxide (Mn_2O_7), (c) manganate ions (MnO_4^{2-}), (d) potassium permanganate ($KMnO_4$)?

SOLUTION
a) Assign an oxidation number of -2 to oxygen. Multiply the single oxidation number of oxygen by two to obtain the total oxidation number of oxygen, $2(-2) = -4$. Since MnO_2 is a neutral substance, we determine the positive charge required to exactly balance the -4 total oxidation number contributed by oxygen. The answer is $+4$. That is, -4 from oxygen added to $+4$ from manganese gives a zero overall charge for MnO_2.

b) Assign an oxidation number of -2 to oxygen. Multiply by seven to obtain the total oxidation number of oxygen, $7(-2) = -14$. Since Mn_2O_7 has no overall charge, manganese must, therefore, contribute a total oxidation number of $+14$ to the formula in order to achieve a zero overall charge. Since there are two manganese atoms per formula, we divide $+14$ by 2 to obtain the single oxidation number of $+7$.

c) Assign an oxidation number of -2 to oxygen. Multiply by four to obtain the total oxidation number of oxygen, $4(-2) = -8$. Since a manganate ion bears an overall charge of $2-$, we determine what oxidation number must be added to -8 to yield a $2-$ overall charge on the ion, $(-8) + x = 2-$; $x = +6$. Therefore, manganese in MnO_4^{2-} has an oxidation number of $+6$.

d) Assign an oxidation number of -2 to oxygen and $+1$ to potassium. Determine the total oxidation numbers of oxygen and potassium, respectively; oxygen $= 4(-2) = -8$, potassium $= +1$. Determine the total oxidation number contributed by oxygen and potassium combined, $(-8) + 1 = -7$. Since the formula has an overall charge of zero, manganese must contribute a $+7$ oxidation number in order to balance exactly the -7 oxidation number. Hence, its oxidation number in $KMnO_4$ is $+7$.

FOLLOW-UP PROBLEM
Determine the single oxidation number of the underlined atom in each of the following species: (a) $\underline{C}rO_4^{2-}$, (b) $\underline{N}H_2^-$, (c) $\underline{C}_2H_2$, (d) $\underline{P}_4O_{10}$, (e) $\underline{Fe}_3O_4$, (f) $\underline{S}_2O_3^{2-}$, (g) $\underline{S}O_4^{2-}$, (h) $\underline{N}_2O_3$.

By examining the formulas of the substances in the equation for a chemical reaction, we can determine the oxidation number of specified atoms or ions. Thus, we can determine whether the oxidation number of a species has increased or decreased during the course of a reaction. We will first consider redox reactions in which the reactants are both added to the same reaction vessel. In these reactions, the electrons are transferred directly from one species to another, and the decrease in potential energy of the system appears as heat energy given off to the surroundings. Our primary objective will be to supply the coefficients that balance the equations for the reactions. For balancing these equations, we will use a method based on changes in oxidation number.

Determining changes in oxidation numbers allows you to establish whether or not the reaction is a redox reaction.

13-3

Balancing Redox Equations Using Changes in Oxidation Numbers

When balancing redox equations, note that the total increase in the oxidation number of the reducing agent must equal the total decrease in the oxidation number of the oxidizing agent.

Figure 13-1
A simple redox reaction. In this reaction, Ag^+ ions oxidize Cu atoms to Cu^{2+} ions. Thus, silver ions are a stronger oxidizing agent than copper ions. All ions in water solution are hydrated.

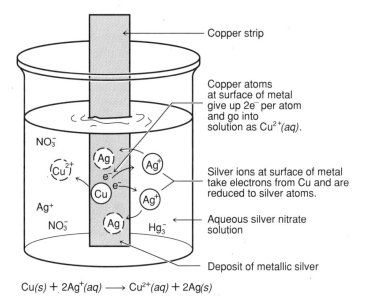

Copper strip

Copper atoms at surface of metal give up $2e^-$ per atom and go into solution as $Cu^{2+}(aq)$.

Silver ions at surface of metal take electrons from Cu and are reduced to silver atoms.

Aqueous silver nitrate solution

Deposit of metallic silver

$$Cu(s) + 2Ag^+(aq) \longrightarrow Cu^{2+}(aq) + 2Ag(s)$$

One of the simpler types of redox reactions involves the reactions of neutral atoms or molecules with ions. For example, when a piece of copper (Cu) is placed in a colourless solution of silver nitrate (a soluble ionic solid), metallic silver (Ag) forms on the surface of the copper and the solution acquires a light blue colour (Fig. 13-1). Analysis reveals that the blue colour is that of hydrated copper(II) ions. On the basis of these observations we can write

$$Cu(s) + Ag^+(aq) \longrightarrow Cu^{2+}(aq) + Ag(s) \qquad [13\text{-}1]$$

The nitrate ions are not involved. To balance the oxidation-reduction equation, we apply the following criteria:

1. The number of atoms on the left side of the equation must equal the number of atoms on the right. In other words, there must be a mass, or material, balance.

2. The net ionic charge on the left must equal the net ionic charge on the right. This means there must be an electric balance.

3. The total increase in oxidation number experienced by the reducing agent must equal the total decrease in oxidation number of the oxidizing agent. In other words, the electrons lost by the reducing agent must equal those gained by the oxidizing agent.

The four coefficients needed to balance Equation 13-1 can be obtained by equalizing the changes in oxidation numbers (criterion 3). To accomplish this, we must first determine the oxidation number and the change in oxidation number for each agent:

$$\begin{array}{c}
\overset{\text{increase of 2}}{\overset{\displaystyle\longrightarrow}{}} \\[-4pt]
\overset{0}{Cu(s)} \;+\; \overset{+1}{Ag^+(aq)} \;\longrightarrow\; \overset{+2}{Cu^{2+}(aq)} \;+\; \overset{0}{Ag(s)} \\[-4pt]
\underset{\text{decrease of 1}}{\underset{\displaystyle\longrightarrow}{}}
\end{array}$$

We then multiply the two changes in oxidation numbers and the species at the end of each line by whatever factors are needed to make the increase equal the decrease. In this case, the factors are 1 for the copper species and 2 for the silver species.

$$Cu(s) \;+\; \underset{\substack{\text{reducing}\\\text{agent}}}{2Ag^+(aq)} \;\longrightarrow\; \underset{\substack{\text{oxidizing}\\\text{agent}}}{Cu^{2+}(aq)} \;+\; 2Ag(s)$$

FOLLOW-UP PROBLEM

Balance the following equations:
a) $Al(s) + Ag^+(aq) \longrightarrow Al^{3+}(aq) + Ag(s)$
b) $Al(s) + Cu^{2+}(aq) \longrightarrow Al^{3+}(aq) + Cu(s)$
c) $Cl_2(g) + Br^-(aq) \longrightarrow Br_2(l) + Cl^-(aq)$

The observations we used to write Equation 13-1 and our analysis of the reaction in terms of changes in oxidation numbers indicate that copper metal (Cu) is oxidized and silver ions (Ag^+) are reduced. Thus, in this reaction, Ag^+ is the oxidizing agent and $Cu(s)$ is the reducing agent.

If we place a strip of silver metal in a solution of copper(II) nitrate, no reaction is observed to occur:

$$Ag(s) + Cu^{2+}(aq) \longrightarrow \text{no reaction} \qquad [13\text{-}2]$$

We can interpret our observations of the two reactions represented by Equations 13-1 and 13-2 as follows:

1. Silver ions can oxidize (remove electrons from) copper atoms (Equation 13-1).

2. Copper(II) ions do not oxidize silver atoms (Equation 13-2).

3. Silver ions are a better oxidizing agent than copper ions.

4. Copper atoms can reduce silver ions (Equation 13-1).

5. Silver atoms do not reduce copper(II) ions (Equation 13-2).

6. Copper is a better reducing agent than silver.

Cleaning Silver Using Redox Reactions
Although silver does not oxidize readily, it does tarnish when reacted with traces of hydrogen sulfide in the air. The tarnish can be removed by simply using an oxidation-reduction reaction: The tarnished silver object is heated in a pot that has been lined with aluminum foil and filled with a dilute solution of table salt or baking soda. Essentially, the aluminum is oxidized and transfers electrons to the silver; the silver atoms then plate on the object. In the overall reaction, the aluminum reacts with the sulfur and restores the silver:

$3Ag_2S(s) + 2Al \longrightarrow Al_2S_3(s) + 6Ag(s)$

Single replacement reactions have equations that suggest that one element replaces an ion of a second element from the compound containing the second element. For example, zinc is said to replace hydrogen ions from hydrochloric acid:

$Zn(s) + 2HCl(aq) \longrightarrow$
$H_2(g) + ZnCl_2(aq)$

We can rank silver ions and copper ions in order of their oxidizing ability. The oxidizing ability of silver ions is related to their tendency to gain electrons and become silver atoms. We can represent the relative oxidizing ability of the two ions in terms of the equations

$$Ag^+ + e^- \rightleftharpoons Ag(s)$$
$$Cu^{2+} + 2e^- \rightleftharpoons Cu(s)$$

The relative order of these equations shows that Ag^+ have a greater tendency to be reduced (gain electrons) than Cu^{2+}. This means that Ag^+ is a stronger oxidizing agent than Cu^{2+}. Therefore, we can predict that Ag^+ can oxidize $Cu(s)$, which is below $Ag(s)$ on the right side of the equation, but that Cu^{2+} cannot oxidize $Ag(s)$. In general, a given oxidizing agent can spontaneously oxidize the reduced form of another oxidizing agent weaker than itself.

In a similar manner, we can represent the relative reducing ability of copper atoms and silver atoms in terms of the equations

$$Cu(s) \rightleftharpoons Cu^{2+} + 2e^-$$
$$Ag(s) \rightleftharpoons Ag^+ + e^-$$

These equations show that $Cu(s)$ has a greater tendency to be oxidized (lose electrons) than $Ag(s)$ and is, therefore, a stronger reducing agent than $Ag(s)$. Notice that the last two equations, which represent reduction processes, can be obtained by reversing the first two equations, which represent oxidization processes.

Reduction processes always result in a decrease in the oxidation number of a species. Thus, silver is reduced from a +1 to a zero oxidation number. *Oxidation processes always result in an increase in the oxidation number of a species.* Thus, copper is oxidized from zero to +2. Note that metals do not exhibit negative oxidation numbers; that is, neutral metallic atoms do not gain electrons. Therefore, metals do not act as oxidizing agents.

As a result of many experiments similar to those described above, scientists have compiled tables of oxidizing and reducing agents listed in order of their relative strengths (Table 13-1). Note that the reactions of the elements in this table are all written as reduction processes. In this table, chlorine gas is the strongest oxidizing agent. This means that Cl_2 can oxidize or take electrons from any species below it on the right side of the equation.

The information in Table 13-1 can be used to write what are sometimes referred to as *single replacement reactions*. A rule of thumb often used by students to predict and write equations for these reactions is: *Any species on the left side of the arrows reacts spontaneously with any species on the right side that is below it in the series.* For example, H^+ ions react with metallic zinc and form H_2 and Zn^{2+}:

$$2H^+(aq) + Zn(s) \longrightarrow H_2(g) + Zn^{2+}$$

TABLE 13-1

IONS, ATOMS AND MOLECULES THAT BEHAVE AS OXIDIZING AND/OR REDUCING AGENTS

	Oxidized Form	Reduced Form	
Strongest → oxidixing agent	$Cl_2 + 2e^- \longrightarrow 2Cl^-$		
	$Br_2(l) + 2e^- \longrightarrow 2Br^-$		
	$Hg^{2+} + 2e^- \longrightarrow Hg(l)$		
	$Ag^+ + e^- \longrightarrow Ag(s)$		
	$Fe^{3+} + e^- \longrightarrow Fe^{2+}$		
	$I_2(s) + 2e^- \longrightarrow 2I^-$		
	$Cu^{2+} + 2e^- \longrightarrow Cu(s)$		
	$Sn^{4+} + 2e^- \longrightarrow Sn^{2+}$		
	$2H^+ + 2e^- \longrightarrow H_2(g)$		
	$Pb^{2+} + 2e^- \longrightarrow Pb(s)$		
	$Sn^{2+} + 2e^- \longrightarrow Sn(s)$		
	$Ni^{2+} + 2e^- \longrightarrow Ni(s)$		
	$Cd^{2+} + 2e^- \longrightarrow Cd(s)$		
	$Fe^{2+} + 2e^- \longrightarrow Fe(s)$		
	$Zn^{2+} + 2e^- \longrightarrow Zn(s)$		
	$Al^{3+} + 3e^- \longrightarrow Al(s)$		
	$Mg^{2+} + 2e^- \longrightarrow Mg(s)$	← Strongest reducing agent	

Oxidizing strength increases

Reducing strength increases

FOLLOW-UP PROBLEM

Using the techniques described above and the equations in Table 13-1, write net ionic equations for the following reactions (all aqueous solutions except g). If no reaction occurs, write *no reaction*.

a) chlorine + tin(II) nitrate $\longrightarrow$

b) iron(II) nitrate + potassium iodide $\longrightarrow$

c) silver and hydrochloric acid $\longrightarrow$

d) cadmium + sulfuric acid $\longrightarrow$

e) zinc + nickel nitrate $\longrightarrow$

f) iron(II) nitrate + aluminum nitrate $\longrightarrow$

g) bromine(I) + magnesium $\longrightarrow$

Many polyatomic ions are also common oxidizing agents. Equations involving these agents are more complicated than those involving only simple ions and atoms.

Consider the reaction of sodium sulfite (Na_2SO_3) with potassium permanganate ($KMnO_4$) in an acid solution. When purple

$KMnO_4$ solution is slowly added to colourless Na_2SO_3 solution, the colour disappears until stoichiometric quantities are present. Ion tests reveal that sulfate ions (SO_4^{2-}) and manganese(II) ions are formed. Since both Na_2SO_3 and $KMnO_4$ are soluble ionic compounds, we can write the skeleton equation as

$$MnO_4^- + SO_3^{2-} \longrightarrow Mn^{2+} + SO_4^{2-}$$

To balance this equation, we follow these steps:

1. Identify the elements that change oxidation numbers. Check that these elements appear in equal numbers on both sides of the equation. Connect the oxidized and reduced forms of each by lines, and write the oxidation numbers above both symbols. The information in Tables 13-2 and 13-3 will help you identify the elements that commonly undergo a change in oxidation number.

2. Write the increase in oxidation number experienced by the reducing agent and the decrease in oxidation number experienced by the oxidizing agent:

3. Find the lowest common multiple of the decrease and increase of the oxidation numbers. In this case, the common multiple is 10. Multiply the species joined by the lines by the necessary factors: 2 for the manganese and 5 for the sulfur.

4. If the solution is acid, then add H^+ to balance the ionic charge. If the solution is basic, add OH^- to balance the charge. The net charge on the left side of the above equation is 12−; that on the right side is 6−. Because the solution is acid, we must add $6H^+$ to the left side:

$$2MnO_4^- + 5SO_3^{2-} + 6H^+ \longrightarrow 2Mn^{2+} + 5SO_4^{2-}$$

5. Add H_2O to balance the hydrogen atoms. In the above equation,

addition of $3H_2O$ to the right side will balance the $6H^+$ on the left:

$$2MnO_4^- + 5SO_3^{2-} + 6H^+ \longrightarrow 2Mn^{2+} + 5SO_4^{2-} + 3H_2O$$

6. Check by counting oxygen atoms on each side. Note that it is often easier to convert a formula equation into an ionic equation before balancing it. This can be accomplished by removing inactive ions such as Na^+ and K^+. If you want to convert a balanced ionic equation into an equation showing neutral formulas, simply add the same number and kind of those ions to each side of the equation.

TABLE 13-2
COMMON OXIDIZING AGENTS

Oxidizing Agent	Formula (Underlined Element Is Reduced)	Oxidation State of Element That Is Reduced
Permanganate ions	$\underline{Mn}O_4^-$	+7
Nitrate ions	$\underline{N}O_3^-$	+5
Dichromate ions	$\underline{Cr}_2O_7^{2-}$	+6
Chlorate ions	$\underline{Cl}O_3^-$	+5
Cerium(IV) ions	$\underline{Ce}^{4+}$	+4
Iron(III) ions	Fe^{3+}	+3
Chlorine	Cl_2	0
Bromine	Br_2	0
Metallic ions in higher oxidation state	X^{n+}	$+n$

TABLE 13-3
COMMON REDUCING AGENTS

Reducing Agent	Formula (Underlined Element Is Oxidized)	Oxidation State of Element That Is Oxidized
Metallic atoms	Zn, Na	0
Nonmetallic atoms	C, S, P	0
Metallic ions in lower oxidation states	X^{n+}	$+n$
Nonmetallic ions	I^-, Br^-, Cl^-	−1
Hydrogen sulfide	H_2S	−2
Oxalic acid	$H_2\underline{C}_2O_4$	+3
Molecules or polyatomic ions containing atoms in lower oxidation states	$\underline{C}O$ $\underline{S}O_3^{2-}$ $\underline{N}O$	lower oxidation state

Let us balance another reaction using the change-in-oxidation-number method. Consider the reaction

$$KMnO_4 + FeSO_4 + H_2SO_4 \longrightarrow$$
$$K_2SO_4 + MnSO_4 + Fe_2(SO_4)_3 + H_2O$$

To balance this equation, we follow these steps:

1. Assign oxidation numbers to *all* of the atoms in the equation:

$$\overset{+1 \ +7 \ -2}{KMnO_4} + \overset{+2 \ +6 \ -2}{FeSO_4} + \overset{+1 \ +6 \ -2}{H_2SO_4} \longrightarrow$$
$$\overset{+1 \ +6 \ -2}{K_2SO_4} + \overset{+2 \ +6 \ -2}{MnSO_4} + \overset{+3 \ +6 \ -2}{Fe_2(SO_4)_3} + \overset{+1 \ -2}{H_2O}$$

2. Identify the elements that undergo a change in oxidation number. Mn changes from +7 in the $KMnO_4$ to +2 in the $MnSO_4$ (a reduction) and Fe changes from +2 in the $FeSO_4$ to +3 in the $Fe_2(SO_4)_3$ (an oxidation).

3. Balance the number of atoms that undergo a change in oxidation number. Since there are two Fe atoms on the product side, we must balance the Fe atoms on the reactant side by putting a 2 in front of the $FeSO_4$, as shown:

$$KMnO_4 + 2FeSO_4 + H_2SO_4 \longrightarrow$$
$$K_2SO_4 + MnSO_4 + Fe_2(SO_4)_3 + H_2O$$

Note that this coefficient may have to be changed later during the balancing of the rest of the equation.

4. Balance the number of electrons lost and gained in the reaction. Place the coefficients into the equation.

$$(5e^- \text{ lost}) \times 2 = 10e^- \text{ total}$$

$$2KMnO_4 + 5 \times 2FeSO_4 + H_2SO_4 \longrightarrow K_2SO_4 + 2MnSO_4 + 5Fe_2(SO_4)_3 + H_2O$$

$$(2e^- \text{ gained}) \times 5 = 10e^- \text{ total}$$

5. Balance the rest of the equation by inspection:

$$2KMnO_4 + 10FeSO_4 + 8H_2SO_4 \longrightarrow$$
$$K_2SO_4 + 2MnSO_4 + 5Fe_2(SO_4)_3 + 8H_2O$$

As a general rule, balance the metals first, then the nonmetals and finally the hydrogens and oxygens.

FOLLOW-UP PROBLEM

Balance the following equations. For each reaction, indicate (i) the oxidizing agent, (ii) the reducing agent, (iii) the element being oxidized, (iv) the element being reduced. Write all equations as net ionic equations.

a) $BrO_3^- + I^- + H^+ \longrightarrow Br^- + I_2 + H_2O$

b) $SeO_4^{2-} + Cl^- + H^+ \longrightarrow SeO_3^{2-} + Cl_2 + H_2O$

c) $Al(s) + NO_3^- + OH^- + H_2O \longrightarrow NH_3 + AlO_2^-$

d) $Zn(s) + NO_3^- + H^+ \longrightarrow Zn^{2+} + NH_4^+ + H_2O$

e) $KMnO_4 + KNO_2 + H_2SO_4 \longrightarrow$
$$MnSO_4 + H_2O + KNO_3 + K_2SO_4$$

f) $ClO_2(g) + SbO_2^- \longrightarrow ClO_2^- + Sb(OH)_6^-$ (basic)

g) $Cr_2O_7^{2-} + I^- \longrightarrow Cr^{3+} + I_2$ (acid)

h) $CN^- + CrO_4^{2-} \longrightarrow CNO^- + Cr(OH)_3(s)$ (basic)

i) $I_2 + ClO_3^- \longrightarrow IO_3^- + Cl^-$ (acid)

j) $MnO_4^- + NH_3 \longrightarrow MnO_2(s) + NO_3^-$ (basic)

k) $Mg(s) + ReO_4^- \longrightarrow Mg^{2+} + Re^-$ (acid)

l) $Ag(s) + NO_3^- \longrightarrow Ag^+ + NO$ (acid)

13-4
Balancing Redox Equations Using the Half-Cell Method

In the half-cell method, a reaction is divided into two separate, simpler reactions, allowing us to balance redox reactions without using oxidation numbers.

It is possible to balance oxidation-reduction equations without using oxidation numbers. This method, known as the *half-cell method*, involves writing two half-cell reactions and adding them to obtain a net equation for the overall reaction. One of the half-cell reactions is an oxidation; the other is a reduction.

In order to construct half-cell reactions, we must know both the oxidized and reduced forms of both agents. The oxidized and reduced forms of a number of common agents are listed in Table 13-4. Note that the oxidizing strength of a species and the product formed often depend on whether the solution is acid or basic. In Table 13-4, the strongest oxidizing agents are located at the upper left and the strongest reducing agents at the lower right.

As in Table 13-1, the data in Table 13-4 can be used to predict whether a redox reaction is likely to occur between two species. It also enables us to predict the products of the reaction. In general, a species on the left reacts spontaneously with a species below it on the right. The more separated the two species are in the table, the more tendency there is for a reaction to occur. For example, Cu^{2+} has more tendency to react with $Mg(s)$ than with $Pb(s)$ and does not react spontaneously with $Ag(s)$. In addition to predicting the

TABLE 13-4
OXIDIZED AND REDUCED FORMS OF SOME COMMON AGENTS IN AQUEOUS SOLUTION

Oxidized Form	Reduced Form
Co^{3+}	Co^{2+}
H_2O_2 (acid)	H_2O
MnO_4^- (acid)	Mn^{2+}
BrO_3^- (acid)	Br^-
ClO_4^- (acid)	Cl^-
Cl_2	Cl^-
$Cr_2O_7^{2-}$ (acid)	Cr^{3+}
O_2 (acid)	H_2O
$Br_2(l)$	Br^-
NO_3^- (acid)	$NO(g)$
ClO^- (basic)	Cl^-
Hg^{2+}	$Hg(l)$
Ag^+	$Ag(s)$
Fe^{3+}	Fe^{2+}
MnO_4^- (basic)	$MnO_2(s)$
$I_2(s)$ (acid)	I^-
Cu^+	$Cu(s)$
$O_2(g)$	OH^-
Cu^{2+}	$Cu(s)$
Cu^{2+}	Cu^+
$S(s)$ (acid)	$H_2S(g)$
H^+ (acid)	H_2
Pb^{2+}	$Pb(s)$
Ni^{2+}	$Ni(s)$
Co^{2+}	$Co(s)$
Cd^{2+}	$Cd(s)$
Fe^{2+}	$Fe(s)$
$S(s)$ (basic)	S^{2-}
Cr^{3+}	$Cr(s)$
Zn^{2+}	$Zn(s)$
H_2O (basic)	$H_2(g)$
Mn^{2+}	$Mn(s)$
Al^{3+}	$Al(s)$
Mg^{2+}	$Mg(s)$
Na^+	$Na(s)$
Ca^{2+}	$Ca(s)$
Cs^+	$Cs(s)$
K^+	$K(s)$

Decreasing strength as oxidizing agent →

Increasing strength as reducing agent →

feasibility of reactions, the data in Table 13-4 enables us to construct half-cell reactions. By following a proper sequence of steps, we can combine half-cell reactions to obtain an equation for any desired redox reaction.

We will balance an equation for the reaction between permanganate ions (MnO_4^-) and iron(II) in an acid solution using the half-cell method. In an acid solution, MnO_4^- acts as an oxidizing agent and is reduced to Mn^{2+} ions by iron(II), the reducing agent. Iron(II) is oxidized by MnO_4^- ions to iron(III). The skeleton equation for this reaction is

$$MnO_4^- + Fe^{2+} \longrightarrow Mn^{2+} + Fe^{3+}$$

To balance this equation, we follow these steps:

1. Divide the skeleton equation into two half-cell reactions. Each half-cell reaction must show either an oxidizing or a reducing agent on the left side and the product(s) on the right side. The unbalanced half-cell reactions are

$$MnO_4^- \longrightarrow Mn^{2+} \qquad [13\text{-}3]$$
$$Fe^{2+} \longrightarrow Fe^{3+} \qquad [13\text{-}4]$$

We will first balance Equation 13-3 and then follow the same steps to balance Equation 13-4.

2. Balance all atoms other than hydrogen and oxygen. In Equation 13-3 the manganese atoms are already in balance.

3. Count the number of oxygen atoms and balance them by adding the proper number of water molecules to the side deficient in oxygen atoms. In Equation 13-3 there are four oxygen atoms on the left side. Thus, $4H_2O$ must be added to the right side of the equation to balance the oxygen atoms:

$$MnO_4^- \longrightarrow Mn^{2+} + 4H_2O$$

4. By adding water to only one side of the reaction, we now have an imbalance of hydrogen atoms. Balance them by adding the proper number of H^+ from the acid solution to the side deficient in hydrogen. Since there are $8H^+$ on the right side, add $8H^+$ to the left side of the equation:

$$8H^+ + MnO_4^- \longrightarrow Mn^{2+} + 4H_2O$$

5. Bring the two sides of the equation into electric balance. This can be done by counting the total ionic charge on each side and adding electrons to the side that needs additional negative charge to bring it into balance. In the equation, the ionic charge on the right side is 2+; on the left, it is 7+. Adding $5e^-$ to the left side reduces the charge to 2+:

$$5e^- + 8H^+ + MnO_4^- \longrightarrow Mn^{2+} + 4H_2O \qquad [13\text{-}5]$$

6. Repeat steps 2 through 4 for Equation 13-4. This yields

$$Fe^{2+} \longrightarrow Fe^{3+} + e^-$$ [13-6]

7. Balance the number of electrons in Equations 13-5 and 13-6. The number of electrons must be the lowest common multiple of the numbers shown in the two equations. Multiply each factor in each half-cell reaction by the number that makes the number of electrons in the two half-cell reactions equal. Therefore, multiply Equation 13-5 by 1 and Equation 13-6 by 5:

$$5e^- + 8H^+ + MnO_4^- \longrightarrow Mn^{2+} + 4H_2O$$
$$5Fe^{2+} \longrightarrow 5Fe^{3+} + 5e^-$$

8. Algebraically add the two half-cell reactions, right and left sides separately. The net equation is

$$8H^+ + MnO_4^- + 5Fe^{2+} \longrightarrow Mn^{2+} + 5Fe^{3+} + 4H_2O$$

In order to obtain an equation for a redox reaction in basic solution, it is necessary to add an extra step to eliminate the H^+ ions, since equations for reactions in basic solution cannot show the presence of excess H^+ ions. For example, we will write an equation for the reaction between permanganate and cyanide ions (CN^-) in basic solution. In this reaction, MnO_4^- is reduced to MnO_2, and CN^- ions are oxidized to cyanate ions (CNO^-). The skeleton equation is

$$MnO_4^- + CN^- \longrightarrow MnO_2(s) + CNO^-$$

We follow these steps:
1. Same as acid solution.

$$MnO_4^- \longrightarrow MnO_2(s)$$ [13-7]
$$CN^- \longrightarrow CNO^-$$ [13-8]

2. Same as acid solution.

$$MnO_4^- \longrightarrow MnO_2(s) + 2H_2O$$

3. Same as acid solution.

$$4H^+ + MnO_4^- \longrightarrow MnO_2(s) + 2H_2O$$

3a. Remove the H^+ ions from the half-cell reaction by adding the same number of OH^- ions to both sides of the equation. If an equal number of OH^- ions are not added to both sides, the balance of atoms and electric charge would be upset. In this equation, $4OH^-$ are required to neutralize the $4H^+$ and must therefore be added to both sides of the equation:

$$4H^+ + MnO_4^- \longrightarrow MnO_2(s) + 2H_2O$$
$$\underline{4OH^- \qquad\qquad\qquad\qquad\qquad + 4OH^-}$$
$$4HOH + MnO_4^- \longrightarrow MnO_2(s) + 2H_2O + 4OH^-$$

In our study of acids and bases, it was useful to express $H^+(aq)$ as H_3O^+. In redox systems, this notation is of little value. For this reason, H_3O^+ will be generally noted as H^+ or $H^+(aq)$ in this chapter.

This operation results in the appearance of water molecules on both sides of the equation. Simplification yields

$$2H_2O + MnO_4^- \longrightarrow MnO_2 + 4OH^-$$

4. Same as acid solution.

$$3e^- + 2H_2O + MnO_4^- \longrightarrow MnO_2(s) + 4OH^- \quad [13\text{-}9]$$

5. Repeating steps 2 through 4 for Equation 13-8 yields

$$2OH^- + CN^- \longrightarrow CNO^- + H_2O + 2e^- \quad [13\text{-}10]$$

6. Balance the electrons by multiplying Equation 13-9 by 2 and Equation 13-10 by 3.

$$6e^- + 4H_2O + 2MnO_4^- \longrightarrow 2MnO_2(s) + 8OH^-$$
$$6OH^- + 3CN^- \longrightarrow 3CNO^- + 3H_2O + 6e^-$$

7. Adding the two equations and collecting like terms gives

$$H_2O + 2MnO_4^- + 3CN^- \longrightarrow 2MnO_2(s) + 2OH^- + 3CNO^-$$

If valid half-cell equations are not required, removing H^+ ions from the equations can be postponed until the last step.

FOLLOW-UP PROBLEMS

1. Use the half-cell method to write equations for the following reactions.
   a) $NO_3^- + Bi \longrightarrow Bi^{3+} + NO_2$ (acid)
   b) $Cr_2O_7^{2-} + I^- \longrightarrow Cr^{3+} + I_2$ (acid)
   c) $Cr^{3+} + ClO_3^- \longrightarrow ClO_2 + Cr_2O_7^{2-}$ (acid)
   d) $CHCl_3 + MnO_4^- \longrightarrow Cl_2 + CO_2 + Mn^{2+}$ (acid)
   e) $MnO_4^- + NO_2^- \longrightarrow MnO_2(s) + NO_3^-$ (basic)
   f) $ClO^- \longrightarrow Cl^- + ClO_3^-$ (basic)
   g) $Al + NO_3^- \longrightarrow Al(OH)_4^- + NH_3$ (basic)
   h) $O_2 + H_2O + I^- \longrightarrow I_2 + OH^-$ (basic)

2. Use the data in Table 13-4 to write net ionic equations for the following reactions (all aqueous solutions except e):
   a) hydrogen peroxide (H_2O_2) with manganese(II) sulfate ($MnSO_4$) (acid)
   b) potassium dichromate with $H_2S(g)$ (acid)
   c) sodium perchlorate with iron(II) nitrate (acid)
   d) metallic sodium plus water (basic)
   e) oxygen (O_2) and hydrogen sulfide (H_2S) (acid)

ELECTROCHEMICAL CELLS

13-5

Defining Terms

Electrochemical cells are a source of electric energy.
Oxidation-reduction reactions can be used as a source of electric energy when they occur in an electrochemical cell such as an ordinary flashlight cell. An electrochemical cell is made up of two half-cells, each involving a different reaction. The process occurring in each half-cell is known as a **half-cell reaction**. When a flashlight is operating, for example, an oxidation half-cell reaction is occurring at the surface of one electrode (the zinc container), while a reduction process is occurring at the other electrode (central rod). The sum of the equations for the two half-cell reactions constitutes the equation for the overall cell reaction.

Most of you know that an ordinary flashlight cell has a voltage of about 1.5 V and produces a current that can be measured in amperes (A). Because these and other terms associated with electric phenomena are used to describe cell characteristics, we will define them in order to provide background for later discussions.

When a flashlight is turned on, energy is being transferred. The source of this energy is the chemical reaction taking place in the cell. That is, chemical energy is being transformed into electric energy, which is being transferred and is doing electric work when it is used to operate any electric device. The work is done by the cell as it forces electrons through the wires and other parts of the **circuit**. The **voltage** of the cell is a measure of its ability to do electric work. The **current** is measured in terms of the number of electrons that flow through a circuit per second. An **ampere** (A) can be defined as a flow of 6.24×10^{18} electrons per second. The electric charge carried by this quantity of electrons is called a **coulomb** (C). An ampere is also defined in practical units as *one coulomb per second*. The energy transferred or work done by 6.24×10^{18} e$^-$ (1 C) is called one **joule** (J). The **volt** (V) can be defined as the energy transferred or work done by the cell when it drives one coulomb through the circuit. In other words,

$$1 \text{ V} = \frac{1 \text{ J}}{\text{C} (6.24 \times 10^{18} \text{ e}^-)}$$

$$= \frac{1.6 \times 10^{-19} \text{ J}}{\text{e}^- \text{ (electric charge)}}$$

A circuit is the external path that electrons follow from one electrode of a cell to the other electrode.

A coulomb (C) is a measure of the amount of charge that passes a given point in a circuit when current of one ampere (A) flows for one second (s). Thus,

$$1 \text{ C} = 1 \text{ A·s}$$

and

$$1 \text{ A} = \frac{1 \text{ C}}{\text{s}}$$

Thus, the electric energy supplied is equal to the voltage times the charge. This means the energy transferred when 1 V drives one electron equals 1.6×10^{-19} J. We will now examine the principles underlying the operation of an electrochemical cell and show how it can be used to determine the spontaneity of a reaction, the equilibrium constant and other factors associated with reactions.

13-6
Electrochemical Cells

If two half-cells—one an oxidation and the other a reduction—are physically separated, a spontaneous reaction involving the transfer of electrons through an external circuit will occur.

Electron transfer between an oxidizing agent and a reducing agent occurs when the reaction is carried out in electrochemical cells. These cells are devices in which oxidation-reduction reactions take place indirectly; that is, the oxidation and reduction reactions each take place at separate surfaces called *electrodes*. In this way, the chemical energy of the participants in a reaction may be largely converted to electric energy. For example, zinc metal reacts with aqueous silver nitrate. The equation for the reaction is

$$Zn(s) + 2Ag^+ \rightleftharpoons Zn^{2+} + 2Ag(s)$$

> Electrodes allow the conduction of electrons into and out of solution. For example, if the electrodes are connected to a battery, they take on an electric charge, thus oxidizing and reducing the ions in the solution.

When the reaction takes place in a single beaker, the two reactants are in direct contact so that the decrease in potential energy of the system appears as heat given off to the surroundings. When, however, the reaction is carried out in an electrochemical cell, the reactants are physically separated. Electron transfer takes place through a wire that connects the electrodes. The decrease in potential energy of the system appears, in part, as electric energy, which can be used to light a small bulb or produce a reading on an *ammeter* (an instrument used for measuring electric current). Let us examine the construction and operation of the electrochemical cell shown in Fig. 13-2.

The overall electrochemical cell is composed of two half-cells. These consist of two beakers, one of which contains a 1 mol/L Zn^{2+} ion solution and a strip of zinc metal; the other a 1 mol/L Ag^+ ion solution and a strip of silver. The metal electrodes are connected through the meter by a *metallic conductor* (wire). The two solutions are then connected by a *salt bridge* containing an electrolytic solution such as KNO_3.

When the electrodes are connected through an ammeter, there is ample evidence that a reaction is taking place. The deflection of the ammeter needle indicates that electric current is passing through the meter. The zinc strip starts to disintegrate and the concentration of the Zn^{2+} ions in solution increases. The silver strip increases in mass as silver metal deposits on its surface.

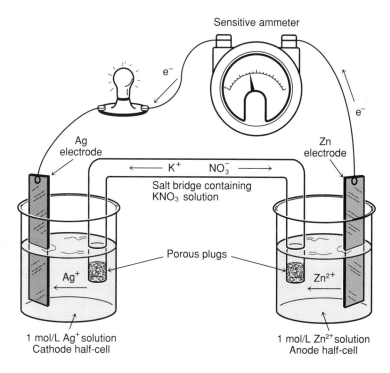

Figure 13-2
A simple electrochemical cell.

Simultaneously, the concentration of Ag^+ ions in solution decreases. As the reaction proceeds, the meter deflection falls off, showing a decrease in the flow of current. The deposition of metallic silver on the silver strip resulting from the reduction of Ag^+ ions in solution is evidence that electrons are flowing from the zinc strip through the wire to the silver strip.

The chemical reactions taking place at the surface of each electrode can be represented by equations. The oxidation reaction taking place at the zinc electrode is

$$Zn(s) \longrightarrow Zn^{2+} + 2e^- \qquad\qquad [13\text{-}11]$$

The reduction reaction taking place at the silver electrode is

$$Ag^+ + e^- \longrightarrow Ag(s) \qquad\qquad [13\text{-}12]$$

By definition, the electrode at which reduction occurs is the **cathode**. Oxidation occurs at the **anode**. Thus, the zinc strip is the anode and the silver strip is the cathode.

The migration of ions through the salt bridge completes the electric circuit and preserves the electric neutrality of the solutions. The salt bridge is necessary to prevent the solutions from becoming electrically charged. If the salt bridge were missing, zinc ions resulting from the dissolution of the zinc strip would accumulate around the electrode and give the solution a positive charge and, thus, prevent electrons from flowing to the silver

Remember:
Oxidation occurs at the *anode*.
Reduction occurs at the *cathode*.

compartment. At the cathode, the deposition of silver ions would leave the solution negatively charged with an excess of negative ions. The salt bridge allows negative ions (anions) to move toward the anode compartment and positive ions (cations) to move toward the cathode compartment. The diffusion of ions maintains the electric neutrality of the solutions. Electrons are then free to flow from the anode to the cathode in the external circuit.

The overall oxidation-reduction reaction taking place in the electrochemical cell is the sum of two half-cell reactions. The reactions represented by Equations 13-11 and 13-12 are half-cell reactions. In order to obtain the overall equation for the reaction taking place in the cell illustrated in Fig. 13-2, we must add these half-cell reactions as follows:

Anode reaction (oxidation):
$$Zn(s) \longrightarrow Zn^{2+} + 2e^-$$
Cathode reaction (reduction):
$$2Ag^+ + 2e^- \longrightarrow 2Ag(s)$$

Total cell reaction:
$$Zn(s) + 2Ag^+ \longrightarrow 2Ag(s) + Zn^{2+} \qquad [13\text{-}13]$$

Note that Equation 13-12 was multiplied by a factor of 2 before it was added to Equation 13-11. This was done to equalize the number of electrons gained by the silver and the number lost by the zinc. Equation 13-13 represents the overall, or net, reaction.

In theory, any oxidation-reduction reaction can be separated into half-cell reactions. The half-cell reactions can be balanced and combined to yield an equation for the overall oxidation-reduction reaction.

13-7
Cell Potential and Potential Difference

The cell potential (E_{cell}) is a measure of the relative abilities of each half-cell to attract electrons.

In Fig. 13-2, the flow of electrons through the meter from the zinc to the silver electrode indicates that the silver metal–silver ion system in the one beaker has more attraction for electrons than the zinc metal–zinc ion combination in the other beaker. The electron-attracting ability of a half-cell is called its ***cell potential*** (E_{cell}). The difference in electron-attracting ability between two half-cells is a measure of the tendency for the overall cell reaction to take place. The difference between the cell potentials of two half-cells is called the ***potential difference*** and is usually expressed as a voltage.

The potential difference between two half-cells is also referred to as the *electromotive force* (emf) or the driving force behind the reaction.

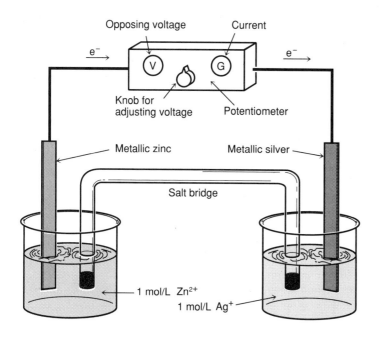

Figure 13-3
The potentiometer contains a variable voltage source that opposes the spontaneous flow of electrons, as shown in the cell at left. The voltage-adjust knob on the potentiometer is turned until the current meter (galvanometer, G) reads zero. At this point, there is no current flowing in the external circuit and the voltage read on the meter is numerically equal to the cell potential.

Precise differences in potential between two electrodes are measured with a *potentiometer* (Fig. 13-3). This instrument is a source of opposing voltage adjusted so that no current flows through the cell whose voltage is being measured. Any current drawn from the cell during measurement results in a slight voltage

A volt is defined as the potential difference necessary to cause one ampere of current to flow through a conductor that has a resistance of one ohm.

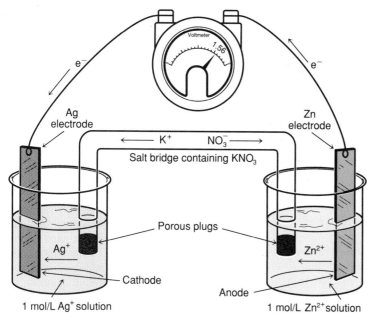

Figure 13-4
The voltage (1.56 V) of this cell is a measure of the tendency for the reaction

Zn(s) + 2Ag$^+$(aq) $\longrightarrow$
Zn^{2+}(aq) + 2Ag(s)

to take place when the ion concentrations are 1 mol/L and the temperature is 25°C.

drop and, therefore, a low reading of the cell potential. A current through the cell also changes the composition of the solution. For convenience in laboratory experiments, high-resistance *voltmeters*, which draw an insignificant current, are used to measure cell potentials. A voltmeter connected to the electrodes of the zinc-silver electrochemical cell shown in Fig. 13-4 reads approximately 1.56 V. This means that the Ag-Ag$^+$ half-cell has 1.56 V more electron-attracting ability than the Zn-Zn^{2+} half-cell. If the potential of the zinc half-cell were known, then the potential of the silver half-cell could be determined by adding 1.56 V to the potential of the zinc half-cell. The absolute potential of an isolated half-cell, however, like the total energy content of a chemical species, cannot be measured experimentally. *Only the difference in potential between two half-cells can be measured.*

13-8
Standard Potential and Reduction Potential

The hydrogen half-cell is assigned a standard potential of zero volts and becomes the reference standard for the determination of all other half-cell potentials.

If the potential of a standard half-cell is assumed to be zero, then the experimentally measured difference in potential between the standard and a second half-cell is the relative potential of the second half-cell. Scientists have developed a useful table of standard half-cell potentials ($E°$) by determining the voltages of hundreds of half-cells coupled to a standard reference half-cell with an arbitrarily assigned potential of 0 V (Table 13-5). The standard

The standard reduction potential ($E°$) is the reduction potential of a half-cell reaction at standard conditions.

TABLE 13-5
STANDARD REDUCTION POTENTIALS

	Half-Cell Reaction					$E°$ (volts)	
Increasing oxidizing ability	$F_2(g)$	$+ 2e^-$	$\rightleftharpoons$		$2F^-$	+2.85	Increasing reducing ability
	$O_3(g) + 2H^+$	$+ 2e^-$	$\rightleftharpoons$	$O_2(g) +$	H_2O	+2.08	
	$S_2O_8^{2-}$	$+ 2e^-$	$\rightleftharpoons$		$2SO_4^{2-}$	+2.05	
	Co^{3+}	$+ e^-$	$\rightleftharpoons$		Co^{2+}	+1.82	
	$H_2O_2 + 2H^+$	$+ 2e^-$	$\rightleftharpoons$		$2H_2O$	+1.77	
	$MnO_4^- + 4H^+$	$+ 3e^-$	$\rightleftharpoons$		$MnO_2(s)$	+1.70	
	Ce^{4+}	$+ 2e^-$	$\rightleftharpoons$		Ce^{3+}	+1.61	
	$BrO_3^- + 6H^+$	$+ 5e^-$	$\rightleftharpoons$	$\frac{1}{2}Br_2 +$	$3H_2O$	+1.52	
	$MnO_4^- + 8H^+$	$+ 5e^-$	$\rightleftharpoons$	$4H_2O +$	$4Mn^{2+}$	+1.52	
	Mn^{3+}	$+ e^-$	$\rightleftharpoons$		Mn^{2+}	+1.51	
	Au^{3+}	$+ 3e^-$	$\rightleftharpoons$		$Au(s)$	+1.50	

TABLE 13-5 (continued)

Half-Cell Reaction				$E°$ (volts)
$PbO_2(s) + 4H^+$	$+ 2e^-$	$\rightleftharpoons Pb^{2+} +$	$2H_2O$	+1.46
$ClO_4^- + 8H^+$	$+ 8e^-$	$\rightleftharpoons 4H_2O +$	Cl^-	+1.39
$Cl_2(g)$	$+ 2e^-$	$\rightleftharpoons$	$2Cl^-$	+1.36
$Cr_2O_7^{2-} + 14H^+$	$+ 6e^-$	$\rightleftharpoons 7H_2O +$	$2Cr^{3+}$	+1.33
$MnO_2(s) + 4H^+$	$+ 2e^-$	$\rightleftharpoons 2H_2O +$	Mn^{2+}	+1.23
$IO_3^- + 6H^+$	$+ 5e^-$	$\rightleftharpoons \frac{1}{2}I_2(s) +$	$3H_2O$	+1.20
Pt^{2+}	$+ 2e^-$	$\rightleftharpoons$	$Pt(s)$	+1.20
$SeO_4^{2-} + 4H^+$	$+ 2e^-$	$\rightleftharpoons H_2SeO_3 +$	H_2O	+1.15
$Br_2(l)$	$+ 2e^-$	$\rightleftharpoons$	$2Br^-$	+1.06
ICl_2^-	$+ e^-$	$\rightleftharpoons \frac{1}{2}I_2(s) +$	$2Cl^-$	+1.06
$NO_3^- + 4H^+$	$+ 3e^-$	$\rightleftharpoons 2H_2O +$	$NO(g)$	+0.96
$NO_3^- + 4H^+$	$+ 2e^-$	$\rightleftharpoons HNO_2 +$	H_2O	+0.94
$HO_2^- + H_2O$	$+ 2e^-$	$\rightleftharpoons$	$3OH^-$	+0.88
$AuCl_4^-$	$+ 3e^-$	$\rightleftharpoons Au(s) +$	$4Cl^-$	+0.86
$Cu^{2+} + I^-$	$+ e^-$	$\rightleftharpoons$	$CuI(s)$	+0.86
Hg^{2+}	$+ 2e^-$	$\rightleftharpoons$	$Hg(l)$	+0.85
$\frac{1}{2}O_2(g) + 2H^+$	$+ 2e^-$	$\rightleftharpoons$	H_2O	+0.82
Ag^+	$+ e^-$	$\rightleftharpoons$	$Ag(s)$	+0.80
Fe^{3+}	$+ e^-$	$\rightleftharpoons$	Fe^{2+}	+0.77
$O_2(g) + 2H_3O^+$	$+ 2e^-$	$\rightleftharpoons H_2O_2 +$	$2H_2O$	+0.68
$MnO_4^- + 2H_2O$	$+ 3e^-$	$\rightleftharpoons 4OH^- +$	$MnO_2(s)$	+0.59
$H_3AsO_4 + 2H^+$	$+ 2e^-$	$\rightleftharpoons H_3AsO_3 +$	H_2O	+0.56
$I_2(s)$	$+ 2e^-$	$\rightleftharpoons$	$2I^-$	+0.54
I_3^-	$+ 2e^-$	$\rightleftharpoons$	$3I^-$	+0.54
Cu^+	$+ e^-$	$\rightleftharpoons$	$Cu(s)$	+0.52
$NiO_2(s) + 2H_2O$	$+ 2e^-$	$\rightleftharpoons Ni(OH)_2(s) +$	$2OH^-$	+0.49
$SO_2 + 4H^+$	$+ 4e^-$	$\rightleftharpoons S(s) +$	$2H_2O$	+0.45
$Ag(NH_3)_2^+$	$+ e^-$	$\rightleftharpoons 2NH_3 +$	$Ag(s)$	+0.37
Cu^{2+}	$+ 2e^-$	$\rightleftharpoons$	$Cu(s)$	+0.34
$Hg_2Cl_2(s)$	$+ 2e^-$	$\rightleftharpoons 2Hg(l) +$	$2Cl^-$	+0.28
$IO_3^- + 3H_2O$	$+ 6e^-$	$\rightleftharpoons I^- +$	$6OH^-$	+0.26
$AgCl(s)$	$+ e^-$	$\rightleftharpoons Ag(s) +$	Cl^-	+0.22
$SO_4^{2-} + 4H^+$	$+ 2e^-$	$\rightleftharpoons H_2SO_3 +$	H_2O	+0.17
Cu^{2+}	$+ e^-$	$\rightleftharpoons$	Cu^+	+0.15
Sn^{4+}	$+ 2e^-$	$\rightleftharpoons$	Sn^{2+}	+0.15
$S + 2H^+$	$+ 2e^-$	$\rightleftharpoons$	H_2S	+0.14
$S_4O_6^{2-}$	$+ 2e^-$	$\rightleftharpoons$	$2S_2O_3^{2-}$	+0.08
$AgBr(s)$	$+ e^-$	$\rightleftharpoons Ag(s) +$	Br^-	+0.071
$Ag(S_2O_3)_2^{3-}$	$+ e^-$	$\rightleftharpoons Ag(s) +$	$2S_2O_3^{2-}$	+0.01
$2H^+$	$+ 2e^-$	$\rightleftharpoons$	$H_2(g)$	0.00
$Hg_2I_2(s)$	$+ 2e^-$	$\rightleftharpoons 2Hg(l) +$	$2I^-$	−0.04
HgI_4^{2-}	$+ 2e^-$	$\rightleftharpoons Hg(l) +$	$4I^-$	−0.04
Pb^{2+}	$+ 2e^-$	$\rightleftharpoons$	$Pb(s)$	−0.13
Sn^{2+}	$+ 2e^-$	$\rightleftharpoons$	$Sn(s)$	−0.14
$AgI(s)$	$+ e^-$	$\rightleftharpoons Ag(s) +$	I^-	−0.15
Ni^{2+}	$+ 2e^-$	$\rightleftharpoons$	$Ni(s)$	−0.24

Increasing oxidizing ability ↑

Increasing reducing ability ↓

TABLE 13-5 (continued)

Half-Cell Reaction				$E°$ (volts)
$H_3PO_4 + 2H^+$	$+ 2e^-$	$\rightleftharpoons H_3PO_3 +$	H_2O	−0.27
$PbCl_2(s)$	$+ 2e^-$	$\rightleftharpoons Pb(s) +$	$2Cl^-$	−0.27
Co^{2+}	$+ 2e^-$	$\rightleftharpoons$	$Co(s)$	−0.28
$PbBr_2(s)$	$+ 2e^-$	$\rightleftharpoons Pb(s) +$	$2Br^-$	−0.28
$Ag(CN)_2^-$	$+ 2e^-$	$\rightleftharpoons Ag(s) +$	$2CN^-$	−0.31
In^{3+}	$+ 3e^-$	$\rightleftharpoons$	$In(s)$	−0.34
Tl^+	$+ e^-$	$\rightleftharpoons$	$Tl(s)$	−0.34
$Hg(CN)_4^{2-}$	$+ 2e^-$	$\rightleftharpoons Hg(l) +$	$4CN^-$	−0.37
$PbI_2(s)$	$+ 2e^-$	$\rightleftharpoons Pb(s) +$	$2I^-$	−0.37
Cd^{2+}	$+ 2e^-$	$\rightleftharpoons$	$Cd(s)$	−0.40
$2H_2O$	$+ 2e^-$	$\rightleftharpoons H_2(g) +$	$2OH^-$	−0.41
$PbSO_4(s)$	$+ 2e^-$	$\rightleftharpoons Pb(s) +$	SO_4^{2-}	−0.41
Fe^{2+}	$+ 2e^-$	$\rightleftharpoons$	$Fe(s)$	−0.44
Ga^{3+}	$+ 3e^-$	$\rightleftharpoons$	$Ga(s)$	−0.56
$PbO(s) + H_2O$	$+ 2e^-$	$\rightleftharpoons Pb(s) +$	$2OH^-$	−0.58
$SO_4^{2-} + 4H_2O$	$+ 8e^-$	$\rightleftharpoons 8OH^- +$	S^{2-}	−0.68
$Ag_2S(s)$	$+ 2e^-$	$\rightleftharpoons 2Ag(s) +$	S^{2-}	−0.69
$HgS(s)$	$+ 2e^-$	$\rightleftharpoons Hg(l) +$	S^{2-}	−0.72
Cr^{3+}	$+ 3e^-$	$\rightleftharpoons$	$Cr(s)$	−0.74
Zn^{2+}	$+ 2e^-$	$\rightleftharpoons$	$Zn(s)$	−0.76
$Fe(OH)_2(s)$	$+ 2e^-$	$\rightleftharpoons Fe(s) +$	$2OH^-$	−0.88
$SO_4^{2-} + H_2O$	$+ 2e^-$	$\rightleftharpoons SO_3^{2-} +$	$2OH^-$	−0.93
$PbS(s)$	$+ 2e^-$	$\rightleftharpoons Pb(s) +$	S^{2-}	−0.95
$CNO^- + H_2O$	$+ 2e^-$	$\rightleftharpoons CN^- +$	$2OH^-$	−0.97
$Zn(NH_3)_4^{2+}$	$+ 2e^-$	$\rightleftharpoons Zn(s) +$	$4NH_3$	−1.01
$N_2(g) + 4H_2O$	$+ 4e^-$	$\rightleftharpoons N_2O_4 +$	$4OH^-$	−1.16
V^{2+}	$+ 2e^-$	$\rightleftharpoons$	$V(s)$	−1.18
Mn^{2+}	$+ 2e^-$	$\rightleftharpoons$	$Mn(s)$	−1.18
$CdS(s)$	$+ 2e^-$	$\rightleftharpoons Cd(s) +$	S^{2-}	−1.21
$Zn(CN)_4^{2-}$	$+ 2e^-$	$\rightleftharpoons Zn(s) +$	$4CN^-$	−1.26
$ZnS(s)$	$+ 2e^-$	$\rightleftharpoons Zn(s) +$	S^{2-}	−1.44
Ti^{2+}	$+ 2e^-$	$\rightleftharpoons$	$Ti(s)$	−1.63
Al^{3+}	$+ 3e^-$	$\rightleftharpoons$	$Al(s)$	−1.66
U^{3+}	$+ 3e^-$	$\rightleftharpoons$	$U(s)$	−1.79
Sc^{3+}	$+ 3e^-$	$\rightleftharpoons$	$Sc(s)$	−2.02
Mg^{2+}	$+ 2e^-$	$\rightleftharpoons$	$Mg(s)$	−2.34
$Mg(OH)_2(s)$	$+ 2e^-$	$\rightleftharpoons Mg(s) +$	$2OH^-$	−2.69
Na^+	$+ e^-$	$\rightleftharpoons$	$Na(s)$	−2.71
Ca^{2+}	$+ 2e^-$	$\rightleftharpoons$	$Ca(s)$	−2.76
Sr^{2+}	$+ 2e^-$	$\rightleftharpoons$	$Sr(s)$	−2.89
Ba^{2+}	$+ 2e^-$	$\rightleftharpoons$	$Ba(s)$	−2.90
K^+	$+ e^-$	$\rightleftharpoons$	$K(s)$	−2.92
Rb^+	$+ e^-$	$\rightleftharpoons$	$Rb(s)$	−2.93
Li^+	$+ e^-$	$\rightleftharpoons$	$Li(s)$	−3.04

Increasing oxidizing ability ↑

Increasing reducing ability ↓

Note: All species are in an aqueous state unless otherwise specified.

reference half-cell is illustrated in Fig. 13-5 and consists of a platinum electrode in a solution in which the [H^+] is 1 mol/L with hydrogen gas at a pressure of 101.3 kPa bubbled over the electrode. Constant temperature is maintained at 25°C.

Let us now examine, interpret and apply the data given in Table 13-5. All half-cell reactions in this table are written so that the *forward reaction (to the right) is a reduction*. The tendency of a half-cell reaction to proceed as a reduction reaction is called the **reduction potential** of the cell. Strong oxidizing agents are associated with reduction half-cell reactions that have high reduction potentials. Thus, the strongest oxidizing agent, F_2, is at the top left. The poorest is the lithium ion, Li^+, at the bottom left. The oxidizing agents are listed in decreasing order of oxidizing strength.

The tendency for the reduction half-cell reaction to proceed to the right is indicated by the magnitude of the half-cell potential. A positive potential for a reduction half-cell reaction means that the oxidizing agent is a stronger oxidizing agent than hydrogen ions (H^+). A negative potential means that the oxidizing agent is a weaker oxidizing agent than hydrogen ions. Thus, Ag^+ ions are a stronger oxidizing agent than H^+ ions, but Zn^{2+} ions are a weaker oxidizing agent than H^+ ions.

It should be noted that there are various ways to list the reduction half-cell reactions and potentials. In some texts, the reactions with the largest negative reduction potential are at the top of the list. Regardless of the order, *the oxidized species of the half-cell reaction having the highest positive reduction potential is the best oxidizing agent*. It can, therefore, oxidize the reduced species of any half-cell reaction having a lower positive reduction potential. Conversely, *the reduced species of the half-cell reaction having the most negative reduction potential is the best reducing agent*. Consider the following alphabetical arrangement of half-cell reduction reactions:

$$Al^{3+} + 3e^- \longrightarrow Al(s) \qquad E° = -1.66 \text{ V}$$
$$Cl_2(g) + 2e^- \longrightarrow 2Cl^- \qquad E° = +1.36 \text{ V}$$

Applying the rule noted above, we can say that in the standard state, chlorine (Cl_2) oxidizes $Al(s)$ and forms Al^{3+}. The chlorine at the same time is reduced to chloride ions (Cl^-). Of the four species above, $Al(s)$ is the best reducing agent and $Cl_2(g)$ is the best oxidizing agent.

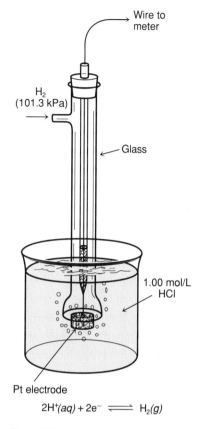

Wire to meter

H_2 (101.3 kPa)

Glass

1.00 mol/L HCl

Pt electrode

$2H^+(aq) + 2e^- \rightleftharpoons H_2(g)$

Figure 13-5
A standard hydrogen electrode.

13-9
The Silver-Hydrogen Cell

A silver half-cell has a greater tendency to be reduced than the hydrogen half-cell.

Figure 13-6 shows a standard hydrogen half-cell coupled to a standard silver half-cell in which the [Ag⁺] is 1 mol/L. The voltmeter reading shows that there is a potential difference of 0.80 V between the hydrogen half-cell and that of the silver–silver ion half-cell. The potential of the standard hydrogen half-cell is arbitrarily taken as zero. Therefore, the potential of the silver half-cell is 0.80 V relative to that of the standard.

Figure 13-6
A silver-hydrogen cell.

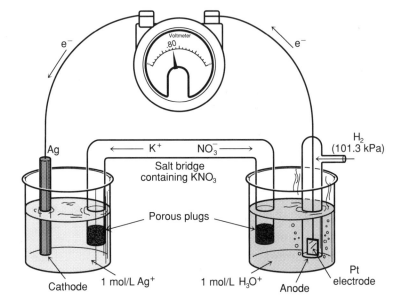

Experiments reveal that electrons flow from the hydrogen half-cell to the silver half-cell and that the acidity of the solution in the hydrogen half-cell increases. In other words, the silver half-cell has an electron-attracting ability that is 0.80 V greater than that of the hydrogen standard half-cell. The reduction of silver ions at the silver electrode implies that *the electron-attracting ability of a half-cell is related to the reduction process* and, therefore, the voltage, 0.80 V, is called the *reduction potential*. The tendency for silver ions to be reduced to silver atoms in the half-cell

$$Ag^+ + e^- \rightleftharpoons Ag(s)$$

is greater by 0.80 V than the tendency for H⁺ ions to be reduced to H₂ in the half-cell

$$2H^+ + 2e^- \rightleftharpoons H_2(g)$$

13-10
The Zinc-Hydrogen Cell

The hydrogen half-cell has a greater tendency to be reduced than a zinc half-cell.

Figure 13-7 shows that when a standard hydrogen and a standard zinc half-cell are coupled, the voltmeter reads 0.76 V. Experiments show that the acidity of the solution in the hydrogen half-cell decreases and that the electrons are flowing from zinc through the external circuit to the hydrogen electrode. There they reduce H^+ ions to H_2 gas. This means that the tendency for zinc ions to be reduced to zinc atoms in the half-cell

$$Zn^{2+} + 2e^- \rightleftharpoons Zn(s)$$

is 0.76 V less than the tendency for H^+ ions to be reduced to H_2 in the half-cell

$$2H^+ + 2e^- \rightleftharpoons H_2(g)$$

Since the electron-attracting ability of a hydrogen half-cell is represented by a potential of zero volts, that of the zinc half-cell would be −0.76 V.

The electron-attracting ability of a silver half-cell is 0.80 V more than that of a hydrogen half-cell, and the electron-attracting ability of a zinc half-cell is 0.76 V less than that of a hydrogen half-cell. Therefore, the electron-attracting ability of a silver half-cell must be 1.56 V more than that of a zinc half-cell. This relationship is represented in Tables 13-6 and 13-7.

TABLE 13-6
HALF-CELL POTENTIALS

Half-Cell	Relative Electron-Attracting Ability
Silver	0.80 V
Hydrogen	0.00 V
Zinc	−0.76 V

TABLE 13-7
CELL POTENTIALS

Cell	Anode	Cathode	E°_{cell}
Hydrogen-silver	H_2	Ag	0.80 V
Zinc-hydrogen	Zn	H_2	0.76 V
Zinc-silver	Zn	Ag	1.56 V

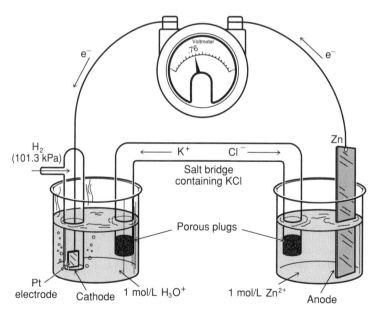

**Figure 13-7
A zinc-hydrogen cell.**

13-11
The Zinc-Silver Cell

When the standard reduction potentials of two half-cells are known, the standard cell potential can be calculated.

When a standard silver and a standard zinc half-cell are coupled, the voltmeter reads 1.56 V (Fig. 13-4). This is the standard cell potential (E°_{cell}) difference between the two half-cells in their standard states. The voltage represents the tendency for the cell reaction

$$2Ag^+ + Zn(s) \rightleftharpoons 2Ag(s) + Zn^{2+}$$

to take place when all participants are at standard state (25°C, 101.3 kPa, 1.00 mol/L concentrations). The value of the standard cell potential can be thought of as a measure of the driving force of the reaction. The positive sign of the cell voltage indicates that the reaction with which it is associated tends at standard-state conditions to proceed spontaneously as written. A negative voltage indicates that the reverse reaction tends to proceed spontaneously at a standard state. This does not mean that no reaction occurs when a reaction has a negative voltage. It simply means that the products are not formed in their standard-state concentrations. We will see later that the magnitude and sign of the voltage are related to the magnitude of the equilibrium constant. A negative voltage is associated with a small equilibrium constant.

STANDARD CELL POTENTIALS

13-12

Calculating Standard Cell Potentials

The standard cell potential (E°_{cell}) is the potential of a cell at standard conditions; that is, when the concentrations of all solutes are 1.00 mol/L, the pressure is 101.3 kPa and the temperature is 25°C.

Calculating the standard cell potential (E°_{cell}) provides information on the direction of electron flow between two half-cells. A net equation for an oxidation-reduction reaction can be obtained by combining any two half-cell reactions in Table 13-5 so that the electrons algebraically cancel. One method is to write one half-cell reaction as a reduction and the other as an oxidation, and then add the two. Note that because all reactions in Table 13-5 are written as reductions, one of them must be reversed before adding. Generally, the half-cell reaction with the lower reduction potential is reversed and then added to the one with the higher reduction potential. This is because the one with the higher reduction potential has the greater tendency to occur and because addition then yields a spontaneous reaction (one with a positive voltage).

Consider the following half-cell reactions taken from Table 13-5:

$$Ag^+ + e^- \rightleftharpoons Ag(s) \qquad E^\circ = 0.80 \text{ V} \qquad [13\text{-}14]$$
$$Cu^{2+} + 2e^- \rightleftharpoons Cu(s) \qquad E^\circ = 0.34 \text{ V} \qquad [13\text{-}15]$$

Before adding, we must multiply Equation 13-14 by 2 in order to balance the electrons, and reverse Equation 13-15 to represent an oxidation. The two new equations become

$$2Ag^+ + 2e^- \rightleftharpoons 2Ag(s) \qquad E° = 0.80 \text{ V} \qquad [13\text{-}16]$$
$$Cu(s) \rightleftharpoons Cu^{2+} + 2e^- \qquad E° = -0.34 \text{ V} \qquad [13\text{-}17]$$

Note that we did not multiply the potential of the silver half-cell reaction by 2. This is not necessary, since the potential is not a function of the number of electrons. Adding Equations 13-16 and 13-17 yields the following equation for the cell reaction:

$$2Ag^+ + Cu(s) \rightleftharpoons Cu^{2+} + 2Ag(s) \qquad E°_{cell} = 0.46 \text{ V} \qquad [13\text{-}18]$$

The positive sign of the cell voltage indicates that the reaction tends to proceed spontaneously at standard-state conditions. When standard half-cell reactions are taken from a table of reduction potentials, the cathode reaction at standard state will always be the one with the higher reduction potential.

The anode and cathode can be identified if we apply the rule that *oxidation occurs at the anode and reduction at the cathode*. Once the electrodes have been identified, the direction of electron flow and ion migration can be determined.

An electrochemical cell is often represented schematically by a single line to separate an electrode from a solution and by a double line to represent the porous partition, or salt bridge, that separates two solutions. In this notation, the copper-silver cell discussed above would be represented as

$$Cu(s) \mid Cu^{2+}(1.00 \text{ mol/L}) \parallel Ag^+(1.00 \text{ mol/L}) \mid Ag(s)$$

By convention, the two couples are usually shown with the anode on the left and the cathode on the right.

The species listed in Table 13-5 are arranged so that any oxidizing agent (on the left side) in the table tends to react spontaneously at standard state with any reducing agent (on the right side) that is below it in the table. Thus, Br_2 oxidizes Cu, I^-, and Zn but not Cl^-. In this table, the more separated the oxidizing and reducing agents are, the greater will be the tendency for the reaction to take place. In general, the greater the distance between the agents, the greater is the difference in their potentials and the greater is the driving force of the reaction.

Standard reduction potential ($E°$) values can be used to predict whether a reaction is probable but not whether it will actually take place at an appreciable rate. The standard cell potential, or cell voltage ($E°_{cell}$), can be used to predict whether or not a certain reaction is probable or spontaneous. It does not indicate, however, whether a reaction rate is fast enough for the reaction to be detected, nor does it allow us always to predict which of several possible products are actually obtained.

Many oxidizing agents can be reduced in steps, yielding products with various oxidation states. For example, HNO_3 is a

In the copper-silver cell, the copper acts as the anode and the silver acts as the cathode.

Electrochemistry and Your Teeth
Dental amalgam, made up of silver in mercury, is a common filling material for teeth. If you have metal fillings in your mouth, you are probably aware of the unpleasant sensation that occurs when you accidentally bite down on a piece of aluminum from a gum or chocolate-bar wrapper. This is an example of electrochemistry at work in your mouth. The aluminum is a stronger reducing agent ($E° = +1.66$ V) than the silver-mercury ($E° = +0.85$ V). Thus, when a piece of aluminum comes in contact with a metal dental filling, the aluminum acts as an anode, the filling as a cathode and the saliva as a salt bridge, producing an electric current. The result of this reaction will shock you!

powerful oxidizing agent that can be reduced to NO_2, N_2O_3, NO, N_2O, N_2 or NH_4^+ ions. Reduction potentials for each of the above reductions are available in any chemistry handbook. The reduction of HNO_3 to N_2 has the highest potential difference, while the reduction to NO_2 has the lowest value. Thus, it would seem that HNO_3 has the greatest tendency to be reduced to N_2. In other words, N_2 is the most stable of the reduction products, and its formation from HNO_3 would represent the greatest decrease in energy. However, at room temperature, NO_2 is usually produced. This is because the reduction reaction that produces NO_2 has a lower activation energy and proceeds at a faster rate than the conversion to N_2. In general, the reaction with the fastest rate is the one that is observed. At higher temperatures, the yield of N_2 increases. Thus, temperature plays an important role in determining which product is formed.

FOLLOW-UP PROBLEMS

1. Which of the following equations represent reactions that tend to proceed spontaneously to the right (at standard-state conditions), tend to proceed spontaneously to the left (at standard state) or do not occur?

a) $2Ag^+ + Cu(s) \rightleftharpoons Cu^{2+} + 2Ag(s)$

b) $Zn(s) + Cu^{2+} \rightleftharpoons Cu(s) + Zn^{2+}$

c) $I_2(s) + 2Cl^- \rightleftharpoons Cl_2(g) + 2I^-$

d) $Fe(s) + Cl_2(g) \rightleftharpoons 2Cl^-(g) + Fe^{2+}$

e) $MnO_4^- + 8H^+ + Cu^{2+} \rightleftharpoons Mn^{2+} + 4H_2O + Cu(s)$

2. What are the E°_{cell} values for the following oxidation-reduction reactions? Which, if any, proceed spontaneously to the left?

a) $5Fe^{2+} + MnO_4^- + 8H^+ \rightleftharpoons 5Fe^{3+} + Mn^{2+} + 4H_2O$

b) $Sn^{2+} + Cl_2(g) \rightleftharpoons Sn^{4+} + 2Cl^-$

c) $3Br_2(l) + 2Cr^{3+} + 7H_2O \rightleftharpoons Cr_2O_7^{2-} + 14H^+ + 6Br^-$

Answers:

1. **(a), (b) and (d) to right; (c) to left; (e) no reaction**

2. **(a) 0.75 V, (b) 1.21 V, (c) −0.27 V (to left)**

NONSTANDARD CELL POTENTIALS

13-13

Effect of Changing Concentration on Cell Potential

Changing the concentrations of the ions in a half-cell changes the electron-attracting ability of its electrode.

You are probably aware that the voltage of a battery does not remain constant. After continued use, the voltage gradually decreases. Let us examine the changes that take place in the zinc-silver cell as it discharges. We can use Le Châtelier's principle to predict how these changes affect the voltage of the cell.

The equilibrium for the cell reaction

$$2Ag^+ + Zn(s) \rightleftharpoons 2Ag(s) + Zn^{2+}$$

shows that as the reaction proceeds, the concentration of Ag^+ ions decreases and the concentration of Zn^{2+} ions increases. According to Le Châtelier's principle, decreasing the concentration of the Ag^+ ions or increasing the concentration of the Zn^{2+} ions causes the equilibrium to shift to the left. Since a shift to the left opposes the cell reaction, the voltage decreases.

Originally, the electron-attracting ability of the Ag-Ag^+ half-cell was much greater than that of the Zn-Zn^{2+} half-cell, and the electrons travelled from the zinc electrode to the silver electrode. As the concentration of the Ag^+ ions in the cathode compartment decreases, the electron-attracting ability of the cathode half-cell decreases. At the same time, the increasing concentration of the Zn^{2+} ions in the anode compartment causes an increase in the electron-attracting ability of the anode half-cell. When the electron-attracting abilities of the two half-cells equalize, there is no further net reaction, and the system is at equilibrium. Thus, *at equilibrium, the cell voltage is zero, and the ion concentrations are equilibrium concentrations*. A voltage of zero indicates that the cell is "dead."

Application of Le Châtelier's principle indicates that increasing the concentration of the reactant in the cathode solution increases the cell voltage. This implies that changing concentrations may cause a change in the spontaneity of a reaction. That is, if concentration changes cause E°_{cell} to change from a positive to a negative value, then the reverse reaction becomes spontaneous.

13-14
Calculating Nonstandard Cell Potentials Using the Nernst Equation

The Nernst equation lets us calculate cell potentials when the concentrations of the ions are not at standard conditions.
In 1889, Walter Nernst (1864–1941), a German scientist, developed a mathematical relationship that lets us calculate cell potentials and the direction of a spontaneous reaction at other than standard-state conditions. For a general oxidation-reduction reaction,

The value 0.059 is obtained by substituting numerical values in the expression

$$\frac{2.3\ RT}{nF}$$

where R is the universal gas constant expressed in J/mol K, T is the Kelvin temperature (298 K), F is the charge on a mole of electrons (96 500 C), n is the number of moles of electrons transferred and 2.3 is the factor used to convert natural logs to base-10 logs. You can verify the value of 0.059 by performing the indicated operations.

$$a A + b B \rightleftharpoons c C + d D$$

the *Nernst equation*, which has been experimentally verified, has the form

$$E_{cell} = E^{\circ}_{cell} - \frac{0.059}{n} \log \frac{[C]^c [D]^d}{[A]^a [B]^b} \qquad [13\text{-}19]$$

where E°_{cell} is the standard cell potential, n is the number of electrons exchanged in the reaction and 0.059 is a constant at 298 K. The concentrations of ions are expressed in terms of mol/L. Note that concentrations of solids and liquid solvents are considered constant and are therefore not included in the expression.

EXAMPLE 13-2
Applying the Nernst Equation
Calculate the cell potential of the following electrochemical cell:

$$Zn(s) \mid Zn^{2+}(0.001\ \text{mol/L}) \parallel Ag^+(0.1\ \text{mol/L}) \mid Ag(s)$$

SOLUTION
1. Identify the cathode and anode half-cells and write the half-cell reactions. Then add the anode and cathode reactions to obtain the cell reaction and the standard cell potential:

Cathode	$2Ag^+ + 2e^- \longrightarrow 2Ag(s)$	$E^{\circ} = +0.80$ V
Anode	$Zn(s) \longrightarrow Zn^{2+} + 2e^-$	$E^{\circ} = +0.76$ V
Cell	$Zn(s) + 2Ag^+ \rightleftharpoons Zn^{2+} + 2Ag(s)$	$E^{\circ}_{cell} = 1.56$ V

2. Substitute the values into the Nernst equation and solve for E_{cell}:

$$E_{cell} = E^{\circ}_{cell} - \frac{0.059}{n} \log \frac{[Zn^{2+}]}{[Ag^+]^2}$$

$$E_{cell} = 1.56 - \frac{0.059}{2} \log \frac{[10^{-3}]}{[10^{-1}]^2}$$

$$= 1.56 - 0.03 \log 10^{-1}$$

$$= 1.56 + 0.03$$

$$= 1.59 \text{ V}$$

FOLLOW-UP PROBLEMS
1. Calculate the voltage for the following electrochemical cell:

$$Zn(s) \mid Zn^{2+}(0.10 \text{ mol/L}) \parallel Cu^{2+}(0.010 \text{ mol/L}) \mid Cu(s)$$

2. a) What is the cell voltage for the following electrochemical cell?

$$Co(s) \mid Co^{2+}(0.1 \text{ mol/L}) \parallel Ni^{2+}(0.001 \text{ mol/L}) \mid Ni(s)$$

b) Using the concentrations in (a), state in which direction the following reaction proceeds spontaneously:

$$Co(s) + Ni^{2+} \rightleftharpoons Co^{2+} + Ni(s)$$

c) In which direction does the reaction proceed spontaneously at standard-state conditions?

Answers:

1. 1.07 V   2. (a) –0.02 V, (b) to left, (c) to right

EQUILIBRIUM CONSTANTS FOR REDOX REACTIONS

13-15

Determining Equilibrium Constants From Standard Cell Potentials

Standard cell potentials provide an alternative way of determining equilibrium constants.

We have suggested that both the standard cell potential (E°_{cell}) and the equilibrium constant (K_e) for a reaction are measures of the tendency for a reaction to take place. It seems reasonable that the two factors should be related. To develop this relationship, recall that when the cell potential is zero, the reaction is at equilibrium. Thus, the existing concentrations are equilibrium concentrations, and the logarithm term in Equation 13-19 becomes $\log K_e$. At equilibrium, when the standard cell potential is zero, Equation 13-19 can be written

Recall from Chapter 10:

$$K_e = \frac{[products]}{[reactants]}$$

$$0 = E^\circ_{cell} - \frac{0.059}{n} \log K_e \qquad \text{[13-20]}$$

$$\log K_e = \frac{nE^\circ_{cell}}{0.059} \qquad \text{[13-21]}$$

$$K_e = 10^{\frac{nE^\circ_{cell}}{0.059}} \qquad \text{[13-22]}$$

Equation 13-22 reveals that the equilibrium constant for any oxidation-reduction reaction can be calculated using the standard cell potential. The same principles apply to redox reactions that involve a direct transfer of electrons as to those that occur in electrochemical cells. Equation 13-22 shows that a reaction with a positive E°_{cell} has a $K_e > 1$, while a reaction with a negative E°_{cell} has a $K_e < 1$. The following example illustrates the calculation and use of equilibrium constants and cell potentials.

EXAMPLE 13-3
Calculating K_e
Calculate the equilibrium constant for the reaction between silver nitrate and metallic zinc. Is the reaction complete or incomplete?

SOLUTION
1. Write the equation for the reaction:

$$2Ag^+(aq) + Zn(s) \rightleftharpoons Zn^{2+}(aq) + 2Ag(s) \quad E^\circ_{cell} = 1.56 \text{ V}$$

2. Substitute values in Equation 13-20:

$$0 = 1.56 - 0.03 \log K_e$$
$$-1.56 = -0.03 \log K_e$$
$$\log K_e = \frac{-1.56}{-0.03} = 52$$
$$K_e = 1 \times 10^{52}$$

The large value of K_e indicates that the reaction is complete.

FOLLOW-UP PROBLEM
Calculate the equilibrium constant for the reaction between metallic zinc and copper(II) sulfate. Is the reaction complete?

Answer: 4.6×10^{36}. Reaction is complete.

Many equilibrium mixtures contain extremely large and extremely small concentrations of ions. Chemical analysis of such a mixture would present a formidable problem. Thus, measuring cell potentials provides a relatively simple way to measure ion concentration and equilibrium constants. The *electrometric (potentiometric) method* is widely applied in determining solubility product constants (K_{sp}) and equilibrium constants in which the equilibrium concentrations of the ions are very small. Consider the solubility product constant for AgCl. In a saturated solution of AgCl, the ion concentrations are so small that accurate measurement by ordinary chemical analysis is difficult. However, by measuring the voltage of an appropriate cell, we can calculate the K_{sp} for AgCl. One standard half-cell of such a cell consists of a metal electrode in a saturated solution of a slightly soluble salt of the metal. The other half-cell could be a standard-state half-cell of the same metal–metallic ion couple, or any other reference half-cell whose accurate E°_{cell} value is known. In Fig. 13-9, for example, the anode consists of a piece of metallic silver immersed in a 1 mol/L Cl^{-} ion solution. The cathode is a standard Ag-Ag^{+} half-cell.

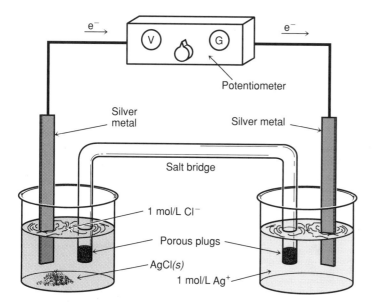

Potentiometer

Silver metal

Silver metal

Salt bridge

1 mol/L Cl^{-}

Porous plugs

AgCl(s)

1 mol/L Ag^{+}

STANDARD FREE-ENERGY CHANGE

13-16
Calculating Standard Free-Energy Change From Standard Cell Potentials

Standard cell potentials can be used to determine the change in free energy in a redox reaction.

In Chapter 10 we found that the change in free energy (ΔG) associated with a reaction could be used as a criterion of reaction spontaneity. That is, a spontaneous reaction has a positive E_{cell} value and is associated with a decrease in free energy (ΔG is negative). These relationships suggest that cell potentials (E_{cell})

Figure 13-9
Electrochemical cell for determining solubility product (K_{sp}) for AgCl. The schematic for the cell is

$$Ag(s) \mid AgCl(s) \mid Cl^{-}(1 \text{ mol/L}) \parallel Ag^{+}(1 \text{ mol/L}) \mid Ag(s)$$

The anode half-cell potential at standard state for the reaction

$$Ag(s) + Cl^{-} \rightleftharpoons AgCl(s) + e^{-}$$

is –0.22 V. The standard cathode potential for the reaction

$$Ag^{+} + e^{-} \rightleftharpoons Ag(s)$$

is 0.80 V. Thus, the standard cell potential for the reaction

$$Ag^{+} + Cl^{-} \rightleftharpoons AgCl(s)$$

is 0.58 V. At equilibrium, we can calculate K_e using Equation 13-20:

$$0 = 0.58 \text{ V} - \frac{0.059}{1.0 \text{ mol}} \log \frac{1}{[Ag^{+}][Cl^{-}]}$$

$$-0.58 = 0.059 \log [Ag^{+}][Cl^{-}]$$

Recall from Chapter 11:

$$K_{sp} = [\text{products}][\text{reactants}]$$

Therefore,

$$\log K_{sp} = -9.8$$
$$K_{sp} = 1.6 \times 10^{-10}$$

must be related to changes in the free energy (ΔG) of a reacting system. The relationship between standard free-energy change ($\Delta G°$) and standard cell potential ($E°_{cell}$) is given by

$$\Delta G° = -nFE°_{cell} \qquad [13\text{-}23]$$

where n is the number of electrons transferred in the cell reaction, $E°_{cell}$ is the standard cell potential expressed in volts and F is the charge carried by a mole of electrons, or 96 500 coulombs (C).

We can interpret Equation 13-23 by saying the $\Delta G°$ *is numerically equal to the useful electric work that a chemical system can do on its surroundings.* Electric work is done when a charge is moved through a voltage difference. In the operation of an electrochemical cell, the voltage or potential difference between two half-cells drives the electrons through the circuit, where they perform electric work.

Equation 13-23 enables scientists to determine values for changes in standard free energy by measuring standard cell potentials. As we learned in Chapter 10, ΔG is related to enthalpy and entropy changes in a system. Since $E°_{cell}$ and $\Delta G°$ are related, we can assume that ΔH and ΔS also affect $E°_{cell}$.

EXAMPLE 13-4
Calculating $\Delta G°$
Calculate $\Delta G°$ for the zinc-silver cell at standard-state conditions.
1. Obtain the standard half-cell reduction potentials from Table 13-5 and determine $E°_{cell}$ by using the relation

$$E°_{cell} = E_{reduction} + E_{oxidation}$$
$$E°_{cell} = 0.80 + 0.76 = 1.56 \text{ V} = 1.56 \text{ J/C}$$

2. Substitute all known values in Equation 13-23 and solve for $\Delta G°$:

$$\begin{aligned}
\Delta G° &= -nFE°_{cell} \\
&= -2(96\ 500 \text{ C})(1.56 \text{ J/C}) \\
&= -3.01 \times 10^5 \text{ J} \\
&= -301 \text{ kJ}
\end{aligned}$$

FOLLOW-UP PROBLEM
Calculate $\Delta G°$ for the reaction between zinc and copper(II) using the data in Table 13-5.

Answer: -212 kJ

APPLICATIONS OF ELECTROCHEMICAL CELLS

There are many applications of electrochemical principles and voltaic cells. The research chemist may use them to determine the spontaneity of reactions, the values for equilibrium constants or the concentrations of ions. Manufacturing chemists apply electrochemical principles when they use pH meters to monitor the acidity of solutions. The chemical engineer is concerned with electrochemical principles and processes when devising methods to prevent corrosion. The same principles are being used by scientists who are engaged in developing fuel cells that will efficiently convert chemical energy into electric energy. All of us depend on electrochemical cells every time we drive a car or turn on a flashlight. Let us briefly consider a few of these applications.

13-17
Lead Storage Battery

Lead storage batteries provide electric power in automobiles. The 12 V lead storage battery consists of six voltaic cells connected in series, that is, in such a manner that their voltages are additive.

The anodes are made of spongy lead and the cathodes of lead(IV) oxide (PbO_2). The electrodes are in a solution of sulfuric acid. When the cells are producing electricity, the reaction at the anode is

$$Pb(s) + HSO_4^- \rightleftharpoons PbSO_4(s) + H^+ + 2e^- \quad [13\text{-}24]$$

The reaction at the cathode is

$$PbO_2(s) + HSO_4^- + 3H^+ + 2e^- \rightleftharpoons PbSO_4(s) + 2H_2O \quad [13\text{-}25]$$

Addition of Equations 13-24 and 13-25 gives the following overall cell reaction:

$$Pb(s) + PbO_2(s) + 2H^+ + 2HSO_4^- \rightleftharpoons 2PbSO_4(s) + 2H_2O$$
$$[13\text{-}26]$$

Equation 13-26 shows that the HSO_4^- ions from the electrolyte react with the Pb^{2+} ions formed by the oxidation of the Pb anode and the reduction of the PbO_2 cathode. The lead sulfate deposits on both electrodes.

During the discharge of the cell, the concentration of H_2SO_4 decreases as the sulfate ions precipitate out and as the H^+ ions form water. As the concentration of the sulfuric acid decreases, the

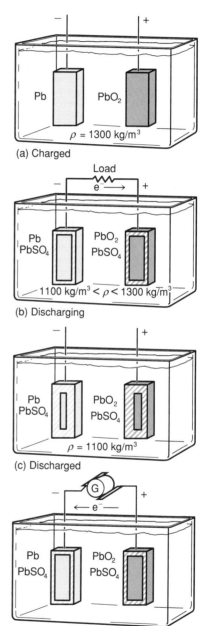

(a) Charged

(b) Discharging

(c) Discharged

(d) Charging

Figure 13-10
Changes that occur during the operation of (a) a fully charged cell, (b) a discharging cell, (c) a fully discharged cell and (d) a storage cell being charged by an external source or direct current.

density of the solution decreases. Thus, the condition of the battery can be easily checked by measuring the density of the sulfuric acid solution with a hydrometer. A low density (specific gravity) indicates a partially discharged cell. The sulfuric acid solution in a fully charged battery has a density of 1200 kg/m^3 to 1300 kg/m^3 (Fig. 13-10(a)). The acid solution in a discharged battery has a density of 1100 kg/m^3 to 1150 kg/m^3 (Fig. 13-10(b)).

The battery can be recharged by connecting it to an external source of direct current and reversing the flow of electrons (Fig. 13-10(d)). This reverses the reactions, forming lead on the anode and lead dioxide on the cathode, and increases the concentration of the sulfuric acid. The charging reaction is

$$2PbSO_4(s) + 2H_2O \rightleftharpoons Pb(s) + PbO_2(s) + 2H^+ + 2HSO_4^-$$

13-18
Dry-Cell Battery

Voltaic cells provide portable sources of electric power.
Some familiar applications of the common dry-cell battery are in portable radios and cassette players. This battery, a zinc-carbon dry cell, is relatively inexpensive and will generate about 1.5 V. Figure 13-11 shows a cutaway diagram of a dry-cell battery.

The outside terminal is attached to a zinc container, which acts as the anode. The centre terminal is connected to a rod of carbon and manganese dioxide, which acts as the cathode. The zinc container is filled with a moist paste of zinc chloride, ammonium chloride, water and an inert filler such as asbestos. A porous liner prevents the zinc from coming into direct contact with the paste and serves as a salt bridge. The anode reaction is

$$Zn(s) \longrightarrow Zn^{2+}(aq) + 2e^-$$

The cathode reaction is

$$2MnO_2(s) + NH_4^+(aq) + 2e^- \longrightarrow MnO_2(s) + 2NH_3(aq) + H_2O$$

In addition, the zinc ion reacts with the ammonia produced at the cathode to produce a complex ion:

$$Zn^{2+}(aq) + 4NH_3(aq) \longrightarrow Zn(NH_3)_4^{2+}(aq)$$

While these dry cells are relatively inexpensive, they rapidly lose power because the products of the reaction cannot diffuse away from the electrodes rapidly enough.

A slightly more expensive battery, called an *alkaline dry cell*, uses the same reactants as the normal dry cell; however, the

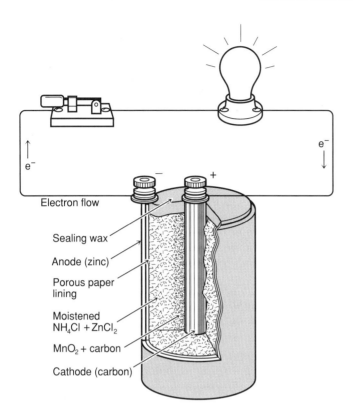

Figure 13-11
A cutaway view of a dry-cell battery showing the interior of the battery as well as the electron flow through an external circuit. Note that a porous liner in the battery prevents the zinc from coming into direct contact with the paste and serves as a salt bridge.

reactions occur in a basic (alkaline) medium. The half-cell reaction at the anode is

$$Zn(s) + 2OH^-(aq) \longrightarrow ZnO(s) + H_2O + 2e^-$$

The cathode reaction is

$$2MnO_2(s) + H_2O + 2e^- \longrightarrow Mn_2O_3(s) + 2OH^-(aq)$$

This battery will produce about 1.54 V. While more expensive, it has a longer shelf life than the normal dry-cell battery and is able to produce more electric current for longer periods of time. However, neither the normal dry cell nor the alkaline batteries are rechargeable.

13-19
Mercury and Silver Oxide Batteries

Mercury and silver oxide batteries are able to maintain a constant potential.

The *mercury battery* (Fig. 13-12) is a small battery that has been used since the 1960s. The anode reaction is the same as the zinc oxidation that occurs in the dry-cell battery. The cathode reduction reaction is

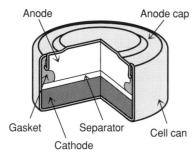

Anode   Anode cap

Gasket   Separator   Cell can

Cathode

Figure 13-12
A mercury battery.

$$HgO(s) + H_2O(l) + 2e^- \longrightarrow Hg(l) + 2OH^-(aq)$$

These batteries generate about 1.35 V. Mercury batteries are useful because they maintain a constant potential throughout their life. Dry-cell batteries, in comparison, have a steadily dropping potential due to the slow diffusion of products away from the cathode. The provision of a constant potential is very important for the proper functioning of precision electronic devices. The major disadvantage of mercury batteries is that mercury has been shown to be an environmental poison.

A recently developed alternative to mercury batteries is the *silver oxide battery*. It is very similar to the mercury battery except that the cathode reaction is

$$Ag_2O(s) + H_2O(l) + 2e^- \longrightarrow 2Ag(s) + 2OH^-(aq)$$

These batteries produce 1.5 V. Because they are made of silver, silver oxide batteries are quite expensive and are used only in high-quality wristwatches, some calculators, hearing aids and some 35 mm automatic cameras.

13-20
Lithium Batteries

Lithium batteries provide a constant potential for many years. Lithium batteries are a relatively new development. Although they are similar to mercury batteries, they produce twice the energy potential for the same size of battery and last many times longer. In fact, some manufacturers claim a lifespan of up to 25 years for their lithium batteries. The long life of the lithium battery, along with its thin shape, has made it extremely useful in the development and implementation of artificial pacemakers. Today, cardiac pacemakers can be made as thin as 9 to 16 mm and can weigh as little as 32 g to 80 g. Another advantage to using lithium batteries in pacemakers is that the reactants do not produce gases and can therefore be hermetically sealed. Because they last for years, the frequency of surgical replacement is low.

13-21
Nickel-Cadmium Battery

Nickel-cadmium batteries can be recharged over and over again.
The nickel-cadmium battery produces about 1.4 V and is rechargeable as the reactions at the anode and cathode are reversible. The half-cell reaction at the anode is

$$Cd(s) + 2OH^-(aq) \rightleftharpoons Cd(OH)_2(s) + 2e^-$$

The reaction at the cathode is

$$NiO_2(s) + 2H_2O(l) + 2e^- \rightleftharpoons Ni(OH)_2(s) + 2OH^-(aq)$$

This battery is more expensive than the other kinds of batteries. It is used to power rechargeable calculators, power tools, camera battery packs and electric shavers.

A Canadian company, Battery Technologies Inc., has developed a new *manganese dioxide battery* that is apparently 50% cheaper to produce than nickel-cadmium batteries and delivers 50% more energy.

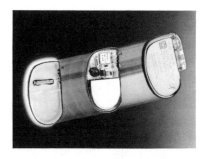

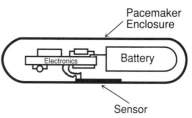

Figure 13-13
The heart has a natural pacemaker that generates electric impulses at an average rate of about 70/min. When injury, disease or birth defects impair the operation of the natural pacemaker, an artificial pacemaker, such as that shown above (top) and in cross-section, may be implanted in a patient's body.

13-22
Corrosion

Corrosion is an electrochemical process in which most metals, particularly iron, deteriorate.

The corrosion of metals has been a problem since the process of obtaining metals from their ores was first developed. While most metals will rust, the rusting of iron is our most serious problem since iron has so many applications in our lives. Experimental evidence indicates that the corrosion of iron is an electrochemical phenomenon. Very pure samples of iron seem to resist corrosion; however, when a piece of iron containing specks of impurities such as copper is exposed to moist air, the iron becomes pitted by rust spots. Rust spots indicate the locations at which the iron has been oxidized and represent the anode half-cells of electrochemical cells.

Impurities such as copper serve as the cathode half-cells and are located in unaffected areas adjacent to the rust spots. The electrons travel through the iron from the anode to the cathode. A film of moisture serves as the medium through which ions travel to complete the circuit (Fig. 13-14).

The electrochemical theory of corrosion is supported by the observation that iron exposed to perfectly dry air does not corrode. Three half-cell reactions represent possible reactions for the corrosion of iron:

Anode: $\qquad$ $Fe(s) \rightleftharpoons Fe^{2+} + 2e^-$ $\quad$ [13-27]

Cathode (neutral solution):
$\qquad \frac{1}{2}O_2(g) + H_2O(l) + 2e^- \rightleftharpoons 2OH^-$ $\quad$ [13-28]

Cathode (acid solution): $\quad 2H^+ + 2e^- \rightleftharpoons H_2(g)$ $\quad$ [13-29]

The overall cell reaction can be obtained by adding Equations 13-27 and 13-28 or 13-27 and 13-29. The former addition gives

$$Fe(s) + \frac{1}{2}O_2(g) + H_2O(l) \rightleftharpoons Fe(OH)_2(s) \quad [13-30]$$

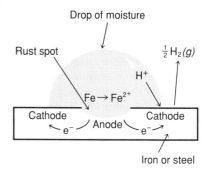

Figure 13-14
Corrosion of impure iron in contact with moisture.

Figure 13-15
The corrosion of this car was caused by the deterioration of metals in an oxidation-reduction reaction. Rust forms when the metal is oxidized by oxygen in the presence of water. For corrosion to occur there must be an anodic area, which can occur at cracks in the oxide coating, at boundaries between different metal phases or around impurities. There must also be a cathodic area, which can occur at the metal oxide coating or around other metal compounds.

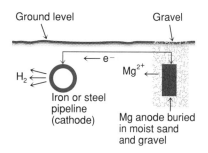

Figure 13-16
Underground iron pipes can be cathodically protected from corrosion if the pipe is connected to a more easily oxidized metal such as zinc or magnesium. For example, the Alaska Pipeline has a zinc wire buried alongside the pipeline itself, acting as the anode and the steel pipe as the cathode.

If the iron object is further exposed to oxygen and water, iron(III) oxide is produced:

$$4Fe(OH)_2(s) + O_2(g) \longrightarrow 2Fe_2O_3 \cdot H_2O(s) + 2H_2O(l)$$

This is the red-brown oxide that forms on cars and bridges.

Salt (NaCl) that is spread on roads in the winter to melt ice and snow also contributes to the corrosion of iron. The chloride ion from the NaCl is relatively small and diffuses through the coating of metal oxide and forms iron chlorides. These iron chlorides are more soluble in water than the iron oxides and hydroxides, and thus diffuse back out through the coating of the metal. This forms a pathway for further attack by oxygen and water into the interior of the iron. As a result, automobiles begin to show small pits in the metal after the winter season, along with the familiar red-brown iron(III) oxide (Fig. 13-15).

13-23
Prevention of Corrosion

Due to the enormous economic cost of corrosion, many industries have been working to find methods of slowing down the rusting process. Although many methods have been devised, none have proven totally successful.

The simplest method for preventing corrosion is to paint the metal. For many years, this was the only protection for the surface metal on automobiles; however, paint is easily chipped and scratched, thus exposing the surface to oxidation.

A second method involves coating iron with another metal that is more resistant to corrosion. One of the most common coating metals is tin. A tin can, used to contain many food items, is really a steel can that has been plated with a protective layer of tin. However, if the tin is scratched and the steel underneath exposed to water or oxygen, the iron will actually rust more quickly than if there had been no tin coating. The reason for this is that iron is a more reactive metal than tin and electrons pass from the iron to the tin, changing the Fe to Fe^{2+}.

A more effective method of protecting iron is to coat it with zinc. Iron so treated is called *galvanized* iron. If the zinc coating is scratched, the zinc will corrode rather than the iron since zinc is a more reactive metal than iron. For this reason, many modern cars have galvanized body parts to protect them from excessive corrosion. However, zinc-coated iron cannot be used for canned food because most zinc compounds are poisonous.

Another method of slowing down corrosion is called *cathodic protection*. In this method, iron is made the cathode half-cell so that it will not lose electrons and corrode. This is accomplished by attaching a more active metal such as magnesium or zinc to the iron or by connecting the iron to the cathode of an external power source. These devices are frequently used to protect underground pipes and tanks (Fig. 13-16) and even the hulls of ships. Steel hulls are especially vulnerable to corrosion because the bronze propeller acts as a cathode, salt water as a salt bridge and the hull as an anode. The problem has been solved by attaching large pieces of magnesium, zinc or aluminum to the hull (Fig. 13-17). The magnesium, zinc or aluminum, being more easily oxidized than iron, acts as an anode, making the steel hull the cathode. Because anodes corrode and cathodes don't, the attached anode material is corroded and dissolved, while the steel hull remains unaffected.

Figure 13-17
A semi-submersible drill rig, currently operating in offshore Atlantic Canadian waters, showing the locations of sacrificial aluminum alloy anodes. The aluminum metal attached to the hull of the ship protects the ship from corrosion by acting as an anode. Since oxidation occurs at the anode, it is the aluminum that is oxidized instead of the steel hull. Aluminum anodes are one-third the weight of zinc anodes and are used for floating structures where loading weight is a consideration.

13-24

The pH Meter

A pH meter is an instrument that measures the potential difference between a reference half-cell and a half-cell whose potential changes when [H⁺] varies.

The development of reference electrodes and indicator electrodes makes it possible to use cell potentials to determine the concentration of a specific ion in a solution. Reference electrodes maintain a constant half-cell potential independent of the concentration of the solution, and indicator electrodes respond to changes in the concentration of specific ions. The potential difference between the indicator and reference electrodes as read on a meter can be related to the concentration of the specific ion. One of the most familiar applications of this relationship is found in the use of pH meters to

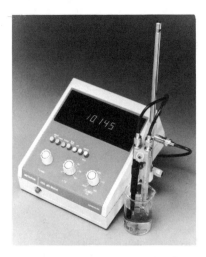

Figure 13-18
A modern pH meter.

determine the [H⁺] of a solution. The potential of a cell changes when the concentration of a reaction participant is varied. When H⁺ ions are a reactant, both the electrode voltage and the pH change when the H⁺ ion concentration is varied. This implies that the pH of a solution is related to the voltage of a cell in which H⁺ ions are a reactant.

The potential of the standard hydrogen electrode varies when [H⁺] is changed. When this half-cell is coupled to a reference half-cell that maintains a constant potential, the variation in the overall cell potential is a measure of the variation in the H⁺ ion concentration of the solution. With the use of the Nernst equation, it can be shown that a change of one pH unit (10-fold [H⁺] change) causes a change in the overall cell potential of 0.059 V.

A pH meter measures the potential difference between a reference half-cell and a half-cell and translates the potential difference into pH values. The dial of the meter is often graduated in both pH and millivolt units. The hydrogen electrode is not a convenient half-cell to use for most laboratory pH measurements. Instead, pH meters are generally equipped with a standard reference electrode and a rugged, portable "glass" electrode whose half-cell potential is sensitive to changes in [H⁺]. A pH meter is shown in Fig. 13-18.

Figure 13-19
An experimental pH meter. The calomel electrode is a reference electrode that maintains a constant potential. The potential across the glass electrode varies with the [H⁺] of the solution.

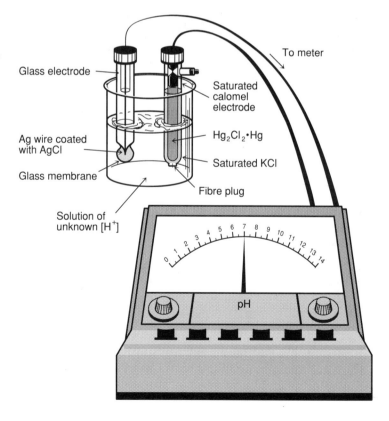

An experimental arrangement for determining pH is shown in Fig. 13-19.

The saturated calomel (Hg_2Cl_2) electrode shown in Fig. 13-19 is commonly used as a reference electrode. The half-cell reaction for this electrode is

$$Hg_2Cl_2 + 2e^- \rightleftharpoons 2Hg + 2Cl^- \qquad E = 0.242 \text{ V}$$

In the so-called normal calomel electrode, the KCl is 1.0 mol/L and the half-cell potential is 0.280 V.

FUEL CELLS: A SPACE-AGE POWER SOURCE

Imagine the type of electric power source that would be needed on the Space Shuttle: it would have to be very efficient at converting the chemical energy of a fuel directly into electricity and also be very convenient to use. The fuel cell, which has already been used successfully on the Space Shuttle, has proved itself to be an efficient and convenient power source for the space age.

Fuel cells, like storage batteries, are electrochemical devices that generate usable electric current. Unlike voltaic cells, a fuel cell's electrodes and electrolytes remain unchanged. Furthermore, the reactants must be continuously supplied from an external storage tank. As the reaction proceeds, the products are removed, preventing the reaction from reaching equilibrium. This allows the cell to run indefinitely as long as the reactants are supplied.

Fuel cells are not new. The first one was built in 1839 by W.R. Grove in England. Early fuel cells were developed in an effort to produce electricity from direct electrochemical oxidation of coal and coal products. Further efforts to develop this technology were dropped when it became evident that fuel cells were unable to compete with steam-driven electric generators. However, in the 1960s, fuel cell research received new impetus from the United States space program, as well as from rising concerns about atmospheric pollution from power plants and internal-combustion engines.

Modern fuel cells are very efficient and provide a steady, dependable supply of electricity without the need to replace or regenerate the electrodes as in a normal storage battery. The most successful fuel cell is the *hydrogen-oxygen cell*, which has been used in the Gemini, Apollo and Space Shuttle programs. This cell involves the oxidation of hydrogen by oxygen to form water. Instead of reacting directly, the fuel cell is designed so that the oxygen is pumped to the cathode where it is reduced, and the hydrogen is pumped to the anode where it is oxidized to water. The electrolyte is a hot, concentrated solution of potassium hydroxide. The electrodes are hollow tubes made of porous, compressed carbon impregnated with a catalyst. The half-cell reaction at the anode is

$$H_2(g) + 2OH^- \rightleftharpoons 2H_2O + 2e^-$$

The reaction at the cathode is

$$O_2(g) + 2H_2O + 4e^- \rightleftharpoons 4OH^-$$

When the two equations are balanced and added together, the following overall equation is obtained:

$$2H_2(g) + O_2(g) \rightleftharpoons 2H_2O(l)$$

As you can see, the only product of the reaction is water. In fact, it is this process that produces the drinking water for orbiting

astronauts.

This method of converting fuel energy directly into electric energy is far more efficient than the old steam-driven turbines. To date, fuel cells are 75% efficient, compared with the 35 to 40% efficiency of power plants and the 25 to 30% efficiency of gasoline or diesel engines. If fuel cells derived from fossil fuels or their products were developed, the consumption of non-renewable petroleum reserves could be reduced significantly.

In all fuel cells, oxygen or air (containing oxygen) is supplied to the cathode as an oxidant, and fuel is supplied to the anode. Hydrogen has been the most successful fuel, but other gases such as carbon monoxide, methyl alcohol, hydrazine and some simple hydrocarbons have also been used. Ballard Technologies of Vancouver has developed a solid polymer fuel cell that uses methanol as a fuel in a cell made with a solid ion-exchange membrane sandwiched between two electrodes. A thin layer of platinum acts as a catalyst. Methanol fuel cells have been used to power television repeater stations and navigation beacons in remote areas that are not supplied with electric power lines.

Fuel cells have the potential to provide an alternative source of electricity that would lower the demands on our fossil-fuel supply and on the environment.

ELECTROLYTIC CELLS

In electrochemical cells, spontaneous chemical reactions take place, liberating electric energy and resulting in a decrease in the chemical energy of the system. Cells in which nonspontaneous reactions take place by the addition of electric energy to the system undergo an increase in potential energy. They are known as *electrolytic cells*. The decomposition of water by electrolysis is an example of an electrolytic-cell reaction (see Fig. 13-20). The reaction

$$2H_2O(l) \rightleftharpoons 2H_2(g) + O_2(g)$$

is a nonspontaneous reaction. Electric energy must be added to the system to bring about the decomposition. The products, H_2 and O_2, possess more potential energy than the H_2O. In theory, the electric energy put into the system can be recovered by allowing the H_2 and O_2 to react, as in a fuel cell.

13-25
Electrolysis of Melted Binary Salts

Electrolysis uses electricity to provide the energy for a nonspontaneous chemical reaction.

In the electrolysis of melted salts, cations are reduced at the cathode, and anions are oxidized at the anode. The products of such an electrolysis are generally metals at the cathode and nonmetals at the anode. Let us examine the operation of an electrolytic cell containing melted sodium chloride, schematically illustrated in Fig. 13-21.

The external source of electric energy may be a dry cell or any source of direct current. The terminals of the battery are connected to inert electrodes A and B by copper wire. The electrodes dip into melted sodium chloride.

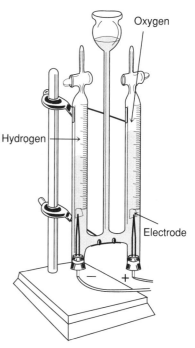

As long as the temperature remains above 800°C, the melting point of sodium chloride, the sodium and chloride ions are able to move freely and transport an electric charge through the liquid. When the circuit is completed, the electric field produced by the battery forces electrons through the wires in the direction shown

Figure 13-20
A series of El-250 cells (above left) that use water electrolysis to produce high-purity hydrogen and its by-products: electrolytic oxygen and heavy water. The El-250 cells have a nominal current of 100 000 A and each cell produces 42 Nm³/h of hydrogen and 21 Nm³/h of oxygen. Each cell works in the same manner as the Hoffman apparatus (above right), which is used to electrolyze small quantities of water.

Electrolysis is usually the preferred method for producing hydrogen when the reliability and economics of production are important factors, when there is a demand for the by-products (oxygen and heavy water) or when gas purity is critical.

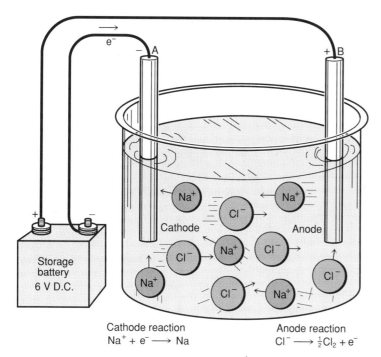

Cathode reaction
$$Na^+ + e^- \longrightarrow Na$$

Anode reaction
$$Cl^- \longrightarrow \tfrac{1}{2}Cl_2 + e^-$$

Figure 13-21
The electrolysis of melted sodium chloride.

by the arrows. That is, electrons are forced toward electrode A and pulled away from B. Positive sodium ions in the liquid are attracted to electrode A, where they pick up one electron per ion and are reduced to neutral sodium atoms. Chloride ions migrate toward the positive electrode, where there is a deficiency of electrons. There they give up one electron per ion to the electrode and become neutral chlorine atoms. Two chlorine atoms combine and form diatomic molecules of Cl_2 gas. The electrode reaction at the cathode is

$$Na^+(l) + e^- \rightleftharpoons Na(l)$$

The reaction at the anode is

$$Cl^-(l) \rightleftharpoons \tfrac{1}{2}Cl_2(g) + e^-$$

The overall reaction can be obtained by adding the anode and cathode reactions:

$$\text{electric energy} + Na^+(l) + Cl^-(l) \rightleftharpoons Na(l) + \tfrac{1}{2}Cl_2(g)$$

13-26
Electrolysis of Aqueous Solutions

There are several different oxidation and reduction reactions that can occur during the electrolysis of water solutions.

When inert electrodes are used in the electrolysis of water solutions, two possible reactions at each electrode must be considered. At the anode, these are the oxidation of water,

$$H_2O(l) \rightleftharpoons \tfrac{1}{2}O_2(g) + 2H^+ + 2e^-$$

and the oxidation of a nonmetallic ion (X^-),

$$2X^- \rightleftharpoons X_2 + 2e^-$$

Experimentally, it is found that for fairly concentrated aqueous solutions of Cl^-, Br^- or I^- ions, the free halogen rather than oxygen is discharged at the anode. Note that oxidation potentials indicate that it should be easier to oxidize H_2O ($[H^+] = 1 \times 10^{-7}$ mol/L) than to oxidize Cl^- and Br^- ions. That is, the *oxidation potential* for the water half-cell reaction is higher than that for the Cl^- or Br^- ion half-cell. This observation suggests that other factors must be taken into consideration. Since a discussion of these factors is beyond the scope of this text, we will use experimental observations as a basis for our statement. When the salt solution contains sulfate ions as the anion, water is oxidized to oxygen. This is because the oxidation of SO_4^{2-} ions requires a much greater potential (driving force) than the oxidation of water.

At the cathode, the two possible reactions are the reduction of a metallic ion (M^{2+}),

$$M^{2+} + 2e^- \rightleftharpoons M$$

and the reduction of water,

$$2H_2O + 2e^- \rightleftharpoons H_2(g) + 2OH^-(10^{-7} \text{ mol/L}) \quad E = -0.41 \text{ V}$$

Use the Nernst equation to verify that $E = -0.41$ V.

The species with the highest possible reduction potential should be the easiest to reduce. In general, therefore, metallic ions such as Cu^{2+} and Ag^+ with reduction potentials greater than that for water should be reduced to the metal at the cathode. On the other hand, water is reduced to hydrogen gas at the cathode in solutions containing Na^+, K^+, Li^+ and other ions with large negative reduction potentials. When an aqueous solution of Na_2SO_4 is electrolyzed using inert electrodes, hydrogen gas is observed at the cathode and oxygen gas at the anode. These observations can be interpreted in terms of the relevant half-cell reactions given below:

$$2H_2O + 2e^- \rightleftharpoons H_2(g) + 2OH^-(10^{-7} \text{ mol/L}) \quad E = -0.41 \text{ V} \quad [13\text{-}31]$$
$$Na^+(aq) + e^- \rightleftharpoons Na(s) \qquad\qquad E° = -2.71 \text{ V} \quad [13\text{-}32]$$
$$2H_2O \rightleftharpoons O_2(g) + 4H^+(10^{-7} \text{ mol/L}) + 4e^- \quad E = -0.815 \text{ V} \quad [13\text{-}33]$$
$$2SO_4^{2-} \rightleftharpoons S_2O_8^{2-} + 2e^- \qquad\qquad E° = -2.01 \text{ V} \quad [13\text{-}34]$$

Equations 13-31 and 13-32 represent the possible cathode reactions. Equation 13-31, which represents the reduction of water, has a higher reduction potential than Equation 13-32. Therefore, water is easier to reduce than $Na^+(aq)$. On this basis, we can assume that Equation 13-31 represents the cathode reaction.

Equations 13-33 and 13-34 represent possible anode reactions. Equation 13-33, which represents the oxidation of water, has a higher oxidation potential than Equation 13-34. Therefore, water is easier to oxidize than SO_4^{2-} ions. On this basis, we can assume that Equation 13-33 represents the anode reaction. The overall reaction can be obtained by multiplying Equation 13-31 by 2 and adding it to Equation 13-33:

$$6H_2O \rightleftharpoons 2H_2(g) + O_2(g) + 4OH^- + 4H^+$$

The Na^+ ions and SO_4^{2-} ions maintain electric neutrality around the electrode as the water is electrolyzed.

The problem of predicting products is complicated even further by using electrodes that may react. Consider the electrolysis of a copper(II) sulfate solution using copper metal as the electrode. This electrolytic cell is illustrated in Fig. 13-22 on the next page. At the cathode, the possible reactions are

$$Cu^{2+} + 2e^- \rightleftharpoons Cu(s) \qquad\qquad E° = 0.34 \text{ V} \quad [13\text{-}35]$$
$$2H_2O + 2e^- \rightleftharpoons H_2(g) + 2OH^-(10^{-7} \text{ mol/L}) \quad E = -0.41 \text{ V}$$

The half-cell potentials indicate that Equation 13-35 is the cathode reaction. At the anode there are now three possibilities: the oxidation of H_2O, the oxidation of SO_4^{2-} and the oxidation of copper metal. The half-cell potentials of

$$Cu(s) \rightleftharpoons Cu^{2+} + 2e^- \qquad E° = -0.34 \text{ V} \qquad [13\text{-}36]$$
$$2H_2O \rightleftharpoons O_2(g) + 4H^+ + 4e^- \quad E° = -0.82 \text{ V}$$
$$2SO_4^{2-} \rightleftharpoons S_2O_8^{2-} + 2e^- \qquad E° = -2.01 \text{ V}$$

indicate that copper metal is the easiest of the three species to oxidize. Therefore, Equation 13-36 represents the anode reaction. The cell described above is characteristic of many electroplating cells. In these cells, the object to be plated is made the cathode, a bar of the plating metal is made the anode, and the solution contains a soluble salt of the plating metal. In a copper-plating cell, Cu^{2+} ions from the solution gain electrons and are deposited on the cathode as copper atoms. As fast as Cu^{2+} ions are removed from solution, copper atoms from the anode bar lose electrons and go into solution as Cu^{2+} ions. In this way, the copper(II) concentration of the solution remains constant at an optimum value. At this point, we should note that it is not always possible to predict exactly what products will be discharged in an electrolytic cell by referring to reduction or oxidation potentials. Such factors as rates, current levels, concentration, polarization and overvoltage must also be considered.

Figure 13-22
An electrolytic cell used for electroplating copper. The object to be plated is connected to the negative terminal of the electrochemical cell, which serves as the source of electrons. The copper anode of the electrolytic cell is connected to the positive terminal of the electrochemical cell.

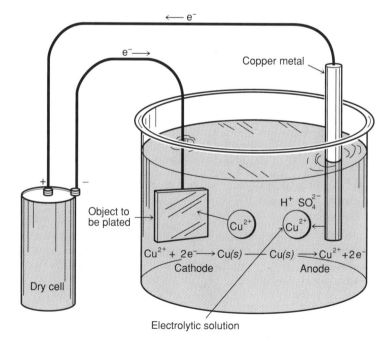

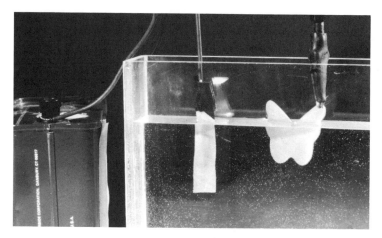

13-27
Industrial Applications of Electrolysis

Electrolysis is used industrially in electroplating, producing hydrogen and oxygen gas from water, and refining metals. In this section we will look specifically at the production of pure metals.

Electrolytic processes are widely used in electroplating (Fig. 13-23) and to prepare metals in a highly pure state. The production of pure copper and pure magnesium are familiar examples. Inco Limited's Canadian operations alone electrolytically refine about 125 million kilograms of copper in a year. In this process, impure copper slabs, known as *blister copper*, act as anodes in an electrolytic cell (Fig. 13-24 on the next page). The cathodes are thin sheets of pure copper and the electrolyte is a copper(II) sulfate solution containing sulfuric acid. During electrolysis the copper in the impure anode goes into solution as Cu^{2+} ions. The Cu^{2+} ions migrate to the cathode and plate out as pure copper. Impurities such as silver and gold, which have more negative oxidation potentials than copper, are not oxidized but fall to the bottom of the tank as the anode disintegrates. In this way, valuable metals are salvaged in the "anode mud." Impurities with higher oxidation potentials than copper are also oxidized and dissolved as ions in the solution. These ions have a lower reduction potential than Cu^{2+} and, therefore, do not plate out unless most of the copper(II) ions have been removed from the solution. This is avoided by the use of impure copper anodes.

One important industrial process for preparing metallic sodium involves the electrolysis of melted NaCl. The reaction is carried out in a ***Downs cell*** similar to that illustrated in Fig. 13-25 on the next page. In this cell, the electrodes are separated by an iron screen that permits passage of ions but prevents the products from

Figure 13-23
Silver is often plated on jewellery made from less expensive metals. In the electroplating of silver onto other metals, the object to be plated acts as the cathode in the reaction. The silver ions in the electroplating silver cyanide solution are reduced to pure silver metal at the cathode and are deposited on the object.

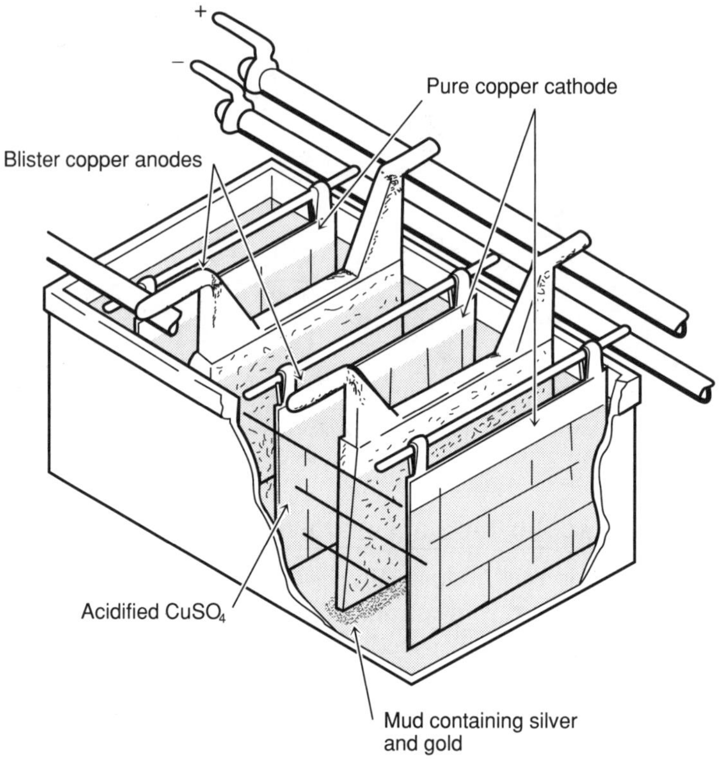

Figure 13-24
The final step in the refining of copper is an electrolytic process. The reduction potential of the copper half-cell is less than that of water. Hence, the Cu^{2+} ions are reduced rather than the water.

Blister copper anodes

Pure copper cathode

Acidified $CuSO_4$

Mud containing silver and gold

interacting. All of the alkali metals can be prepared by the electrolytic decomposition of their melted salts. This was the method used by Sir Humphrey Davy, the discoverer of the elements sodium, potassium and lithium.

Magnesium is primarily used as a structural material. Magnesium-aluminum alloys are used extensively in the aircraft and space industries because of their strength and light weight.

Figure 13-25
Melted sodium chloride is electrolyzed in a Downs cell. Chlorine gas is formed over the central positive carbon electrode, and melted sodium metal is produced at the negative iron electrode.

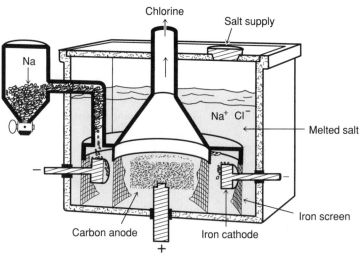

Chlorine

Salt supply

Na

Na^+ Cl^-

Melted salt

Carbon anode

Iron cathode

Iron screen

Although magnesium is a strong reducing agent, it resists corrosion by forming a layer of basic carbonate ($MgCO_3 \cdot Mg(OH)_2$) on the surface. Large quantities of magnesium are obtained from the sea. The last step in the production of magnesium from the sea is the electrolysis of melted $MgCl_2$ in airtight electrolytic cells. At the cathode, magnesium ions (Mg^{2+}) are reduced to metallic magnesium. The chlorine produced at the anode is used to produce the hydrochloric acid required for the process. The quantity of magnesium and chlorine produced depends on the current flow. In the industrial preparation of magnesium, currents of 50 000 A are used.

13-28
Quantitative Aspects of Electrolysis

By measuring the amount of current used, we can determine the amount of chemical change that occurs during the electrolysis.

The masses of products liberated at the electrodes of an electrolytic cell are related to the quantity of electricity passed through the cell and the electrode reactions.

In the electrolysis of melted NaCl, for example, one mole of electrons, which is called one *faraday* (F) of electric charge, is required to reduce one mole of Na^+ ions at the cathode. At the same time, one mole of electrons must be removed from one mole of Cl^- ions at the anode, forming one-half mole of chlorine molecules. Thus, one faraday discharges one mole of metallic sodium and one-half mole of chlorine gas. The mass of a metal discharged by one faraday depends on the number of electrons required to reduce each ion. The following cathode reactions show that one faraday reduces one mole of sodium ions, one-half mole of calcium ions and one-third mole of aluminum ions:

$$Na^+(l) + e^- \rightleftharpoons Na(l)$$
$$Ca^{2+}(l) + 2e^- \rightleftharpoons Ca(s)$$
$$Al^{3+}(l) + 3e^- \rightleftharpoons Al(l)$$

The number of electrons associated with the discharge of any species at the electrode of an electrolytic cell can be determined from the electrode reaction.

EXAMPLE 13-5
Calculating the Number of Faradays
An electrochemist trying out a small-scale experiment in the laboratory wishes to reduce 2.93 g of nickel ions from molten $NiCl_2$. How many faradays will be required?

SOLUTION

1. Write the equation for the reduction of Ni^{2+}:

$$Ni^{2+}(l) + 2e^- \rightleftharpoons Ni(s)$$

2. Determine the amount of nickel in 2.93 g:

$$2.93 \text{ g} \times 1 \text{ mol}/58.7 \text{ g} = 0.0500 \text{ mol}$$

3. Multiply the number of moles of nickel by the number of faradays per mole as shown by the number of electrons in the reduction equation:

$$0.0500 \text{ mol} \times 2 \text{ F/mol} = 0.100 \text{ F}$$

FOLLOW-UP PROBLEM

How many faradays are required to reduce 10 g of calcium from melted calcium chloride?

Answer: 0.500 F

Figure 13-26
These three electrolytic cells are connected in series to a source of direct current (battery). It can be seen from the data in the table that the amounts of different elements discharged at the cathode by the same quantity of electric charge form whole-number mole ratios. Determine these ratios from the data.

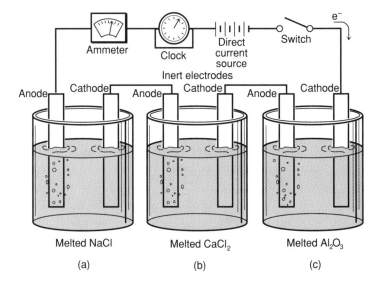

Melted NaCl	Melted CaCl$_2$	Melted Al$_2$O$_3$
(a)	(b)	(c)

The mass (grams) of a chemical substance discharged at an electrode by one faraday of electricity is called a *gram-equivalent mass*.

Cell	Metal Discharged at Cathode	Current (A)	Time (s)	Charge (C)	Mass of Metal Discharged (g)	Molar Mass of Metal
(a)	Na	2.0	48 250	96 500	23	23
(b)	Ca	2.0	48 250	96 500	20	40
(c)	Al	2.0	48 250	96 500	9	27

Experimentally, the quantity of electric charge *(Q)* transferred through an electrolytic cell is determined by measuring the time and magnitude of the current flow. The time is measured in seconds with a stopwatch or timer. The current *(I)* is measured in amperes with an ammeter. The product of the current and time is equal to the quantity of electric charge expressed in terms of coulombs. That is,

$$Q = It \qquad [13\text{-}37]$$

Equation 13-37 indicates that one coulomb is the quantity of electric charge transferred when a current of one ampere flows for one second. One coulomb is the charge carried by 6.24×10^{18} e$^-$. It can be shown that one faraday is equal to approximately 9.65×10^4 C. The relationship between coulombs and faradays is

$$F = C \times \frac{1\ F}{9.65 \times 10^4\ C} \qquad [13\text{-}38]$$

MICHAEL FARADAY
1791–1867
Michael Faraday, the son of a London blacksmith, received only a very elementary education. He was apprenticed to a bookbinder in 1804, during which time he read every book he could. His contact with scientific publications stimulated his interest in science.

Many of the terms in electrochemistry can be traced to Faraday. He coined the words *electrode, electrolyte, electrolysis, anode, cathode, ion, anion* and *cation.*

Faraday's contributions to the field of physics probably exceeded those to the field of chemistry. He believed that since electricity could produce a magnetic field, a moving magnet must be capable of producing an electric current. His experiments laid the groundwork for transformers and motors. Faraday did not believe, as Newton did, that a force could act through a distance but, rather, that a "field" existed. Many scientists feel that his "field theory" was his single most important contribution.

Faraday believed that there must be some fundamental relationship between gravitational and electromagnetic forces, and he performed many experiments to discover the nature of this relationship. He wrote: "Here end my trials for the present. The results are negative. They do not shake my strong feeling of the existence of a relation between gravity and electricity, though they give no proof that such a relation exists."

EXAMPLE 13-6
Applying the Electric Charge Equation

To electroplate a small statue with silver, a jeweller needs to reduce a total of 20.0 g of silver from a silver nitrate solution using a 15.0 A current. How much time will it take to properly electroplate the statue?

SOLUTION

1. Determine the number of faradays required to reduce 1 mol of silver ions by writing the equation for the reduction of silver ions:

$$Ag^+(aq) + e^- \longrightarrow Ag(s)$$

2. Determine the amount of silver in 20.0 g:

$$20.0\ g \times 1\ mol/108\ g = 0.185\ mol$$

3. Determine the number of faradays required to reduce 0.185 mol of silver. Because one silver ion requires one electron, one mole of silver ions requires one faraday of electric charge, and 0.185 mol requires 0.185 F.

4. Determine the number of coulombs in 0.185 F using Equation 13-38:

$$0.185\ F \times 9.65 \times 10^4\ C/F = 17\ 852\ C$$

5. Solve Equation 13-37 for *t* and substitute the known values. Note that 1C = 1A·s.

$$t = \frac{17\ 852\ C}{15.0\ C/s} = 1190\ s$$

ALTERNATE SOLUTION

$$\left(\frac{20.0 \text{ g Ag}}{15.0 \text{ A}}\right)\left(\frac{\text{mol Ag}}{108 \text{ g Ag}}\right)\left(\frac{F}{\text{mol Ag}}\right)\left(\frac{96\,500 \text{ C}}{F}\right)\left(\frac{\text{A}\cdot\text{s}}{\text{C}}\right) = 1191 \text{ s}$$

FOLLOW-UP PROBLEM

A current of 5.0 A is passed through melted KCl for 1000 s. How many grams of potassium are produced?

Answer: 2.03 g

EXAMPLE 13-7
Applying the Faraday-Coulomb Equation
a) What mass of copper is deposited from a plating bath in an electrolysis plant by a current of 3.0 A flowing for a period of 2.0 h?
b) What volume of oxygen gas will be evolved at the anode if the temperature is 27°C and the pressure is 98.6 kPa?
c) If the cell originally contained 1.0 L of 0.20 mol/L $CuSO_4$ and a platinum (inert) anode, what is the concentration of $CuSO_4$ after the electrolysis, assuming no volume change?
d) If the anode is a bar of copper, what is the concentration of $CuSO_4$ after the electrolysis?

SOLUTION
a) The electrode reaction is

$$Cu^{2+}(aq) + 2e^- \rightleftharpoons Cu(s)$$

Calculate the coulombs passed through the cell:

$$Q = It = (3.0 \text{ A})(2.0 \text{ h})\left(\frac{3600 \text{ s}}{\text{h}}\right) = 2.16 \times 10^4 \text{ C}$$

Calculate the faradays of electricity:

$$F = (2.16 \times 10^4 \text{ C})\left(\frac{F}{9.65 \times 10^4 \text{ C}}\right) = 0.224 \text{ F}$$

Calculate the grams of Cu deposited. The electrode reaction shows there are 2 F/mol (63.6 g) of copper.

$$(0.224 \text{ F})\left(\frac{63.6 \text{ g Cu}}{2 \text{ F}}\right) = 7.12 \text{ g Cu}$$

b) The electrode reaction is

$$2H_2O \rightleftharpoons O_2(g) + 4H^+ + 4e^-$$

Calculate the mass of O_2 evolved by 1 F. From the electrode reaction, 4 F (4 mol of e^-) are associated with the discharge of one mole of O_2.

$$\left(\frac{32 \text{ g } O_2}{\text{mol } O_2}\right)\left(\frac{\text{mol } O_2}{4 \text{ F}}\right) = \frac{8.0 \text{ g } O_2}{\text{F}}$$

Calculate the mass of O_2 evolved by passage of 0.224 F (from part a):

$$(0.224 \text{ F})\left(\frac{8.0 \text{ g } O_2}{\text{F}}\right) = 1.8 \text{ g } O_2$$

Convert 1.8 g O_2 into litres at 27°C and 98.6 kPa:

$$(1.8 \text{ g } O_2)\left(\frac{\text{mol } O_2}{32 \text{ g } O_2}\right)\left(\frac{22.4 \text{ L } O_2}{\text{mol } O_2}\right)\left(\frac{300 \text{ K}}{273 \text{ K}}\right)\left(\frac{101.3}{98.6}\right)$$

$$= 1.4 \text{ L } O_2$$

c) Calculate the original moles of Cu^{2+}:

$$n = (0.20 \text{ mol/L})(1.0 \text{ L}) = 0.20 \text{ mol}$$

Calculate the moles of Cu deposited:

$$(0.224 \text{ F})\left(\frac{\text{mol Cu}}{2 \text{ F}}\right) = 0.11 \text{ mol Cu}$$

Calculate the moles of Cu^{2+} remaining:

$$0.20 \text{ mol} - 0.11 \text{ mol} = 0.090 \text{ mol}$$

Calculate the concentration of the solution:

$$\text{Concentration} = \frac{\text{mol } Cu^{2+}}{\text{L}} = \frac{0.090 \text{ mol}}{1.0 \text{ L}} = 0.090 \text{ mol/L}$$

d) The concentration will be the same as the original concentration. The anode furnishes Cu^{2+} to the solution as fast as the Cu^{2+} is removed.

FOLLOW-UP PROBLEM

How many litres of H_2 are evolved at 20°C and 102.6 kPa when 2.0 A is passed through a cell containing sulfuric acid for 3.0 h?

Answer: 2.7 L

BHT AND BHA: KEEPING CHIPS FRESH

Anyone who has tasted butter that has been left sitting in sunlight for a period of time is familiar with the odour and taste of rancid fat—the effects of atmospheric oxidation. Atmospheric oxidation is responsible for destroying the unsaturated fats and fatty portions in food.

Natural fats and oils are mixtures of esters of glycerol and fatty acids. Fatty acids consist of unbranched carbon chains that can be saturated (contain no carbon-to-carbon double bonds) or unsaturated (contain double bonds); the most common unsaturated fatty acid is oleic acid ($CH_3(CH_2)_7CH=CH(CH_2)_7COOH$). Fatty acids can be used as energy or stored in fat cells. As well, some fatty acids, known as *essential fatty acids*, cannot be synthesized by the body, although our systems require them.

There are three types of essential fatty acids: linoleic acid, linolenic acid and arachidonic acid. Linoleic acid ($CH_3(CH_2)_4$ $(CH=CHCH_2)_2(CH_2)_6COOH$) is the most important essential fatty acid because it is the precursor of the other two essential fatty acids. Linolenic acid ($CH_3CH_2(CH=CHCH_2)_3(CH_2)_6COOH$) and arachidonic acid ($CH_3(CH_2)_4(CH=CHCH_2)_4(CH_2)_2COOH$) are precursors of prostaglandins—hormone-like compounds that affect blood pressure, body temperature and relaxation and con-

traction of smooth muscle. As well, arachidonic acid is an essential component of biological membranes.

The mechanism of oxidation of unsaturated fats involves a chain-reaction process. First, an oxygen molecule removes a hydrogen atom from a carbon atom adjacent to a double bond, resulting in the formation of two free radicals:

$$RH + O_2 \longrightarrow R\bullet + H_2O\bullet$$
$$\text{fat} \qquad\qquad \text{free radicals}$$

These free radicals further react to form a hydroperoxide (ROOH) and a free radical:

$$R\bullet + O_2 \longrightarrow ROO\bullet$$

$$ROO\bullet + RH \longrightarrow ROOH + R\bullet$$
$$\text{hydro-}$$
$$\text{peroxide}$$

Hydroperoxides are unstable compounds that readily break down to a mixture of alcohols, aldehydes and ketones. Oleic acid, for example, breaks down by the following reaction:

$$CH_3(CH_2)_7CH=CH(CH_2)_7COOH + O_2 \longrightarrow$$
$$CH_3(CH_2)_7CHO + OCH(CH_2)_7COOH$$

Aldehydes and ketones are responsible for the odour and taste of rancid fat and can be tasted at concentrations below 1 ppm.

If kept covered, cold and dry, most foods can be protected from oxidation reactions for relatively long periods of time. As well, *antioxidizing agents* can be added to prevent oxidation by essentially "mopping up" the free radicals as they are formed. Among the most popular antioxidants commonly found in potato chips, vegetable oils, baked goods and breakfast cereals are *butylated hydroxytoluene (BHT)* and *butylated hydroxyanisole (BHA)*:

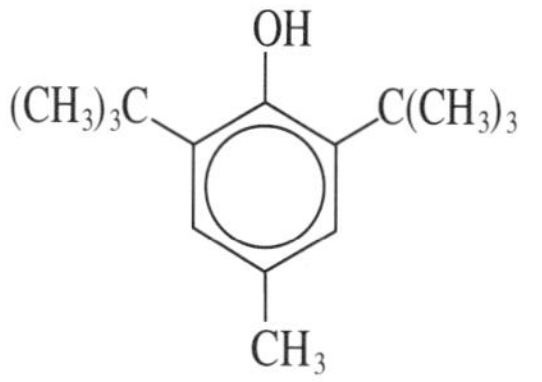

2,6-di-t-butyl-4-methylphenol
(butylated hydroxytoluene)
BHT

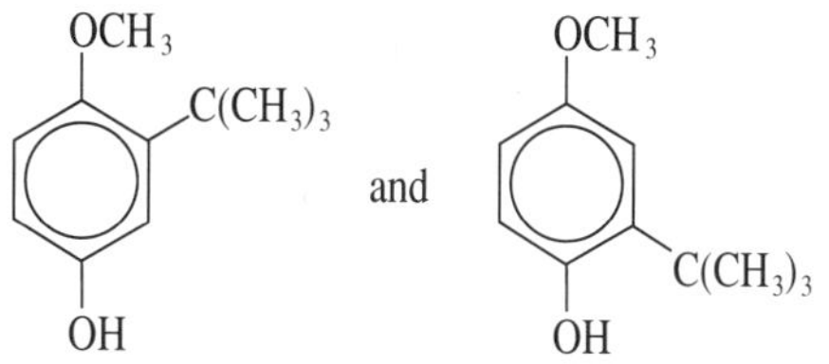

2- and 3-t-butyl-4-hydroxyanisole
(butylated hydroxyanisole)
BHA

Antioxidants prevent the oxidation of fats by donating a hydrogen atom from the hydroxyl group (—OH) to the free radical, thus stopping the chain reaction. The antioxidant becomes a relatively stable aromatic radical:

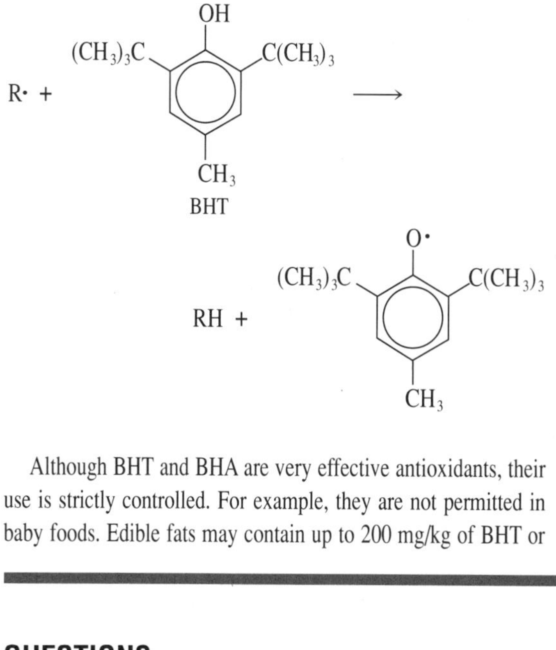

Although BHT and BHA are very effective antioxidants, their use is strictly controlled. For example, they are not permitted in baby foods. Edible fats may contain up to 200 mg/kg of BHT or BHA or any mixture of the two. Both BHT and BHA are used in potato flour, flakes or granules to a maximum of 25 mg/kg. BHT is used in chewing gum in amounts up to 200 mg/kg.

The average daily human intake of both BHT and BHA is 0.1 mg per kg of body weight. Tests done with experimental animals show that extremely large amounts in excess of 500 times this dose cause the liver to enlarge. BHT and BHA may also stimulate the activity of steroid hormones with adverse effects on reproductive systems.

Different species vary in their response to BHT and BHA. Larger doses of BHA than of BHT have caused harmful effects in dogs and rodents; less of BHA than BHT causes harmful effects in monkeys. Long-term studies have determined that, by themselves, BHT and BHA do not cause cancer and, in some cases, may even reduce the occurrence of some tumours.

In the clamour against food additives, what is often overlooked is the important role they play in maintaining the quality and nutritive value of food. Antioxidants such as BHT and BHA not only prevent fats from going rancid but also preserve essential fatty acids in the food, and have so far proved to be more of a benefit than a risk.

QUESTIONS

1. Define the following concepts:
   a) oxidizing agent,
   b) oxidized substance,
   c) reducing agent,
   d) reduced substance.

2. For each of the following, state whether the change is an oxidation or a reduction reaction.
   a) MnO_4^- becomes MnO_4^{2-}
   b) K becomes K^+
   c) N_2 becomes NH_3
   d) NH_3 becomes N_2O
   e) P_4O_{10} becomes P_4O_6
   f) SO_4^{2-} becomes SO_3^{2-}
   g) $HClO_4$ becomes HCl and H_2O
   h) O_2 becomes O^{2-}
   i) $Cr_2O_7^{2-}$ becomes Cr^{3+} and H_2O
   Answers: (b) and (d) oxidation

3. Balance the following equations (ions are hydrated) and identify the oxidizing and reducing agent in each. Change to net ionic form before balancing.

a) $I_2 + H_2S \rightleftharpoons H^+ + I^- + S$

b) $Cu + HNO_3 \rightleftharpoons Cu(NO_3)_2 + NO_2 + H_2O$

c) $H_2SO_4 + Zn \rightleftharpoons S + H_2O + ZnSO_4$

d) $CuO + NH_3 \rightleftharpoons Cu + H_2O + N_2$

e) $H_2O + ClO_3^- + SO_2 \rightleftharpoons SO_4^{2-} + H^+ + Cl^-$

f) $K_2Cr_2O_7 + HCl \rightleftharpoons$
$\qquad KCl + CrCl_3 + H_2O + Cl_2$

g) $MnO_4^- + CH_3OH + H^+ \rightleftharpoons$
$\qquad MnO_2 + CH_2O + H_2O$

h) $P + HNO_3 + H_2O \rightleftharpoons H_3PO_4 + NO$

i) $HIO_3 + H_2SO_3 \rightleftharpoons I_2 + H_2SO_4 + H_2O$

j) $Zn + HNO_3 \rightleftharpoons$
$\qquad Zn(NO_3)_2 + NH_4NO_3 + H_2O$

4. Balance the following equations by the half-cell method. Show both half-cell reactions and identify them as oxidation or reduction.

a) $SO_3^{2-} + MnO_4^- + H^+ \rightleftharpoons$
$\qquad Mn^{2+} + SO_4^{2-} + H_2O(l)$

b) $Cu(s) + NO_3^- + H^+ \rightleftharpoons$
$\qquad Cu^{2+} + NO(g) + H_2O(l)$

c) $Cl_2(g) + OH^- \rightleftharpoons Cl^- + ClO_3^- + H_2O(l)$

d) $Cl_2(g) + H_2O \rightleftharpoons Cl^- + ClO^- + H^+$

e) $SO_4^{2-} + I^- + H^+ \rightleftharpoons S^{2-} + I_2(s) + H_2O(l)$

f) $NH_4NO_2(s) \rightleftharpoons N_2(g) + H_2O(g)$

g) $Zn(s) + SO_4^{2-} + H^+ \rightleftharpoons$
$\qquad S(s) + Zn^{2+} + H_2O(l)$

h) $MnO_4^- + C_2O_4^{2-} + H^+ \rightleftharpoons$
$\qquad MnO_2(s) + CO_2(g) + H_2O(l)$

i) $SO_3^{2-} + IO_3^- + H^+ \rightleftharpoons$
$\qquad I_2(s) + SO_4^{2-} + H_2O(l)$

j) $ClO_3^- \rightleftharpoons Cl^- + ClO_4^- + O_2(g)$

5. For each of the following combinations of reactants, write an equation for a likely reaction. Assume 1 mol/L concentration of ions, 101.3 kPa pressure and 25°C for gases.

a) $Mg(s) + Al^{3+}$ f) $Zn(s) + Br_2(l)$

b) $Hg^+ + Ag(s)$ g) $Sn(s) + H^+$

c) $Cl^- + I_2(s)$ h) $Cu(s) + I^-$

d) $Fe(s) + Sn^{2+}$ i) $H_2(g) + Cl_2(g)$

e) $Al(s) + Zn^{2+}$ j) $H_2(g) + Ag^+$

6. Would it be practical to store a 0.5 mol/L $Fe_2(SO_4)_3$ solution in an aluminum container? Explain.

7. Explain why a salt bridge is necessary in an electrochemical cell.

8. Define (a) anode and (b) cathode.

9. Use the data in Table 13-5 to explain in general terms the reason that hydrogen can be prepared in the laboratory by reacting zinc metal with hydrochloric acid, but not by copper with hydrochloric acid.

10. Use the data in Table 13-5 to explain in general terms why hydrogen is produced when zinc reacts with hydrochloric acid, but NO, NO_2 or NH_4^+ is produced when zinc reacts with nitric acid.

11. Explain why silver dissolves in 1 mol/L nitric acid but not in hydrochloric acid.

12. Concentrated $HCl(aq)$ can be used to clean oxidized copper (copper containing a coat of copper(II) oxide) without attacking the metallic copper. Explain.

13. Why is it not possible to prepare an alkali metal by electrolyzing an aqueous solution of ions of that metal?

14. Explain why magnesium metal does not corrode as rapidly as a less active metal such as iron.

15. If we know the composition of a solution and the electrode potentials, it is possible to predict the products of electrolysis. Explain.

16. a) Explain why the silver and gold found in blister (impure) copper do not go into solution when the anode disintegrates during the electrolytic refining of copper.
b) If Ag^+ ions were present in the electrolyte, would they interfere with the production of pure copper cathodes? Explain.

c) If Al^{3+} ions were present, would they interfere with the production of pure copper cathodes? Explain.

17. What is meant by *cathodic protection against corrosion*?

18. Why should aluminum nails be electrically insulated when used with sheet iron?

19. a) What metal might you fasten to the hull of an aluminum boat to give it cathodic protection in sea water?
b) Name two metals you would not use.

PROBLEMS

1. Determine the oxidation numbers of the underlined elements in the following formulas:

a) H$\underline{\text{Cl}}$O
b) K$\underline{\text{Cl}}$O$_3$
c) $\underline{\text{Mn}}$O$_2$
d) $\underline{\text{Pb}}$O$_2$
e) $\underline{\text{Pb}}$SO$_4$
f) K$_2$$\underline{\text{S}}O_4$
g) $\underline{\text{N}}$H$_4^+$
h) Na$_2$$\underline{\text{O}}_2$
i) $\underline{\text{Fe}}$O
j) $\underline{\text{Fe}}_2$O$_3$
k) Na$\underline{\text{I}}$O$_4$
l) $\underline{\text{Fe}}_3$O$_4$
m) $\underline{\text{Cr}}_2$O$_7^{2-}$
n) $\underline{\text{Mn}}$O$_4^{2-}$
o) $\underline{\text{N}}$O$_3^-$
p) $\underline{\text{Cl}}$O$_3^-$

Answers: (c) +4, (f) +6, (l) $+\frac{8}{3}$ (p) +5

2. If we used the silver–silver ion electrode as the standard for $E°$ values instead of the hydrogen electrode, what would be the standard reduction potentials ($E°$) for the following half-cell reactions?

a) F$_2$(g) + 2e$^-$ $\rightleftharpoons$ 2F$^-$
b) O$_2$(g) + 4H$^+$ + 4e$^-$ $\rightleftharpoons$ 2H$_2$O
c) Fe^{3+} + e$^-$ $\rightleftharpoons$ Fe^{2+}
d) 2H$^+$ + 2e$^-$ $\rightleftharpoons$ H$_2$(g)
e) Mg^{2+} + 2e$^-$ $\rightleftharpoons$ Mg(s)

3. An iron-nickel electrochemical cell uses a salt bridge to join a half-cell containing a strip of iron in a 1.0 mol/L solution of Fe^{2+} to a half-cell that contains a strip of nickel in a 1.0 mol/L Ni^{2+} solution. A voltmeter connects the two metal strips.

a) In which cell does reduction occur?
b) Write the half-cell reactions involved.
c) Which metal is the anode?
d) In which direction are electrons passing through the voltmeter?
e) What is the expected voltmeter reading?

f) What would be the effect on the voltmeter reading if the Fe^{2+} concentration were increased?
g) What would be the effect on the reading if the [Ni^{2+}] were increased? decreased?
h) What is the voltmeter reading when the cell reaches equilibrium?
i) What is the value of ΔG when the cell reaches equilibrium?
j) Calculate K_e for the reaction from $E°$ values.

Answers: (d) from the iron to the nickel; (g) If [Ni^{2+}] is increased, voltage of cell increases.

4. Observations: (i) A reacts spontaneously with 1 mol/L BNO$_3$, 1 mol/L D(NO$_3$)$_2$ and dilute sulfuric acid. A does not react with 1 mol/L C(NO$_3$)$_2$. (ii) B does not react spontaneously with any of the 1 mol/L solutions above or with dilute sulfuric acid. (iii) C reacts spontaneously with dilute sulfuric acid and with 1 mol/L solutions of all the other metallic salts. (iv) D reacts spontaneously with 1 mol/L BNO$_3$. It does not react with dilute sulfuric acid.

a) Use the observations and arrange the following five reduction half-cell reactions in order, the one with the largest positive reduction potential listed first.

$$A^{2+} + 2e^- \longrightarrow A(s)$$
$$B^+ + e^- \longrightarrow B(s)$$
$$C^{2+} + 2e^- \longrightarrow C(s)$$
$$D^{2+} + 2e^- \longrightarrow D(s)$$
$$2H^+ + 2e^- \longrightarrow H_2(g)$$

b) Which metal is the best reducing agent?

c) Which ion is the best oxidizing agent?

5. a) Which of the following is the best oxidizing agent at standard state: I_2, I^-, Au, Au^{3+}, Mg or Mg^{2+}?

b) Which is the best reducing agent?

6. Calculate the voltage of a standard cell with the following half-cell reactions:

$$Ni(s) \longrightarrow Ni^{2+} + 2e^-$$
$$2e^- + Cl_2(g) \longrightarrow 2Cl^-$$

7. In a copper-zinc cell the following half-cell reactions occur:

$$Cu^{2+} + 2e^- \longrightarrow Cu(s)$$
$$Zn(s) \longrightarrow Zn^{2+} + 2e^-$$

What would be the effect on the voltage if

a) sulfide ions (S^{2-}) were added to the Cu^{2+} ion compartment?

b) $CuSO_4$ were added to the Cu^{2+} ion compartment?

c) sulfide ions were added to the Zn^{2+} ion compartment?

d) the size of the zinc electrode were doubled?

e) water were added to both compartments?

8. Consider the following equation:

$$\tfrac{1}{2}Cl_2(g) + Br^- \longrightarrow \tfrac{1}{2}Br_2(l) + Cl^- \quad E° = 0.30 \text{ V}$$

a) Calculate the equilibrium constant for the cell reaction at equilibrium.

b) What is the voltage of the cell if the concentration of Br^- is increased tenfold?

Answer: $K_e = 1 \times 10^5$

9. Calculate the standard cell potentials ($E°_{cell}$) for the following reactions:

a) $Cl_2 + Ni(s) \rightleftharpoons Ni^{2+} + 2Cl^-$

b) $2Ce^{4+} + 2I^- \rightleftharpoons 2Ce^{3+} + I_2$

c) $Sn^{4+} + Cd(s) \rightleftharpoons Sn^{2+} + Cd^{2+}$

d) $Br_2 + 2Fe^{2+} \rightleftharpoons 2Br^- + 2Fe^{3+}$

10. Calculate the potential for each of the following cells. Identify the anode in each case.

a) $Fe(s) \mid Fe^{2+}(0.10 \text{ mol/L}) \parallel$
$Cd^{2+}(0.0010 \text{ mol/L}) \mid Cd(s)$

b) $Mg(s) \mid Mg^{2+}(10^{-3} \text{ mol/L}) \parallel$
$Ag^+(2.0 \text{ mol/L}) \mid Ag(s)$

c) $Pt(s), H_2(101.3 \text{ kPa}) \mid$
$H^+(1.0 \times 10^{-4} \text{ mol/L}) \parallel$
$Cl^-(1.0 \text{ mol/L}), Hg_2Cl_2(sat) \mid Hg$

d) $Pt(s), H_2(101.3 \text{ kPa}) \mid H^+(0.10 \text{ mol/L}) \parallel$
$H^+(1.0 \times 10^{-5} \text{ mol/L}) \mid$
$H_2(101.3 \text{ kPa}), Pt(s)$

11. Can iodine oxidize (a) Fe^{2+} to Fe^{3+}? (b) Sn to Sn^{2+}? Use the data in Table 13-5 to help explain your answers.

12. Which of the reactions below (i) goes spontaneously at standard state to the right as written? (ii) goes spontaneously to the left (reverse reaction is spontaneous)? (iii) is an impossible reaction (does not take place in either direction)? Assume standard-state conditions and concentrations. Note that the half-cell potential is 1.44 V for

$$BrO_3^- + 6H_3O^+ + 6e^- \longrightarrow 9H_2O + Br$$

a) $BrO_3^- + H_3O^+ + I^- \longrightarrow I_2 + Br^- + H_2O$

b) $Cu^{2+} + Fe^{2+} \longrightarrow Fe^{3+} + Cu(s)$

c) $MnO_4^- + H_3O^+ + Co^{2+} \longrightarrow$
$ Co(s) + H_2O + Mn^{2+}$

d) $Cr_2O_7^{2-} + H_3O^+ + Fe^{2+} \longrightarrow$
$\phantom{Cr_2O_7^{2-} + H_3O^+} 2Cr^{3+} + H_2O + Fe^{3+}$

e) $Fe^{2+} + I_2 \longrightarrow Fe^{3+} + I^-$

f) $Cr_2O_7^{2-} + 14H^+ + 6Ce^{3+} \longrightarrow$
$\phantom{Cr_2O_7^{2-} + 14H^+} 2Cr^{3+} + 7H_2O + 6Ce^{4+}$

13. Write equations for reactions that occur when equal volumes of the following 2 mol/L solutions are mixed. If no reaction occurs, write N.R.

a) sulfurous acid and potassium permanganate

b) iron(III) nitrate, potassium bromide and

potassium iodide

c) sodium chloride and aqueous bromine

d) potassium dichromate, hydrogen peroxide and sulfuric acid

14. Consider the following equations:

$$Au^{3+} + 3e^- \longrightarrow Au(s) \qquad E° = 1.50 \text{ V}$$
$$AuCl_4^- + 3e^- \longrightarrow Au(s) + 4Cl^- \quad E° = 1.00 \text{ V}$$

a) Which of these species is the best oxidizing agent?

b) Explain why an $AuCl_4^-$ half-cell has a lower reduction potential than an Au^{3+} half-cell.

c) Could Au be plated better from an aqueous solution of $AuCl_4^-$ or Au^{3+}?

d) At which electrode would the gold be deposited?

Answers: (a) Au³⁺, (d) cathode

15. a) How does decreasing the pH (increasing the acidity) of a nitrate solution affect the reduction potential and the oxidizing strength of the nitrate system?

b) Write the formulas of two other oxidizing agents whose strength is affected by $[H^+]$.

c) Write the formulas of two oxidizing agents whose strength is not affected by the $[H^+]$.

16. Predict the principal product discharged at each electrode during the electrolysis of the following 1 mol/L solutions. Assume platinum electrodes are used. (a) KI, (b) H_2SO_4, (c) HCl

17. a) Draw a diagram for an experiment that demonstrates how a copper-plated spoon could be plated with silver.

b) Identify the cathode and anode.

c) How much silver will be plated out of solution by a current of 1.0 A flowing for 27 h?

Answer: (c) 108 g

18. What charge is required to electroplate
a) 7.00 g of lithium?

b) 20.0 g of calcium?

c) 17.3 g of chromium from a solution of Cr^{3+}?

d) 27.0 g of Al?

Answer: (c) 96 500 C

19. By the electrolysis of water, 11.2 L of oxygen at STP was prepared. (a) What charge was required? (b) If a current of 0.5 A was used, how long did it take?

20. If a constant current passing through a copper sulfate solution plated 2.00 g of copper in 90.0 min, what was the current in amperes?

21. What mass (in kg) of magnesium can be produced per hour by a plant that uses a current of 50 000 A to electrolyze melted $MgCl_2$?

22. Electrolysis of 1.500 L of a 0.500 mol/L copper(II) sulfate solution is accomplished by passing 5 A through the cell for 4 h. Inert electrodes are used. Assume there is no change in the volume of the solution during electrolysis.

a) During electrolysis, does the potential energy of the chemical system increase or decrease? Explain.

b) Write an equation for the half-cell reaction occurring at the anode.

c) As electrolysis proceeds, does the solution become more acidic, less acidic, or does it maintain a constant pH value?

d) How many electrons pass through the system during the electrolysis?

e) How many grams of copper are deposited?

f) What volume of gas is collected by displacement of water at 26°C and 100 kPa? (Water vapour pressure at 26°C is 3.3 kPa.)

g) What is the concentration of Cu^{2+} at completion of the electrolysis?

Answer: (g) 0.25 mol/L

APPENDICES

APPENDIX 1

Mathematical Operations and Concepts

Scientific, or Exponential, Notation

Scientific work frequently involves the use of large and small numbers. Multiplying and dividing such numbers as 0.000 000 065 3 and 605 000 000 000 would be extremely tedious unless these numbers were expressed as powers of ten. A convenient method of expressing these large and small numbers in exponential form is called *scientific*, or *exponential, notation*. The large or small number in this system is expressed as a number between one and ten with some power of ten used to indicate the placement of the decimal point. Multiplying by a positive power of ten indicates that the decimal point must be moved to the right:

$$1.48 \times 10^6 = 1\ 480\ 000$$
$$1.23 \times 10^2 = 123$$

Multiplying by a negative power of ten indicates that the decimal point must be moved to the left:

$$1.66 \times 10^{-4} = 0.000\ 166$$

1. *Addition and Subtraction.* When adding or subtracting two numbers expressed in scientific notation, first make the powers of ten equal. The numbers are then added or subtracted as appropriate:

$$1.55 \times 10^4 + 1.643 \times 10^5$$
$$= 0.155 \times 10^5 + 1.643 \times 10^5$$
$$= 1.798 \times 10^5$$

2. *Multiplication.* When multiplying numbers that are expressed in scientific notation, add the exponents:

$$(1.40 \times 10^4)(2.00 \times 10^6) = 2.80 \times 10^4 \times 10^6$$
$$= 2.80 \times 10^{10}$$

3. *Division.* When dividing numbers expressed in scientific notation, subtract the exponents:

$$\frac{6.88 \times 10^6}{2.00 \times 10^7} = 3.44 \times 10^{-1}$$

$$\frac{4.50 \times 10^{-6}}{6.66 \times 10^{-7}} = 0.676 \times 10^{-6-(-7)}$$
$$= 0.676 \times 10^1$$
$$= 6.76$$

The rule of division of exponents tells us that any number raised to the zero power is equal to one:

$$\frac{5^2}{5^2} = 5^{2-2}$$
$$= 5^0$$
$$= 1$$

4. *Extracting Roots of Numbers.* When calculating the root of a number expressed in scientific notation, divide the exponent by two when taking the square root and by three when taking the cube root:

$$\sqrt{1.6 \times 10^7} = \sqrt{16 \times 10^6}$$
$$= \sqrt{16} \times \sqrt{10^6}$$
$$= 4.0 \times 10^3$$
$$\sqrt[3]{2.7 \times 10^{10}} = \sqrt[3]{27 \times 10^9}$$
$$= \sqrt[3]{27} \times \sqrt[3]{10^9}$$
$$= 3.0 \times 10^3$$

Significant Figures

In many areas of scientific work, measurements obtained to a given degree of certainty are used to derive other data. We will follow the general rule that derived values can be no more certain than the original measured data. Derived values should be expressed with the same number of significant figures as the original measurements. For example, to determine the area of a rectangle, we measure the length and width to some degree of certainty; their product is the area. In this case, uncertainty is compounded when we measure the length and width. If the length is measured as 25.1 cm and the width as 12.4 cm, the uncertainty in each measurement is ±0.05 cm. Thus, the area lies between

$$25.05 \text{ cm} \times 12.35 \text{ cm}$$

and

$$25.15 \text{ cm} \times 12.45 \text{ cm}$$

This area can be properly expressed to three significant figures, which is the same number of significant figures contained in the measurements. Thus,

$$25.1 \text{ cm} \times 12.4 \text{ cm} = 311.24 \text{ cm}^2$$
$$= 311 \text{ cm}^2$$

1. *Addition and Subtraction.* When numbers are added or subtracted, the answer can be expressed only to the same number of figures after the decimal point as the number that contains the fewest digits after the decimal point.

$$
\begin{array}{r}
25.632 \\
1.48 \\
2.766 \\
\hline
29.878
\end{array}
$$

Note that the answer must be rounded off to two numbers after the decimal point to give 29.88.

2. *Multiplication and Division.* When numbers are multiplied or divided, the answer is rounded off so that it is as precise as the least precise of the numbers used in the calculation:

$$(6.42 \times 10^{-3})(4.0111 \times 10^{-5}) = 2.58 \times 10^{-7}$$
$$\frac{12.05}{3.1} = 3.9$$

3. *Rounding Off Numbers.* When a number is rounded off, the procedure is as follows:
a) When the last digit of a number is greater than five, the last digit retained is increased by one unit. For example, 20.147 to four significant figures is 20.15.

b) When the last digit is less than five, it is dropped, leaving the last remaining digit unchanged. For example, 12.33 to three significant figures is 12.3.
c) When the last digit is five, the number is rounded off so that the last remaining digit is even. For example, 21.5 to two significant figures is 22, and 26.25 to three significant figures is 26.2.

4. *Exact Numbers.* Numbers that are exact have no uncertainty and are precise. For example, if we count twelve beakers, the number 12 does not represent an approximation but means exactly 12.

5. *Zeros.* Zeros are significant only if they are not being used exclusively to locate the decimal point. Thus, zeros to the left of the first non-zero number are not significant; zeros to the right of the last non-zero numbers are significant. Consider the following examples:
a) 0.0032 mm contains only two significant figures. The zeros are needed only to locate the decimal point and are not significant.
b) 302 mL contains three significant figures. The zero in this case indicates the number of tens.
c) 25.000 cm contains five significant figures. The zeros are all significant because they are not needed to locate the decimal point. The last zero indicates the estimate was made to 0.0005 cm.
d) 6000 contains only one significant figure. This measurement could have been made with greater certainty than one significant figure. We can indicate the number of significant figures by expressing the number in scientific notation:

6×10^3 contains one significant figure.
6.0×10^2 contains two significant figures.
6.00×10^3 contains three significant figures.
6.000×10^4 contains four significant figures.

6. *Logarithms of Numbers.* When we are calculating the logarithm of a number, the number(s) to the right of the decimal point, which are called the *mantissa*, should contain as many significant digits as contained in the number used in the computation. The number(s) to the left of the decimal, called the *characteristic*, is derived

from the power to which ten is raised and is not related to the precision of the number. For example,

$$\log 5.8 \times 10^2 = \log 5.8 + \log 10^2$$
$$= 0.7634 + 2$$
$$= 2.76$$

Note that there are two digits after the decimal, the same number of significant figures as in 5.8.

Logarithms

A logarithm is an exponent. There are two types of logarithms used in this text: common logarithms with base 10 and natural logarithms with base e equal to 2.718 28. Generally,

$$\log x = a, \text{ where } x = 10^a$$

and

$$\ln x = b, \text{ where } x = e^b$$

Note that we can represent the relationship between log and ln as

$$\ln x = 2.303 \log x$$

Logarithms are exponents and, as such, represent the power to which the base is raised; the base is 10 in common logarithms and e in natural logarithms. For example,

$$\log 1000 = 3, \text{ since } 10^3 = 1000$$
$$\log 100 = 2, \text{ since } 10^2 = 100$$
$$\log 10 = 1, \text{ since } 10^1 = 10$$
$$\log 1 = 0, \text{ since } 10^0 = 1$$
$$\log 0.1 = -1, \text{ since } 10^{-1} = 0.1$$
$$\log 0.01 = -2, \text{ since } 10^{-2} = 0.01$$

The logarithms of such numbers as 0.01, 0.1, 1 and 10 can be easily found by inspection. However, logs that cannot be expressed as simple powers of ten can be found by means of a scientific calculator or log tables. Note that because the log 1 = 0 and the log 10 = 1, the logs of all numbers between 1 and 10 lie between 0 and 1.

To find the logarithm of a number that is greater than ten or less than one, we can express the number using scientific notation. For example,

$$\log 6400 = \log (6.4 \times 10^3)$$

Since logarithms are exponents, the logs of products are added and the logs of quotients are subtracted. For example,

$$\log ab = \log a + \log b$$
$$\log \frac{a}{b} = \log a - \log b$$

In the example above,

$$\log (6.4 \times 10^3) = \log 6.4 + \log 10^3$$

Using a calculator, we can calculate the log of 6.4 as 0.806. Note that the log of 10^3 is 3. Therefore,

$$\log (6.4 \times 10^3) = 0.806 + 3$$
$$= 3.806$$
$$= 3.81$$

Note that we round off 3.806 to two significant digits after the decimal point. *The number of significant digits after the decimal point in the logarithm must equal the number of significant digits in the original number.*

If we are given the log of a number, for example 3.81, we must find the antilog. Because the number 3.81 is an exponent and

$$\log x = a, \text{ where } x = 10^a$$

we can write it as

$$x = 10^{3.81} = 10^{0.81} \times 10^3$$
$$= 6.4 \times 10^3$$

Quadratic Equations

A quadratic equation is any equation with a variable raised to an exponent of two. The equation $x^2 = 4$ is a quadratic expression and, like all quadratics, has two solutions for the variable x. Either $+2$ or -2 satisfies the value for x.

All quadratic equations can be expressed in the standard form, $ax^2 + bx + c = 0$. The general solution to all quadratic equations in this form is the quadratic formula:

$$x = \frac{-b \pm \sqrt{b^2 - 4ac}}{2a}$$

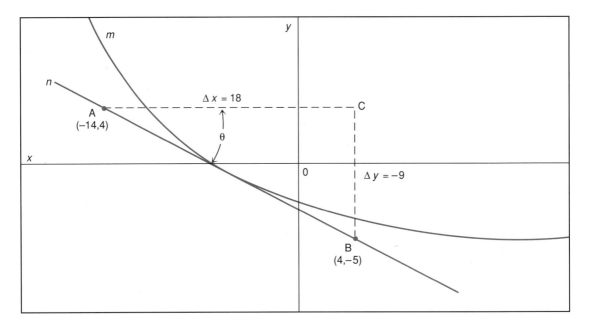

Note that when we are dealing with any physical reality, one of the possible roots may turn out to be meaningless, in which case it is simply discarded. For example, if the term x in a given expression represents concentration, and one root of the equation turns out to be negative, you can simply disregard this root since it has no real significance. It is impossible to have a negative concentration.

Figure 1
The slope of the line, *n*, is given by the relationship $\Delta y/\Delta x$, where

$$\frac{\Delta y}{\Delta x} = \frac{-5-(4)}{4-(-14)} = \frac{-9}{18} = -\frac{1}{2}$$

The Slope of a Line

The slope of a line is given by the ratio of the change in x and y co-ordinates from one point to another on the line. We indicate the change in the y co-ordinate as Δy and the change in the x co-ordinate as Δx. In Fig. 1, points A and B are two points on line n. The slope of this line is given as $\Delta y/\Delta x$, which in this case has a value of $-\frac{1}{2}$. The sign on the slope gives an indication of its direction of inclination. The slope of l_1 in Fig. 2 is negative, while that of l_2 is positive.

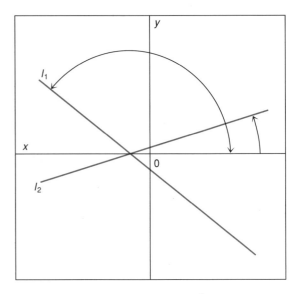

Figure 2
If the inclination is greater than 90°, as in l_1, the slope is negative. If the inclination is less than 90°, as in l_2, the slope is positive.

Frequently, it is desirable to find the slope of a curved line, such as *m* in Fig. 1. Obviously, the curved line does not have a constant slope at all points. Therefore, we describe its slope at a given point. The slope at a given point on a curve can be determined by drawing a line tangent to the curve at that point and then determining the slope of the tangent. In Fig. 1, the slope of the curved line *m* at the point of tangency with line *n* is $-\frac{1}{2}$, the same as the slope of line *n*.

The slope of a line is also defined as the value of the trigonometric function, called the tangent (tan). The tan of the angle theta, θ, in Fig. 1, is defined as the opposite side of the angle θ, CB, divided by the adjacent side of the angle θ, AC. In this co-ordinate system, the value of CB is -9 and the value of AC is 18. Thus, the tan $\theta = -\frac{1}{2}$.

APPENDIX 2

The Metric System

The system of measurement used in science courses is called the International System of Units, or the SI (Système international d'unités) metric system. This system was first adopted by the General Conference on Weights and Measures in 1960. The major advantage of this system is that it employs only a few base units with fractional parts or multiples based on the decimal system.

The metre is the standard unit of length in the metric system. Originally, a fraction of a certain quadrant of the earth was arbitrarily chosen to serve as the standard of length in the metric system. In 1960, however, it was determined that the metre should be redefined as 1 650 763.73 times the wavelength of the orange-red spectral line of light emitted by krypton-86. Thus, the metre is now standardized to the atom rather than to one of the earth's quadrants.

The metre, centimetre and millimetre are often too large for conveniently expressing the dimensions on the molecular or atomic scale. For this purpose, the micrometre (μm), nanometre (nm) and the picometre (pm) are used. For example, the atomic diameters of atoms range from 0.1 to 0.5 nm. SI prefixes and their multiplying factors are given in Table 1.

Note that a number of non-SI units are permitted for use with the SI system. Such units include the electron volt (eV), minute (min), hour (h), day (d), year (a), hectare (ha) and litre (L). Because Canada is still undergoing metric conversion, some imperial units are also permitted, where such units are in general use and therefore necessary for practical applications. For example, an experiment that requires a 64 mm nail rather than a $2\frac{1}{2}$ inch nail might create confusion. However, SI units are to be used as much as possible.

TABLE 1
SI PREFIXES

Prefix	Multiplying Factor
Exa (E)	10^{18}
Peta (P)	10^{15}
Tera (T)	10^{12}
Giga (G)	10^{9}
Mega (M)	10^{6}
Kilo (k)	10^{3}
Hecto (h)	10^{2}
Deca (da)	10^{1}
Deci (d)	10^{-1}
Centi (c)	10^{-2}
Milli (m)	10^{-3}
Micro (μ)	10^{-6}
Nano (n)	10^{-9}
Pico (p)	10^{-12}
Femto (f)	10^{-15}
Atto (a)	10^{-18}

APPENDIX 3

Useful Tables

TABLE 1
VALUES OF SOME PHYSICAL CONSTANTS

Quantity	Symbol	Value
Avogadro's number	N_A	$6.022\ 137 \times 10^{23}$ /mol
Coulomb's constant	k	9.0×10^9 N·m^2/C
Electronic charge	e	$1.602\ 177 \times 10^{-19}$ C
Faraday's constant	F	9.648×10^4 C/mol electrons
Mass of electron	m_e	$9.109\ 939 \times 10^{-31}$ kg
		0.000 55 g/mol
Mass of neutron	m_n	$1.674\ 929 \times 10^{-27}$ kg
		1.008 66 g/mol
Mass of proton	m_p	$1.672\ 623 \times 10^{-27}$ kg
		1.007 28 g/mol
Pi	π	3.141 592 653
Planck's constant	h	$6.626\ 076 \times 10^{-34}$ J·s
Speed of sound in air	v	331.29 m/s
Velocity of light in vacuo	c	$2.997\ 924 \times 10^8$ m/s

TABLE 2
ELECTRON CONFIGURATION OF THE ELEMENTS

Atomic Number	Element	Principal Energy Levels / Orbitals	1	2		3			4				5				6				7
			1s	2s	2p	3s	3p	3d	4s	4p	4d	4f	5s	5p	5d	5f	6s	6p	6d	6f	7s
1	Hydrogen		1																		
2	Helium		2																		
3	Lithium		2	1																	
4	Beryllium		2	2																	
5	Boron		2	2	1																
6	Carbon		2	2	2																
7	Nitrogen		2	2	3																
8	Oxygen		2	2	4																
9	Fluorine		2	2	5																
10	Neon		2	2	6																
11	Sodium		2	2	6	1															
12	Magnesium		2	2	6	2															
13	Aluminum		2	2	6	2	1														
14	Silicon		2	2	6	2	2														
15	Phosphorus		2	2	6	2	3														
16	Sulfur		2	2	6	2	4														
17	Chlorine		2	2	6	2	5														

TABLE 2 (continued)
ELECTRON CONFIGURATION OF THE ELEMENTS

Atomic Number	Element	Principal Energy Levels / Orbitals:	1	2		3			4				5				6				7
			1s	2s	2p	3s	3p	3d	4s	4p	4d	4f	5s	5p	5d	5f	6s	6p	6d	6f	7s
18	Argon		2	2	6	2	6														
19	Potassium		2	2	6	2	6		1												
20	Calcium		2	2	6	2	6		2												
21	Scandium		2	2	6	2	6	1	2												
22	Titanium		2	2	6	2	6	2	2												
23	Vanadium		2	2	6	2	6	3	2												
24	Chromium		2	2	6	2	6	5	1												
25	Manganese		2	2	6	2	6	5	2												
26	Iron		2	2	6	2	6	6	2												
27	Cobalt		2	2	6	2	6	7	2												
28	Nickel		2	2	6	2	6	8	2												
29	Copper		2	2	6	2	6	10	1												
30	Zinc		2	2	6	2	6	10	2												
31	Gallium		2	2	6	2	6	10	2	1											
32	Germanium		2	2	6	2	6	10	2	2											
33	Arsenic		2	2	6	2	6	10	2	3											
34	Selenium		2	2	6	2	6	10	2	4											
35	Bromine		2	2	6	2	6	10	2	5											
36	Krypton		2	2	6	2	6	10	2	6											
37	Rubidium		2	2	6	2	6	10	2	6			1								
38	Strontium		2	2	6	2	6	10	2	6			2								
39	Yttrium		2	2	6	2	6	10	2	6	1		2								
40	Zirconium		2	2	6	2	6	10	2	6	2		2								
41	Niobium		2	2	6	2	6	10	2	6	4		1								
42	Molybdenum		2	2	6	2	6	10	2	6	5		1								
43	Technetium		2	2	6	2	6	10	2	6	6		1								
44	Ruthenium		2	2	6	2	6	10	2	6	7		1								
45	Rhodium		2	2	6	2	6	10	2	6	8		1								
46	Palladium		2	2	6	2	6	10	2	6	10										
47	Silver		2	2	6	2	6	10	2	6	10		1								
48	Cadmium		2	2	6	2	6	10	2	6	10		2								
49	Indium		2	2	6	2	6	10	2	6	10		2	1							
50	Tin		2	2	6	2	6	10	2	6	10		2	2							
51	Antimony		2	2	6	2	6	10	2	6	10		2	3							
52	Tellurium		2	2	6	2	6	10	2	6	10		2	4							
53	Iodine		2	2	6	2	6	10	2	6	10		2	5							
54	Xenon		2	2	6	2	6	10	2	6	10		2	6							
55	Cesium		2	2	6	2	6	10	2	6	10		2	6			1				
56	Barium		2	2	6	2	6	10	2	6	10		2	6			2				
57	Lanthanum		2	2	6	2	6	10	2	6	10		2	6	1		2				
58	Cerium		2	2	6	2	6	10	2	6	10	2	2	6			2				
59	Praseodymium		2	2	6	2	6	10	2	6	10	3	2	6			2				

TABLE 2 (continued)
ELECTRON CONFIGURATION OF THE ELEMENTS

Atomic Number	Element	Principal Energy Levels / Orbitals: 1s	2s	2p	3s	3p	3d	4s	4p	4d	4f	5s	5p	5d	5f	6s	6p	6d	6f	7s
60	Neodymium	2	2	6	2	6	10	2	6	10	4	2	6			2				
61	Promethium	2	2	6	2	6	10	2	6	10	5	2	6			2				
62	Samarium	2	2	6	2	6	10	2	6	10	6	2	6			2				
63	Europium	2	2	6	2	6	10	2	6	10	7	2	6			2				
64	Gadolinium	2	2	6	2	6	10	2	6	10	7	2	6	1		2				
65	Terbium	2	2	6	2	6	10	2	6	10	9	2	6			2				
66	Dysprosium	2	2	6	2	6	10	2	6	10	10	2	6			2				
67	Holmium	2	2	6	2	6	10	2	6	10	11	2	6			2				
68	Erbium	2	2	6	2	6	10	2	6	10	12	2	6			2				
69	Thulium	2	2	6	2	6	10	2	6	10	13	2	6			2				
70	Ytterbium	2	2	6	2	6	10	2	6	10	14	2	6			2				
71	Lutetium	2	2	6	2	6	10	2	6	10	14	2	6	1		2				
72	Hafnium	2	2	6	2	6	10	2	6	10	14	2	6	2		2				
73	Tantalum	2	2	6	2	6	10	2	6	10	14	2	6	3		2				
74	Tungsten	2	2	6	2	6	10	2	6	10	14	2	6	4		2				
75	Rhenium	2	2	6	2	6	10	2	6	10	14	2	6	5		2				
76	Osmium	2	2	6	2	6	10	2	6	10	14	2	6	6		2				
77	Iridium	2	2	6	2	6	10	2	6	10	14	2	6	9		0				
78	Platinum	2	2	6	2	6	10	2	6	10	14	2	6	9		1				
79	Gold	2	2	6	2	6	10	2	6	10	14	2	6	10		1				
80	Mercury	2	2	6	2	6	10	2	6	10	14	2	6	10		2				
81	Thallium	2	2	6	2	6	10	2	6	10	14	2	6	10		2	1			
82	Lead	2	2	6	2	6	10	2	6	10	14	2	6	10		2	2			
83	Bismuth	2	2	6	2	6	10	2	6	10	14	2	6	10		2	3			
84	Polonium	2	2	6	2	6	10	2	6	10	14	2	6	10		2	4			
85	Astatine	2	2	6	2	6	10	2	6	10	14	2	6	10		2	5			
86	Radon	2	2	6	2	6	10	2	6	10	14	2	6	10		2	6			
87	Francium	2	2	6	2	6	10	2	6	10	14	2	6	10		2	6			1
88	Radium	2	2	6	2	6	10	2	6	10	14	2	6	10		2	6			2
89	Actinium	2	2	6	2	6	10	2	6	10	14	2	6	10		2	6	1		2
90	Thorium	2	2	6	2	6	10	2	6	10	14	2	6	10		2	6	2		2
91	Protactinium	2	2	6	2	6	10	2	6	10	14	2	6	10	2	2	6	1		2
92	Uranium	2	2	6	2	6	10	2	6	10	14	2	6	10	3	2	6	1		2
93	Neptunium	2	2	6	2	6	10	2	6	10	14	2	6	10	4	2	6	1		2
94	Plutonium	2	2	6	2	6	10	2	6	10	14	2	6	10	6	2	6			2
95	Americium	2	2	6	2	6	10	2	6	10	14	2	6	10	7	2	6			2
96	Curium	2	2	6	2	6	10	2	6	10	14	2	6	10	7	2	6	1		2
97	Berkelium	2	2	6	2	6	10	2	6	10	14	2	6	10	8	2	6	1		2
98	Californium	2	2	6	2	6	10	2	6	10	14	2	6	10	10	2	6			2
99	Einsteinium	2	2	6	2	6	10	2	6	10	14	2	6	10	11	2	6			2
100	Fermium	2	2	6	2	6	10	2	6	10	14	2	6	10	12	2	6			2
101	Mendelevium	2	2	6	2	6	10	2	6	10	14	2	6	10	13	2	6			2
102	Nobelium	2	2	6	2	6	10	2	6	10	14	2	6	10	13	2	6	1		2
103	Lawrencium	2	2	6	2	6	10	2	6	10	14	2	6	10	14	2	6	1		2

TABLE 3
COMMON IONS AND THEIR CHARGES

Ion	Symbol and Charge	Ion	Symbol and Charge
Acetate	$C_2H_3O_2^-$	Hydrogen sulfide (bisulfide)	HS^-
Arsenate	AsO_4^{3-}	Hydrogen sulfite (bisulfite)	HSO_3^-
Arsenite	AsO_3^{3-}	Hydroxide	OH^-
Benzoate	$C_7H_6O_2^{2-}$	Hypochlorite	ClO^-
Borate	BO_3^{3-}	Iodate	IO_3^-
Bromate	BrO_3^-	Iodide	I^-
Bromide	Br^-	Monohydrogen phosphate	HPO_4^{2-}
Carbonate	CO_3^{2-}	Nitrate	NO_3^-
Chlorate	ClO_3^-	Nitrite	NO_2^-
Chloride	Cl^-	Orthosilicate	SiO_4^{4-}
Chlorite	ClO_2^-	Oxalate	$C_2O_4^{2-}$
Chromate	CrO_4^{2-}	Oxide	O^{2-}
Cyanate	CNO^-	Perchlorate	ClO_4^-
Cyanide	CN^-	Periodate	IO_4^-
Dihydrogen phosphate	$H_2PO_4^-$	Permanganate	MnO_4^-
Fluoride	F^-	Peroxide	O_2^{2-}
Hydride	H^-	Phosphate	PO_4^{3-}
Hexacyanoferrate(III) (ferricyanide)	$Fe(CN)_6^{3-}$	Pyrophosphate	$P_2O_7^{4-}$
Hexacyanoferrate(II) (ferrocyanide)	$Fe(CN)_6^{4-}$	Sulfate	SO_4^{2-}
Hydrogen carbonate (bicarbonate)	HCO_3^-	Sulfite	SO_3^{2-}
Hydrogen oxalate (bioxalate)	$HC_2O_4^-$	Thiocyanate	SCN^-
Hydrogen phthalate (biphthalate)	$HC_8H_4O_4^-$	Thiosulfate	$S_2O_3^{2-}$
Hydrogen sulfate (bisulfate)	HSO_4^-		

TABLE 4
STANDARD ENTROPY VALUES

Substance	$S°$ (J/mol·K)	Substance	$S°$ (J/mol·K)
Al	28.3	$BiCl_3$	177
$AlCl_3$	110.7	Bi_2O_3	151
Al_2O_3	51.0	BCl_3	290
$Al_2(SO_4)_3$	239	B_2H_6	232
AsH_3	223	B_2O_3	53.8
As_2O_5	105	$B(OH)_3$	88.8
Ba	66.9	$Br_2(l)$	152.2
$Ba^{2+}(aq)$	9.6	$Br_2(g)$	245.4
$BaCO_3$	112	HBr	198.5
$BaCl_2$	125	Br^-	82.4
BaO	70.4	$Cd(s)$	51.8
$Ba(OH)_2$	−8	$Cd^{2+}(aq)$	−73.2
$Ba(NO_3)_2$	214	$CdCl_2$	115
$BaSO_4$	132	CdO	54.8
$BeCl_2$	89.9	CdS	64.9
BeO	14	$CdSO_4$	123

TABLE 4 (continued)
STANDARD ENTROPY VALUES

Substance	$S°$ (J/mol·K)	Substance	$S°$ (J/mol·K)
$Ca(s)$	41.4	Cr_2O_3	81.2
$Ca^{2+}(aq)$	−53.1	CrO_3	72
$CaCO_3$	92.9	$Co(s)$	30
CaF_2	80.3	$Co^{2+}(aq)$	−110
$CaCl_2$	114	$CoCl_2$	106
$CaBr_2$	130	$Co(NO_3)_2$	192
CaI_2	143	CoO	53
CaO	40	CoS	67.4
$Ca_3(PO_4)_2$	241	Cu	33.2
$CaSO_4$	107	$Cu^{2+}(aq)$	−99.6
$CaSO_4 \cdot 2H_2O$	131	$CuCl$	86.2
C (graphite)	5.69	$CuCl_2$	119
C (diamond)	2.4	Cu_2O	93.1
$CCl_4(l)$	214.4	CuO	42.6
$CO(g)$	197.9	Cu_2S	121
$CO_2(g)$	213.6	CuS	66.5
$CO_2(aq)$	117.6	$CuSO_4$	109
$H_2CO_3(aq)$	187.4	$F_2(g)$	202.7
$HCO_3^-(aq)$	91.2	$F^-(aq)$	−13.8
$CO_3^{2-}(aq)$	−56.9	$HF(g)$	173.5
$CS_2(l)$	151.3	Au_2O_3	125
$HCN(g)$	201.7	$AuCl_3$	148
$CN^-(aq)$	94.1	$H_2(g)$	130.6
$CH_4(g)$	186.2	$H_2O(l)$	69.9
$C_2H_2(g)$	200.8	$H_2O(g)$	188.7
$C_2H_4(g)$	219.8	$H_2O_2(l)$	109.6
$C_2H_6(g)$	229.5	$H_2Se(g)$	219
$C_3H_8(g)$	269.9	I_2	116.1
$C_4H_{10}(g)$	310.2	$I_2(g)$	260.7
$C_6H_6(l)$	173.3	$HI(g)$	206
$CH_3OH(l)$	126.8	Fe	27
$C_2H_5OH(l)$	161	$Fe^{2+}(aq)$	−137.7
$HCHOO(g)$	251	$Fe^{3+}(aq)$	−315.9
$CH_3COOH(l)$	160	Fe_2O_3	90
$CH_2O(g)$	218.8	Fe_3O_4	146.4
$(CH_3)_2CO(l)$	200.4	FeS	60.3
C_6H_5COOH	167.6	FeS_2	52.9
$CO(NH_2)_2$	104.6	Pb	64.8
$CO(NH_2)_2(aq)$	173.8	$Pb^{2+}(aq)$	10.5
$Cl_2(g)$	223	$PbCl_2$	136
$Cl^-(aq)$	56.5	PbO	68.7
$HCl(g)$	186.7	PbO_2	68.6
$HCl(aq)$	56.5	$Pb(OH)_2$	88
$HClO(aq)$	106.8	PbS	91.2
$Cr(s)$	23.8	$PbSO_4$	149
$CrCl_2$	115	Li	28.4
$CrCl_3$	126	$Li^+(aq)$	10.3

TABLE 4 (continued)
STANDARD ENTROPY VALUES

Substance	$S°$ (J/mol·K)	Substance	$S°$ (J/mol·K)
LiF	35.7	$K^+(aq)$	102.5
LiCl	59.3	KF	66.6
LiBr	66.9	KCl	82.6
Li_2O	37.9	KBr	95.9
Li_3N	37.3	KI	106.3
Mg	32.5	KOH	78.9
$Mg^{2+}(aq)$	−138.1	K_2SO_4	176
$MgCO_3$	65.7	$SiH_4(g)$	205
MgF_2	79.9	SiO_2	41.8
$MgCl_2$	89.5	Ag	42.6
MgO	26.9	$Ag^+(aq)$	72.7
$Mg(OH)_2$	63.1	AgCl	96.2
Mn	32	AgBr	107.1
$Mn^{2+}(aq)$	−74.9	$AgNO_3$	141
$MnO_4^-(aq)$	191	Ag_2O	121.3
$KMnO_4$	171.7	Na	51
MnO	60.2	$Na^+(aq)$	59
MnO_2	53.1	NaF	51.5
$MnSO_4$	112	NaCl	72.4
Hg(l)	76.1	NaBr	83.7
Hg_2Cl_2	192.5	NaI	91.2
$HgCl_2$	146	$NaHCO_3$	102
HgO	70.3	Na_2CO_3	136
Ni	30	Na_2O_2	94.6
$NiCl_2$	97.5	Na_2O	72.8
NiO	38	Na_2OH	64.2
$NiSO_4$	77.8	Na_2SO_4	149.5
$NiCO_3$	91.6	S (rhombic)	31.8
$N_2(g)$	191.5	$SO_2(g)$	248
$NH_3(g)$	192.5	$SO_3(g)$	256
$NH_4^+(aq)$	113	$H_2S(g)$	206
NH_4Cl	94.6	$H_2SO_4(l)$	157
NO(g)	210.6	$H_2SO_4(aq)$	20.1
$NO_2(g)$	240.5	$SF_6(g)$	292
$N_2O(g)$	220	Sn	51.6
$N_2O_4(g)$	304	$Sn^{2+}(aq)$	−17
$HNO_3(aq)$	155.6	$SnCl_4(l)$	258.6
$NO_3^-(aq)$	146.4	SnO	56.5
$O_2(g)$	205	SnO_2	52.3
$OH^-(aq)$	−10.8	Zn	41.6
$P_4(g)$	163.2	$Zn^{2+}(aq)$	−112.1
$PCl_3(g)$	311.8	$ZnCl_2$	111
$PCl_5(g)$	364.6	ZnO	43.6
$PH_3(g)$	210.2	ZnS	57.7
P_4O_{10}	228.9	$ZnSO_4$	120
H_3PO_4	110.5		

INDEX

INDEX

PHOTO AND ILLUSTRATION CREDITS

CHEMICAL SYMBOLS, UNITS, PREFIXES AND ABBREVIATIONS

a	year
A	ampere
α	alpha ray
(aq)	aqueous solution
β	beta ray
Bq	becquerel
c	specific heat capacity
C	coulomb
centi (c)	10^{-2}
°C	degree Celsius
ρ	density
deci (d)	10^{-1}
Δ	change in (delta)
δ^-, δ^+	partial charge
$e^-, _{-1}e$	electron
$_{+1}e$	positron
E	energy
E_k	kinetic energy
E_p	potential energy
F	Faraday constant
(g)	gas
G	Gibbs free energy
ΔG	change in free energy
$\Delta G°$	change in standard free energy
γ	gamma ray
h	hour
H	enthalpy
$\Delta H°$	standard change in enthalpy
$H_f°$	standard enthalpy of formation
$H_r°$	standard enthalpy of reaction
IUPAC	International Union of Pure and Applied Chemistry
J	joule

K	kelvin
kilo (k)	10^3
K_a	acid dissociation constant
K_b	base dissociation constant
K_e	equilibrium constant
K_{sp}	solubility product constant
K_w	ion product constant for water
(l)	liquid
micro (μ)	10^{-6}
milli (m)	10^{-3}
min	minute
mol	mole
n	number of moles
$_0n$	neutron
nano (n)	10^{-9}
π	pi
p	pressure
$_1p, _1H$	proton
pH	measure of relative acidity
pico (p)	10^{-12}
Q	heat energy or electric charge
S	entropy
$\Delta S°$	standard change in entropy
σ	sigma
s	second
(s)	solid
SI	International System of Units (Système international d'unités)
t	time
$t_{1/2}$	half-life
T	temperature
u	atomic mass unit
V	volume